NON-CRYSTALLINE SOLIDS

V. D. Fréchette, Editor
State University of New York College of Ceramics
at Alfred University

Conference on
Non-crystalline Solids
Alfred, New York
September 3–5, 1958

Sponsored by
National Academy of Sciences-
National Research Council and
Air Force Office of Scientific
Research, Air Research and
Development Command

NEW YORK · LONDON   John Wiley & Sons, Inc.

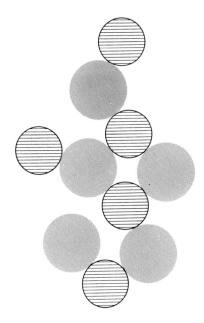

NON-CRYSTALLINE SOLIDS

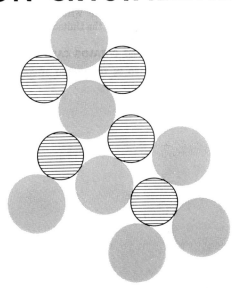

Foreword

For over ten years now a committee of the National Academy of Sciences-National Research Council, Division of Physical Sciences, has initiated activities which cross the traditional, and often only inertial, boundaries between various sciences interested in solids. The major activity of this committee has been the organization of a series of specialized conferences at which invited groups of speakers and discussers present, compare, and clarify the status of their knowledge and understanding of the subject. The first, held at Cornell University in 1948, dealt with "Phase Transformations in Solids." This was followed in turn by "Imperfections in Nearly Perfect Crystals," Pocono, Pennsylvania, in 1950; "Structure and Properties of Solid Surfaces," Lake Geneva, Wisconsin, in 1952; and, finally, the "Non-crystalline Solids" as reported in the current book. The present committee consists of Drs. Harvey Brooks, M. J. Buerger, Morris Cohen, P. P. Ewald, V. D. Fréchette, J. G. Kirkwood, F. Seitz, and R. Smoluchowski, Chairman.

The topic of this most recent conference—non-crystalline solids—was chosen in response to the great need for an authoritative survey of this field in which both the theory and the experiment have recently made great strides. The committee was especially pleased to have Professor V. D. Fréchette of Alfred University accept the onerous responsibilities of serving as Chairman of the conference. With the able assistance of Drs. O. L. Anderson, S. H. Bauer, T. H. Davies, N. J. Kreidl, and J. A.

Krumhansl an excellent program was organized and the conference expertly run. The presence of several speakers and discussers from abroad was particularly gratifying. It is a pleasure to express—in the name of the National Academy of Sciences-National Research Council Committee on Solids—our sincere appreciation to Dr. Fréchette and to his committee and to the officers and faculty of Alfred who extended the facilities of the University and a personal hospitality which contributed greatly to the success of the conference.

Special thanks are also due to the Office of Scientific Research of the Air Research and Development Command not only for the financial support under Contract No. AF49(638)–419, which made the conference and this volume possible, but also for the effective assistance received from its staff members in planning the many details of the meetings.

Committee on Solids
National Research Council
ROMAN SMOLUCHOWSKI, Chairman

Preface

Non-crystalline is essentially a negative term describing a state of matter which does not have a crystalline character. In consequence, the meaning of the term *non-crystalline solid* has changed with every development in our understanding of the complementary term, *crystalline solid*.

We once considered non-crystalline all solids which showed no crystal facets or cleavage faces to the naked eye. But we were forced to restrict the term to successively fewer materials as the evidence for crystallinity came to include the criteria of microscopy and then of x-ray diffraction; from these the idea of the crystalline state emerged as that state in which the spatial arrangement of atoms could be described as translationally repetitive. Still later, theoretical considerations together with additional evidence from catalytic, electrical, and microscopic studies forced realization that the concept of absolutely regular repetition of atomic groupings in a crystal had to be modified, both with respect to register (which, however, may be perfect up to a "mosaic limit") and with respect to details of the repeating motif. It is now clear that the crystal and its properties can be discussed best in terms of a defined ideally repetitive atomic arrangement together with a description of the departure of the real crystal from the ideal model, specifying the nature, location, and concentration of such *defects*.

In some instances regularity appears to be limited to two dimensions, as in some graphites, or to one dimension (keratin), in which translational repetition with only occasional lapse occurs. Such materials may be described as two-dimensionally and one-dimensionally crystalline respectively; by corollary they are two-dimensionally and one-dimensionally non-crystalline. A few solids are known in which no translational repetition whatever exists, and these must be termed wholly non-crystalline. Yet, even in these, the atomic arrangement is by no means strictly random; in some of them identical atomic groups of some complexity are to be found throughout the structure at varying intervals and having various orientations constituting *short range order*. The boundary between crystalline and non-crystalline solids is evidently an indistinct and overlapping one, and elements of both conditions characterize many real materials.

Study of the non-crystalline solids has been handicapped by the diffuse nature of the physical and chemical phenomena and the relatively great variability in structure which are characteristic of them, and which cause difficulty in relating observed data to structural models. Nevertheless, strong advances in dealing with these problems have recently been made. Activity in this field is to be found in a broad range of disciplines including physics, chemistry, metallurgy, and ceramics. It was the aim of the conference, and of this book which emerges from it, to bring these scattered contributions together in one place where the interplay of opinions in discussion could provide a degree of perspective, defining the area of non-crystalline solids in common terms and supplying individual contributions in a form suitable for general use.

The first five chapters deal with the *scattering of radiation* by non-crystalline materials. The *correlation function* plays the same role in a non-crystalline medium that the lattice and the distribution of atoms within the unit cell play in crystalline media. Derivation of the correlation function from the angular distribution of scattered radiation is discussed in the special cases of x-rays and visible light. The x-ray method is illustrated by examination of gel catalysts, while the scattering of visible light near the critical point of gas condensation or liquid mixing is shown to yield a correlation length indicative of the range of molecular forces. The analysis of x-ray diffraction data is extended to deal with separate identical molecules or of semiregular linear high polymers. Experimental and theoretical considerations are further developed in relation to the problem of protein structure. As an example of high temperature x-ray diffraction by non-crystalline materials, it was possible to confirm the existence of "holes" or fluctuating fissures between ion clusters of one or two ionic shells surrounding a central ion in molten alkali halides.

Electronic structure is discussed in Chapters 6 to 8, the discussion beginning with an analysis of one-dimensional disordered arrays. The fine structure of the x-ray K-absorption edge can be interpreted in terms of the electron environment of the absorbing element to yield information concerning such features as state of ionization, type of bonding, and band structure; a qualitative introduction to this new approach is given with examples of applications in catalysis work. The methods of magnetic resonance spectroscopy are described in relation to the study of molecular structure, motions of molecules and groups, chemical bonding, and electronic configurations in paramagnetic solids, with special reference to glasses.

Chapters 9 through 12 deal with *relaxation phenomena*. Development of irreversible thermodynamics in the study of relaxation processes yields moderate success in providing macroscopic equations of motion, but the attempts toward corresponding microscopic indications are less satisfactory. If temperature, pressure, or other stress is applied to a liquid for a time which is short compared to the structural relaxation time, the liquid will exhibit properties typical of an amorphous solid; ultrasonic investigations are described in this connection. The kinetics of mechanical relaxation effects in inorganic glasses are developed in relation to the internal friction, strain retardation, and impact methods of study at appropriate temperatures. It is suggested that the fictive temperature theory relating to glass relaxation can be treated as a special case of Eyring's recently proposed general equilibration theory of transient phenomena.

The last eight chapters are concerned with the *structure and properties of special systems*. As in preceding chapters where kinetic theory and methods of study are illustrated in terms of special systems, in these concluding chapters not merely the characteristics of specific non-crystalline materials but also definitive remarks of general significance are introduced. For example, in discussion of the structures of amorphous sulfur and selenium, Prins notes three classes of materials tending to form glasses for different reasons: (1) the network or coordination glasses resulting from the difficulty of readjusting, once formed, a wrongly connected configuration; (2) the linear polymers, in which long, worm-like molecules disentangle reluctantly to assume an ordered array; and (3) glucose and related substances resembling the coordination glasses but with hydroxyl bonds substituted for valency bonds. The kinetics of ion movement in thin films of Ta_2O_5 are related to their resistance to chemical attack and to structural changes with changing electric field and temperature. Optical absorption, electrical conductivity and superconductivity, and x-ray and electron diffraction measurements indicate the degree of lattice disorder in amorphous layers of metals and metal halides prepared by condensation at very low temperatures, in some cases with the aid of a second substance condensed simultaneously to disturb crystallization. Review of the chemical features of the glassy state suggests that glass formation is essentially a kinetic problem, in which the physical properties of glasses of systematically varied composition can afford guidance for physical theories; electrical and rheological properties of silicate glasses are examined in illustration. A nomenclature is proposed for the network defects in glass before and after irradiation with x-rays and fast neutrons. Explanations are offered for the apparent anomalies in specific heat, shear modulus, refractive index, thermal expansion, ultrasonic and dielectric relaxation, and bulk modulus of vitreous silica, whose pressure and temperature dependence is opposite that of crystalline silica. The time dependence of the strength of amorphous solids, traceable to the growth of flaws under the simultaneous influence of tensile stress and chemical attack, requires a time term in the statistical treatment of fracture. The low thermal conductivity of non-crystalline solids has implications with regard to structure that become understandable in the case of low temperatures, as indicated by the example of vitreous silica. Experimental data on other materials are needed to test the suggestion that low temperature thermal conductivity may prove to be a sensitive, and perhaps not inconvenient, indication of crystallinity.

The discussions following each chapter supply additional valuable results and interpretations, lending emphasis to some points and highlighting the many questions that still remain.

I acknowledge with gratitude the assistance of the members of the Conference Committee, Dr. O. L. Anderson, Professor S. H. Bauer, Dr. T. H. Davies, Dr. N. J. Kreidl, and Professor J. A. Krumhansl, in preparation of the manuscript.

V. D. Fréchette

April, 1960

Participants

O. L. Anderson
Bell Telephone Laboratories, Murray Hill, New Jersey

S. Bateson
Duplate Canada Limited, Oshawa, Ontario, Canada

S. H. Bauer
Department of Chemistry, Cornell University, Ithaca, New York

A. B. Bestul
Mineral Products Division, National Bureau of Standards, Washington 25, D. C.

Neill M. Brandt
Mellon Institute, 4400 Fifth Avenue, Pittsburgh 13, Pennsylvania

M. J. Buerger
Department of Geology and Geophysics, Massachusetts Institute of Technology, Cambridge 39, Massachusetts

R. J. Charles
General Electric Research Laboratory, P.O. Box 1088, Schenectady, New York

Alvin Cohen
Mellon Institute, 4400 Fifth Avenue, Pittsburgh 13, Pennsylvania

H. Cole
Pilkington Brothers Limited, St. Helens, England

John S. Coleman
Division of Physical Sciences, National Research Council, 2101 Constitution Avenue, Washington 25, D. C.

Ralph H. Condit
Solid State Sciences Division, Air Force Office of Scientific Research, Washington 25, D. C.

J. H. Crawford, Jr.
Solid State Division, Oak Ridge National Laboratory, Oak Ridge, Tennessee

T. H. Davies
Mellon Institute, 4400 Fifth Avenue, Pittsburgh 13, Pennsylvania

R. O. Davies
Queen Mary College, Mile End Road, E1, London, England

P. Debye
Department of Chemistry, Cornell University, Ithaca, New York

G. J. Dienes
Brookhaven National Laboratory, Upton, L. I., New York

R. W. Douglas
Department of Glass Technology, The University, Northumberland Road, Sheffield 10, England

H. A. Elliott
Royal Military College of Canada, Kingston, Ontario, Canada

J. C. Fisher
General Electric Research Laboratory, P.O. Box 1088, Schenectady, New York

Thomas Fox
Mellon Institute, 4400 Fifth Avenue, Pittsburgh 13, Pennsylvania

V. D. Fréchette
State University of New York College of Ceramics at Alfred University, Alfred, New York

H. L. Frisch
Bell Telephone Laboratories, Murray Hill, New Jersey

J. E. Goldman
Physics and Chemistry Departments, Scientific Laboratory, Ford Motor Company, Dearborn, Michigan

T. J. Gray
State University of New York College of Ceramics at Alfred University, Alfred, New York

C. H. Greene
State University of New York College of Ceramics at Alfred University, Alfred, New York

J. R. Hensler
Bausch & Lomb Optical Company, Rochester 2, New York

R. Hilsch
First Physics Institute, University of Göttingen, Göttingen, Germany

Maurice L. Huggins
Research Laboratories, Eastman Kodak Company, Rochester 4, New York

Robert E. Hughes
University of Pennsylvania, Philadelphia 4, Pennsylvania

J. C. King
Whippany Laboratory, Bell Telephone Laboratories, Whippany, New Jersey

P. L. Kirby
Welwyn Electrical Laboratories Ltd., Bedlington, England

P. G. Klemens
Division of Physics, National Standards Laboratory, University Grounds, City Road, Chippendale, N. S. W., Sydney, Australia

N. J. Kreidl
Bausch & Lomb Optical Company, Rochester 2, New York

J. A. Krumhansl
Department of Physics, Cornell University, Ithaca, New York

A. B. Lidiard
Physics Research Laboratory, Upper Redlands Road, Reading, England

Howard Lillie
Corning Glass Works, Corning, New York

Theodore A. Litovitz

Catholic University of America, Washington 17, D. C.

R. D. Maurer

Corning Glass Works, Corning, New York

John Michener

Owens-Corning Fiberglas Corporation, Research Center, Newark, Ohio

R. E. Mould

Preston Laboratories, Inc., Box 149, Butler, Pennsylvania

Eugene F. Poncelet

Stanford Research Institute, Menlo Park, California

J. A. Prins

Laboratory of Technical Physics, Technical University of Delft, Mijnbouwplein 11, Delft, Netherlands

Taikyue Ree

Department of Chemistry, University of Utah, Salt Lake City, Utah

D. C. Rich

Pittsburgh Plate Glass Co., Box 11472, Pittsburgh, Pennsylvania

D. P. Riley

Intertechnical Consultants, Inc., 70 Rue du XXI Décembre, Geneva, Switzerland

Guy Rindone

Department of Ceramic Technology, The Pennsylvania State University, University Park, Pennsylvania

Murray A. Schwartz

Metallurgy Branch WCLTL, Aeronautical Research Laboratory, Wright Air Development Division, Wright-Patterson AFB, Ohio

Ronald E. Sellers, Jr.

Solid State Sciences Division, Air Force Office of Scientific Research, Washington 25, D. C.

I. Simon

Arthur D. Little, Inc., 30 Memorial Drive, Cambridge 42, Massachusetts

W. P. Slichter

Bell Telephone Laboratories, Murray Hill, New Jersey

Roman Smoluchowski
Department of Physics, Carnegie Institute of Technology, Pittsburgh 13, Pennsylvania

J. M. Stevels
Philips Research Laboratories, N. V. Philips Gloeilampenfabrieken, Eindhoven, Netherlands

R. A. Van Nordstrand
Sinclair Research Laboratories, Inc., 400 East Sibley Boulevard, Harvey, Illinois

D. A. Vermilyea
General Electric Company, P.O. Box 1088, Schenectady, New York

A. H. Weber
Department of Physics, University of St. Louis, St. Louis, Missouri

W. A. Weyl
Division of Mineral Technology, The Pennsylvania State University, University Park, Pennsylvania

A. E. R. Westman
Ontario Research Foundation, 43 Queens Park, Toronto 5, Ontario, Canada

Edgar F. Westrum, Jr.
Department of Chemistry, University of Michigan, Ann Arbor, Michigan

J. Zarzycki
Saint-Gobain, Laboratoires de la Villette, 52, Boulevard de la Villette, Paris 19, France

Contents

1

by

P. Debye

Cornell University

Scattering of Radiation by Non-crystalline Media

Formulation of the Interference Principle

One rather powerful, but by no means all-powerful, method for investigating the structure of non-crystalline substances can be based on the observation of the angular distribution of the intensity of scattered radiation. The kind of information about the structure we can obtain in this way, obvious for crystalline media, is not so evident for non-crystalline media. A prime objective of our discussion therefore is a proper definition of such structures. In order to avoid complications unnecessary for this purpose only cases will be considered in which, in the scattering process, the interaction between the radiation and the atoms of the medium is small in magnitude. This certainly covers with a high degree of accuracy the scattering of visible light and of x-rays. Cases of stronger interaction have been considered by van Hove (1954, 1958).

Let us assume a medium with an average dielectric constant ε on top of which local fluctuations $\delta\varepsilon$ of random character are superimposed. Through this medium we send a primary plane light wave which is polarized and in which the electric force has the amplitude E_0. Suppose also that the fluctuations $\delta\varepsilon$ are confined to a small volume which, however, may be large compared to the wavelength λ. By a straightforward application of Maxwell's equations, we then find that this volume is the center of scattered radiations. At a large distance R from this volume (large compared to the dimensions of the volume) and within the medium of dielectric constant ε, the scattered wave has an amplitude and phase (both measured in the usual way by writing for the electric force E of the scattered wave) which lie in the plane defined by the directions of E_0 and R and is perpendicular to R:

$$E = E_0 \frac{e^{-ikR}}{R} \frac{k^2}{4\pi} \sin \vartheta \int \frac{\delta\mathcal{E}}{\mathcal{E}} e^{ik(\mathbf{s},\mathbf{r})} \, d\tau. \tag{1}$$

In this relation λ is the wavelength in the medium and $k = 2\pi/\lambda$. The angle between the directions of E_0 and of R is called ϑ. $\mathbf{s}$ is a vector which is the difference between a unit vector $\mathbf{S}$ in the direction of R and another unit vector $\mathbf{S}_0$ in the direction of propagation of the primary wave. If we call the angle between these two vectors θ, the absolute value of the difference vector $\mathbf{s}$ becomes $2 \sin (\theta/2)$. Finally $\mathbf{r}$ is a vector defining the position of the volume element $d\tau$ in the scattering volume with respect to an arbitrary center; from it the large distance R is measured. The integration has to be carried out over the scattering volume; the factor $e^{ik(\mathbf{s},\mathbf{r})}$ measures the interference between the wavelets emitted by the different volume elements.

The Correlation Function

From relation (1) we obtain the scattered intensity by multiplying E and its conjugate complex. We call the primary intensity $\mathcal{I}_0$ and the secondary intensity $\mathcal{I}$, and this process leads immediately to the relation

$$\frac{\mathcal{I}}{\mathcal{I}_0} = \frac{k^4}{16\pi^2} \frac{\sin^2 \vartheta}{R^2} \iint \left(\frac{\delta\mathcal{E}}{\mathcal{E}}\right)\left(\frac{\delta\mathcal{E}}{\mathcal{E}}\right)' e^{ik(\mathbf{s},\mathbf{r}-\mathbf{r}')} \, d\tau \, d\tau' \tag{2}$$

This is the instantaneous intensity. Only the average value, which, in the case of fluctuations $\delta\mathcal{E}$ which vary with time, is a time average. If the fluctuations are frozen in, we can replace the time average by a space average since the position of the sample under investigation obviously has no influence on the observed intensity. In order to be able to perform the integration we have to know the average value of the product

$$(\delta\mathcal{E}/\mathcal{E})_A (\delta\mathcal{E}/\mathcal{E})_B$$

in which the first fluctuation is measured in a point A and the second in another point B. In the case of stationary fluctuations we shall obtain this average by letting the measuring stick AB take up all possible positions and orientations within the scattering medium. We shall consider only the isotropic case; then we can say that the product in question will be a function of the distance AB only, which we shall call r. For $r = 0$ this product takes the value

$$\mathrm{Av}\ \langle(\delta\varepsilon/\varepsilon)^2\rangle$$

For large values of r the product obviously tends to zero. We now introduce the correlation function $C(r)$ by the definition

$$\mathrm{Av}\left\langle\left(\frac{\delta\varepsilon}{\varepsilon}\right)_A\left(\frac{\delta\varepsilon}{\varepsilon}\right)_B\right\rangle = \mathrm{Av}\left\langle\left(\frac{\delta\varepsilon}{\varepsilon}\right)^2\right\rangle C(r) \tag{3}$$

which makes $C(r)$ dimensionless and makes it start with 1 for $r = 0$. The same problem has appeared in many different connections, and it leads in all cases to equivalent mathematical formulations. As examples can be mentioned: (a) the theory of turbulence (Taylor, 1920, 1938); (b) the scattering of sound in water (Pekeris, 1947); (c) the scattering of radio waves (Booker and Gordon, 1950). After the introduction of C the integration in (2) can be performed; it leads to the result

$$\frac{\mathcal{I}}{\mathcal{I}_0} = \frac{k^4}{16\pi^2}\frac{\sin^2\vartheta}{R^2}V\,\mathrm{Av}\left\langle\left(\frac{\delta\varepsilon}{\varepsilon}\right)^2\right\rangle \int_0^\infty C(r)\frac{\sin ksr}{ksr}\,d\tau \tag{4}$$

in which V is the volume illuminated by the primary light wave. The right-hand side is dimensionless as it should be, since the integral represents a volume. This volume depends on the angle of observation through the inclusion of s in its definition and measures the interference effect due to the irregularities in the medium. It is obvious that this effect appears as a result of the correlation of the fluctuations in neighboring points. It can easily be seen that, should the primary radiation be unpolarized, it is only necessary to replace $\sin^2\vartheta$ by $\frac{1}{2}(1 + \cos^2\theta)$.

The Special Case of X-rays

The scattering of x-rays is due mainly to the electrons dispersed in the medium, and for many practical cases these electrons can be treated as free. Under the influence of a periodic electric field,

$$Ee^{i\omega t}$$

the amplitude x of an electron with charge e and mass m will be

$$x = -\frac{eE}{m\omega^2}e^{i\omega t}$$

The polarization P due to n such free electrons per cubic centimeter will be

$$P = -\frac{ne^2}{m\omega^2}Ee^{i\omega t}$$

which means that the dielectric constant ε will be

$$\varepsilon = 1 - \frac{4\pi n e^2}{m\omega^2} \tag{5}$$

which is very little different from unity and shows that the phase velocity in the medium is larger than the velocity of light in vacuum. The only thing necessary to describe the x-ray scattering is to replace the dielectric constant in (4) by its value (5). The result is

$$\frac{\mathcal{I}}{\mathcal{I}_0} = \left(\frac{e^2}{mc^2}\right)^2 \frac{\sin^2 \vartheta}{R^2} V \text{ Av } \langle (\delta n)^2 \rangle \int_0^\infty C(r) \frac{\sin ksr}{ksr} d\tau \tag{6}$$

The factor $(e^2/mc^2)^2$ can be called the scattering cross section of the single free electron; it has the value 8.06×10^{-26} cm^2. Owing to the dispersion peculiar for free electrons, the usual characteristic dependence of Rayleigh scattering on the wavelength is wiped out. Equation (6) can be read as saying that the scattering of the $Vn = \mathfrak{N}$ electrons contained in volume V is equivalent to that of

$$\mathfrak{N}^* = V \text{ Av } \langle (\delta n)^2 \rangle \int_0^\infty C(r) \frac{\sin ksr}{ksr} d\tau \tag{6'}$$

independent free electrons. Their number $\mathfrak{N}^*$ varies of course with s, that is, with the angle of observation θ. Since $\delta\varepsilon$ is proportional to δn, the correlation function $C(r)$ can here be defined by the relation

$$\text{Av } \langle \delta n_A \, \delta n_B \rangle = \text{Av } \langle (\delta n)^2 \rangle \, C(r)$$

Calculation of the Correlation Function from the Intensity Distribution

It is clear that for the definition of the structure of a non-crystalline medium the correlation function plays the same role as the lattice structure and the distribution of the atoms within the lattice cell for a crystalline medium. For this reason it is important to see how the correlation function can be derived from observations about the angular distribution of the scattered intensity. It turns out that the solution of this problem is given immediately by the application of a Fourier inversion. We know that if

$$f(x) = 2 \int_0^\infty \varphi(u) \sin 2\pi x u \, du$$

the function $\varphi(u)$ can be found by calculating

$$\varphi(u) = 2 \int_0^\infty f(x) \sin 2\pi u x \, dx$$

Now we can say, as is seen from the preceding paragraphs, that the experiment provides us with a curve the ordinates of which represent a volume Ω as a function of $s = 2 \sin (\theta/2)$ defined by

$$\Omega(ks) = \int_0^\infty C(r) \frac{\sin ksr}{ksr} \, d\tau \qquad (7)$$

Since $k = 2\pi/\lambda$, this relation can also be written in the form

$$\frac{s}{\lambda} \Omega \left(\frac{s}{\lambda} \right) = 2 \int_0^\infty rC(r) \sin 2\pi \frac{s}{\lambda} r \, dr \qquad (7')$$

which by application of Fourier's theorem leads immediately to

$$rC(r) = 2 \int_0^\infty \frac{s}{\lambda} \Omega \left(\frac{s}{\lambda} \right) \sin 2\pi r \frac{s}{\lambda} \, d \left(\frac{s}{\lambda} \right) \qquad (8)$$

In actual practice it never is possible to match the mathematical elegance of this solution for the simple reason that the range of $s = 2 \sin (\theta/2)$ is limited from 0 to 2 and therefore the curve for $\Omega(s/\lambda)$ is known only for a finite interval instead of the required range from 0 to ∞.

In some important cases it can be shown that the correlation function is a simple exponential,

$$C(r) = e^{-r/a} \qquad (9)$$

a relation which defines immediately a correlation length a. If this is so, the angular intensity distribution is represented by a simple formula. The integration by which the volume Ω is defined can be performed readily and leads to

$$\Omega = \frac{8\pi a^3}{(1 + k^2 s^2 a^2)^2} \qquad (10)$$

The corresponding intensity distribution can be checked by plotting the reciprocal of the square root of the scattered intensity as a function of s^2. If the correlation function is indeed a simple exponential, this procedure gives a straight line the slope of which is a measure for the correlation length a.

Equation (10) shows, with reference to our general formula for the scattered intensity, that for large enough values of s this intensity decreases in proportion to s^{-4}. This feature is quite general, independent of the special form of the correlation function. Substituting σ for ks, our formula (7) for the definition of the volume Ω, which in essence describes the angular intensity distribution, can be written in the form

$$\Omega = -4\pi \frac{1}{\sigma} \frac{d}{d\sigma} \int_0^\infty C(r) \cos \sigma r \, dr$$

By repeated partial integration the integral can be developed in powers of $1/\sigma$, and the first approximation obtained in this way is

$$\int_0^\infty C(r) \cos \sigma r \, dr = \frac{C'(0)}{\sigma^2} + \cdots$$

which makes

$$\Omega = -8\pi \frac{C'(0)}{\sigma^4} + \cdots = -\frac{8\pi}{k^4} \frac{C'(0)}{s^4} + \cdots \qquad (11)$$

This result is correct provided $C(r)$ vanishes strongly enough for large values of r and, what is more important, provided a finite gradient of $C(r)$ for $r = 0$ exists.

The Analysis of Hole Structures

(See Debye and Bueche, 1949; Debye, Anderson, and Brumberger, 1957; Guinier, Fournet, Walker, and Yudowitch, 1955.) In catalytic processes structures are used which have a high specific surface S/V, which, deviating from the usual custom, we shall define as the surface per unit volume and not per unit weight. Values of, for example, 100 m^2/cc are common. Such a specific surface has the dimension of a reciprocal length, and 100 m^2/cc corresponds to a length of 100 Å. It is evident that, in case we want to investigate such structures by their x-ray scattering, we shall have to concentrate on small angle scattering if the usual x-rays of wavelengths about 1 Å are used. As soon as we do this, however, we deliberately concentrate on geometrical properties of the hole structure and cannot expect to find any indication of the atomic structure of the solid material, which can appear only at larger angles. For our purpose, then, the structure can be considered as consisting of material parts in which the electron density n is constant and holes in which the electron density is zero. If we take χ to represent the porosity (quotient of volume of holes to total volume) the average electron density will be

$$n_{av} = n(1 - \chi) + 0\chi = n(1 - \chi)$$

and the local fluctuations Δ_M in material and Δ_H in holes will be

$$\Delta_M = n - n(1 - \chi) = n\chi$$

$$\Delta_H = 0 - n(1 - \chi) = -n(1 - \chi) \qquad (12)$$

which leads to

$$\mathrm{Av}\langle\Delta^2\rangle = (1 - \chi)\Delta_M{}^2 + \chi\Delta_H{}^2 = n^2\chi(1 - \chi) \tag{13}$$

We must now define the correlation function. In the special case of our hole structure the measuring stick AB which we introduced to define the correlation function can appear only in four different positions depending on whether end A or end B is in material or in a hole. In order to calculate the average value of $\Delta_A \Delta_B$ we introduce the four probabilities

$$
\begin{array}{cc}
p_{00} & p_{01} \\
p_{10} & p_{11}
\end{array}
\tag{14}
$$

where p_{01} is the probability that our measuring stick, being with end A in a hole (index 0), will have end B in material (index 1). The other three possibilities are defined in an analogous way. We now can calculate the average value of the product $\Delta_A \Delta_B$ for a given length of the measuring stick and obtain

$$\mathrm{Av}\langle\Delta_A \Delta_B\rangle = \chi p_{00} \Delta_H{}^2 + [\chi p_{01} + (1 - \chi)p_{10}] \Delta_M \Delta_H$$
$$+ (1 - \chi)p_{11} \Delta_M{}^2 \tag{15}$$

The four probabilities we introduced are not independent of each other. Obviously the following three relations must hold.

$$p_{00} + p_{01} = 1 \qquad p_{10} + p_{11} = 1 \qquad \chi p_{01} = (1 - \chi)p_{10} \tag{16}$$

and this means that we must have

$$
\begin{array}{ll}
p_{00} = 1 - (1 - \chi)R & p_{01} = (1 - \chi)R \\
p_{10} = \chi R & p_{11} = 1 - \chi R
\end{array}
\tag{17}
$$

in which R is an as yet unknown function of the length of the stick. Substituting (17) in (15) gives, by using (12), the result

$$\mathrm{Av}\langle\Delta_A \Delta_B\rangle = n^2\chi(1 - \chi)(1 - R)$$

Now according to (13) the factor on the right-hand side represents $\mathrm{Av}\langle\Delta^2\rangle$, so we come to the result that our former correlation function $C(r)$ and the new function $R(r)$ are connected by the relation

$$C(r) = 1 - R(r) \tag{18}$$

Since the correlation function $C(r)$ can be derived from the angular intensity distribution, the same is now true for $R(r)$, and we can, according to (17), also evaluate the four probabilities p. It is easier to condense the whole information by asking for the probability p_{diss}, i.e., that the ends of our measuring stick will be dissimilar (hole and material or material and hole). For this probability we find

$$p_{\text{diss}} = \chi p_{01} + (1 - \chi)p_{10} = 2\chi(1 - \chi)R = 2\chi(1 - \chi)[1 - C] \quad (19)$$

The curve for p_{diss} so obtained can be considered, in a qualitative way, as a representation of the distribution of hole sizes. It starts with 0 for $r = 0$ and ends with the ordinate $2\chi(1 - \chi)$ for large values of r.

The Relation between Correlation Function and Specific Surface

(See G. Porod, 1951, 1952; Guinier et al., 1955). If we consider the probability of dissimilar ends p_{diss} for very small lengths of our stick, this stick will have to cut through the surface, and in evaluating the value of the probability we shall have to follow this surface through the whole volume. From this it is evident that a relation should exist which connects p_{diss} with the specific surface. A simple geometrical argument (Debye, Anderson, and Brumberger, 1957) shows that, in the limit for very small lengths r of our stick in a volume V which contains a surface S,

$$p_{\text{diss}} = (S/2V)r \quad (20)$$

On the other hand, relation (19) shows that for small values of r we have

$$p_{\text{diss}} = -2\chi(1 - \chi)C'(0)r \quad (20')$$

Comparison of these two relations then shows that the specific surface S/V can be determined by evaluating the tangent of the correlation curve for $r = 0$ according to the relation

$$S/V = -4\chi(1 - \chi)C'(0) \quad (21)$$

In case the correlation function is a simple exponential function as in (9), this boils down to

$$S/V = 4\chi(1 - \chi)(1/a) \quad (21')$$

In this case the representation of the intensity curve in the manner described on page 5 provides immediately a measure of the specific surface by the slope of the straight line in question.

In an experimental investigation (Debye, Anderson, Brumberger, 1957) Anderson and Brumberger showed that in many practical cases of gel catalysts the straight-line representation of the reciprocal square root of the intensity versus the square of the scattering angle fitted the experimental results. That brought up the question: Why should the special exponential correlation curve appear at all? It could be shown (Debye, Anderson, and Brumberger, 1957) that an absolutely random arrangement of the interfaces between holes and material inside the sample indeed leads to the exponential correlation function. In equation (11) it was shown that for sufficiently large values of s the scattered intensity should decrease proportionately with the reciprocal fourth power of s, and the proportionality was found to be proportional to $C'(0)$. Since in the meantime we have seen that $C'(0)$ is proportional to the specific surface (equation 21), we see that for sufficiently large values of s the observed intensity itself should be a measure of the specific surface. Starting with equation (6) for the equivalent number $\mathfrak{N}^*$ of free electrons, the Av $\langle(\delta n)^2\rangle$ can be expressed by the electron density n of the material and the porosity χ according to equation (13). For the integral Ω (see equation 7) appearing as the second factor which determines $\mathfrak{N}^*$, we can substitute its asymptotic value according to (11). In this way we arrive at

$$\mathfrak{N}^* = -\frac{8\pi}{k^4} V n^2 \chi (1 - \chi) \frac{C'(0)}{s^4}$$

Finally $C'(0)$ and the specific surface are connected by relation (21). Thus we have in the range of larger angles

$$\mathfrak{N}^* = \frac{2\pi}{k^4} \frac{n^2 S}{s^4} \tag{22}$$

It is interesting to note that in the case of gel catalysts and by a purely experimental approach Van Nordstrand came to the conclusions that (a) the scattered intensity decreased at larger angles in proportion to the reciprocal 4th power of the angle, and (b) in this range the intensity was proportional to the surface as derived from adsorption measurements, as long as samples of the same material were compared (Van Nordstrand and Hach, 1953; Van Nordstrand and Johnson, 1954).

Angular Dissymmetry of Critical Opalescence

Under ordinary circumstances the scattering of liquids is rather small and for visible light does not show any peculiar angular intensity distribution; it is essentially like that of an infinitely small dipole. However, in condensing a simple gas to a liquid and observing it in the vicinity of the critical point or in experimenting with two liquids in the vicinity of their critical mixing temperature, very strong scattering of visible light is observed. At the same time the scattered intensity becomes concentrated more and more in the forward direction (the direction of propagation of the primary beam) the nearer the temperature comes to the critical temperature (Zimm, 1950; Fuerth and Williams, 1954). In the light of our general formula, equation (4), this must mean that under such circumstances an appreciable correlation has to exist between the density or concentration fluctuations or the corresponding fluctuations of the refractive index over distances which are comparable with the wavelength of visible light. This is clear since the main angular dependence of the scattered intensity from the angle of observation is represented by the integral over the correlation function $C(r)$, and this integral will show appreciable variations with s only when $C(r)$ has not yet reached its final value of zero for distances r which make kr of the order of magnitude 1 or r of the order magnitude $\lambda/2\pi$.

From equation (4) only, we cannot yet calculate the intensity of scattering. It will be proportional to

$$\mathrm{Av}\left\langle\left(\frac{\delta\varepsilon}{\varepsilon}\right)^2\right\rangle \Big/ \int_0^\infty (Cr)\, d\tau$$

at least under ordinary circumstances, when the correlation distance is small compared with the wavelength of the light, but the value of this factor can be determined only after we have specified the reason for the fluctuations. From now on we shall consider only the case of the condensation of a gas, since this sufficiently illustrates the situation.

Following Einstein (1910), we accept as the reason for the fluctuations the thermal molecular motion. For the actual calculation, however, it will be more appropriate for our purpose to use a line of reasoning followed by Brillouin (1922). He considers the thermal motion in the liquid a superposition of elastic (sonic) waves, the same way as has been found to be practical for the calculation of the specific heat of solids. He starts out by calculating from equation (1) the scattered intensity of a homogeneous liquid through which a plain sonic wave travels which induces small periodic fluctuations η of the dielectric constant ε. Experiments showing the scattering of light by artificial supersonic waves were made by Debye and Sears (1932). Such fluctuations can be represented by

$$\eta = \eta_0 e^{i\omega t} e^{-iK(\mathbf{S},\mathbf{r})}$$

for waves of frequency ω and a direction indicated by the unit vector $\mathbf{S}$. Brillouin then accepts for the number of such waves, dZ, all independent from each other in volume V and in the interval $d\Omega$ (with $d\Omega$ indicating the element of solid angle) the usual relation

$$dZ = \frac{V}{(2\pi)^3} K^2 \, dK \, d\Omega$$

Performing the integration over the whole volume, which is illuminated (taken to be a sphere for the purpose of the actual calculation), he finds:

(a) Of all the thermal waves which are traversing the liquid only one is effective for the scattering. It is a wave with a front such that the scattered light can be considered as primary light reflected at this front.

(b) Between the wavelength λ of the light and the wavelength Λ of the reflecting sonic wave, Bragg's relation must hold. This relation is written

$$s/\lambda = 1/\Lambda \tag{23}$$

If now the amplitude of the dielectric constant fluctuation in this special wave is called η_0, Brillouin's calculations show that the intensity scattered by a volume V is proportional to the square of the amplitude. They lead to the relation

$$\frac{g}{g_0} = \frac{k^4}{16\pi^2} \frac{\sin^2 \vartheta}{R^2} V^2 \left(\frac{\eta_0}{\varepsilon}\right)^2 \tag{24}$$

The total energy of such a wave filling volume V is

$$\frac{V}{2\kappa} \left(\frac{\sigma_0}{\rho}\right)^2 \tag{25}$$

if in the usual way κ indicates the compressibility and if the amplitude of the density fluctuations is σ_0 whereas ρ is the average density of the liquid. This must be equal to βT in thermal equilibrium (β is Boltzmann's constant); therefore

$$\left(\frac{\sigma_0}{\rho}\right)^2 = \frac{2\kappa\beta T}{V} \tag{26}$$

Since we can express η_0 in σ_0 by the relation

$$\eta_0 = \sigma_0 \frac{d\varepsilon}{d\rho}$$

we come to the final result

$$\frac{g}{g_0} = \frac{k^4}{16\pi^2} \frac{\sin^2 \vartheta}{R^2} V 2\kappa\beta T \left(\frac{\rho}{\varepsilon} \frac{d\varepsilon}{d\rho}\right)^2 \tag{27}$$

This is the result first derived by Einstein (1910). In this formula there is not any indication of an angular dissymmetry. Obviously there is a flaw somewhere in the reasoning, and it comes to the foreground in experiments near the critical point. The next paragraph deals with the necessary correction.

Molecular Energy in an Inhomogeneous Medium

The wavelength of the sound waves on which the scattered light can be considered as reflected changes with the angle θ between primary and secondary ray. According to Bragg's relation it goes from ∞ for $\theta = 0$ to $\lambda/2$ for $\theta = \pi$. In this way a range of frequencies going roughly from 0 to 10^4 megacycles is covered. The observation of the intensity of the scattered light, when θ goes from 0 to π, can be interpreted as a measurement of the square of the amplitude of the thermal supersonic waves over the corresponding range of wavelengths. Einstein's result is equivalent to saying that because of the law of equipartition those amplitude squares are all the same for the sound waves of the whole interval. In scrutinizing the details, it is seen that this statement rests on the assumption that the potential energy involved in the propagation of the sound waves is due to the compressibility. This compressibility gets bigger the nearer we come to the critical point. In this point itself it is infinite, and this has the effect that the energy involved in the compression to a given amplitude approaches zero near the critical point, as shown by equation (25). Under these circumstances it is essential to consider the existence of any other source of energy, even if it is unimportant under ordinary circumstances. The fact that surface tension exists, showing that juxtaposition of two different densities involves an extra energy, indicates that if we want to be exact in calculating the energy in a wave not only the amplitude but also the spatial gradient of the amplitude has to be considered (Roccard, 1933). This remark can be formulated in a quantitative way by the following reasoning.

Suppose that the potential energy between two molecules is solely a function of their mutual distance r. Thinking of universal molecular attraction, we call it $-\varepsilon(r)$. The number of molecules around a central molecule in a shell of radius r and thickness dr is

$$4\pi n r^2\, dr = n\, d\tau$$

The potential energy of one central molecule due to action of its surroundings therefore is

$$w = -\int n\varepsilon(r)\, d\tau \tag{28}$$

where in our simplified picture of molecular forces we let the integration go from the distance of contact to infinity. Around the position of the central molecule we can develop the molecular density n in powers of the coordinates around this center. If we break this series off at the second power of these coordinates, the result is

$$w = -I_0 n - \frac{I_2}{6} \Delta n \tag{29}$$

in which Δ stands for the Laplace operator calculated at the position of the central molecule and I_0 and I_2 are defined by the integrals

$$I_0 = \int \mathcal{E}(r)\, d\tau \qquad I_2 = \int r^2 \mathcal{E}(r)\, d\tau \tag{29'}$$

We can define a length l by making

$$l^2 = I_2/I_0 \tag{30}$$

We shall call this length the range of molecular forces. We can now calculate the total potential energy $\mathfrak{U}$ in a volume V containing $\mathfrak{N}$ molecules and find, by integrating over the whole volume,

$$2\mathfrak{U} = -I_0 \int n^2\, d\tau - \frac{I_0}{6} l^2 \int n\, \Delta n\, d\tau \tag{31}$$

We are trying here to discuss a theory in its most simple formulation. For this reason it will be sufficient not to go beyond the classical reasoning of van der Waals. For the potential energy of a liquid he writes

$$\mathfrak{U} = -a/V$$

This shows, according to (31), that the van der Waals constant a can be identified with

$$a = \mathfrak{N}^2(I_0/2) \tag{32}$$

We can also remark that by partial integration the second integral in (31) can be given the form

$$\int n\, \Delta n\, d\tau = \int n\, \frac{\partial n}{\partial \nu}\, d\sigma - \int (\text{grad } n)^2\, d\tau$$

in which the first integral is to be taken over the boundary surface with the normal ν. Combining all this, we come to the conclusion that in a liquid with densities variable from point to point we not only have per unit volume the van der Waals energy density

$$u_1 = -a/V^2 = -(I_0/2)n^2 \tag{33}$$

but also an additional energy density

$$u_2 = (I_0/12)(l \operatorname{grad} n)^2 \qquad (33')$$

Angular Distribution of the Scattered Intensity

If we use the classical van der Waals equation of state for a volume V containing $\mathfrak{N}$ molecules,

$$p = \frac{\mathfrak{N}\beta T}{V - b} - \frac{a}{V^2}$$

the critical parameters are

$$p_c = \frac{1}{27}\frac{a}{b^2} \qquad V_c = 3b \qquad \mathfrak{N}\beta T_c = \frac{8}{27}\frac{a}{b} \qquad (34)$$

Using the reduced parameters

$$\varphi = \frac{V}{V_c} \quad \text{and} \quad \tau = \frac{T}{T_c} \qquad (35)$$

the reciprocal compressibility calculated from the equation of state comes out to be

$$\frac{1}{\kappa} = 6p_c \left[\frac{4\varphi}{(3\varphi - 1)^2} \tau - \frac{1}{\varphi^2} \right] \qquad (36)$$

We shall suppose, for the sake of simplicity in the formulas, that the scattering experiment is carried out at constant volume and decreasing temperature and that the density is kept equal to the critical density. In this case $\varphi = 1$ and

$$1/\kappa = 6p_c(\tau - 1) \qquad (36')$$

In equation (25) we calculated the energy, due to the compressibility, contained in a volume V through which a supersonic wave passes. If the value in (36') for the compressibility is substituted, this energy becomes

$$V3p_c(\tau - 1)(\sigma_0/\rho)^2 \qquad (37)$$

Half of this is potential energy.

In order to calculate the additional potential energy due to density gradients, we observe that, (a) the relative density fluctuations are the same as the relative fluctuations of the number of molecules per unit volume and (b) the operation gradient performed on a wave of the form

$$A \cos (\omega t - Kx)$$

merely changes this expression into

$$KA \sin (\omega t - Kx)$$

From equation (33') we then conclude that the additional energy in volume V is

$$\frac{V}{2} \frac{I_0 n^2}{12} K^2 l^2 \left(\frac{\sigma_0}{\rho}\right)^2 \tag{37'}$$

On the other hand, by application of equations (32) and (34) it is found that

$$n^2 I_0 = \frac{2a}{V^2} = \frac{2}{g} \frac{1}{\varphi^2} \frac{a}{b^2} = \frac{6 p_c}{\varphi^2}$$

The ratio of the additional to the compressional potential energy therefore is

$$\frac{1}{6} \frac{K^2 l^2}{\tau - 1} \tag{38}$$

if again, as before, we assume that the experiment is carried out at $\varphi = 1$. Upon taking the additional potential energy into account one obtains, because of equipartition, the relationship

$$\frac{V}{2\kappa} \left(\frac{\sigma_0}{\rho}\right)^2 \left[1 + \frac{1}{6} \frac{K^2 l^2}{\tau - 1}\right] = \beta T \tag{39}$$

instead of equation (26), derived previously by Einstein. Remembering that $K = 2\pi/\Lambda$ and that Bragg's relation holds between the wavelength Λ of the supersonic wave and the wavelength λ of the optical wave, we come now, instead of to equation (27), to the final result,

$$\frac{g}{g_0} = \frac{k^4}{16\pi^2} \frac{\sin^2 \vartheta}{R^2} V \left(\frac{\rho \, d\varepsilon}{\varepsilon \, d\rho}\right)^2 \frac{2\kappa\beta T}{1 + \dfrac{2\pi^2}{3} \dfrac{l^2}{\lambda^2} \dfrac{s^2}{\tau - 1}} \tag{40}$$

Since according to (36') κ is proportional to $1/(\tau - 1)$, relation (40) represents the familiar fact that, with the approach to the critical point, the intensity increases strongly. More important, because of the denominator, the angular dissymmetry increases at the same time. Assuming $l = 10$ Å and $\lambda = 3000$ Å, a value of $\tau - 1 = 0.73 \times 10^{-4}$ will make the factor of s^2 in the denominator equal to unity, which means a strongly pronounced dissymmetry. On the other hand, for a critical temperature $T_c = 300$ it would only be necessary to approach the critical temperature to a distance of 0.022°C in order to establish that dissymmetry.

It is clear that similar relations will hold for the case of the critical mixing point if the energy relations are discussed, as this is usually done in defining the cohesive energy density. If the foregoing explanation is accepted, this means that the angular dissymmetry in the vicinity of the critical point is a measure for the range of molecular forces. From this point of view measurements of this type become important.

The Correlation Function

We started by showing that in scattering by inhomogeneous media the correlation function is of fundamental importance. At first glance it may seem, from the text of the immediately preceding paragraphs, as if we now had completely lost sight of this point of view. This section is added in order to show what the correlation function is which corresponds to relation (40) and to our physical picture of critical opalescence. Consider two points A and B in the liquid. If a wave passes through the liquid in a direction indicated by the unit vector $\mathbf{S}$, the density fluctuation σ in a point at position $\mathbf{r}$ can be represented by the formula

$$\sigma = \sigma_0 e^{i[\omega t - K(\mathbf{S}, \mathbf{r})]}$$

The average value of the product of the two density fluctuations in points A and B is

$$\text{Av} \langle \sigma_A \sigma_B \rangle = \frac{\sigma_0^2}{2} \cos K(\mathbf{S}, \mathbf{r}_B - \mathbf{r}_A) \tag{41}$$

All the different thermal waves are independent of each other. Remembering that the number of waves in the interval $K^2\, dK\, d\Omega$ (with $d\Omega$ indicating the element of solid angle) is

$$dZ = \frac{V}{(2\pi)^3} K^2\, dK\, d\Omega$$

we find immediately

$$\text{Av} \langle \sigma_A \sigma_B \rangle = \frac{V}{(2\pi)^3} \int \frac{\sigma_0^2}{2} \cos K(\mathbf{Sr}) K^2\, dK\, d\Omega$$

if the vector from A to B now is called $\mathbf{r}$. The integration over the solid angle can be carried out immediately with the result that

$$\text{Av} \langle \sigma_A \sigma_B \rangle = 4\pi \frac{V}{(2\pi)^3} \int_0^{K_m} \frac{\sigma_0^2}{2} \frac{\sin Kr}{Kr} K^2\, dK \tag{42}$$

The integration starts at $K = 0$, it ends at $K = K_m$, where, as in the case of the specific heats, K_m is determined by the fact that the liquid has a finite number of degrees of freedom. This leads to the relation

$$\frac{V}{(2\pi)^3}\frac{4\pi}{3}K_m{}^3 = 3\mathfrak{N} \tag{43}$$

In our case, where we have taken account of the existence of an energy additional to the compressional energy due to density gradients, we found that equipartition leads to relation (39). Substituting the value for $\sigma_0{}^2$, from this relation gives the result

$$\mathrm{Av}\left\langle\frac{\sigma_A}{\rho}\frac{\sigma_B}{\rho}\right\rangle = \frac{4\pi\kappa\beta T}{(2\pi)^3}\frac{1}{r}\int_0^{K_m}\frac{\sin Kr}{1 + K^2/K_0{}^2}K\,dK \tag{44}$$

with

$$K_0{}^2 = 6\frac{\tau - 1}{l^2} \tag{44'}$$

For $r = 0$ this leads to

$$\mathrm{Av}\left\langle\left(\frac{\sigma}{\rho}\right)^2\right\rangle = \frac{4\pi\kappa\beta T}{(2\pi)^3}\int_0^{K_m}\frac{K^2\,dK}{1 + K^2/K_0{}^2}$$

$$= \frac{4\pi\kappa\beta T}{(2\pi)^3}K_0{}^3\left[\frac{K_m}{K_0} - \arctan\frac{K_m}{K_0}\right] \tag{45}$$

The correlation function is the quotient of (44) and (45). If now we consider first a case in which the experiment is carried out near the critical point, we observe that, since according to (43) and (44')

$$K_m = 2\pi\left(\frac{g}{4\pi}\frac{\mathfrak{N}}{V}\right)^{1/3} \quad \text{and} \quad K_0 = \frac{2\pi}{l}\sqrt{\frac{3}{2\pi^2}(\tau - 1)}$$

the quotient K_m/K_0 will be very large. In this case a good approximation will be achieved by substituting ∞ for the upper limit of the integration. Since

$$\int_0^\infty\frac{\sin\alpha x}{1 + x^2}\,dx = \frac{\pi}{2}e^{-\alpha}$$

we find for the correlation function the approximation

$$C(r) = \frac{\pi}{2}\frac{e^{-K_0 r}}{K_m{}^2} \tag{46}$$

An exponential approximation for the correlation function has been mentioned before (Ornstein and Zernike, 1918). In another paper of the same authors (Ornstein and Zernike, 1926), essentially the same formula as our relation (40) for the scattered intensity has been proposed. The reasoning, however, is quite different from that followed here. We are on common ground concerning the importance of correlation, the introduction of which was the outstanding featurre of Zernike's thesis (Zernike, 1916, 1917). It should also be noted that the introduction of the correlation concept provides a quantitative description of what Volmer (1957) calls: "The colloidal nature of liquid mixtures near the critical state."

From the derivation it is clear that the approximation (46) becomes invalid for small values of r. For $r = 0$ we always have $C(r) = 1$.

It is interesting to see what the correlation function expressed by the integral in equation (44) becomes for ordinary cases, for example, in a liquid at a temperature much lower than the critical temperature. In this case it is more appropriate not to try to calculate the compressibility but to use its experimental value. It is easily seen from expression (37′) for the additional energy, in substituting for $n^2 I_0$ its expression in terms of the critical pressure p_c and the reduced volume φ, that K_0^2 can be defined by the formula

$$K_0^2 = \frac{\varphi^2}{\kappa p_c} \frac{1}{l^2} \tag{47}$$

Taking as an example benzene at 20°C, it is found, applying equation (43) for K_m and equation (47) for K_0, that

$$K_m = \frac{2\pi}{5.9} \, \text{Å}^{-1} \quad \text{and} \quad K_0 = \frac{2\pi}{0.12l} \, \text{Å}^{-1}$$

K_m and K_0 are now both of the same order of magnitude, although K_m probably is a few times smaller than K_0. Taking, for instance, $l = 10$ Å gives $K_m/K_0 = \frac{1}{5}$. If we introduce now $x = K_m r$ as a new parameter and use in the integral the variable $\xi = K/K_m$ we have according to (44):

$$\text{Av}\left\langle \frac{\sigma_A}{\rho} \frac{\sigma_B}{\rho} \right\rangle = \frac{4\pi\kappa\beta T}{(2\pi)^3} \frac{K_m^3}{x^3} \int_0^1 \frac{\sin x\xi}{1 + (K_m^2/K_0^2)\xi^2} \xi \, d\xi \tag{48}$$

Since $K_m^2/K_0^2 = 1/25$, it will be a good approximation to neglect the part $(K_m^2/K_0^2)\xi^2$ in the denominator. So we obtain the approximation

$$\text{Av}\left\langle \frac{\sigma_A}{\rho} \frac{\sigma_B}{\rho} \right\rangle = \frac{4\pi\kappa\beta T}{(2\pi)^3} K_m^3 \frac{\sin x - x \cos x}{x^3} \tag{48′}$$

where $x = K_m r$. From this, taking the limiting value for $x = 0$, or from an approximate value calculated from (45) in the limit for $K_m/K_0 = 0$, the correlation function follows immediately as

$$C(r) = 3 \frac{\sin x - x \cos x}{x^3} \tag{49}$$

where $x = K_m r$. This is an interesting theoretical result in view of the well-known experimental results obtained by x-ray scattering for the radial distribution function of the atoms around a single central atom in a liquid, as introduced by Zernike and Prins (1927). Maxima and minima in the scattering diagram of liquids were first observed in 1916 (Debye and Scherrer). They were originally interpreted as the result of interference between the atoms in the molecule. This point of view, however, was soon corrected (Debye, 1925, 1927) and was experimentally proved to be untenable by the observation of a scattering pattern of monatomic liquids (Keesom and de Smedt, 1923).

The effect of approaching the critical temperature can be expressed very simply if, next to a range l of molecular forces, we introduce a range L of correlation by the definition

$$L^2 = \frac{\int C(r) r^2 \, d\tau}{\int C(r) \, d\tau}$$

From equation (4) it is evident that (after corrections for polarization effects) the first variation of the scattered intensity with s will be proportional to s^2 and be represented by a formula of the form

$$\frac{\mathcal{I}}{\mathcal{I}_0} = 1 - \frac{k^2 s^2}{6} L^2$$

According to equation (40) we also have for small values of s

$$\frac{\mathcal{I}}{\mathcal{I}_0} = 1 - \frac{2\pi^2}{3} \frac{l^2}{\lambda^2} \frac{s^2}{\tau - 1}$$

Since $k = 2\pi/\lambda$, we see at once that

$$L^2 = l^2/(\tau - 1) \tag{50}$$

We cannot, of course, apply (50) directly to the experiments of Zimm (1950) on the mixture of carbon tetrachloride and perfluoromethyl-cyclohexane. However, we can determine L by plotting the scattered intensity as a function of s^2 and measuring the tangent of this curve for $s = 0$. From Figure 6 in Zimm's publication it follows, for instance, that for a temperature distance of 0.02°C from the critical temperature we have $L/\lambda = 0.43$, which would make $L = 1300$ Å for an assumed value of the optical wavelength of 3000 Å. Moreover, Zimm's curves for different values of $T - T_c$ give values of L which follow relation (50) in their dependence on the temperature distance from the critical temperature, although, strictly speaking, our derivation of that relation does not apply directly to the case of liquid mixtures. We conclude that observations of the angular intensity distribution near the critical temperature can be used to investigate the range of molecular forces since, in order to obtain the correlation range in this vicinity, we have to multiply by such a big factor that the last-named range becomes comparable to the wavelength of visible light.

REFERENCES

Booker, H. G., and Gordon, W. E., *Proc. I.R.E.* **38**, 401 (1950).

Brillouin, L., *Ann. phys.* **17**, 88 (1922).

Debye, P., *J. Math. Phys.* **4**, 133 (1925).

Debye, P., *Physik. Z.* **28**, 135 (1927).

Debye, P., Anderson, H. R., and Brumberger, H., *J. Appl. Phys.* **28**, 679 (1957).

Debye, P., and Bueche, A. M., *J. Appl. Phys.* **20**, 518 (1949).

Debye, P., and Scherrer, P., *Goettinger Nachr.* **16** (1916).

Debye, P., and Sears, F. W., *Proc. Natl. Acad. Sci. U. S.* **18**, 409 (1932).

Einstein, A., *Ann. Physik* **33**, 1275 (1918).

Fuerth, R., and Williams, C. L., *Proc. Roy. Soc. (London)* **A224**, 104 (1954).

Guinier, A., Fournet, G., Walker, G B., and Yudowitch, K. L., *Small Angle Scattering of X-rays*, Wiley, New York, 1955.

Keesom, W. H., and de Smedt, J., *J. phys. radium* [6] **4**, 144 (1923).

Ornstein, L. S., and Zernike, F., *Physik. Z.* **19**, 134 (1918).

Ornstein, L. S., and Zernike, F., *Physik. Z.* **27**, 761 (1926).

Pekeris, C. L., *Phys. Rev.* **71**, 268 (1947).

Porod, G., *Kolloid Z.* **124**, 83 (1951).

Porod, G., *Kolloid Z.* **125**, 51, 109 (1952).

Roccard, Yves, *J. phys. radium* **4**, 165 (1933).

Taylor, G. I., *Proc. London Math. Soc.* **20**, 196 (1920).

Taylor, G. I., *Proc. Roy. Soc. (London)* **164**, 478 (1938).

van Hove, L., *Phys. Rev.* **95**, 249 (1954).

van Hove, L., *Physica* **24**, 404 (1958).

Van Nordstrand, R. A., and Hach, K. M., in a paper presented to the A.C.S. Meeting, Chicago, Sept. 1953.

Van Nordstrand, R. A., and Johnson, M. F. L., in a paper presented to the A.C.S. Meeting, New York, Sept. 1954.

Volmer, M., *Z. physik. Chem.* **207**, 307 (1957).

Zernike, F. (Thesis), *Proc. Acad. Sci. Amsterdam* **17**, 793 (1916).

Zernike, F. (Thesis), *Arch. néerl. sci.* **Ser. 3A**, **4**, 74 (1917).

Zernike, F., and Prins, J. A., *Z. Physik* **41**, 184 (1927).

Zimm, B. H., *J. Phys. & Colloid Chem.* **54**, 1306 (1950).

DISCUSSION

J. A. PRINS

I wish to call attention to the fact that the correlation function so clearly expounded by Professor Debye may be derived more completely from small-angle x-ray scattering than from optical scattering; the latter provides only an integral over the curve, while the former gives the entire curve. When the intensity of scattering in the optical region is plotted versus s (rather than s^2, as shown by Debye), it follows the shape a in Fig. 1 in the neighborhood of the critical point.

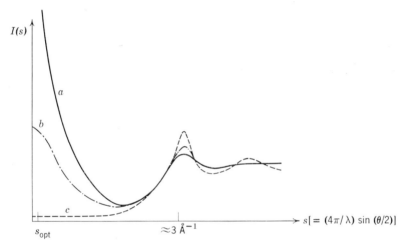

Fig. 1. Schematic representation of scattering curves on approach of the critical temperature T_c. Curve a, at $T = T_c$; b, at $T \approx 0.9T_c$; c, at $T \approx 0.1T_c$. (Note that the half-width of a is *smaller* than that of b, indicating larger "clusters.")

Of course, the intensity of scattering in the optical region is much stronger under these conditions than it would be farther removed from the critical point; it is determined by the compressibility. Please note that my value of s includes the reciprocal of the wavelength, so that a single scale may be used both for the optical regions and for the small-angle x-ray region. The optical scattering reaches only to s_{opt} because the wavelength is so very large.

It is well known that, in the region corresponding to a few reciprocal angstroms, there are peaks in the correlation function due to the interference at intra- and intermolecular distances. Of course, one never observes these with optical scattering. Now, Debye's theory gives correlations due to intermolecular scattering at large distances, and the formula he derived permits an analysis over the entire region by means of a single expression. Of course, in the application, the formula is always approximate.

Figure 2 gives experimental data in the neighborhood of the critical point for He, but not so very close to it. They are due to the x-ray group at Columbus, Ohio. The curve for 4.2 Å corresponds roughly to curve b of Fig. 1. The shape of the curve implies that there are fluctuations in this temperature region which may be conceived as spacings due to supersonic waves, in the neighborhood of about 100 Å. Note that the critical temperature for helium is 4.6°K, and the experiment was done rather distant in the Debye sense, but still the effect of the critical temperature is showing up in the data. If one were at the critical temperature, the scattering would be very large and would increase proportionately

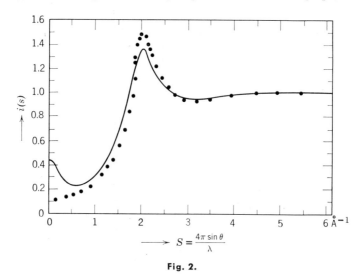

$$S = \frac{4\pi \sin \theta}{\lambda}$$

Fig. 2.

with s^{-2}, as shown in Fig. 1. In this region of Fig. 2 relatively far from the critical point, periodicities in the fluctuation of densities in liquid occur, and they are of the order of hundreds of angstroms, as proved by the fact that the scattered intensity at $s \approx 0.01$ is appreciable. This is in good accord with the considerations presented by Professor Debye.

In Fig. 3 are given data on x-ray scattering at very small angles by glass recorded by Porai-Koshits and Andreyev and published in *Nature* **182,** 336 (1958). The experimental work was done as follows. A very thin piece of glass was used as a sample, and a parallel x-ray beam was passed through it. They determined the scattering at very small angles, of the order of 5 minutes of arc. This corresponds to very large distances between discontinuities; hence they considered the effect due to domains which have many molecules. Such domains differ in density, though ordinarily glass is considered homogeneous. Even in the optical scattering region, there is no intense scattering. The x-ray data indicate the presence of discontinuities; that is, there are no actual voids, but there are regions which are lighter and denser (i.e., regions with lower and with higher refractive indices) at distances of some hundreds of angstroms.

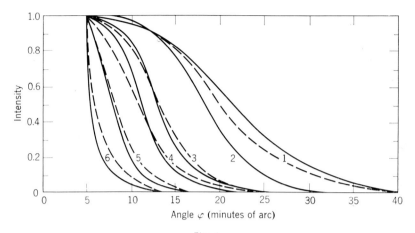

Fig. 3.

Note that the intensities have been reduced to an arbitrary scale for all the cases cited.

It is possible to accentuate these fluctuations by a simple trick. One merely treats the glass with some solvent and dissolves out more of one type of the domain than of another, so that the fluctuations are enhanced by a factor of thousands. The other graphs were thus obtained; they are a thousand times stronger than the broken curve, but they have been reduced to fit the same scale.

P. DEBYE

I had indicated that the scattering in helium should be studied close to the critical point. I did not know that it has been done. I suggested such an experiment because at this critical point effects due to quantum restrictions might appear. At this point, the thermal energy is not kT. I hoped that these departures would show up, since the square of the amplitude would not be proportional to kT, and indeed such a study has now been reported.

As far as glasses are concerned, several years ago Bueche tried to determine the amount of light scattered by glass and found that glass was inhomogeneous. At that time, we introduced a correlation function of the exponential form $e^{-R/A}$, only because it appeared to be a simple form [Debye and Bueche, *J. Appl. Phys.* **20**, 664 (1949)]. It may well be that the work done by Porai-Koshits and Andreyev (*loc. cit.*) concerned data on Vycor glass, which does have a lot of holes in it. However, in that case, the dimensions should be smaller, with an average around 25 Å [Debye and Brumberger, *J. Phys. Chem.* **61**, 1623 (1957)].

J. A. PRINS

They did use Vycor glass, but it was annealed first.

P. G. KLEMENS

The correlation function introduced by Professor Debye is also important in the scattering of phonons in amorphous solids which, in turn, determines the thermal conductivity. I shall discuss this later.

P. DEBYE

The correlation function has appeared in many different connections and leads in all cases to equivalent mathematical formulations. As examples, one can mention (a) the theory of turbulence and (b) the scattering of sound in water, wherein one finds that sound is highly attenuated due to inhomogeneities in the medium. It also appears (c) in the Booker and Gordon theory of radio scattering in the troposphere.

T. A. LITOVITZ

Fabelinski of Lebedev Institute has measured the scattering of light by hypersonic waves in liquids. Under these conditions, he informed me, he found a Doppler shift in the frequency. However, when he repeated the experiment with fused quartz, he could not observe the Doppler shift lines. It seems very strange that there are hypersonic waves in liquids with sufficiently low attenuation to cause a measurable Doppler shift but that such hypersonic waves do not appear in quartz. Could any explanation of this be given in terms of correlation function?

P. DEBYE

I do not know. It may well be that the hypersonic waves do not exist in quartz, because in a glass they are scattered too much and may, therefore, be highly attenuated. Of course, such scattering is necessary to explain the thermal conductivity, for it is clear that unless there is attenuation by scattering due to inhomogeneities there can be no thermal conductivity; such inhomogeneities are frozen-in in the glass. In this connection, it seems also appropriate to quote the following references: P. Debye and F. W. Sears, *Proc. Natl. Acad. Sci. U. S.* **18**, 409 (1932); P. Debye, H. Sack, and F. Conlon, *Compt. rend.* **198**, 922 (1934); E. H. L. Meyer and W. Ramm, *Physik. Z.* **33**, 270 (1932); W. Ramm, *Physik. Z.* **35**, 111, 756 (1934). These four papers discuss the Doppler shift.

D. P. RILEY

It is true, is it not, that it is impossible by scattering means alone to distinguish between a structure and its complementary structure? By which I mean the structure where nothing becomes one, and one becomes nothing. Of course, in most such cases, one may introduce other criteria such as the density, but in the field of disordered structures it is often difficult to derive a model which one can definitely say is a "pore" structure as opposed to a "particle" structure from scattering experiments alone. Very often an important technological factor is dependent on what we might call the topology or connectivity of the internal surfaces, and it would be interesting to have an experiment to explore this. I would suggest that many rather definite structural pictures presented in the literature are really subjective. One is measuring, as you correctly stressed, a correlation function, and, unless there is other evidence which allows one to define the topology, one is unjustified in drawing a precise picture of the configuration.

S. H. BAUER

I presume that one should stress that there are two steps in the analysis and presentation of diffraction data. From the experimental data one may deduce directly the correlation function, but it is up to the investigator to provide a model which is suggested by the correlation function. Professor Debye's presentation clearly illustrates the power and limitations of diffraction techniques for the determination of the structure of matter. One would like to be able to sit on a selected atom and describe the structure as it extends in any selected direction, as a function of distance away from the point of observation. Unfortunately, this cannot be done by a scattering experiment, because an average is obtained over the entire sample. For a disordered system, the most that can be obtained directly is a function which depends only on the scattering angle and is independent of the orientation of the specimen, and, under those conditions, the most that can be derived from the diffraction data is a correlation function. The investigator must then postulate a model which on testing will be found either to agree or disagree with these observations. This is specifically illustrated by Debye's discussion of the determination of the molecular energy integral from scattering data near the critical temperature. The integral is taken over all of space, of the energy as a function of the radial distance from a given atom. But this is an average function; one would prefer to have the potential energy as a function of the orientation of adjacent molecules (unless they are spherical) but can only deduce the equivalent spherical distribution.

ROMAN SMOLUCHOWSKI

Is it correct to conclude that a knowledge of percent porosity and of scattering data alone is not sufficient to permit a decision whether the scattering pores are connected?

P. DEBYE

That is correct.

by

D. P. Riley

Intertechnical Consultants Inc.

Spherically Symmetric Fourier Transforms and Medium Range Radial Distribution Functions in the X-ray Determination of Complex Molecular Structures

Statement of the Problem

Knowledge of a chemical molecule can conveniently be classified into three parts: (a) precise knowledge of the immediate environment of each atom in the molecule, i.e., bond lengths and bond angles; (b) a less exact picture of the structure of the whole molecule, i.e., the molecular configuration; and (c) the over-all size and shape of the molecule.

For small molecules it is unprofitable to make these distinctions, as exact knowledge of the molecule in all its aspects is relatively easy to obtain. With larger, more complex molecular structures, however, such distinctions are not only imposed by limitations in analytical techniques but are also of definite help in understanding and interpreting the various properties of the molecule, whether chemical, physical, or technological. The purpose of this chapter is to discuss a means of deriving a general picture of molecular structure on the intermediate scale by x-ray scattering methods. The most sensitive range of interatomic distances in this context is that between 4 Å and 11 Å, roughly.

The ideal diffraction experiment would record the spatial distribution of intensity scattered by a single molecule as a function of its orientation relative to the primary beam and would completely exclude confusing intermolecular interference effects. While it is experimentally very difficult to derive the molecular intensity function with this degree of explicitness, it is simple to measure its average value over all orientations. This is the basis of those methods, using the diffraction of either x-rays or electrons, which determine the structure of simple molecules in the gas or vapor state. In a gas each molecule is effectively an independent scatterer, and the observed intensity is the sum of the intensities given by many molecules in random orientation. Debye (1915, 1930) was the pioneer of the method, and it has been extensively applied by Pauling and Brockway (1934) and others, in its electron diffraction aspect, to the study of simple molecules. In particular, Warren and his collaborators (i.e., Warren and Gingrich, 1934) have investigated the structure of some relatively simple amorphous solids by similar x-ray means.

A molecular solution free of aggregation effects, i.e., an ideal solution, would correspond to the gas state. The effects of intermolecular interference are, however, relatively non-confusing with large molecules and are localized in the low angle region of scattering. It is, therefore, permissible to examine such substances in the form of isotropic solid specimens and to consider that the major part of the intensity curve, which is due to intramolecular interference, is not appreciably influenced by the state of aggregation. In this respect large molecules are simpler to deal with than small ones (Riley and Arndt, 1954).

Outline of Methods

The experimental procedure used is the measurement over a wide angular range of the intensity of monochromatic x-rays scattered by an isotropic specimen. The term "isotropic" signifies that the molecules within the irradiated volume possess random orientation, it being understood that for true randomness the number of molecules is necessarily very large. Frequently, in the case of high polymers, interest centers on regularly constructed *parts* of the molecule rather than on the whole molecule considered as a chemical entity. In that event, it is these constituent parts that need to be randomly oriented. In general, the method aims at investigating the structure of identical, or nearly identical, atomic groupings, irrespective of whether these groupings constitute a molecule or only part of one. The use of the word "molecule" in what follows is intended to cover such cases as a matter of convenience. In principle, the isotropic specimen can be solid, liquid, or gaseous; in practice, a compressed powder or similar random aggregate is used if possible, although solutions have also been employed.

Two ways of interpreting the experimental data are possible. The first takes as its starting point a number of possible models of the molecular structure and calculates from them the intensity curves to which they would give rise; the second starts with the observed intensity curve and transforms it with the minimum of assumptions into a radial distribution curve characteristic of the average atomic environment in the molecule. Comparison between theory and experiment is made using intensity curves in the first method and radial distribution curves in the second. Strictly speaking, only one basic method is involved, one procedure being the reverse of the other. In the practical sense, however, the two approaches are not precisely equivalent, and they differ in sensitivity and usefulness in ways described later.

It is a *sine qua non* of this type of investigation that the experimental intensity curve be obtained with considerable accuracy and refer to the specimen only. The accurate measurement of intensity scattered from an amorphous substance of medium-to-low scattering power presents some difficulty, especially since strictly monochromatic radiation must be employed. At high angles the scattering is very feeble but is important in connection with the establishment of a normalized scale of intensity. The low angle region may be of interest in reflecting molecular-packing phenomena. It is therefore desirable to use a technique which allows, in one continuous experiment, the recording of intensity over a very wide angular range. A convenient subtractive technique for eliminating the effects of extraneous scattering is only possible using a counter method of intensity measurement, which is also commendable because of its inherent precision. In order to achieve monochromatic conditions conveniently, a technique has been developed (Arndt and Riley, 1952; Lang, 1952) employing a proportional counter as the x-ray detector.

No novelty is claimed for the method as such. Its application to complex structures containing large numbers of atoms, however, raises problems. It was my aim, in collaboration with Dr. U. W. Arndt, to devise simplified, self-consistent techniques which could be used even with highly complicated molecules. The relations derived permit the close comparison of identical functions, the functions being, on the one hand, calculated from postulated molecular models according to a simplified standard procedure of general applicability and, on the other, derived from experimental observations on the material specimen. It should be noted that the definition of the functions used is not identical with that of other authors, notably Warren, Krutter, and Morningstar (1936), although the practical differences are not great in the case of organic structures.

Fundamental Relations

The basic relation on which all calculations are based is due to Debye (1930), and it expresses the average intensity per molecule scattered coherently by an assemblage of independent molecules in random orientation:

$$I(s) = \sum_i \sum_j f_i(s)f_j(s) \frac{\sin sl_{ij}}{sl_{ij}} \tag{1}$$

Throughout this chapter, the angle variable is defined as

$$s = 4\pi \frac{\sin \theta}{\lambda} \tag{2}$$

where 2θ is the angle of scattering and λ is the wavelength of the x-radiation employed. The double summation embraces all pairs of atoms in the molecule, each pair being counted twice except for the self-identity cases where $i = j$. The symbol l_{ij} refers to the distance between the two atoms, i and j, constituting a pair, while $f_i(s)f_j(s)$ represents the product of their scattering, or form, factors. Debye's expression can be applied to any rigid assembly of atoms acting as an independent scattering unit.[*]

It is desirable to separate out the portion of the scattered intensity that is due to interatomic interferences, as this is the only part that is sensitive to the molecular structure. The total intensity $I(s)$ can be split into two parts:

$$I(s) = A(s) + B(s) \tag{3}$$

$A(s)$ corresponds to the cases where $i = j$ in equation (1) and represents the intensity due to the atoms present scattering independently of each other. Its value is given by

$$A(s) = \sum_i f_i^2(s) \tag{4}$$

the sum of the squares of the atomic scattering factors of all the atoms in the structure. The interference scattering, where $i \neq j$, is represented by

$$B(s) = \sum_i \sum_j^{i \neq j} f_i(s)f_j(s) \frac{\sin sl_{ij}}{sl_{ij}} \tag{5}$$

[*] The effect of thermal motion can be allowed for separately.

For substances that are mainly constituted of atoms which do not differ too widely in atomic number, it is possible to effect a considerable simplification. The assumption can then reasonably be made that the atomic scattering factors all have the same dependence on the angle variable s (i.e., the same "shape") and differ only in magnitude, as defined by the atomic number Z:

$$f_Z(s) = Zf(s) \tag{6}$$

where $f(s)$, the normalized factor, is identical for each atom. It is now possible to bring $f^2(s)$ outside the summations in (5). This being so, if the intensity function $i(s)$ is defined as the ratio of interference scattering to independent scattering,

$$i(s) = B(s)/A(s) \tag{7}$$

it follows that

$$i(s) = \nu^{-1} \sum_i^{i\neq j} \sum_j W_{ij} \frac{\sin sl_{ij}}{sl_{ij}} \tag{8}$$

where $\nu = \Sigma Z^2$, the sum of the squares of the atomic numbers of all the atoms concerned, and $W_{ij} = Z_i Z_j$, the product of atomic numbers in the pair of atoms i, j. We shall term $i(s)$ the *interference intensity function*. As it is the ratio of two intensities, it has the dimensions of a pure number and is independent of the nature of $f(s)$, which does not therefore require definition. The interference intensity function provides a convenient means of comparing theory with experiment, as an equivalent function is derivable from the experimental data.

Equation (8) is not in a suitable form for routine calculation with desk machines owing to the large number of different values of $(\sin x)/x$ that may be involved. While with small molecules the use of $(\sin x)/x$ tables is obligatory, with a large molecule (such as a high polymer) advantage can be taken of its size to rewrite (8) as the equivalent Fourier integral,

$$\nu s i'(s) = \int_0^\infty \frac{\phi(r)}{r} \sin sr \, dr \tag{9}$$

in which the smoothed continuous radial distribution function $\phi(r)$ replaces the discontinuous point function $W_{ij}(l_{ij})$ in (8). The latest Beevers-Lipson strips (Beevers, 1952) provide a convenient means of evaluating such integrals.

The *radial distribution function* is defined as

$$\phi(r) = \int_0^\infty H(l)\sigma(r-l) \, dl \tag{10}$$

where $\sigma(x)$ is a smoothing function folded into the discontinuous histogram $H(l)$ representative of the distribution of W_{ij} in terms of l_{ij},

$$H(l) = \sum_{l}^{l+\Delta l} W_{ij}(l_{ij}) \tag{11}$$

The intensity function in (9) has been marked with a prime because it includes an effect due to the smoothing function. This can be eliminated by dividing $i'(s)$ by the Fourier transform, $\tau(s)$, of $\sigma(x)$:

$$i(s) = i'(s)/\tau(s) \tag{12}$$

The exact form of the smoothing function is therefore merely a matter of convenience. The justification for this procedure lies in the theorem which states that the Fourier transform of the convolution (or fold) of two functions is equal to the product of the Fourier transforms of the separate functions [see, for instance, Titchmarsh (1937)]. Normally, a Gaussian smoothing function is employed, as its Fourier transform is easily calculated, being itself a Gaussian. With organic substances, $\sigma(x) = e^{-9.5x^2}$ has been found to be a convenient choice and corresponds roughly to the electronic distribution around a typical atom.

$i(s)$, as finally derived via (9) and (12) in this way, differs from the function defined by (8) only by as much as the histogram (11) is an inexact representation of the molecule. By choosing Δl to be 0.1 Å, the deviation can be made negligible.

An alternative method of computation treats the exact relations (4), (5), and (7) to give $i(s)$ but necessitates, with complex molecules, the use of an electronic digital machine, suitably programmed (Gilles and Riley, in preparation). The appropriate atomic scattering factors are recorded on tape, once for all, for use in any problem.

Reduction of Experimental Data

The intensity curve observed experimentally, even after all corrections have been applied (see "Experimental Procedure and Reliability of Results" below), necessarily includes the effect of incoherent (or Compton) scattering. This is removed by the following procedure which also serves to place the resulting coherent intensity data on an absolute scale. For this to be achieved, it is necessary to know, at least approximately, the elementary composition of the specimen. The intensity of coherent plus incoherent scattering from hypothetical material of this composition, in which all the atoms are presumed to scatter independently, is first computed from tabulated atomic scattering factors of both types and is called I_{tot}. At high values of s, the observed curve I_{expt} will approximate this total independent scattering curve because of the unimportance of interatomic interference effects in this region. The procedure is to match I_{expt} with I_{tot} over a range of high values of s and thus place the two curves on the same scale. It is convenient to express I_{tot} in normalized form such that its value is unity at $s = 0$; in this way different experimental curves can easily be compared absolutely on a normalized intensity scale.

Once I_{expt} has been normalized in this way, $i(s)$ can be derived from the relation

$$i(s) = (I_{expt} - I_{tot})/I_{coh} \tag{13}$$

where I_{coh} represents the coherent part of the normalized independent scattering. It is evident that I_{coh} is equivalent to the $A(s)$ of equation (3), and the numerator in (13) to $B(s)$.

The principal disadvantage of the procedure is the subjective nature of the process of curve matching. The greater the range of s embraced in I_{expt}, the better the matching is likely to be, but great effort spent on always extending the s range would be wasted owing to the limited accuracy with which atomic scattering factors are known.

Uncertainty is obviously involved in the derivation of $i(s)$ from an experimental intensity curve, both because of the matching procedure and by virtue of the technical experimental problems discussed later. The uncertainty, however, affects only the position of the whole curve relative to the zero abscissa; it lifts or lowers the curve roughly as if it were hinged about the matching point. The number of singularities in the curve remains the same, as does their shape; only their relative importance can be modified. Assuming that these practical difficulties can be overcome, the function $i(s)$ given by the experimental data is exactly equivalent to that defined in equations (9) and (12). Precise comparison between theory and experiment is therefore permissible except over the low angle range of s.

The Influence of Low Angle Scattering

The reservation made above regarding low values of s arises because the relations used in computing $i(s)$ from molecular models assume that the specimen is truly gas-like, i.e., that the individual molecules are widely separated in a random way. The principal effect due to this assumption is the presence of a considerable amount of scattering at fairly low values of s, rising to a maximum at zero angle. A high low angle peak due to this cause is therefore included when $i(s)$ is calculated from the relations of the previous section, whether exact or approximate. This peak will not be observed in practice unless the specimen is either a gas or a dilute solution. In dense systems, notably in solids, it is replaced by the effects due to intermolecular interferences. As was stated in the first section, these effects are distinguishable with relative ease for large molecules. With such substances, even when examined as solids, close comparison of the intramolecular portion of $i(s)$ given by experiment can be made over the appropriate range of s with $i(s)$ calculated from postulated molecular models via the gas-scattering relations.

The Use of Radial Distribution Curves

It is evident from equations (10) and (11) that a radial distribution function $\phi(r)$ can be calculated from the atomic positions in any postulated molecular model and that this function will be characteristic of the molecule, however complex. If, therefore, an equivalent function can be derived from the intensity of x-ray scattering by the material specimen, an alternative means of testing structural hypothesis by experiment is provided.

The derivation of a radial distribution function from experimental intensity curves is a well-known procedure. For example, Fourier transformation of (9) gives

$$\frac{\phi(r)}{r} = \frac{2\nu}{\pi} \int_0^\infty si'(s) \sin sr \, ds \qquad (14)$$

As $i'(s)$ can easily be obtained from the experimentally observed values of $i(s)$ via (12), it would be possible, with a gas-like specimen, to derive by experiment a radial distribution function with exactly the same significance as $\phi(r)$ computed for a hypothetical molecule. Precise comparison would then be possible.

In practice, $\phi(r)$ is not directly given by Fourier transformation of the observed intensity function, as the contribution of the low angle scattering is excluded. As stated above, apart from the rare cases of nearly ideal specimens, gas-type low angle scattering will not be observed in reality, and particularly not with solids. This unobserved low angle scattering is due to the molecule considered as a structureless volume of uniform electron density; in other words, it is related to its shape only. Rewriting (9) in order to bring out this distinction, we obtain

$$\nu si'(s) = \int_0^\infty \frac{\{\phi(r) - \bar{\phi}(r)\}}{r} \sin sr \, dr + \int_0^\infty \frac{\bar{\phi}(r)}{r} \sin sr \, dr \qquad (15)$$

in which the second integral represents the unobserved scattering at low s values, or "shape transform." The significance of $\bar{\phi}(r)$ will be discussed below. If the observable part of the experimental intensity curve leads to $i'_{\text{obs}}(s)$, where the prime has the usual significance, then

$$\nu s i'_{\text{obs}}(s) = \int_0^\infty \frac{\{\phi(r) - \bar{\phi}(r)\}}{r} \sin sr \, dr \tag{16}$$

which, by Fourier transformation, becomes

$$\frac{\{\phi(r) - \bar{\phi}(r)\}}{r} = \frac{2\nu}{\pi} \int_0^\infty s i'_{\text{obs}}(s) \sin sr \, ds \tag{17}$$

In other words, the radial distribution curve directly derived from the experimental data is the difference function $\phi(r) - \bar{\phi}(r)$, and not $\phi(r)$ itself.

$\bar{\phi}(r)$, or the "shape function," is not easily defined with exactitude for molecules of finite size and arbitrary shape. It may be considered the radial distribution curve of the uniformly filled shape of the molecule, but it should be noted that the shape may, in some instances, possess re-entrant surfaces or be hollow. $\bar{\phi}(r)$ is evidently a relatively featureless curve representing a grossly smoothed version of $\phi(r)$. The function $\phi(r)$ oscillates above and below $\bar{\phi}(r)$, and the difference radial distribution curve $\phi(r) - \bar{\phi}(r)$ refers these structure-sensitive fluctuations to a straight base line.

While the main features of the peak system in $\phi(r)$ will be reproduced in $\phi(r) - \bar{\phi}(r)$, precise comparison between the two types of curves is clearly impossible. In the general case, the shape function $\bar{\phi}(r)$ is not evaluable analytically, so derivation of $\phi(r)$ from the difference function is not practicable with certainty and precision. On these grounds alone, close comparison between hypothesis and experiment is better made by means of $i(s)$ curves, as in this case the equivalent discrepancy is confined to the low s region and is easily recognized.

There are other reasons which favor the use of $i(s)$ curves. In the derivation of a radial distribution curve from the experimental data, equal weight is given to all parts of the intensity curve, although the precision of their measurement varies. It is consequently less easy to make allowance for such uncertainties when testing a structural hypothesis. Again, the computation of $i(s)$ via equation (9) is based on Fourier transformation of the convergent function $\phi(r)/r$, with a subsequent division by s. This is a sounder procedure than is involved in the converse case, which requires Fourier inversion of the abruptly terminated function $s i'_{\text{obs}}(s)$ with the possible occurrence, as a consequence, of false features in the resulting radial distribution curve. The frequently used device of multiplying $si_{obs}(s)$ by an arbitrary "fade-off" factor before inversion can remove true as well as false features. Finally, quite apart from the above considerations, experience has shown (Arndt and Riley, 1955) that distinction between closely related molecular models of high polymers is uncertain on the basis of their calculated $\phi(r)$ curves, whereas the differences between the equivalent $i(s)$ curves are so clear that characterization is unambiguous. In a formal sense, the sensitivity of the two methods is identical since they are only alternative manifestations of the same reality. In practice, the $i(s)$ method is the more sensitive because differences due to small structural modifications tend to be localized in one part of the curve and are, thereby, more readily apparent. Nevertheless, the radial distribution curve method is well suited to rapid diagnosis where a large number of apparently equally suitable molecular models is predicted by chemical reasoning. It then provides a convenient means of narrowing down the field of choice to permit subsequent detailed analysis of $i(s)$ curves as the final procedure.

Sensitivity of the Method

It is evident that homometric structures, defined (Patterson, 1944) as possessing the same interatomic distances terminated by similar pairs of like or different atoms, will give rise to identical scattering and radial distribution curves. In a general sense, the probability of occurrence of nearly homometric structures is considerable where large regularly constructed high polymers are concerned. A linear polymer may be considered to possess interatomic distances l_{ij} and atomic number products W_{ij} of two types. The first arise from atoms within a single monomeric unit, considered to be invariant, and are evidently the same for all chain configurations; the second are due to the relative positions of different monomeric units with respect to each other. The second group of l_{ij} and W_{ij} are defined by the nature of the chain folding, and it is improbable that homometric sets could be produced by different configurations. Apart from the initial region, therefore, different radial distribution curves must result from unlike chain configurations, but the disparity may not always be striking. By virtue of the process of Fourier transformation, the differences are localized and accentuated in the corresponding $i(s)$ curves and are particularly evident in the part between $s \approx 1$ and $s \approx 3.5$ in the case of organic polymers. It is precisely this part of the intensity curve that can be measured with the highest accuracy in normal experiments.

As is shown below under "Some Applications of the Methods," the $i(s)$ method is sufficiently sensitive to permit unequivocal distinction between the two closely related variants, α_1 and α_2, of a helically coiled α-polypeptide chain. These differ essentially only in the way the side chains are attached to the same fundamental helical polypeptide chain. It might be of interest to discuss these structures in more detail here, as they exemplify both the power and limitations of the procedures used.

The basic structure considered is the α-helix of Pauling, Corey, and Branson (1951). There are four different varieties of this helix or, indeed, of any molecule containing optically asymmetric atoms as an integral part of a helical polymer chain. Figure 1 indicates the stereo-

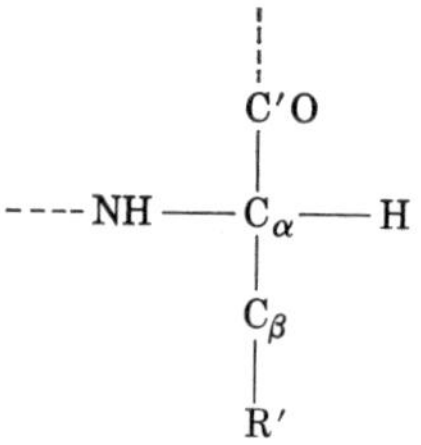

$$\begin{array}{c} \vdots \\ C'O \\ | \\ ----NH-----C_\alpha-----H \\ | \\ C_\beta \\ | \\ R' \end{array}$$

Fig. 1. An amino acid residue in the L-configuration found in natural proteins, drawn according to the usual convention. C_α is the plane of the paper; the bonds to C'O and C_β are below, and those to NH and H above, this plane. (Arndt and Riley, 1955.)

chemistry around the asymmetric C_α atom in a single amino acid residue of a polypeptide chain, $(—NH—C_\alpha HR—C'O—)_n$.

The side chains R consist, in general, of a first carbon atom C_β attached to the C_α atom of the helix, plus other atoms R' attached to C_β. The position of C_β can be defined with precision in any structural hypothesis and is therefore always included in calculations. There are evidently two alternative positions of C_β, called $C_\beta 1$ and $C_\beta 2$, as it can change places with the H atom directly attached to C_α. Four different types of α-helix, consisting of the two enantiomorphous pairs, can consequently be distinguished:

$$\alpha_1 = LH\ C_\beta\ 2\ L\text{-}C_\alpha \quad \text{and its enantiomorph } \alpha_1' = RH\ C_\beta\ 2\ D\text{-}C_\alpha$$

and

$$\alpha_2 = RH\ C_\beta\ 1\ L\text{-}C_\alpha \quad \text{and its enantiomorph } \alpha_2' = LH\ C_\beta\ 1\ D\text{-}C_\alpha$$

The symbols L and D have the usual significance and refer to *levo* and *dextro* asymmetric C_α atoms, respectively; the abbreviations LH and RH signify left-handed and right-handed helices.

As, in general, enantiomorphous structures produce identical scattering or diffraction effects, distinction by x-ray means between α_1 and α_1' is impossible, as it is between α_2 and α_2'. Apart from this basic limitation, the $i(s)$ method is amply sensitive to distinguish between $\alpha_1(\alpha_1')$ and $\alpha_2(\alpha_2')$ or between the equivalent structures for the other helices mentioned below under applications of the method. It should be emphasized that the fundamental polypeptide chain itself, constituted of C_α, C', N, and O atoms, is identical in all helices of the same category apart from a possible change of hand (LH or RH). It will be seen by reference to Figs. 3 and 4 that, whereas the portions of the $i(s)$ curves from $s \approx 3.5$ outwards hardly alter when the position of the C_β atom is changed in a given helix, the parts between $s \approx 1$ and $s \approx 3.5$ are substantially modified.

As described later, the experimental data lead to the α-helix as the most probable predominant chain configuration in most natural α-proteins. It is of interest to remark that Riley and Arndt (1953) were led, in the case of insulin, through a close comparison of its observed $i(s)$ curve with those calculated for both types of α-helix, to suggest that the insulin molecule contained both α_1 and α_2 helices in roughly equal proportions, a fact which was later confirmed by chemical evidence.

Experimental Procedure and Reliability of Results

In order to measure, in a single continuous experiment, the intensity scattered over a very wide angular range, it is advisable to use a parallel-sided block specimen in a symmetrical transmission setting in conjunction with a proportional counter. In general, Cu Kα radiation (λ = 1.542 Å) is used, particularly with organic substances. The use of other wavelengths may, of course, be necessary in certain cases to avoid fluorescent radiation. In the usual Debye-Scherrer method a cylindrical specimen is employed, and the diffraction pattern is recorded on photographic film. The measured intensity ordinates must be corrected for absorption in the sample; although methods of determining this correction have been developed, an accurate knowledge of the atomic composition of the specimen is needed, since the absorption factor cannot be measured directly but must be calculated. In the case of organic polymers containing mainly light atoms, the absorption is often determined by small amounts of heavier atoms whose exact proportion is not known with certainty.

Because of this difficulty it is customary to make accurate intensity measurements using parallel-sided powder blocks and employing a side reflection technique. If the specimen is sufficiently thick to be considered "infinite" from the standpoint of absorption, the correction to be applied becomes invariant with scattering angle. This method, however, cannot be applied for organic molecules, mainly because in this case considerable interest attaches to the part of the diffraction pattern corresponding to values of $\sin \theta/\lambda$ less than 0.1. With the usual characteristic radiations this means that the scattering angle is less than about 18°, and in this range the side reflection technique becomes subject to considerable errors.

With these arguments in mind, the experimental method adopted by Arndt and Riley was one in which the sample was compressed into a parallel-sided powder block used in transmission. By means of a counter and a block specimen, the absorption could be measured very accurately and reliable corrections applied.

The specimens were examined in the form of tightly compressed compacts of powdered material or of finely chopped-up fibers; containing windows were not in general found to be necessary. The intensity was measured by means of a proportional counter used in conjunction with a single-channel pulse amplitude analyzer adjusted so that only quanta in a narrow band centered on the characteristic wavelength emitted by the target metal were counted. When the usual $K\beta$ filter was employed, the degree of monochromatization achieved was ca. 99% in terms of energy (Arndt and Riley, 1952). The diffractometer was fitted with a monitoring counter in the primary beam. In this way the scattering from the specimen was measured in terms of the primary intensity and was not affected by variations in the latter. Details of the diffractometer and of its use have been described elsewhere (Arndt, Coates, and Riley, 1953), together with an account of the correction factors to be employed. Greatly improved stability was achieved by the use of the continuous flow type of counter described by Arndt, Coates, and Crathorn (1954).

The intensity curves obtained in this way refer to the sample only and are corrected in the usual way for experimental factors. They include the incoherent Compton scattering, but the effect of fluorescent radiation is usually negligible. Counting losses can be disregarded when a proportional counter is used, and the total number of counts recorded in the experiments was such that statistical inaccuracies were unimportant. The monitoring device maintained an excellent degree of constancy in the basic intensity. In short, the only appreciable source of error or variation ascribable to the apparatus that could be detected under normal operating conditions was due to occasional small drifts in the counting circuits. Checks for this effect were a matter of routine.

The degree of reproducibility of results for a given sample, if in the form of a fine powder, was very high, even when conditions were deliberately varied in order to constitute a test. The accuracy of measurement of scattered intensity, over a range of s from about 0.1 to 6.5, was within 1% in the most favorable cases, although for the purposes of rapid survey a lower accuracy was accepted.

As discussed above under "Reduction of Experimental Data," the absolute scale of intensity is determined by this high s region, and it is important that it be known accurately. Errors arise in its determination because of the almost grazing angles of incidence that are necessitated in the symmetrical transmission setting. Heavy reliance must therefore be placed on the efficiency of the geometrical volume correction factor, $\cos \theta$, in this region. It is clear that, if the specimen deviates from the assumed shape of a block with perfectly plane and parallel sides, the correction factor will not operate satisfactorily. In particular, any bowing of the specimen into a concave or convex shape will seriously affect the extreme high angle part of the intensity curve, and a satisfactory correction procedure will be impossible. The low and medium angle regions, on the other hand, will not be greatly affected, as the change of irradiated volume with angle is there much less marked.

The alternative reflection setting of the specimen is satisfactory with regard to the high angle region but encounters similar difficulties in the range of moderate and low angles. The nature of the absorption correction is more complicated in this case unless a specimen of "infinite" thickness be used, an impossibility with organic substances owing to their low absorption coefficients. Experience shows that the transmission setting gives a reliable curve except at extremely high angles ($2\vartheta > 160°$) and has the advantage that the absorption correction is easily applied. The exploration of the general trend of the scattering curves at high s values is best done by using a shorter wavelength; i.e., the use of Ag Kα ($\lambda = 0.561$ Å) permits the measurement of intensity up to $s \approx 13$.

There is one other source of error against which it is difficult to guard. It is impossible to be certain that a block specimen of dimensions ca. 10 x 10 x 1 mm, prepared by compression of a powder, is completely homogenous in density. A linear absorption factor measured over the narrow area of the beam at $2\theta = 0°$ may, therefore, not be representative of the whole specimen as it rotates. The effect can be examined by measuring the absorption at a number of angular positions of the specimen relative to the primary beam, so that different paths through it are involved. With compacts made from finely powdered solids, the variation in absorption with angle is small and irregular, and the adoption of an average value is permissible. Flaky specimens give a less satisfactory result. The effect of adopting a wrong absorption correction factor is progressively to raise or lower the corrected intensity curve with increase of s. Without repeating each run a number of times with specimens of different thicknesses, it is difficult to be sure that this has not happened to some extent with a typical sample.

To sum up, it may be said that the measurement of the *whole* course of the corrected intensity curve is necessarily less accurate than that of a limited region. Even slight singularities in the curve can be established beyond doubt, but the exact form of the monotonic curve on which they are superimposed is not capable of determination with equivalent precision. Even so, in carefully measured curves the discrepancy is unlikely to exceed $\pm 5\%$ in the normalized "absolute" height of the principal peak.

Some Applications of the Methods

In principle, the methods described above are of unlimited application if the effects of intermolecular interferences are negligible or, alternatively, are clearly separable from the intramolecular scattering. In practice, the $i(s)$ method is well suited to the investigation of chain configuration in regular or semiregular linear high polymers. The procedures have been subjected to critical test in the case of amorphous proteins and polypeptides, and it has been shown that they are far more sensitive to minor structural differences than might at first be expected. The study of these substances will be described in some detail by way of example.

Various schemes for folding or coiling polypeptide chains have been suggested, and a number of them give with some exactness the coordinates of the atoms C_α, C_β, C', O, and N in a succession of amino acid residues (see Fig. 1). The calculations neglect the contributions of the R' atoms, or non-C_β atoms in the R groups.

Calculations were carried out for the following helical models of a folded polypeptide chain:

$$\alpha, \gamma, \pi, 4_{13}, 3_{10}, 3_8, 2_7 b$$

For each of the first five helices listed, the two alternative positions of the C_β atoms were considered, corresponding to a change of hand of the helix if the L-C_α configuration is preserved as described above under "Sensitivity of the Method."

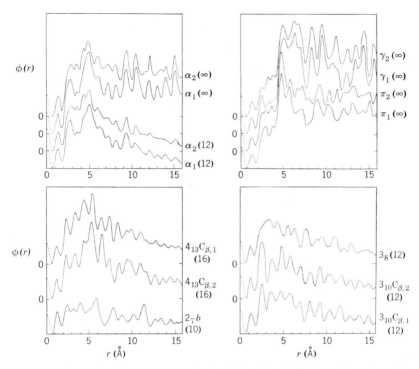

Fig. 2. Radial distribution curves $\phi(r)$ derived various helical configurations of a polypeptide chain. The number of amino acid residues included in the calculations is shown in parentheses. (Arndt and Riley, 1955.)

Figure 2 assembles the radial distribution curves $\phi(r)$ computed for these model structures. In all cases the smoothing function $\sigma(x)$ employed was the Gaussian $e^{-9.5x^2}$.

It is clear that the general trend of the curves depends on the length of the helix, i.e., the number of amino acid residues introduced into the calculation. The effect is exemplified in Figure 2, the number of residues involved being marked for each curve. An infinitely long chain gives rise to a radial distribution function which, at high values of r, oscillates asymptotically about a constant finite value; a chain of finite length gives, after the initial region, a curve that descends steadily until it reaches zero at a value of r approximately equal to the combined folded chain length and diameter. The way in which the shape function $\bar\phi(r)$, mentioned above, depends on the form of the molecule is clearly demonstrated by the general trend of these $\phi(r)$ curves.

As would be expected, the initial part of all the curves is virtually the same, corresponding to nearest and next-nearest atomic neighbors (peaks at 1.5 and 2.6 Å). The region that is most sensitive to chain configuration lies between about $r = 4$ Å and $r = 10$ Å. The prominent peak, between 4 and 5 Å, that occurs in most cases, is related to the average diameter of the helix.

It is also evident that the general similarity between the radial distribution curves for the two variants of the α, π, and 4_{13} helices, for instance, would make distinction between them an uncertain matter.

The interference intensity functions $i(s)$ for the infinitely long α, γ, π, and 4_{13} helices are presented in Fig. 3, the two sets of curves referring to the two alternative positions of the C_β atoms. The equivalent results for the 3_{10}, 3_8, and 2_7 helices are given in Fig. 4.

The function $i(s)$ was computed according to the description given above under "Fundamental Relations" but was modified in one small particular in order to make it more realistic. The modification takes into account the effect of thermal agitation. While James (1932) has shown

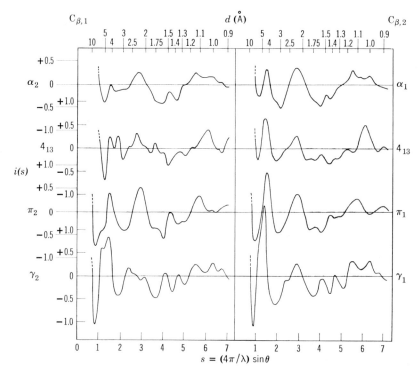

Fig. 3. Interference intensity functions $i(s)$ calculated for independent α, 4_{13}, π, and γ helices of infinite length in random orientation. The left-hand set of curves refers to models in which the C_β atoms are in position 1; the right-hand set refers to the alternative C_β position 2. (Arndt and Riley, 1955.)

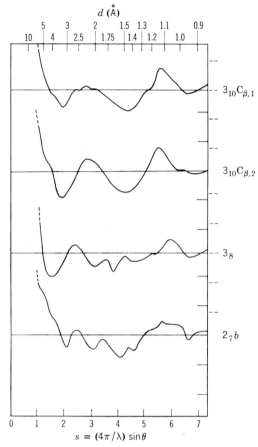

Fig. 4. $i(s)$ functions for the 3_{10}, 3_8, and 2_7 helices; two alternative C_β positions are considered for the 3_{10} helix. The ordinate scale for all curves is as marked for Fig. 3. (Arndt and Riley, 1955.)

that thermal movements of covalently bonded atoms make only a negligible impression on the x-ray scattering curves from free molecules, this cannot be assumed to be so for molecules in which the much weaker hydrogen bonding plays an essential role. The polypeptide chain is held in its helical configuration by hydrogen bonds, and the principal effect of thermal agitation will therefore be a sort of concertina motion along the length of the helix. It was estimated, from the bond energies and atomic masses involved, that this concertina motion would lead to a temperature factor of approximately $e^{-0.013s^2}$ by which $i(s)$, calculated from a rigid model, should be multiplied. All these theoretical $i(s)$ curves are on an absolute scale and are strictly comparable.

The experimental intensity curves given by all α-proteins are very similar, and only six are selected here for illustration. The intensity data were determined with particular care, each protein being examined several times. Each scattering curve was first normalized in the usual way, independently of the others, and the results are depicted in Fig. 5. It will be observed that the curves are all exceedingly alike and differ mainly as regards the normalized height of the inner half of the curve, particularly that of the peak at $s \approx 1.5$. It is also evident that the

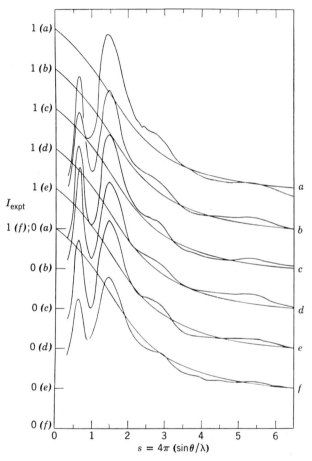

Fig. 5. Intensity curves I_{expt} given by six different α-proteins: a, ribonuclease; b, hemoglobin (ox); c, serum albumin (ox); d, myoglobin (whale); e, myoglobin (horse); f, insulin (ox). (The peak at $s = 0.6$ for ribonuclease lies below the much higher peak for ox hemoglobin and should not be confused with it. Zeros displaced as indicated.) (Arndt and Riley, 1955.)

similarities between the curves are of greater importance than the differences.

The more subtle features of the scattering curves are made more apparent in the mean interference intensity function $i(s)$ reproduced in Fig. 6. This curve was obtained by averaging the six $i(s)$ curves cor-

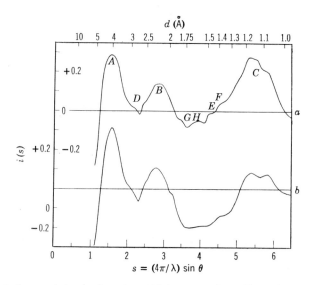

Fig. 6. Interference intensity functions $i(s)$ for α-proteins. Curve (a) is a composite curve obtained by averaging the six $i(s)$ functions derived from the I_{expt} curves in Fig. 5; (b) refers to serum albumin alone. (Arndt and Riley, 1955.)

responding to those in Fig. 5. By this process any interference effects due to the common predominant polypeptide chain configuration would be expected to be enhanced at the expense of any specific side chain effects. The important features are: first, the three principal maxima, A, B, and C, of which the last is seen to possess a central depression in most of the individual curves, e.g., that for serum albumin alone, also reproduced in Fig. 6; the next important feature is the slight, but definite, convexity D; thirdly, some of the curves, but not all, exhibit the slight step at E; finally, all show the shoulder F. The subsidiary convexities G and H are sometimes present.

The first important conclusion to be drawn from the close similarity between the intensity curves for all α-proteins is that the same fundamental polypeptide chain configuration is almost certainly present as the predominant component in every case. It is reasonable to suppose that the nature of this predominant configuration should be revealed by comparing the observed curves with those calculated for various structural models.

By far the most important property of the experimental intensity curves for the α-proteins is the maximum A at $s \approx 1.5$ (Fig. 6) which will be called the "principal peak." This typical and pronounced peak must be primarily a function of the intrinsic regularity of folding of the polypeptide chain. The fact that it is absent in the curves of Fig. 4 allows the immediate exclusion of the 3_{10}, 3_8, and 2_7 helices from further consideration. There are, it is true, slight hesitations in the upward sweep of the low angle intensity in the two 3_{10} curves, but the effect is altogether too trivial to give rise to the actually observed peak under any circumstances.

No other structure can be excluded on this simple basis, but a further rapid examination of the various $i(s)$ curves is sufficient to rule out the $4_{13}(C_{\beta,1})$ and γ_2 helices (Fig. 3). In the former case, a marked extra peak at $s \approx 1.9$ accompanies that at $s \approx 1.5$ and would certainly be apparent in the experimental curves; its complete absence in actuality constitutes ample grounds for rejecting the $C_{\beta,1}$ variant of the 4_{13} helix. The principal peak in the case of γ_2 is doubled by the addition of a shoulder at $s \approx 1.1$ which is not observed in practice. An additional reason for discarding the γ_2 helix is that the next broad maximum contains three peaks at $s \approx 2.4$, 2.8, and 3.2, of which the first is the most pronounced. This region is quite dissimilar to the single broad peak B centered on $s \approx 2.8$ in the experimental curves.

Reasoning based on the normalized height of the principal peak must take into account a number of technical factors, but it is clear that none of them could reasonably be expected to reduce the extreme height of 1.55 for the principal peak in the case of the γ_1 helix to a value of about 0.3 as reliably observed with serum albumin and several other α-proteins. While the corresponding heights, 0.89 and 0.65, are still considerable for the π_1 and 4_{13} $(C_{\beta,2})$ helices, they are not so great as to compel rejection on this ground alone. Nor does the exceptionally low height of the equivalent α_2 peak necessarily exclude this structure, although it is improbable that it could be the sole configuration present.

To sum up the results of these comparisons based on the more obvious features of the $i(s)$ curves, the following configurations are left for further examination: α_1, α_2, π_1, π_2, 4_{13} $(C_{\beta,2})$. The rest can be definitely rejected.

In order to proceed to a choice between the remaining alternatives, consideration must be given to the more subtle characteristics of the interference intensity functions.

Distinction between the α_1 curve and the others is afforded by the region between $s \approx 1.7$ and 2.3. In the $i(s)$ function for α_1, a secondary convexity occurs before the curve descends to form a rather sharply pointed minimum, in contrast with the smooth and rounded shape of this first dip in the π and 4_{13} ($C_{\beta,2}$) curves. This feature is definitely observed experimentally and is clearly seen in the curve in Fig. 6 for serum albumin but is shifted slightly to higher s values. The characteristic dip in the final broad maximum in the α helix curves is also commonly found in the α-protein curves.

On all grounds, the configurational model in best agreement with the experimental data is the α_1 helix. All its features are observed with one or other of the α-proteins examined, and no gross discrepancies are apparent. This conclusion is reinforced if one takes account of the data for the synthetic α-polypeptides. Nevertheless, on the basis of the protein data alone, it is impossible to assert that the π_1, π_2, and 4_{13} ($C_{\beta,2}$) helices are markedly inconsistent with observation. Equally, the admixture of a certain proportion of α_2 would not be an impossibility, although a 100% α_2 structure would seem to be highly improbable.

The length of an undeviated coiled chain in a corpuscular protein can never be very great because of the limited size of the molecule. The $i(s)$ functions for short α helices containing only twelve residues give curves which are very similar to those illustrated for a helix of infinite length, but all the features are somewhat more blurred. An important difference is that the principal peak is appreciably broader in the new α_1 curve and thereby more in conformity with that observed in practice.

In Fig. 7 the curve for an α_1 helix is compared with the composite curve shown in Fig. 6. Figure 7 should be studied in conjunction with Fig. 8, which refers to the synthetic α-polypeptide poly-γ-benzyl-L-glutamate.

Even a cursory examination of the $i(s)$ function given by poly-γ-benzyl-L-glutamate (α-form) is sufficient for its strong qualitative resemblance to the curve for an α_1 helix of infinite length to be perceived. Figure 8 shows that each feature in the theoretical curve is matched by an equivalent one in the experimentally observed function, the important difference being in the height of the principal peak at $s \approx 1.5$, or 4.1 Å in "spacing" terms. This particular discrepancy is the only marked one and may be attributed to the relatively greater importance of the contributions from the large side chains in this synthetic polypeptide.

In the comparisons made in Figs. 7 and 8 the theoretical curves are scaled down by a factor μ which takes into account the side chain atoms omitted in the calculations. This procedure is described in full by Arndt and Riley (1955). It is then permissible to subtract the theoretical from

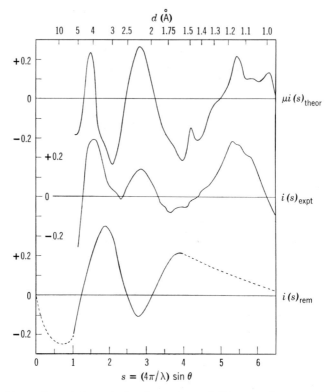

Fig. 7. Comparison of theoretical and experimental $i(s)$ curves for α-proteins, where $\mu i(s)_{\text{theor}}$ refers to an α_1 helix and is appropriately scaled, and $i(s)_{\text{expt}}$ is the composite curve of Fig. 6. $i(s)_{\text{rem}}$ represents the effect of the "remainder" atoms not included in the calculations, i.e., principally the non-C_β atoms in the side chains. (Arndt and Riley, 1955.)

the observed $\mu i(s)$ curve to give a curve, $i(s)_{\text{rem}}$, due to the contributions of the non-C_β side chain atoms. The two simple $i(s)_{\text{rem}}$ curves which result are shown in the lower parts of Figs. 7 and 8. These complications would not arise in the case of simpler polymers.

Other Possible Applications

The methods described are well suited to the investigation of the structure of amorphous high polymers and, in particular, those in which the monomer is relatively simple in the sense that any side chains pendent to the main polymer chain are capable of exact definition with

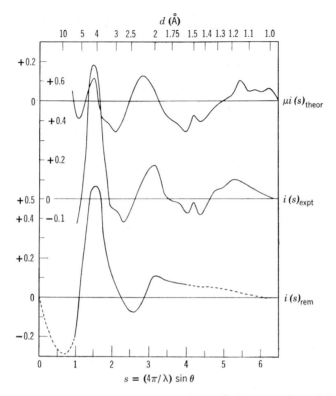

Fig. 8. Comparison of theoretical and experimental $i(s)$ curves for polybenzyl-L-glutamate (α-form) in a way similar to Fig. 7 (Arndt and Riley, 1955).

regard to their atomic coordinates. The example of protein structure chosen above is most unfavorable in this respect: These are some 21 different "side chains" in a protein, hence there is no true monomeric unit; also, many of the side chains are sufficiently complex to defy exact spatial definition when all possibilities of free rotation about single bonds are taken into account.

An ideal polymer for the present type of investigation would be described as follows: (a) it should be composed of single monomeric units or, if a copolymer, have either a completely regular or a completely irregular succession of different monomer residues; (b) all atoms in the molecule (other than H) should be capable of being given reasonably exact coordinate positions in any postulated structure; and (c) there should be no exact registration between neighboring polymer chains, which should preferably be fairly widely separated.

In general, the essential prerequisite for this type of work is that the structure to be tested be expressible in mathematical form, however complex. The spherical transform method, as it may be called, is not capable of leading directly, without any assumptions, to a detailed picture of atomic positions in the way that single-crystal Fourier techniques can with small molecules. Some chemical knowledge must be used and rational guesses made concerning the molecular structure. It is then a relatively simple matter to put these suppositions to the test, and the crux of the matter is whether the method is intrinsically sufficiently sensitive to distinguish between the various possibilities. The above exigent examples show that, in general, it is.

REFERENCES

Arndt, U. W., Coates, W. A., and Crathorn, A. R., *Proc Phys. Soc. (London)* **B67,** 357 (1954).

Arndt, U. W., Coates, W. A., and Riley, D. P., *Proc. Phys. Soc. (London)* **B66,** 1009 (1953).

Arndt, U. W., and Riley, D. P., *Proc. Phys. Soc. (London)* **A65,** 74 (1952).

Arndt, U. W., and Riley, D. P., *Phil. Trans. Roy. Soc. (London)* **A247,** 409 (1955).

Beevers, C. A., *Acta Cryst.* **5,** 670 (1952).

Debye, P., *Ann. Physik* **46,** 809 (1915).

Debye, P., *Physik. Z.* **31,** 419 (1930).

Gilles, D. C., and Riley, D. P., in preparation.

James, R. W., *Physik. Z.* **33,** 737 (1932).

Lang, A. R., *Proc. Phys. Soc. (London)* **A65,** 372 (1952).

Patterson, A. L., *Phys. Rev.* **56,** 195 (1944).

Pauling, L., and Brockway, L. O., *J. Chem. Phys.* **2,** 867 (1934).

Pauling, L., Corey, R. B., and Branson, H. R., *Proc. Natl. Acad. Sci. U. S.* **37,** 205 (1951).

Riley, D. P., and Arndt, U. W., *Nature* **171,** 144 (1953).

Riley, D. P., and Arndt, U. W., *J. Colloid. Sci. Suppl.* **1,** 57 (1954).

Titchmarsh, E. C., *Introduction to the Theory of Fourier Integrals*, Clarendon Press, Oxford, 1937.

Warren, B. E., and Gingrich, N. S., *Phys. Rev.* **46,** 368 (1934).

Warren, B. E., Krutter, H., and Morningstar, O., *J. Am. Ceram. Soc.* **19,** 202 (1936).

DISCUSSION

J. A. PRINS

Do you really insist that it is preferable to use the amorphous state rather than the partially oriented or completely crystalline state for structure determinations? Of course, in inducing orientation, one does influence the molecules a little, but in the partially oriented state one can get so much more information. Personally, I would prefer to work with the crystallized material.

D. P. RILEY

In answer to your question, there are a number of points which should be considered. In the first place, one may not be able to produce the slightly oriented or crystallized form of the high polymer. Only the isotactic high polymers can be truly crystallized. Secondly, one can always induce ordering or semiordering in a high polymer by drawing it out in fiber form, but does not one actually change the chain configuration to some extent in such a drawing process? If one had perfect fibers, I agree with you. However, the partially crystallite fibers present a different story. You know that mathematically it is one of the most difficult things to treat near parallelism. Thus one can treat the spherically symmetric problem and the cylindrically symmetric problem. In fact, the latter has been done. Oster and I worked on this, but one gets into a very difficult situation if the problem cannot be treated as either one or the other.

M. L. HUGGINS

Perhaps we can put it in this way: we can get a certain amount of information which is quantitatively very accurate for a completely random orientation. We can get perhaps more information which is less quantitatively correct if we have partial orientation, especially if the degree of orientation is not accurately known. From both kinds of experiments, we can obtain information which will definitely rule out certain structures and which, in complicated cases, will help us to decide between alternative hypothetical structures. With materials as complicated as the substances you have worked with, it is necessary at some stage to introduce a model and to test it.

P. J. W. DEBYE

May I illustrate the limitations of the information obtainable from such experiments by an example. When I was working with Menke, we obtained a curve of the x-ray intensity scattered by liquid CCl_4 as a function of the scattering angle. What we wanted was not only the probability of finding another molecule at any distance from a central molecule, but also simultaneously the probability of orientation of the distant molecule with respect to orientations of the central molecule. This total probability is a function of at least two variables, and it is impossible to derive such a function from an experiment which furnishes an intensity which is a function of only one variable. Supposing that the probability function concerning the distance could be derived from experiments with monatomic liquids, what could be shown was that mutual orientations are present even in a liquid consisting of such "round" molecules as CCl_4.

D. P. RILEY

I absolutely agree in principle with you, Professor Debye, but I wish to point out that precisely by virtue of the very large size of the protein molecules with which we were dealing it becomes an obvious matter to distinguish between the internal and external effects in the diffraction pattern; in contrast, in carbon tetrachloride or with small molecules generally, it is very difficult, if not impossible, to make such a distinction. In other words, the very complexity of the molecular structure is a help rather than a hindrance and is indeed essential to the methods used by Arndt and myself.

J. A. PRINS

Well, I wish to be a little less pessimistic. With the introduction of some extraneous data, one can determine structures. As an example, from a powder diagram of potassium chloride, one can deduce the structure of the crystal.

S. H. BAUER

One should keep in mind the importance of the subjective step; that is, the introduction of a model in the interpretation of the data. This is very clear from Dr. Riley's analysis. The point is that one cannot fully utilize his data unless he has a model derived from the extensive studies of single crystals of amino acids for which much more than radial distribution curves were available. In other words, one did start with data from other sources, and, taking over the structures of simple units, he could set up a model for the long chain proteins. Were it not possible to utilize extraneous data, but to rely merely on radial distribution curves which follow directly from the inversion of intensities, then Professor Debye's point is essentially limiting.

M. L. HUGGINS

It is certainly possible, by such methods as were used by Dr. Riley, to eliminate a variety of models which have been proposed, and that is probably the most useful function of the procedure outlined by him. Perhaps some of the difficulties of interpretation could be avoided by making solutions of the complicated protein molecules and then freezing them to obtain glasses. In such amorphous solids there are isolated molecules, and, if those molecules are composed of atoms which are sufficiently strong scatterers relative to the atoms in the medium, one can as a first approximation neglect the contribution from the medium and analyze the diffraction data as if they were produced by the complex molecules alone.

by

S. H. Bauer

Cornell University

Electron Diffraction Techniques for the Study of Amorphous Systems

Comments on the Structural Aspects of Non-crystalline Solids

It is clearly possible to imagine a very large range of structural models all of which would fall under the classification of non-crystalline solids. Start with any well-crystallized, highly ordered system as found in nature or prepared in the laboratory, of which there is a great variety, and distort it in one of many possible ways. When the distortion is sufficiently large that an appreciable fraction of the symmetry operations no longer lead to an approximately identical structure, one may call the system "non-crystalline." However, when the distortions become so large that all semblance of order except for neighbors and nearest neighbors has been removed, the system should be described as a rigid liquid, and greater simplicity is achieved.

In the range intermediate between crystal and liquid, it is most instructive to describe the structures from the view one would have were he sitting on a selected atom. Fortunately, there are tools for structure determination which permit one to investigate the symmetry of the fields around a selected atom, but these are rather specialized types of probes. One must infer from the perturbation of some property of the selected atom, brought about by the presence of its neighbors, the configuration of matter in its vicinity. In contrast, the diffraction technique is the most direct tool for the determination of interatomic distances; regrettably, it cannot be made so selective, except under very special circumstances not easily achieved. Deductions of structure depend on one of two procedures. For any given model, one may compute the intensity which would be expected, and this could be compared with the observed diffraction patterns. Figure 1 shows the computed coherent intensity for a sequence of diffraction units of increasing size, illustrating the trend with increasing long range order (Morozumi and Ritter, 1953; see also Chapter 19). Of course, one may then question the uniqueness of the assumed model which was found to agree with the observed diffraction pattern, and this can be tested by determining the magnitudes of the variations of the parameters for the model which can be tolerated and still retain agreement with the recorded data to within the experimental error. The possibility that radically different structures may lead to the same intensity pattern (homometric structures) has been discussed by Patterson (1944). For well-crystallized and highly ordered systems, the intensity distribution provides a direct measure of the symmetry elements which the structure possesses, but this is available only to a rudimentary extent for the highly distorted structures considered here.

The second procedure has already been introduced in Chapter 1 by its originator, Professor Debye. A powerful method of analysis of diffraction data is the computation of a correlation function (or radial distribution function) for the characteristic interatomic distances present in the scatterer; in turn, this suggests a model. As is well known, the radial distribution function involves an averaging, over all points in a sample, of the product of the density of electric potential or scattering matter at each point by the density contained in a shell of radius r. Clearly, up to a certain size the magnitude of the sample affects the average. Conceivably, if one were to illuminate small enough regions of the sample, he could obtain a much more sensitive measure of local order than is generally observed; but corrections will have to be made for diffraction effects due to small sample size. Irrespective of the nature of the radiation used, there are certain limitations which are imposed on the radial distribution or correlation function procedure for reducing the data and thereby deducing a model.

Resolution Limitations on Radial Distribution Curves

Let us assume that by some appropriate procedure extraneous scattering has been properly corrected for, atomic scattering has been subtracted out, and the corrected curve has been divided by a properly

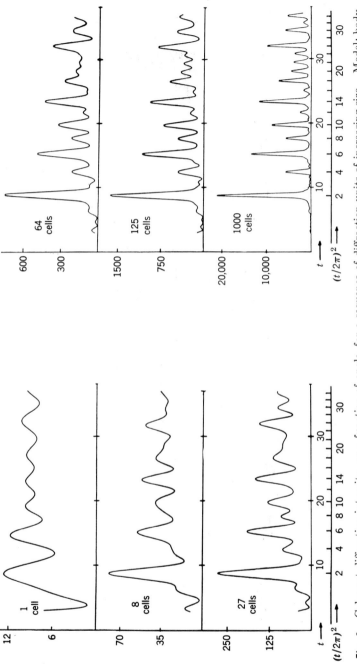

Fig. 1. Coherent diffraction intensity, as a function of angle, for a sequence of diffraction units of increasing size. Model: body-centered cubic lattice; $t \equiv a \cdot s$, where a is the unit translation. Morozumi and Ritter (1953) pointed out that about 60 unit cells (for example, particles 20 Å in diameter) will show diffraction rings characteristic of macroscopic crystals out to about $t = 25$. (After Morozumi and Ritter, 1953.)

averaged atom-form factor function, so that an intensity function is available for an amorphous material, such as would be produced were the nuclei to scatter in proportion to some characteristic constant independent of the scattering angle (for x-rays and electrons this is the atomic number; for neutrons there is a characteristic scattering coefficient for each isotopic species). The structure-sensitive diffraction intensity $i_Z(s)$ as a function of the scattering angle $[s \equiv (4\pi/\lambda) \sin (\theta/2)]$ is given by

$$s \cdot i_Z(s) = \sum_{ij}{}' Z_i Z_j \int_0^\infty \frac{W(r_{ij} - r_{ij}{}^0)}{r_{ij}} \sin s r_{ij} \, dr_{ij} \tag{1}$$

where $W(r_{ij} - r_{ij}{}^0)$ is the probability distribution due to atomic vibrations, molecular rotations, and the like. On application of the Fourier integral theorem, one gets

$$2\pi^2 r D_Z(r) = \int_0^\infty s \cdot i_Z(s) \sin rs \, ds = \frac{\pi}{2} \sum_{ij}{}' \frac{Z_i Z_j}{r_{ij}} W_Z(r_{ij} - r_{ij}{}^0) \tag{2}$$

The physical interpretation of the radial distribution function $r D_Z(r)$ has been extensively discussed.

Specifically, the limitations on the precision with which radial distribution curves may be obtained depend on:

(a) The precision with which the diffracted intensity can be measured. This varies with the nature of the radiation used. One must consider not only such factors as the signal-to-noise ratio but also unavoidable extraneous scattering due to slits, multiple scattering due to excessive sample thickness, and so on.

(b) The proper reduction of the data.

(c) The computational procedures used in the inversion. Here there are two aspects: the finite range of integration, because data are available only from some small angle to a maximum angle determined by the wavelength of the radiation; and the integration is generally replaced by a summation.

A discussion of the proper size for the increment to be used in the summation has been presented by Ino (1957). He suggests that $\Delta s_{\max} \leq \pi/r_{ij(\max)}^0$. IBM programs as currently used by electron diffraction investigators are set up for $\Delta s = \pi/10$; the space interval over which the sum is computed is 0–6 Å, with $\Delta r = 0.04$. For the study of gaseous materials, this interval is adequate. However, were radial distribution procedures applied to the analysis of diffraction data from high polymers or proteins, the Δs interval would have to be reduced to $\pi/20$.

For the unobserved diffraction intensity from zero to some $s_{\min}$, one must always splice in a computed portion based on a reasonable model.

This can be done without prejudicing final conclusions regarding the structure, since the inner part is not sensitive to details of the structure except for very large distances over which there is little correlation in non-crystalline materials. Of much greater concern is the termination of the summation at some maximal s. This has been discussed at length (Klug and Alexander, 1954). It has been empirically observed that a modulating function of the type $\exp(-\gamma^2 s^2)$, with γ adjusted so that the value of the exponential decreases to 0.1 or 0.2 at s_{max}, gives a satisfactory damping of the high frequency terms in the radial distribution curve. Selection of an exponential modulating function is fortunate, because the resulting integrals may be readily evaluated, and because the parameter γ assumes a significance of an "artificial temperature factor." The radial distribution function follows from the reduced intensity function:

$$2\pi^2 r D_Z{}^c(r) = \left(\frac{\pi}{10}\right)^2 \sum_{q=1}^{n} q \cdot i_Z(q) \exp\left[-\gamma^2 \left(\frac{\pi q}{10}\right)^2\right] \sin\left(r\frac{\pi q}{10}\right) \quad (3)$$

$$\frac{10}{\pi} s \equiv q \quad \text{with } q \text{ taken at } 0, 1, 2, 3, \cdots$$

If one assumes the individual atoms to be held to their equilibrium positions by harmonic forces, the probability of displacement from their equilibrium positions is given by a Gaussian:

$$W_Z(r - r_{ij}{}^0) = \frac{1}{2\alpha_{ij}\pi^{1/2}} \exp\left[-\frac{(r - r_{ij}{}^0)^2}{4\alpha_{ij}{}^2}\right] \quad (4)$$

wherein $2\alpha_{ij}{}^2$ is the average of the square of the deviation of r_{ij} from $r_{ij}{}^0$, measured along the line joining the atoms i and j. Then a well-resolved peak in the radial distribution curve has the shape

$$\ln[2\pi^2 r D_Z{}^c(r)] = \ln\frac{\pi^{1/2}}{4}\frac{g_{ij}Z_iZ_j}{(\alpha_{ij}{}^2 + \gamma^2)^{1/2}r_{ij}} + \frac{(r_{ij}{}^0 - r_{ij})^2}{4(\alpha_{ij}{}^2 + \gamma^2)} \quad (5)$$

wherein g_{ij} is the relative weight assigned to the particular atom pair. The maximum height of a peak is $\pi^{1/2}g_{ij}Z_iZ_j/4r_{ij}{}^0(\alpha_{ij}{}^2 + \gamma^2)^{1/2}$, the width of a half maximum is $4(\alpha_{ij}{}^2 + \gamma^2)^{1/2}(\ln 2)^{1/2}$, and the area (height $\times$ width at half-maximum) is $0.833\pi^{1/2}g_{ij}Z_iZ_j/r_{ij}{}^0$. These quantities may be used to measure the accuracy of the computational procedure for the radial distribution function.

Coffin (1951) tested a series of inversions to determine how the upper limit for the summation and the parameter of the modulating function affect resolution. Inversions of the same theoretical intensity curve (nuclear scattering) were made with s_{max} limited to 31.4, 21.7, 17.6, 9.1, and 7.5 (Figs. 2 and 3). These curves clearly argue for the need to re-

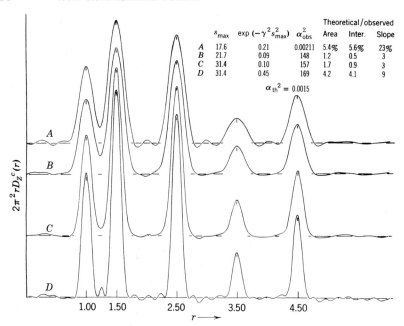

	s_{max}	$\exp(-\gamma^2 s^2_{max})$	α^2_{obs}	Theoretical/observed Area	Inter.	Slope
A	17.6	0.21	0.00211	5.4%	5.6%	23%
B	21.7	0.09	148	1.2	0.5	3
C	31.4	0.10	157	1.7	0.9	3
D	31.4	0.45	169	4.2	4.1	9

$$\alpha^2_{th} = 0.0015$$

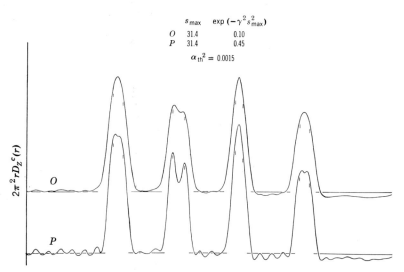

	s_{max}	$\exp(-\gamma^2 s^2_{max})$
O	31.4	0.10
P	31.4	0.45

$$\alpha^2_{th} = 0.0015$$

Fig. 2. Radial distribution functions (A, B, C, D) computed by means of equation (3) from a theoretical intensity curve, based on "nuclear" scattering for $r_{ij}^0 = 1.00$, 1.50, 2.50, 3.50, and 4.50 Å, with $\alpha^2 = 0.0015$. Curves O, P are inversions of an intensity curve for a sequence of paired peaks with spacings 0.16, 0.20, 0.12, and 0.16 Å, to test resolution.

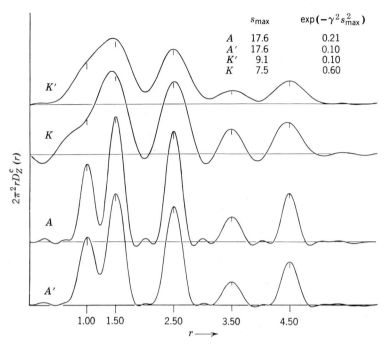

Fig. 3. Further tests on the reliability of R.D. curves, as a function of s_{max}; the model is the same as for curves A–D in Fig. 2.

evaluate some of the published radial distribution curves which have been obtained with copper radiation ($s_{max} \approx 8$) in the study of x-ray diffraction from liquids. Molybdenum radiation properly treated would be almost adequate, but much more reliable results would be obtained were s_{max} as large as 25 (perhaps Ag Kα). The effects of random errors in reading the positions of the diffraction peaks, of measuring the intensity, or of the imposition of an unrecognized uniformly modulating function are shown in Fig. 4. [Klug and Alexander (1954) have reviewed briefly the consequences of discrete errors in the intensity function, errors in curve fitting, and failure to make appropriate absorption corrections.] Obviously, in the interpretation of scattered intensity by means of radial distribution or correlation functions, one must treat with great care the termination of the summation and indeed must make every effort to extend the observed intensities to as large a value of s_{max} as can be achieved. One should note, however, that the limitation by s_{max} probably does not apply to study of long range correlation. We are currently investigating the effect of s_{max} and of measurement errors in the small angle region on the resolution of distances in the 10–20 Å range.

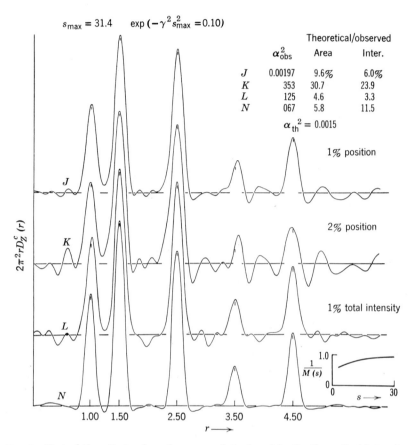

Fig. 4. Test of the effects of random errors introduced in the theoretical intensity curve on the resulting R.D. curves; model as for Fig. 2. Curve N is for a superposed modulating function $M(s)$ of a form shown in the sketch.

A discussion of the limitations imposed by other factors will be presented in the next section.

Special Features Shown by Electrons

For structure determination, electron diffraction possesses some features which are particularly attractive and others which introduce difficulties. The differences between the scattering parameters for x-rays, neutrons, and electrons are summarized in Table 1. Note that the wavelengths for electron beams in the velocity range generally used

Table 1

	X-rays	Neutrons	Electrons
λ	0.5–2.5 Å Cu Kα: 1.5 Å	0.5–4 Å "thermal": 1.1 Å	0.05–0.08 Å 50 kv: 0.055 Å
Scattered by	Electron $\rho(\mathbf{r})$; nuclei not effective	Nuclear forces	Electric potential; Ze^+ modified by $\rho(\mathbf{r})$
Amplitude	$\dfrac{e^2}{mc^2}\dfrac{\rho(\mathbf{r})}{R}\,d\tau$		$\dfrac{2m}{h^2}\dfrac{V(\mathbf{r})}{R}\,d\tau$
Atomic- form factor	F; theory available, given $\rho(\mathbf{r})$	Theory available for magnetic scattering	$f = (Z - F)/s^2$ $[s \equiv (4\pi/\lambda)\sin(\theta/2)]$
F dependence on Z	Roughly $F \doteq \phi Z$; ϕ universal function	Irregular; $F_n = (\sigma_s/4\pi)^{1/2}$	Roughly $f \doteq Z(1 - \phi)/s^2$
F dependence on angle	Decreases monotonically from Z to 0	Independent of scattering angle	$(s^2 f)$ increases monotonically from 0 to Z
Magnitude at $s = 6.3$	$F_{\mathrm{Na}} = 1.14 \times 10^{-12}$ $F_{\mathrm{Cu}} = 3.75$	0.34×10^{-12} 0.76	6700×10^{-12} 15,100
Range in $s/4\pi$ covered	1.4 for Mo Kα	0.95 for "thermal"	2.5 (usually) 4 (sometimes)
Intensity measure- ment	Difficult on absolute basis	Obtainable on absolute basis	Difficult on absolute basis
Polarization	Must be corrected for	Depends on spin-spin interactions	Not significant

are appreciably smaller than those generally utilized in x-ray and neutron diffraction. Hence $s_{\max}$ is correspondingly greater. Indeed, workers at the University of Oslo have recorded electron diffraction patterns for gases with s values up to about 60; efforts to extend the range in s for thin films and powders have not been reported. The larger effective diffraction angles attainable is one favorable aspect of electron diffraction, in that the radial distribution curves deduced show the best resolution in interatomic distances.

Now let us consider the scattering process. Whereas the x-ray diffraction intensity is determined by the electron density distribution, electrons are scattered by the entire electric potential, owing to the positive charge on the nuclei as modified by the surrounding electron density.

The relationship between the various amplitudes of scattering and their radial distribution functions for x-rays and electrons has been given by Viervoll (1955). Let $\rho(\mathbf{r})$ be the position vector specifying the electron density distribution in specimen space, and $\mathbf{s}$ the corresponding vector in reciprocal space. The amplitude for coherent x-ray diffraction scattering by any sample is given by

$$A_X(\mathbf{s}) \propto \int \rho(\mathbf{r}) \exp\left(-ik\mathbf{s}\cdot\mathbf{r}\right) d\tau \tag{6}$$

$$k = 2\pi/\lambda \qquad |\mathbf{s}| = 2\sin(\theta/2) \qquad s = k|\mathbf{s}|$$

The corresponding equation for electron diffraction is

$$A_e(\mathbf{s}) \propto \int V(\mathbf{r}) \exp\left(-ik\mathbf{r}\cdot\mathbf{s}\right) d\tau \tag{7}$$

where $V(\mathbf{r})$ is the electric potential distribution in the specimen. The potential or the electron distribution may be obtained by a Fourier inversion of these amplitude functions, which are related by the Poisson equation.

$$\nabla^2 V(\mathbf{r}) = -4\pi\rho_t(\mathbf{r}) = -4\pi[\rho_Z(\mathbf{r}) - \rho(\mathbf{r})] \tag{8}$$

where $\rho_t(\mathbf{r})$ is the total charge density, and $\rho_Z(\mathbf{r})$ that due to the nuclei only. One may thus transform expression (7) to

$$s^2 A_e(\mathbf{s}) \propto \int \rho_t(\mathbf{r}) \exp\left(-ik\mathbf{r}\cdot\mathbf{s}\right) d\tau \tag{9}$$

or write

$$\left\langle \frac{Z}{Z-F} \right\rangle_{\text{av}} s^2 A_e(\mathbf{s}) \propto \int \rho_Z(\mathbf{r}) \exp\left(-ik\mathbf{r}\cdot\mathbf{s}\right) d\tau \tag{10}$$

The atom-form factor for x-rays is

$$F \equiv \int_0^\infty 4\pi r^2 \rho_{\text{atom}}(r) \frac{\sin sr}{sr} dr$$

For electrons it is $f_i \equiv (Z_i - F_i)/s^2$ to within the validity of the first Born approximation. In expression (10) Viervoll used $(1/s^2)\langle (Z-F)/Z\rangle_{\text{av}}$ as the average atomic (scattering) form factor. For electrons the structure-sensitive portion of the diffraction intensity, when relation (4) is valid, should be computed from

$$J_e(s) = \sum_{ij}{}' f_i f_j \exp\left(-\alpha_{ij}^2 s^2\right) \frac{\sin sr_{ij}^0}{sr_{ij}^0} \tag{11}$$

to replace the idealized expression (1). The relation between the various radial distribution functions can now be stated.

$$2\pi^2 r D_V(r) = \int_0^\infty s \cdot J_e(s) \sin sr \, ds \qquad (12)$$

$$2\pi^2 r D_t(r) = \int_0^\infty s^5 \cdot J_e(s) \sin sr \, ds \qquad (13)$$

$$2\pi^2 r D_Z(r) = \int_0^\infty \left\langle \frac{Z^2}{(Z-F)^2} \right\rangle_{av} s^5 \cdot J_e(s) \sin sr \, ds \qquad (14)$$

On comparing (2) with (14),

$$J_e \left\langle \frac{Z^2}{(Z-F)^2} \right\rangle_{av} s^4 \equiv i_Z(s)$$

$$\frac{d^4}{dr^4} [2\pi^2 r D_V(r)] = 2\pi^2 r D_t(r) \qquad (15)$$

It is evident that, whereas the measured intensity of scattered electrons gives directly the distribution of electric potential throughout the sample, it can be reduced to a distribution which depends on the charge density, and with proper reduction to the nuclear charge density. The latter correction must be looked at carefully, since for both x-rays and electrons it is necessary to factor out a universal atom-form factor, ϕ, to the approximation that for all atoms this function has the same angular dependence. Compare the shapes of both the coherent and the incoherent form factors for x-rays and electrons (Fig. 5). For x-rays the coherent intensity decreases with increasing s and eventually falls below that of the rising incoherent contribution. The magnitudes of neither the ϕ^2 function nor of the structure-sensitive part of the intensity pattern can be measured with precision at large s; yet, it is the ratio F^2/ϕ^2 which determines $D_Z(r)$. Finbak (1949) recommended the computation of $D_{elec}(r)$ rather than of $D_Z(r)$ to avoid this difficulty. Here is the second advantage possessed by electrons: $s^4 f^2$ increases with increasing scattering angle. When a rotating sector is used (see below), such that the recorded intensity is proportional to $s^4 f^2$, it is the ratio of large numbers, $s^4 f^2/[s^4(1-\phi)^2]$, which determines $D_Z(r)$.

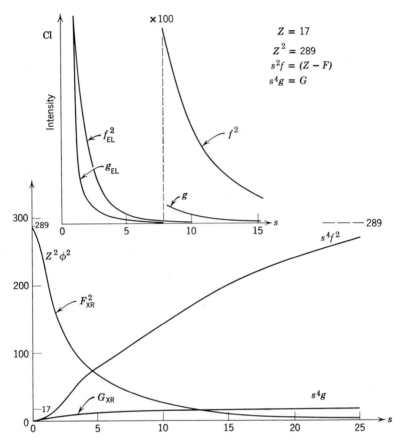

Fig. 5. Coherent and incoherent atom-form factors for Cl. Comparison of the functions for x-rays (F_{XR}^2 and G_{XR}, respectively) and fast electrons (f_{EL}^2 and g_{EL}).

One should, of course, raise the question as to how well a single ϕ function does approximate all atom-form factors. This has not been tested extensively for x-rays, but it does appear to be poor for electrons, particularly at small s values (<8). Coffin (1951) tested a variety of correction procedures for reducing a coherent intensity curve, as per equation (11) so that upon inversion the resulting function would approximate $D_Z(r)$ rather than $D_t(r)$. Several are shown in Fig. 6. The backgrounds of the radial distribution curves F and G are clearly not zero but depend on the way the averaging [implied in (10) and (14)] had been performed. The major difficulty arises from the region in the intensity curve from $s = 0$ to about $s = 4$. Even though the coherent intensity contribution is not structure-sensitive, it is sensitive to the shape of the

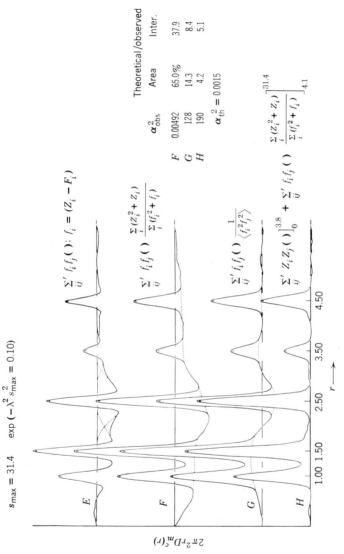

Fig. 6. Radial distribution curves deduced for the model used in Fig. 2, but with the coherent intensity computed with equation (11). Curve E gives $D_t(r)$, corresponds to equation (13); curve F corresponds to equation (14), $s^2 {}_f = s^2 f_i/Z_i \neq (1 - \phi)$, since the f_i values were computed for specific atoms, using Hartree electron distributions, whereas ϕ is a universal function based on the Thomas-Fermi model.

atom-form factors used. It appears to be essential in deducing the correct $D_Z(r)$ from electron diffraction data to compute that part of the curve rather than to use the measured intensity, as is evident from curve H. Perhaps a more satisfactory way to introduce this correction is

$$i_Z^c(s) \equiv J_e(s) \quad + [i_Z^0(s) - J_e^0(s)] \qquad (16)$$

$$\uparrow \qquad\qquad \uparrow$$

experimentally observed over $4 < s < 40$ (minus atomic contributions)

computed for a reasonably satisfactory model, over range $0 < s < 15$

In this manner the experimentally observed intensity curve is adjusted simultaneously for the unavailable low angle region and for the departure of the actual intensity curve from that which would be obtained for nuclear scattering.

One should not conclude the discussion of atom-form factors without calling attention to a major difficulty inherent in electron diffraction. Strictly speaking, the first Born approximation is too crude for accurate structure determinations. It has long been known that this approximation is invalid at very small angles, and within the last decade it has been demonstrated to be invalid even at larger angles, when the difference in atomic number between the scattering atoms is appreciable. A careful study has yet to be made of the best procedure for reducing diffraction data for compounds containing both light and heavy atoms. Under those conditions equation (11) should be rewritten in the form

$$J_e(s) = \sum_{ij}{}' |f_i|\,|f_j| \cos(\Delta\eta_{ij}) \exp(-\alpha_{ij}{}^2 s^2) \frac{\sin s r_{ij}{}^0}{s r_{ij}{}^0} \qquad (17)$$

wherein the atomic scattering factors are complex functions, $f_j = |f_j| \exp(-i\eta_j)$. The scattered amplitude from a given atom pair involves a relative phase shift $\Delta\eta_{ij}$ which is appreciable when the difference in the atomic numbers for the pair ij is appreciable. For example, this "heavy-light split" amounts to about 0.25 Å for the pair lead-carbon in lead tetramethyl. A theoretical analysis of these "splits" has been given by Ibers and Hoerni (1954). Clearly, the phase shift in scattering not only reduces the resolution attainable in the radial distribution curves for molecules containing both light and heavy atoms but also reduces the utility of radial distribution curves for estimating intramolecular motions.

We have pointed out previously that one great advantage which the diffraction of electrons has over x-rays and neutrons is the short wavelength. A minor useful feature is that patterns produced by amorphous or highly distorted materials, which consist of the superposition of broad diffraction maxima, are still easily recognizable visually owing to the compression of the diffraction angle. The early data on the structures of molecules in the gaseous state would have been impossible to interpret were it not for the fact that the eye is very sensitive to adjacent increments in photographic density. Electron diffraction patterns as recorded on film are easily discernible, and the maxima and minima can be measured visually.

The third essential advantage of electron diffraction is that the scattering coefficient of 25–50 kv electrons is very high (Table 1). Electron beams are best suited for the study of surface layers and thin films, as well as of gaseous systems. An estimate of how small a sample size is needed for structure determination by electron diffraction may be obtained from the fact that a jet of carbon tetrachloride less than a half millimeter in diameter, at a pressure of approximately 1 mm Hg, will produce a useful electron diffraction photograph in about 1 minute using a beam current of approximately 0.1 μa. The scattering coefficient for electrons clearly depends on the voltage (their effective wavelength). The total scattering cross section is given by

$$\pi \sigma_e^2 = 2\pi B^2 \left(\frac{\lambda}{2\pi}\right)^2 \int_0^{4\pi/\lambda} \left[\sum_i (f_i^2 + g_i) + \sum_{ij}' f_i f_j \frac{\sin s r_{ij}^0}{s r_{ij}^0} \right] \frac{ds}{s} \quad (18)$$

where $B \equiv 8\pi^2 m e^2/h^2$; to a rough approximation the structure-sensitive part of the integrand may be neglected. Then, owing to the rapid decrement of the argument with s, the magnitude of the integral does not depend greatly on λ, and the scattering cross section is approximately proportional to λ^2.

The very high scattering coefficient provides desirable characteristics but also introduces difficulties. The first and obvious disadvantage is that the diffraction data must be recorded in a high vacuum system, and no windows can be used to confine the sample. (Depending on the accelerating voltage, the ambient pressure in the diffraction apparatus should be no greater than about 10^{-5} mm Hg at 50 kv and correspondingly lower for lower voltages.) Problems associated with selective sampling of the outer layers of thick specimens and difficulties with multiple scattering will be discussed below. At this point, it is worth while to consider briefly some of the experimental techniques and to note structural data derived from gaseous systems which can be carried over to amorphous solids.

Remarks on Experimental Procedures and Results from the Study of Gaseous Compounds

Figure 7 is a schematic arrangement for the study of materials by electron diffraction; as indicated, the sample is a jet of gas moving upwards within the vacuum system through the nozzle. In order to maintain the vacuum at the lowest possible level, the jet is surrounded by liquid nitrogen-cooled surfaces. When thin films, powdered materials, or crystals are studied, a variety of supports have been developed for insertion in place of the gas nozzle. (Figure 8 shows a heated single-crystal goniometer and specimen holder for reflection studies.) A significant development in the recording of electron diffraction data has been the introduction of a "sector," that is, a rotating mask which reduces the exposure of the inner parts of the pattern relative to the outer parts according to a predetermined function of the radius. Thus one may cut a sector such that the background of the pattern is effectively leveled, and the details of the fluctuations above and below that background can be readily microdensitometered. Furthermore, the enormous range in intensity which is introduced by the s^{-4} factor thereby can be removed, so that the photographic film can record accurately the spread in intensities. Under these conditions the recorded pattern is not $J_e(s)$ but, depending on the shape of the sector opening, some modified function. Ideally the sector should be cut, so that the opening is given by

$$\text{Sector opening } \Omega = \frac{1}{\sum_i (f_i^2 + g_i)} \tag{19}$$

Then the recorded intensity (single scattering only) is

$$\frac{I_e \text{ (sector)}}{P_e \text{ (primary)}} = K \left[1 + \Omega \sum_{ij}{}' f_i f_j \exp\left(-\alpha_{ij}^2 s^2\right) \frac{\sin s r_{ij}^0}{s r_{ij}^0} \right] \tag{20}$$

where $K = B^2(N/R^2)$ and N = number of molecules per cubic centimeter in the sample. The structure-sensitive part is the second term in the bracket, and the unit value corresponds to the contribution from the atomic coherent and incoherent scattering. When electron diffraction data thus recorded are properly analyzed and care is taken to eliminate extraneous scattering and other disturbing factors, very good agreement between theory and experiment can be obtained (see Fig. 9; Bartell and Brockway, 1953). Examples of rather complicated molecules are shown

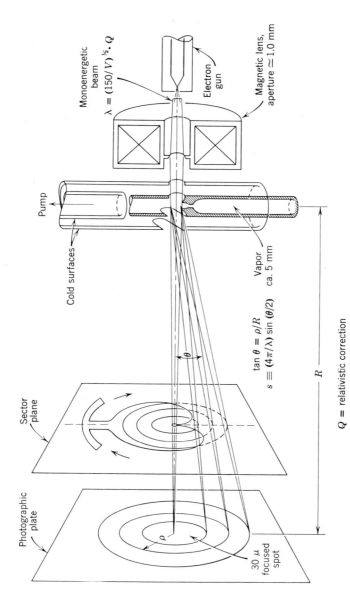

Fig. 7. Schematic arrangement for electron diffraction apparatus. Operating vacuum should be better than 1×10^{-5} mm Hg.

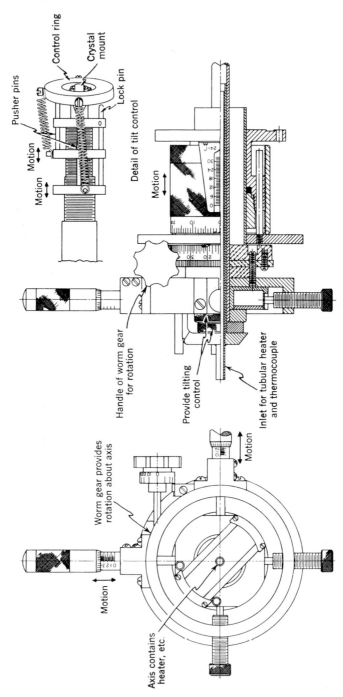

Fig. 8. Heated single-crystal goniometer and specimen holder for reflection studies.

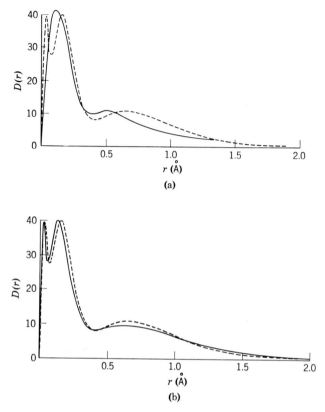

Fig. 9. (a) The radial distribution of electrons in argon computed from x-ray diffraction data (Wollan), and the Hartree distribution; (b) the radial distribution of electrons in argon computed from electron diffraction data, and the Hartree distribution. Broken curves, Hartree theory; solid curves, from x-ray diffraction. (Bartell and Brockway, 1953.)

in Fig. 10; all the interatomic distances for toluene and phenyl silane have been resolved and estimates made of the average vibrational amplitudes (Keidel and Bauer, 1956).

Many structures of low molecular weight organic molecules which are of interest to high polymer chemists have been determined in the gas phase by electron diffraction techniques. These have been confirmed by x-ray diffraction studies of the crystals, by their infrared and microwave spectra. The latter, in particular, have permitted very precise determinations of bond distances and valence angles for sufficiently simple structures. Since many monomers are electronically conjugated systems, such that on polymerization the conjugation is either fully or partially

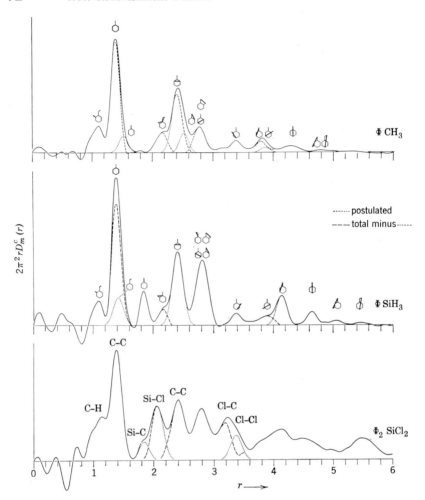

Fig. 10. Radial distribution curves for phenyl methane, phenyl silane, and diphenyl-dichlorosilane (Keidel and Bauer, 1956).

removed, one must estimate the changes which occur on polymerization by studying much smaller model compounds of the unconjugated variety. This information is also available (Bowen et al., 1958; Wheland, 1955; Pinsker, 1953; Stuart, 1952). Interatomic distances which are of special interest to glass technologists are quoted in Table 2.

Multiple Scattering

Owing to the high cross section for electron scattering (equation 18), great care must be taken to reduce extraneous scattering during the recording of the diffraction patterns. An inherent limitation is the appearance of plural and of multiple scattering for sufficiently dense samples. On the one hand, the deduction of reliable radial distribution functions for amorphous films is thereby hindered; on the other, the effect can be advantageously exploited for the "selective sampling" of the outer layers of the specimen.

Preliminary Analysis

To a reasonable approximation, the power in the transmitted beam is

$$J_0 = P_0 \exp\left(-\pi\sigma^2 N t\right)$$
$$N = \text{scattering units/cm}^3$$
$$K \equiv \pi\sigma^2 N \tag{21}$$
$$\varepsilon \equiv 2\left(\frac{s\lambda}{4\pi}\right)^2 \ll 1$$

The intensity of singly scattered electrons is

$$J_1(\text{total}) = P_0 K \int_0^t \exp\left(-Kx_1\right) \exp\left(-K\frac{t-x_1}{1-\varepsilon}\right) dx_1$$
$$\cong P_0(Kt) \exp\left(-Kt\right) \tag{22}$$

$$\text{error } 3.5\% \text{ at } s = 26; \qquad \theta = 15°$$

$$J_n \cong P_0 \frac{(Kt)^n}{n!} \exp\left(-Kt\right); \qquad \sum_{n=1}^{\infty} J_n = P_0[1 - \exp\left(-Kt\right)] \tag{23}$$

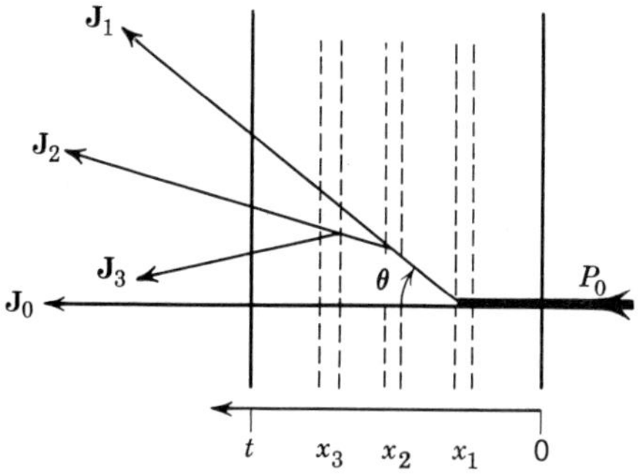

Fig. 11. Transmitted, singly scattered, and multiply scattered electron intensity.

Table 2

DISTANCES (IN ANGSTROMS) AND BOND ANGLES

$Me \equiv CH_3$; IR = infrared; ed → gas phase; xr → crystal structure analysis; xrl → x-ray R. D. analysis.

Substance	Si-O	Si-O-Si	Si-Y	Remarks
$H_3Si\text{-}O\text{-}SiH_3$	1.64 ± 0.01	$142 \pm 4°$ $155\ (\pm 15°)$	1.46 —	ed (Sutton et al., unpublished) IR (Curl and Pitzer, 1958)
$Cl_3Si\text{-}O\text{-}SiCl_3$	1.61 ± 0.03 1.64 ± 0.05	$175 \pm 5°$ —	2.00 ± 0.05 2.02 ± 0.03	xr (Wegener, unpublished) ed (Yamasaki et al., 1950)
$Me_3Si\text{-}O\text{-}SiMe_3$	1.63 ± 0.03	$130 \pm 10°$ $137 \pm 7°$ $160 \pm 15°$	1.88 ± 0.03 — —	ed (Yamasaki et al., 1950) ed (Lucht, unpublished) Dipole moment (Sauer and Mead, 1946) IR (Kriegsmann, 1957); also Raman spectra recorded and correlated
$Me_3Si\text{-}X\text{-}SiMe_3$ $(X = CH_2, NH, O, S)$	—	—		
$(Me_2SiO)_3$	1.66 ± 0.04	$125 \pm 5°$	1.88 ± 0.04	ed (Aggarwal and Bauer, 1950); S_3O_3 rings planar
$(Me_2SiO)_4$	1.65	$142°$	1.92	xr (Steinkink et al., 1955); S_4O_4 rings puckered
$(Me_4Si_2O_3)_2Si$	1.64 ± 0.03	$129\text{-}134°$	1.88 ± 0.03	xr (Roth and Harker, 1948); spiro[5.5]-pentasiloxane; rings planar and perpendicular to each other
$Si(OMe)_4$	1.64 ± 0.03	(Si-O-C) $113 \pm 2°$	(C-O) 1.42 ± 0.02	ed (Yamasaki et al., 1950)

SiO_2 glass	1.60 ± 0.05	$143 \pm 17°$	—	xrl (Zarzycki, 1957); SiO_4 tetrahedra; Si-O-Si becomes larger at higher temperatures
GeO_2 glass	(Ge-O) 1.70 ± 0.05	(Ge-O-Ge) $\sim 140°$ at $20°C$ / $\sim 160°$ at $1200°C$	—	xrl (Zarzycki, 1957); GeO_4 tetrahedra
$(Me_2SiNH)_3$	(Si-N) 1.78 ± 0.03	(Si-N-Si) $117 \pm 4°$	1.87 ± 0.05	ed (Yokoi and Yamasaki, 1953); Si_3N_3 ring puckered
$(Me_2SiNH)_4$	—	$123 \pm 4°$	—	ed (Yokoi and Yamasaki, 1953); Si_4N_4 ring puckered
$(Me_2SiS)_2$	(Si-S) 2.18 ± 0.03	(Si-S-Si) $75°$	—	ed (Yokoi, 1955); Si_2S_2 ring planar
$(Me_2SiS)_3$	2.15 ± 0.03	$110°$	—	ed (Yokoi, 1955); Si_3S_3 ring probably planar
$B(OMe)_3$	(B-O) 1.38 ± 0.02	(B-O-C) $113 \pm 3°$	(O-C) 1.43 ± 0.03	ed (Bauer and Beach, 1941); BO_3 group planar
$(MeBO)_3$	1.39 ± 0.02	(B-O-B) $112 \pm 4°$	(B-C) 1.57 ± 0.03	ed (Bauer and Beach, 1941); B_3O_3 ring planar
B_2O_3 glasses (solid and molten)	≈ 1.38	$\approx 180°$	—	xrl (Herre and Richter, 1957); BO_3 groups planar
	≈ 1.30 at $20°C$ / ≈ 1.50 at $1600°C$	—	—	xrl (Zarzycki, 1956); BO_3 groups planar

Therefore one may use the transmission of the primary beam through the sample as a rough measure of the various fractions which have been scattered once, twice, etc. This is shown in Fig. 12. As a consequence

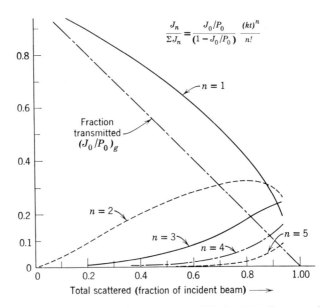

$$\frac{J_n}{\Sigma J_n} = \frac{J_0/P_0}{(1 - J_0/P_0)} \frac{(kt)^n}{n!}$$

Fig. 12. Incident beam fractions transmitted and total scattered.

of secondary scattering, forbidden reflections appear for well-crystallized materials, and the intensities of the allowed reflections are incorrectly recorded; for all types of material, owing to multiple scattering, the background departs appreciably from that computed on the assumption of single scattering. Instead of following approximately an s^{-3} dependence on angle, the slope is much less owing to the superposition of a bell-shaped intensity function on the expected background. This is illustrated by Fig. 13 (see also Ellis, 1952).

A Multiple Scattering Formula

Much more sophisticated but not entirely adequate treatments of multiple scattering have been presented by Viervoll and by Olsen (see Bauer et al., 1958). Formulas have been developed on the assumption that there are no phase relations between the waves scattered from adjacent small units, such as small crystallites, and this is justified when the elementary units are distributed at random with respect to orienta-

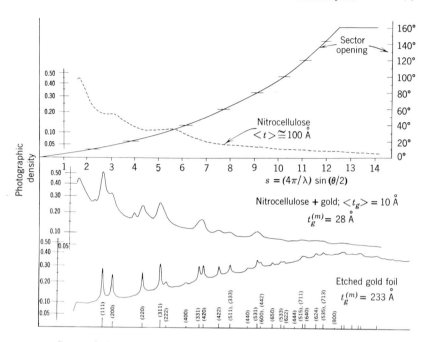

Fig. 13. Sector shape and microphotometer records for nitrocellulose and gold films (M. Friedman, unpublished work). The sector was cut empirically to provide a flat background for {50 Å nitrocellulose + 50 Å gold}. For very small gold crystallites there is little superposed multiple scattering, so that the net background decreases with s. Thicker gold films provide considerable multiple scattering, and the net background increases with s, owing to overcompensation by the sector.

tion and in space. Then one may sum over intensities rather than over amplitudes.

Set the cross section for scattering by a single unit (crystal, particle, etc.) to be $\sigma(\theta)$, θ being the angle of scattering with respect to the initial direction of motion of the electrons. Because of the random distribution of the units there must be over-all rotational symmetry around the initial direction; therefore $\sigma(\theta)$ may be treated as a function of θ only. Neglect energy loss and *differences in path length traversed by the electrons* (i.e., restriction to *small angles*), and define the probability (i.e., the intensity normalized to unity) $I(\mathbf{n}, t)$ that, after traversing a sheet of material of thickness t, the electron will be moving in the direction $\mathbf{n}$. Before reaching the material, all electrons will be moving parallel to the z-axis:

$$I(\mathbf{n} - \mathbf{n}_0, 0) = \delta(\mathbf{n} - \mathbf{n}_0)$$

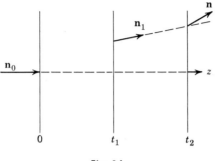

Fig. 14.

The equation of continuity follows from Fig. 14.

$$\int I(\mathbf{n}_1 - \mathbf{n}_0, t_1) I(\mathbf{n} - \mathbf{n}_1, t_2)\, d(\mathbf{n}_1) = I(\mathbf{n} - \mathbf{n}_0, t_1 + t_2) \qquad (24)$$

The integration over $\mathbf{n}_1$ extends over all intermediate directions of $\mathbf{n}_1$. Now introduce $d(\mathbf{n}_1) = dx \cdot dy$ (small angle approximation), and equation (24) may be written

$$\int I(\boldsymbol{\rho}_1, t_1) I(\boldsymbol{\rho} - \boldsymbol{\rho}_1, t_2)\, dx_1\, dy_1 = I(\boldsymbol{\rho}, t_1 + t_2) \qquad (24a)$$

where $\boldsymbol{\rho} = (x, y)$. One may express the intensity as a Fourier integral,

$$I(\boldsymbol{\rho}, t) = \int \exp\,(i\mathbf{k}\cdot\boldsymbol{\rho})\, J(\mathbf{k}, t)\, d(\mathbf{k}) \qquad (25)$$

After a number of integrations and normalization for all t,

$$\int I(\boldsymbol{\rho}, t)\, d(\boldsymbol{\rho}) = 1$$

one may write $d(\boldsymbol{\rho}) = \theta\, d\theta\, d\phi$, and $d(\mathbf{k}) = k\, dk\, d\phi_k$; then integration with respect to ϕ, ϕ_k can be readily performed, giving

$$I(\theta, t) = \frac{1}{2\pi} \int J_0(\theta k) \exp\left[-N\sigma t \left\{ 1 - \frac{1}{\sigma} \int \sigma(\theta') J_0(\theta' k)\theta'\, d\theta' \right\} \right] k\, dk \qquad (26)$$

J_0 being the Bessel function of order zero, and σ the total single scattering cross section. From equations such as (26), one can compute the total intensity expected for a thick, dilute suspension of scatterers of a known structure. Preliminary analyses have also been made in which the amplitudes rather than the intensities are folded. However, the converse problem, how one may correct an observed diffraction pattern for multiple scattering so that he may compute a reliable radial distribution curve, has not yet been solved. For a discussion of multiple scattering in crystals and in gas molecules, the reader is referred to papers by Hoerni (1956) and Kageyama (1956).

One effective way for reducing but not eliminating the extraneous background is to prevent those electrons which have lost energy from being recorded. A number of devices have been designed to accomplish this. The insertion of a Boersch lens (Boersch and Catalina, 1957) permits the rejection of electrons which have lost as little as 3 volts (out of 50 kv); the increase in contrast for thick samples is dramatic (for example, Fig. 15). This technique has great potential for the development

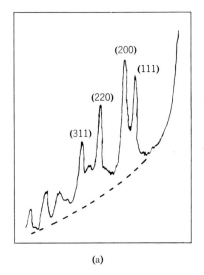 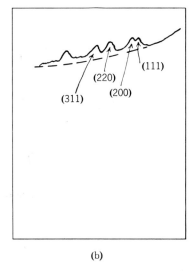

(a)   (b)

Fig. 15. Microphotometer records of diffraction patterns produced by gold films (Ichinokawa and Uyeda, 1954): (a) with filter lens set to deflect $\Delta V \geq 3$ volts; (b) with filter lens set to deflect $\Delta V \geq 30$ volts.

of quantitative recording of electron diffraction intensities, particularly when combined with the use of a rotating sector.

During the past five years, several electron diffraction units have been constructed in which rays selected from the diffraction pattern are passed into a velocity analyzer, to determine characteristic energy losses (Möllensteht, 1952; Marton et al., 1955, 1958). Leder and Simpson (1958) described a retarding voltage arrangement which has several tenths of a volt resolution; typical energy loss spectra through collodion and aluminum films are given. A comparison of the characteristic energy losses of electrons with the fine structure of x-ray absorption spectra has been made (Leder et al., 1956). The observed correlation suggests that many of the characteristic energy losses may be due to the excitation of the valence electrons to higher allowed energy levels.

Selective Sampling

The high scattering cross section of electrons with its inherent troublesome feature of multiple scattering can be advantageously exploited for the study of surface layers. As the voltage is decreased, the scattering cross section increases rapidly; for low voltage electrons (10–1000 ev), single atomic layers can be studied, as has been demonstrated in the classic work of Davisson and Germer. The low voltage range for electron diffraction is currently used by Farnsworth (ASTIA documents) in the study of surface layers of oxygen on crystals of nickel, silicon, and other semiconductors. These experiments must be performed in ultra-high vacuum systems, after thorough baking out of the apparatus and specimens; great care must be exercised in the preparation of the samples and in control of the atmosphere. Use of incident beam voltages in the neighborhood of 10 ev allows one to detect the presence of a few percent of a monolayer of adsorbed gas. After several monolayers of gas become adsorbed, the outer amorphous material completely prevents observation of the diffraction pattern due to the underlying crystal.

In the high voltage range the experimental techniques are considerably simpler, but the sampling is correspondingly less selective. If the assumption is made that only singly scattered electrons constitute the structure-sensitive part of the diffraction pattern, it is clear that the intensity of single scattering will be a maximum for some thickness of the particle, since the amount of single scattering will increase with its thickness, but the fraction lost through multiple scattering will also increase. For transmission experiments the fraction of singly scattered electrons as a function of the sample thickness t is

$$N/N_0 = (1/R^2)\mu_e\rho_a t \exp\left(-\langle\mu_e\rangle\rho_a t\right) \qquad (27)$$

where $\langle\mu_e\rangle$ is the weighted average absorption coefficient, and ρ_a is the atomic density (atoms per cubic centimeter). This function clearly has a maximum at $t_{max} = 1/\mu_e\rho_a$. A more useful form is $t_{max} \cong 10^{-7}/[(7.6)\rho_x\lambda^2]$ (ρ_x in grams per cubic centimeter). Since the intensity lost by the primary beam is due only to scattering (other causes being negligible), the absorption coefficient μ_e is simply the ratio of scattered electrons to incident electrons per unit area for each atom. To the desired approximation one may neglect the small interatomic interference terms relative to the much larger atomic scattering, and then

$$\mu_e \doteq \left(\frac{8\pi^2 me^2}{h^2}\right)^2 \frac{(Z - F)^2 + g}{s^4}$$

For a Thomas-Fermi model for the charge distribution in an atom, Boersch calculated this to be

$$\mu_e = 6.3 \times 10^{-17}\lambda^2 Z^{4/3} \text{ cm}^2 \quad \text{(with } \lambda \text{ in Å)} \tag{28}$$

The intensity of the structure-sensitive part may be assumed to be proportional to N/N_0. A material for which t_{max} is sufficiently small to permit detection of the effect of surface distortion is clearly one with a high density, since a decrease in t_{max} also results in a narrowing of the size range for single scattering (Fig. 16).

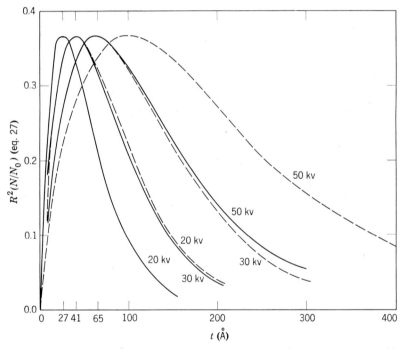

Fig. 16. Fractions of singly scattered electrons, as a function of crystallite size. Broken curve, NiO (200); solid curve, ThO_2 (400).

The fraction of singly scattered photons (x-rays) is

$$\frac{N}{N_0} = \left(\frac{1 + \cos^2\theta}{2}\right)\left(\frac{e^2}{mc^2}\right)\frac{\rho_a}{R^2} F^2 t \exp\left(-\mu_x t\right) \tag{29}$$

For the range of sizes being considered here (50 Å $< t <$ few hundred Å) and for small angles ($F \cong Z$), this reduces to

$$R^2 \frac{N}{N_0} = \left(\frac{e^2}{mc^2}\right)^2 \rho_a Z^2 t = 2.7 \times 10^{-8} t \tag{29a}$$

The maximum for single scattering for electrons for a substance such as NiO occurs at $t = 100$ Å, although single scattering occurs appreciably over a range from 30 to 200 Å. For x-rays the intensity of single scattering increases linearly with t until much greater thicknesses are reached. However, the effective contribution to the x-ray pattern by very small crystallites is less than is indicated by the equation, because the diffraction peaks for crystals ≤ 100 Å are so broad that they merge into the background. When a fairly large range of crystallite sizes is present, it follows that preferential sampling of the small crystallites by electrons will occur, whereas they will be overlooked by x-rays. The possibility of studying surface regions with soft x-rays at first appears attractive. However, except for substances with long repeat distances, the longest wavelength which can be used effectively is about 10 Å. Then, for $\mu_x \approx 15{,}000$, a thickness of 250 Å is needed to provide 50% absorption.

In order to determine the conditions which are necessary to permit detection of a difference between surface and bulk lattice parameters by electron diffraction, one must postulate a function to represent the variation of lattice parameter with thickness. Computations for simple models lead to asymmetric diffraction peaks (Bauer et al., 1958). Studies of selected materials are now in progress. It is of interest to mention that lattice parameters for very small crystallites have been determined by electron diffraction and reported to differ from those given by x-ray diffraction for the same materials or for the bulk substances. There is considerable doubt as to whether most of the reported effects are real. Great care must be taken in the proper reading of the diffraction ring diameters, since they are affected both by the shape of the background and the shape of the rings. A detailed analysis has been presented (Libowitz and Bauer, 1955).

Shape Factor for Thin Films

In order to obtain meaningful radial distribution functions from electron diffraction data on thin films, one must not only correct for (a) atomic coherent scattering, (b) atomic incoherent scattering, and (c) multiple scattering over the observable angular range, but he must also introduce a correction in the vicinity of all intense maxima, and in particular near the central beam for diffraction due to finite sample thickness. This is of significance for films in the 30–500 Å range. An analysis of this effect has been made by Viervoll (see Bauer et al., 1958). The shape factor for small crystallites has been discussed in considerable detail by Ewald, von Laue, and Patterson. The shape transform for electron diffraction by small crystals has recently been discussed by Rees and Spink (1950).

In his calculation of the low angle scattering by a thin film, Viervoll assumed that the sample was structureless. Let the cross section of the sample be a square of length b oriented so that one side is parallel and the other perpendicular to the plane defined by the incident beam and the direction of scattering; the film thickness is t, and N is the number of atoms per unit volume. Define the parameters

$$\alpha \equiv t \sin \theta = \frac{\lambda s}{4\pi} t \qquad \beta \equiv b(1 - \sin^2 \theta)^{\frac{1}{2}} = b\left(1 - \frac{\lambda^2 s^2}{16\pi^2}\right)^{\frac{1}{2}}$$

Then

$$\frac{I(s)}{B(s)} = N \frac{2(1 - \cos s\beta)}{s^2\beta^2} \cdot \frac{2(1 - \cos s\alpha)}{s^2\alpha^2} \tag{30}$$

where $B(s)$ is the total atomic scattering function for N atoms. Both the thickness (t) and the linear dimension (b) determine the diffraction intensity. The half-width of the central peak (at half-maximum) due to the first factor is

$$s\beta_{\frac{1}{2}} = 2.75 \quad \text{and} \quad s_{\frac{1}{2}} = 2.75/b$$

The second factor of (30) provides a similar pattern; zeros appear at $\lambda t s_0^2/4\pi = 2n\pi$ and subsidiary maxima at $\lambda t^2 s_m^2/4\pi = (2n + 1)\pi$. Clearly, the width of the diffraction pattern immediately around the central beam will be determined by the larger dimension (b). To obtain orders of magnitude, suppose

$$\frac{N}{V} = \frac{N}{\beta^2 t} = 0.1 \quad \text{and take} \quad b = 0.1 \text{ mm} = 10^6 \text{ Å}$$

A series of curves have been computed for different values of t (Fig. 17). Two striking features become evident:

(a) There is a considerable contribution to the coherent scattering function at values of s up to about 3 for film thicknesses as high as 100 Å, and up to $s = 1.5$ for films as thick as 500 Å.

(b) The cross-over in intensity from above to below N occurs at increasing s as t gets larger, up to about $t \cong 80$ Å, and then recedes; at the cross-over (dI/ds) is steep.

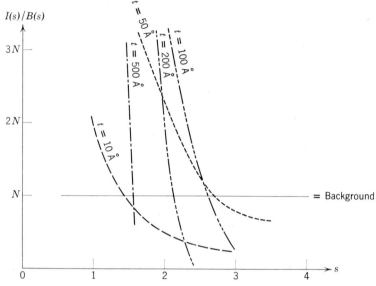

Fig. 17. Relative shape factor for thin films.

A final point which should not be overlooked is that at present the shape of the atom-form factor for electrons at very small angles is known only approximately (Massey, 1952).

Summary of Structural Studies of Amorphous Materials by Electron Diffraction

Germer (1938, 1939) was among the first to study organic films extensively. Both reflection- and transmission-type photographs were obtained; in particular, Germer and co-workers studied the deposition of long chain hydrocarbons and of long chain fatty acids and of their salts on various metal substrates by the dipping technique developed by Blodgett (1937). Conclusions on the orientation and structures of these multilayers followed from the patterns recorded. Over the next decade, a number of papers appeared in which electron diffraction by films of high polymers were taken for the purpose of getting information on their atomic configurations. The first attempts to interpret the patterns were made by assuming a model and comparing the computed with the observed intensities. The reports by Kakinoki (1940) on cellulose are typical. In 1949 Kakinoki, Murata, and Katada computed radial distribution curves for several high polymers, based on patterns which were recorded out to $s = 20$. None the less, the radial distribution curves did not lead to significant structural information, and the interpretation of the data still necessitated the correlation of intensity curves computed for various assumed models with the observed patterns. These investigators found that for a large number of high polymers, ranging from polystyrene through various cellulose derivatives, agar-agar, and gelatin, closely similar patterns were obtained.

One of the problems which has yet not been solved is how to eliminate changes in the structure of these high polymer films due to bombardment by the electron beam. An attempt to reduce these damaging effects was made by Honjo and Watanabe (1957). They cooled the specimens and were able to obtain excellent diffraction patterns for various cellulose fibers. Lowering the accelerating voltage and using low intensities and long exposure times also help prevent deterioration. We shall describe in the next section experiments performed at Cornell which demonstrated changes in density due to irradiation even by low intensity electron beams.

Interesting electron diffraction data have been obtained on the structure of carbon black and of evaporated carbon films. White and Germer (1941) showed that films of pyrolitically deposited carbon consist of pseudo-crystals, each made up of three or four parallel, uniformly spaced, but otherwise randomly disposed atomic planes in which the carbon atoms are arranged as in graphite. More recently Kakinoki and co-workers (1957) compared evaporated carbon films with polystyrene and found the spacings to be quite similar in a number of respects and to differ appreciably from those in graphite. The carbon films used in these studies were the same as generally prepared for the replica method in electron microscopy and were of the order of 100 Å thick. Kakinoki concluded from the diffuse ring positions and from a radial distribution curve that these carbon films consisted of three-dimensional networks, with carbon-carbon bonds of the order of 1.54 Å, but with graphite-like structures over short distances.

As a tool for the study of very thin layers of hydrocarbons deposited on metal surfaces, electron diffraction is of demonstrated utility. A large variety of waxes have thus been examined. The theory for the scattering of electrons by hydrocarbon films supported on metal substrates (such as would appear in lubrication studies) was given by Karle (1946), and typical data wherein the theory was utilized to interpret observed patterns were reported in a subsequent paper (Karle and Brockway, 1947). For long chain molecules this theory permits the estimation of the azimuthal direction and the declination from the vertical as well as the orientation of the hydrocarbon chains about their own axes. For the latter, one requires correct intensity measurements within the separate diffraction orders. Were reliable quantitative intensity data available, the angular distribution of the declination and the orientation of the hydrocarbon films could be obtained. Recently the study of adhesives has been undertaken by Jamaguchi (1957). From his work and others (Natta and Corradini, 1956), it is clear that in such polymer films molecules tend to assume a preferred orientation with respect to the roll or extrusion direction. [Similarly, orientation and preferential growth factors, as well as the imposition of unnatural spacings by the substrate (epitaxy) on evaporated films of inorganic materials, have been extensively investigated.] In this respect the concurrent analyses of polarized infrared absorption data with electron diffraction patterns of oriented films (such as would be obtained by a rolling process) would help to elucidate the structures of such films on a molecular basis. Polarized infrared data give the direction of orientation along which the dipole moment responsible for absorption changes, and this can be correlated with the configuration of the long chain molecule as determined by the diffraction technique. Natta and Corradini studied 1,2-polybutadiene in this manner.

A number of investigations were made of the amorphous-type layer which remains when a metallic surface is lapped with fine grain abrasives. This stratum has been called the "Beilby layer." Raether concluded that it consists of very small crystal grains, so that the diffraction patterns obtained therefrom consist of rather diffuse halos. Recently Nonaka and Kohra (1954) studied the changes which occur in the Beilby layer as a function of temperature, and they found indeed that crystal growth takes place, with the consequent sharpening of the diffraction pattern, and that the time required depends on the temperature, being considerably less at elevated temperatures.

Only within the last five years have serious efforts been made to obtain radial distribution curves for amorphous materials from electron diffraction data. The most intriguing of these has been the development by some Japanese workers (Honjo et al., 1956) of a low temperature specimen mount which could be used both for electron diffraction and electron microscopy. With such a device they were able to record electron diffraction patterns from mercury as a function of the temperature of the substrate upon which the mercury was condensed. In later work they demonstrated that this technique is a powerful one for investigating the structure of highly supercooled liquids. This is feasible because in the process of condensation of a liquid on a crystal substrate in such an apparatus extremely small droplets are formed—so small that there is a small probability for nuclei to be enclosed. The drops remain liquid to temperatures many degrees below the normal freezing point. This procedure was used to study the structure of supercooled liquid bismuth (Takagi, 1956). At temperatures below the freezing point the liquid has a relatively well-ordered structure with spacings comparable to those present in the solid; at temperatures 300° above the melting point, this structure is considerably washed out. In the radial distribution curve for the liquid in the supercooled state, the first peak shows six atoms, in a shell structure almost like that in the solid; at 400°C the number of atoms under the first peak has reached eight, and the second shell has been considerably washed out in amplitude (Fig. 18).

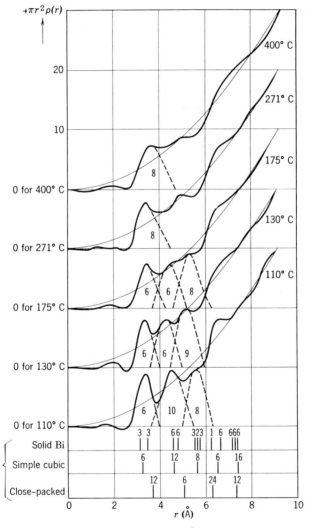

Fig. 18. Obtained radial distribution function $4\pi r^2 \rho(r)$ at 400°, 271°, 175°, 130°, and 110°C; atomic shells in solid Bi, in simple cubic structure and in close-packed structure (Honjo et al., 1956).

Examination of the data, however, shows that this technique is still to be developed. No allowance has been made by these workers for multiple scattering; because the shape factor has not been considered, the question of the correct intensity at small s remains; the diffraction data extended only to about $s = 9$ and thereafter seem to "wash out." The authors did state that the weak point in the data as reported is the limit in the accuracy of the intensity measurements. The introduction of a filter lens and sector will greatly enhance the reliability and extent of the intensity measurements, and interesting structural conclusions will follow from this technique.

Changes in Collodion Film Induced by 50 kv Electrons, as Measured by Transmission Ratios and Diffraction Intensities

Collodion films (obtained by casting solutions in amyl acetate on water substrates) were investigated by measuring the intensity of the "undeflected" beam, transmitted for various film thicknesses, and concurrently recording the diffraction pattern (Andersen and Calvo; see Bauer et al., 1958). Results could not be reproduced until it was recognized that the collodion films changed upon bombardment by low intensity electron beams. This change was so rapid that the time usually taken for aligning the beam with respect to the sample exceeded the time during which significant changes occurred in the film's transmission. It was necessary to study the transmission characteristics before further work on multiple scattering could be pursued.

Measurement of the I/I_0 values (collector aperture $\approx 0.5s$) and the variation of the background in the electron diffraction patterns showed that the rate of change in these films decreased with time, reaching an apparently constant plateau after 3 minutes' exposure to a beam of intensity of 10^{-6} to 10^{-7} amp, and after about 20 minutes at $3-6 \times 10^{-8}$ amp, for all thicknesses (60–1000 Å). The changes were localized to the region at which the beam struck, as could be verified by moving the spot of incidence on the surface of the film. Previous drying of the films in a vacuum oven at about 150°C for several hours reduced but did not eliminate these effects.

In Fig. 19, I/I_0 is shown plotted against exposure time. To check whether this is a desorption phenomenon and exponential in form, we determined the variation of the "desorption" coefficient with thickness. Assume that the intensity I at any time of exposure is related to the final intensity I_f and the intensity recorded at the moment of first exposure I_1,

$$I = I_f - (I_f - I_1) \exp(-\kappa t)$$

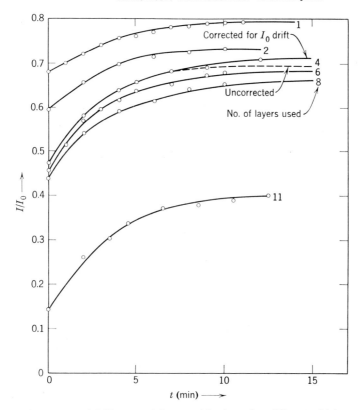

Fig. 19. Variation of I/I_0 central beam with time, for different thicknesses of collodion film.

or

$$\ln \frac{I_f - I}{I_f - I_1} = \kappa t \qquad (31)$$

When $(I_f - I)/(I_f - I_1)$ was plotted on a semilog scale against time, curves for various thicknesses were very close to straight lines, with essentially equal slopes. A measure of the contraction of the film upon exposure, for the various thicknesses, is made in Fig. 20. The values of I_1/I_0 and I_f/I_0 were plotted on a semilog scale as a function of the thickness. The points of constant I/I_0 have been connected. If the thickness scale for the fresh film is expanded by a factor of 3, I/I_0 for the exposed film is obtained. One may conclude that these films contract to about $\frac{1}{3}$ their initial thicknesses (subject to the errors of estimating I_1) upon electron bombardment. Changes in thickness also affect the background diffraction intensity. Since multiple scattering is more prominent for

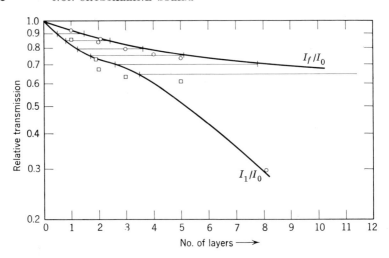

Fig. 20. Two curves for time 0 and ∞ made to estimate change in thickness of the films. A factor of $\frac{1}{3}$ seems to fit.

thicker specimens, the slope of the background should decrease with increasing thickness. Figure 21 shows backgrounds deduced from microphotometer records of diffraction pictures taken after exposure of a 500 Å thick collodion film 0, 1, 4, and 7 minutes to the beam.

König (1951) reported that carbonization takes place when a collodion film is exposed to an electron beam, and he cited the disappearance of the first maximum in the diffraction pattern as evidence. Figure 22 shows microphotometer tracings of electron diffraction patterns produced by a 500 Å film. Even after 7 minutes' exposure to the beam, the first maximum remains. König's failure to use a sector may have caused the first peak to be lost in the steepening background as the collodion shrank. However, it is clear that extended exposure to an intense electron beam could cause the film to carbonize. It is doubtful that the short exposures and low beam intensities usually employed in diffraction experiments do much more than cause the evaporation of solvent and loss of water from the film. Since the contraction is substantial, extensive cross-linking may be taking place.

Departure of the relative transmission versus thickness relation from exponential (Fig. 20) may be semiquantitatively accounted for. One should keep in mind that in these measurements the collecting cage, of necessity, had an aperture which was about five times the diameter of the focused beam. The shape factor, which depends on sample thickness, introduces a low angle scattering function not all of which is collected by the cup. In addition, the effects of multiple scattering enter in a

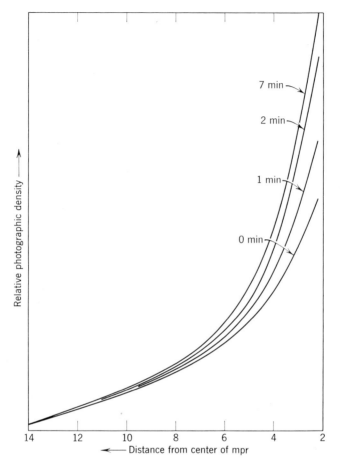

Fig. 21. Backgrounds deduced from electron diffraction photographs (see Fig. 22), taken with a sector, of a 500 Å collodion film, after the indicated times of exposure to the electron beam.

complicated manner. Reduction of the data in Fig. 22 and the computation of radial distribution functions are now in progress.

Prospects

The introduction of modern vacuum technology and the application of current advances in electronics will permit the determination of electron diffraction patterns with high precision, extending to large diffraction angles; use of sectors and filter lens will facilitate these measure-

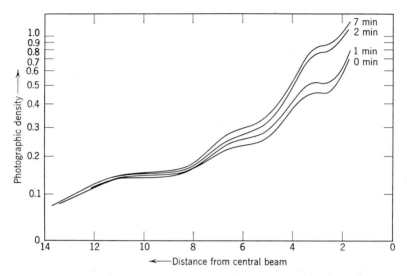

Fig. 22. Electron diffraction intensity curves after 0, 1, 2, and 7 minutes' exposure to the electron beam.

ments. Analysis of the incoherent energy losses and advances in the theory of plural scattering will facilitate our understanding of the structure of the scatterers, both with respect to the arrangement of the atoms and the changes in energy levels characteristic of the condensed state of matter.

REFERENCES

Aggarwal, E. H., and Bauer, S. H., *J. Chem. Phys.* **18**, 42 (1950).

Bartell, L. S., and Brockway, L. O., *Phys. Rev.* **90**, 833 (1953).

Bauer, S. H., and co-workers, Final Technical Report, Contract Nonr-401(06), Project NR 356 296, submitted Feb. 1, 1958.

Bauer, S. H., and Beach, J. Y., *J. Am. Chem. Soc.* **63**, 1394 (1941).

Blodgett, K. S., *Proc. Natl. Acad. Sci. U. S.* **23**, 390 (1937).

Boersch, H., and Catalina, F., *Acta Cryst.* **10**, 339 (1957), and previous publications.

Bowen, H. J. M., et al., Tables of Interatomic Distances and Configurations in Molecules and Ions, *Chem. Soc. (London) Spec. Publ.*, **No. 11** (1958).

Coffin, K. P., Ph.D. Dissertation presented to the Faculty of the Graduate School of Cornell University (Sept. 1951).

Curl, R. F., and Pitzer, K. S., *J. Am. Chem. Soc.* **80**, 2371 (1958).

Ellis, S. T., *J. Appl. Phys.* **23**, 1024 (1952).

Farnsworth, H. E., ASTIA documents Nos. 113,679 (1956), 117,025 (1957), 133,730 (1957).

Finbak, C., *Acta Chem. Scand.* **3**, 1279, 1293 (1949).

Freedman, Miriam (Mrs.), unpublished data, 1951.

Germer, L. H., reviews appear in *J. Appl. Phys.* **9**, 143 (1938), and publication No. 7 of the AAAS, p. 47 (1939).

Herre, F., and Richter, H., *Z. Naturforsch.* **12a**, 545 (1957).

Hoerni, J., *Phys. Rev.* **102**, 1530, 1534 (1956).

Honjo, G., et al., *J. Phys. Soc. Japan* **11**, 527 (1956).

Honjo, G., and Watanabe, H., *Acta Cryst.* **10**, 818 (1957).

Ibers, J. A., and Hoerni, J. A., *Acta Cryst.* **7**, 405 (1954).

Ichinokawa, T., and Uyeda, R., *Proc. Japan Acad.* **30**, 858 (1954).

Ino, Tadashi, *J. Phys. Soc. Japan* **12**, 495 (1957).

Jamaguchi, S., *J. Polymer Sci.* **25**, 118 (1957).

Kageyama, S., *J. Phys. Soc. Japan* **11**, 348 (1956).

Kakinoki, J., *Proc. Phys.-Math. Soc. Japan* **22**, 1010 (1940).

Kakinoki, J., et al., *Acta Cryst.* **10**, 829 (1957).

Kakinoki, J., Murata, H., and Katada, K., *Sci. Papers Osaka Univ.*, **No. 16/17** (1949).

Karle, J., *J. Chem. Phys.* **14**, 297 (1946).

Karle, J., and Brockway, L. O., *J. Chem. Phys.* **15**, 213 (1947).

Keidel, F. A., and Bauer, S. H., *J. Chem. Phys.* **25**, 1218 (1956).

Klug, H. P., and Alexander, L. E., *X-ray Diffraction Procedures*, Wiley, New York, 1954, p. 608.

König, Hans, *Z. Physik* **129**, 483 (1951).

Kriegsmann, H., *Z. Elektrochem.* **61**, 1088 (1957).

Leder, L. B., et al., *Phys. Rev.* **101**, 1460 (1956).

Leder, L. B., and Simpson, J. A., *Rev. Sci. Instr.* **29**, 571 (1958).

Libowitz, G., and Bauer, S. H., *J. Phys. Chem.* **59**, 209, 214 (1955).

Lucht, C. M., unpublished data.

Marton, L., et al., *Advances in Electronics and Electron Phys.* **7**, 183 (1955); *Rev. Sci. Instr.* **29**, 567 (1958).

Massey, H. S. W., *Advances in Electronics and Electron Phys.* **4**, 1 (1952).

Möllensteht, G., *Optica* **9**, 473 (1952).

Morozumi, C., and Ritter, H. L., *Acta Cryst.* **6**, 588 (1953).

Natta, G., and Corradini, P., *J. Polymer Sci.* **20**, 255 (1956).

Nonaka, K., and Kohra, K., *J. Phys. Soc. Japan* **9**, 512 (1954).

Patterson, A. L., *Phys. Rev.* **65**, 195 (1944).

Pinsker, Z. G., *Electron Diffraction*, Butterworths, London, 1953.

Rees, L. G., and Spink, J. A., *Acta Cryst.* **3**, 316 (1950).

Roth, W. L., and Harker, D., *Acta Cryst.* **1**, 34 (1948).

Sauer, R. O., and Mead, D. J., *J. Am. Chem. Soc.* **68**, 1797 (1946).

Steinkink, H., et al., *Acta Cryst.* **8**, 420 (1955).

Stuart, H. A., *Die Physik der Hockpolymeren*, Vol. 1, Springer, Berlin, 1952.

Sutton, L. E., and co-workers, unpublished.

Takagi, M., *J. Phys. Soc. Japan* **11**, 396 (1956).

Viervoll, H., *Acta Cryst.* **8**, 56 (1955).

Wegener, H. A. Richard, unpublished.

Wheland, G. W., *Resonance in Organic Chemistry*, Wiley, New York, 1955.

White, A. H., and Germer, L. H., *J. Chem. Phys.* **9**, 492 (1941).

Yamasaki, K., et al., *J. Chem. Phys.* **18**, 1414 (1950).

Yokoi, M., et al., *J. Am. Chem. Soc.* **77**, 4484 (1955).

Yokoi, M., and Yamasaki, K., *J. Am. Chem. Soc.* **75**, 4139 (1953).

Zarzycki, J., in *Verres et réfractaires* **11**, 3 (1957).

Zarzycki, J., *4th Intern. Congr. on Glass, Paris*, 1956.

DISCUSSION

J. A. PRINS

I wish to raise a point regarding the preparation of samples of very small drops of highly supercooled liquids. I have often tried (and sometimes succeeded) to get electron diffraction patterns from small drops of liquids, but I have encountered great difficulties, because these drops were generally too large. When the atomic number of the material is relatively large, the diameter of the drops should be no more than 100 Å and at most should not be larger than 1000 Å even for very low atomic numbers. I found it difficult to get drops of that size without much larger drops appearing at the same time and introducing spurious effects.

S. H. BAUER

Please note that the Japanese workers devised a very special cooling system and obtained their drops by slow evaporation.

J. A. PRINS

I have attempted to do this with mercury onto collodion films but have not succeeded. One could stop at just the right point, but one always had a mixture of large drops and small drops. It could be that the small drops give the dominant pattern, and the bigger drops merely introduce background effects. On considering the changes in the radial distribution curves as a function of temperature, I have a suspicion that there may be something wrong with the experiment. Bismuth oxide is very easily obtained in the amorphous state; since it is impossible to eliminate oxygen completely from the diffraction system, it could well be that these diffraction patterns were in part due to the oxide of the metal rather than to the highly supercooled liquid.

S. H. BAUER

I can confirm your argument in this respect that, at a pressure at which one normally operates in electron diffraction cameras (for example, 10^{-5} mm Hg), it takes only a second or so to obtain a monolayer of oxygen on the surface. With the surface layer completely covered with oxygen, one may raise the question as to how rapidly and how deeply the oxygen atoms diffuse into the lower substrates and thereby react with the metal at the substrate temperatures utilized in these experiments.

D. P. RILEY

I do not recall the specific reference, but I believe that work on soft x-ray spectra on pure elements suffers from just this difficulty of reaction with the ambient atmosphere. I should think it is highly likely that the description of the experiment as given by Professor Prins is correct.

R. HILSCH

I will later report on bismuth. We have prepared bismuth in the amorphous state at very low temperatures, where it appears in simple cubic surroundings. Therefore one wonders whether at the high temperature of 110°C a different coordination number appears. It may be that this substantiates Professor Prins's arguments.

O. L. ANDERSON

Was I correct in concluding that you believe that in silica-type molecules in the gaseous phase the evidence is in favor of an oxygen bond angle less than 180°?

S. H. BAUER

The evidence seems to be very clear to that effect.

T. J. GRAY

I would like to call attention to data obtained by Professor Cox at Leeds which show, on the basis of electron density determination, that in solid silica the bond angle is less than 180°.

J. ZARZYCKI

X-ray diffraction data on vitreous SiO_2 and GeO_2 [J. Zarzycki, *Verres et réfractaires* **11**, 3 (1957)] clearly indicate that the oxygen bond angle is less than 180°.

by

R. M. Delaney
A. H. Weber

Saint Louis University

Structure of Vitreous Silica by Total Neutron Scattering

Semi-empirical Method for Inelastic Scattering

Theory

The total neutron scattering analysis may be developed by first expressing the theory for structure analysis by x-rays in terms of differential neutron scattering. The radial density distribution for x-rays is

$$4\pi r^2[\rho(r) - \rho_0] = \frac{2r}{\pi} \int_0^\infty si(s) \sin rs \, ds \qquad (1)$$

where $\rho(r)$ is the atomic density as a function of r, ρ_0 is the average atomic density of the sample, $s = 4\pi(\sin \theta)/\lambda = 4\pi\chi$, θ is half the scattering angle, and $i(s) = (I_{eu}/Nf^2) - 1$, where I_{eu} is the differential intensity of scattering in electron units (the ratio of scattered intensity to the intensity scattered by a single electron), N is the number of scattering centers in the sample, and f is the atomic structure factor.

Investigation originally assisted by the Owens-Illinois Glass Company of Toledo, Ohio, and later supported by the Office of Ordnance Research, United States Army.

The section "Semi-empirical Method" is essentially as published in *The Physical Review* **105**, 517–521 (1957).

For neutrons $N(d\sigma_s/d\omega)$ replaces I_{eu} and a (nuclear scattering length) replaces f; also (Weber, 1950; Shull and Wollan, 1951) $4\pi a^2 = \sigma_s{}^b$, where $\sigma_s{}^b$ is the coherent scattering cross section for an isolated, bound scattering center. Hence, for differential scattering of neutrons,

$$i(s) = \left(\frac{4\pi}{\sigma_s{}^b}\frac{d\sigma_s}{d\omega}\right) - 1 \tag{2}$$

so that (1) becomes

$$4\pi r^2[\rho(r) - \rho_0] = \frac{2r}{\pi}\int_0^\infty s\left[\left(\frac{4\pi}{\sigma_s{}^b}\frac{d\sigma_s}{d\omega}\right) - 1\right]\sin rs\, ds \tag{3}$$

where the Debye-Waller factor has been neglected as in (1).

The Fourier transform of (3) is

$$si(s) = \int_0^\infty 4\pi r[\rho(r) - \rho_0]\sin sr\, dr \tag{3a}$$

Integrating the differential scattering cross section over the total solid angle and using $d\omega = 2\pi \sin 2\theta\, d(2\theta)$ yields

$$\sigma_s = \int_0^{4\pi} d\omega(d\sigma_s/d\omega)$$

$$= \int_{2\theta=0}^{2\theta=\pi} 2\pi \sin 2\theta\, d(2\theta)(d\sigma_s/d\omega)$$

$$= 8\pi\lambda^2 \int_0^{1/\lambda} (d\sigma_s/d\omega)\chi\, d\chi \tag{4}$$

where $\chi = (\sin \theta)/\lambda$.

Transmission experiments were conducted with the slow neutron velocity selector (Brill and Lichtenberger, 1947) to measure σ_T the total cross section for neutrons. The intensity ($\propto$ flux) I of a neutron beam measured after it passes through a sample ($4\frac{1}{2}$ x $1\frac{1}{2}$ x $1\frac{1}{4}$ inches with the $1\frac{1}{4}$-inch dimension parallel to the neutron beam) of N_s scattering units per square centimeter is related to the initial beam intensity I_0 by

$$I = I_0 \exp(-N_s\sigma_T) \tag{5}$$

whence

$$\sigma_T = N_s \ln(1/T) \tag{6}$$

where the transmission T is the ratio of I to I_0.

The determination of atomic radial density distribution using transmission data requires the integration of the differential scattering cross section by way of (4), yielding the total scattering cross section which is then experimentally evaluated by using (6). Substituting (2) in (4) and using $s = 4\pi\chi$ yields (writing σ_{Ls}, the total liquid sample scattering cross section, for σ_s)

$$\sigma_{Ls} = \frac{\sigma_s{}^b \lambda^2}{8\pi^2} \left(\int_0^{4\pi/\lambda} s \, ds + \int_0^{4\pi/\lambda} si(s) \, ds \right) \tag{7}$$

Integrating the first term and using (3a) in the second term of the right-hand side of (7) yields

$$\frac{\sigma_{Ls}}{\sigma_s{}^b} = 1 + \frac{\lambda^2}{8\pi^2} \int_0^{4\pi/\lambda} \int_0^{\infty} 4\pi[\rho(r) - \rho_0] \sin sr \, dr \, r \, ds \tag{8}$$

Integration with respect to s yields

$$\frac{\sigma_{Ls}}{\sigma_s{}^b} = 1 + \frac{\lambda^2}{2\pi} \int_0^{\infty} [\rho(r) - \rho_0] \left(1 - \cos \frac{4\pi r}{\lambda} \right) dr \tag{9}$$

Taking

$$\int_0^{\infty} [\rho(r) - \rho_0] \, dr = 0 \tag{10}$$

setting $\alpha = 4\pi/\lambda$ and $i(\alpha) = 1 - \sigma_{Ls}/\sigma_s{}^b$ and rearranging yields

$$\left(\frac{\alpha^2}{4\pi} \right) i(\alpha) = \frac{2}{\pi} \int_0^{\infty} [\rho(r) - \rho_0] \cos \alpha r \, dr \tag{11}$$

Multiplying both sides of (11) by $\cos \alpha r'$ and integrating with respect to α over the range 0 to ∞ yields

$$\frac{1}{4\pi^2} \int_0^{\infty} \alpha^2 i(\alpha) \cos \alpha r' \, d\alpha = \frac{2}{\pi} \int_0^{\infty} \cos \alpha r' \, d\alpha \int_0^{\infty} [\rho(r) - \rho_0] \cos \alpha r \, dr \tag{12}$$

Since the right-hand side of (12) is the Fourier integral representation of $[\rho(r) - \rho_0]$, the radial density distribution is given by the corresponding transform

$$4\pi r^2 [\rho(r) - \rho_0] = \frac{r^2}{\pi} \int_0^{\infty} \alpha^2 i(\alpha) \cos \alpha r \, d\alpha \tag{13}$$

If the analysis is extended to a diatomic substance such as vitreous silica, four radial densities, instead of the single $\rho(r)$ of (13), must be considered: $\rho^{ii}(r)$, the radial density of i-type atoms about an i-type origin atom; $\rho^{jj}(r)$, of j-type atoms about a j-type atom; $\rho^{ij}(r)$, of j-type atoms about an i-type atom; and $\rho^{ji}(r)$, of i-type atoms about a j-type atom. In the present work it is assumed that, of the four distributions involved in the radial densities, the first two and the third and fourth together are independent of one another; that is, they do not overlap. This assumption is substantiated by the ultimate experimental results.

Hence, for vitreous silica, equation (13) (for a monatomic substance) is replaced by the following three expressions.

1. For the i-i system (i-type atoms about an i-type atom),

$$4\pi r^2 f_i\{\rho^{ii}(r) - \rho_i\} = \frac{r^2}{\pi}\int_0^\infty \alpha^2 i_1(\alpha)\cos\alpha r\, d\alpha \tag{14}$$

2. For the j-j system (j-type atoms about a j-type atom),

$$4\pi r^2 g f_j\{\rho^{jj}(r) - \rho_j\} = \frac{r^2}{\pi}\int_0^\infty \alpha^2 i_1(\alpha)\cos\alpha r\, d\alpha \tag{15}$$

3. For the i-j and j-i systems,

$$4\pi r^2 g^{1/2}[f_j\{\rho^{ji}(r) - \rho_i\} + f_i\{\rho^{ij}(r) - \rho_j\}] = \frac{r^2}{\pi}\int_0^\infty \alpha^2 i_1(\alpha)\cos\alpha r\, d\alpha \tag{16}$$

In (14) to (16),

$$i_1(\alpha) = \frac{\sigma_{sc} - (\sigma_{obs} - \sigma_A)}{\sigma_i} \tag{17}$$

where σ_{sc} is the bound isolated scattering cross section for the molecule, σ_{obs} is the total experimentally measured (chopper) cross section, σ_A is the capture cross section for the molecule [thus $\sigma_{obs} - \sigma_A$ replaces σ_{Ls} of (7) to (13)] and σ_i is the bound coherent scattering cross section for the i-type atom. Also, f_i and f_j are the fractions of i- and j-type atoms in the diatomic substance; g is σ_j/σ_i; ρ_i and ρ_j are the average radial densities of the i-type atoms in the i-i system and the j-type atoms in the j-j systems, respectively, and are defined by

$$\rho_i = \frac{\int_0^R 4\pi r^2 \rho^{ii}(r)\, dr}{\int_0^R 4\pi r^2\, dr} \tag{18}$$

$$\rho_j = \frac{\int_0^R 4\pi r^2 \rho^{jj}(r)\, dr}{\int_0^R 4\pi r^2\, dr} \tag{19}$$

It is emphasized that (14) to (16) constitute a "separate-systems" analysis and may be used only when the separate radial densities present act independently. This means, for example, that the i-i system alone produces a peak at distance r in the radial density distribution curve, the effect of the j-j, i-j, and j-i in phase scattering being negligible at the same distance r, and so on. If such is not the case, (14) to (16) must be modified, and this can be done.

Analytical Procedure

The measurement of the total cross section of (6) with the chopper is straightforward. The transmission coefficient is calculated by the ratio of the cadmium difference reading with the sample in the beam to the cadmium difference reading without the sample. Figure 1 shows the

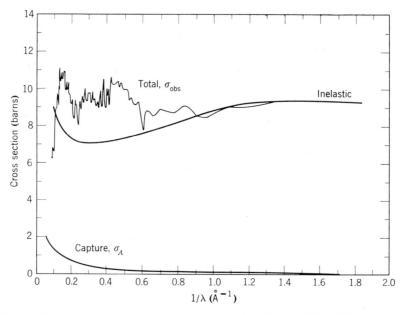

Fig. 1. Neutron cross sections for superpure Corning vitreous silica. The observed total (capture plus scattering) cross section σ_{obs} curve is plotted directly from data obtained with the slow neutron velocity selector. Counting statistics: probable error 5% or smaller. Resolution: $\Delta(1/\lambda)$ at half-maximum is 0.012 $\overset{\circ}{A}^{-1}$ at $1/\lambda = 0.625$ $\overset{\circ}{A}^{-1}$.

total cross section σ_{obs} so obtained for superpure Corning vitreous silica. This observed total cross section includes the coherent liquid scattering (the interferent part), capture (designated by σ_A), incoherent elastic scattering (spin and isotope effects), thermal incoherent scattering (decreased coherent scattering calculated by the Debye-Waller factor), and inelastic scattering.

The capture cross section is readily subtracted [as indicated by (17)] from the total cross section on a σ versus λ plot since σ_A is linear with λ (Bent and Ruderman, 1950). Since the capture cross section is zero for $\lambda = 0$, one other point ("Nuclear Data," 1950) was used to determine the σ_A versus λ straight line.

The incoherent elastic part of the scattering is zero, since for vitreous silica the nuclei involved are monoisotopic and of spin zero. The thermal decreased coherency is small for vitreous silica and so was neglected. The inelastic scattering cross section was evaluated approximately by assuming it to be proportional to the reciprocal Debye temperature and using the curves given by Cassels (Frisch, 1950). The resulting curve was fitted to the experimental curve in the region $1.1 \text{ Å}^{-1} < 1/\lambda < 2 \text{ Å}^{-1}$ as indicated in Fig. 1 and was used as σ_{sc} in (17). This means that $\sigma_{obs} - \sigma_A$ approaches the inelastic cross section at the shorter neutron wavelengths here employed. Also, the resulting correction is a one-phonon correction at large wavelength and a Debye-Waller type of correction at small wavelength and is an approximation. Incidentally, the value of σ_{Ls} at the maximum value of $1/\lambda$ in Fig. 1 is $\sigma_s{}^b$ of (7) to (13).

The integrals of (14) to (17) were evaluated by representing them as finite sums (Danielson and Lanczos, 1950); a 128-point analysis (using an electronic digital computer) was employed to obtain the radial density distribution curves of Fig. 2. The ordinates in Fig. 2 are defined as follows.

$$R_{O,O\text{-}Si,Si}(\rho) \equiv 4\pi r^2[g f_O \rho^{O,O} + f_{Si}\rho^{Si,Si}] = 4\pi r^2[g f_O \rho_O + f_{Si}\rho_{Si}]$$

$$+ \frac{r^2}{\pi} \int_0^\infty i_1(\alpha)\alpha^2 \cos \alpha r \, d\alpha$$

$$R_{Si,Si}(\rho) \equiv 4\pi r^2 f_{Si}\rho^{Si,Si} = 4\pi r^2 f_{Si}\rho_{Si} + \frac{r^2}{\pi} \int_0^\infty i_1(\alpha)\alpha^2 \cos \alpha r \, d\alpha$$

$$R_{O,O}(\rho) \equiv 4\pi g r^2 f_O \rho^{O,O} = 4\pi r^2 g f_O \rho_O + \frac{r^2}{\pi} \int_0^\infty i_1(\alpha)\alpha^2 \cos \alpha r \, d\alpha$$

$$R_{O,Si}(\rho) \equiv 4\pi r^2 g^{\frac{1}{2}}[f_O\rho^{O,Si} + f_{Si}\rho^{Si,O}]$$

$$= 4\pi r^2 g^{\frac{1}{2}}[f_O\rho_{Si} + f_{Si}\rho_O] + \frac{r^2}{\pi} \int_0^\infty i_1(\alpha)\alpha^2 \cos \alpha r \, d\alpha$$

The areas under the peaks of the radial density distribution curves (Fig. 2) yield the number of atoms (O or Si) located about an origin atom (O or Si) at the average distance given by the r value of the peak. In calculating these numbers of atoms the basic unit structure of Warren (1934, 1937) was used as a working model. In this structure each Si atom is tetrahedrally surrounded by four O atoms; the vertices of the first tetrahedron are at the same time vertices of four other tetrahedra, so that each O atom is bound to two Si atoms. (In the glassy state this structure is not repeated at regular intervals; there are distortions, so that some features of a random network are produced.)

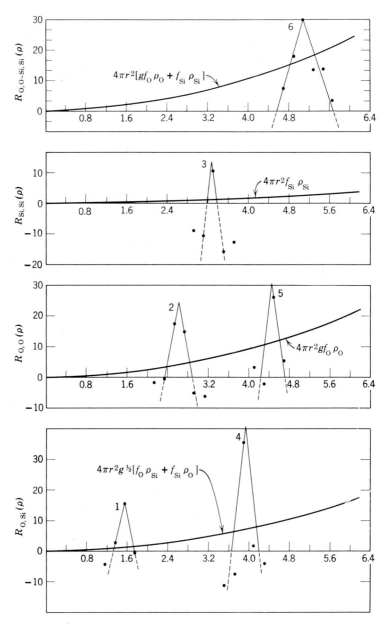

Fig. 2. Atomic radial density distribution for superpure Corning vitreous silica obtained by a 128-point analysis of the data of Fig. 1. The peaks are numbered 1–6 in order of increasing radial distance r: peak 1 is for O atoms, about an Si origin atom or for Si atoms about an O origin atom; peak 2 is for O atoms about an O origin atom; peak 3 is for Si atoms about an Si origin atom; peak 4 is for 2nd Si atoms about an O origin atom or for 2nd O atoms about an Si origin atom; peak 5 is for 2nd O atoms about an O origin atom; peak 6 is for 2nd Si atoms about an Si origin atom and 3rd O atoms about an O origin atom.

Thus, if the first definite peak of Fig. 2 (at $r = 1.6$ Å approximately, labeled 1) is considered to be produced by the smallest Si-O distances, then from (16)

$$G(r) = 4\pi r^2 g^{\frac{1}{2}} \{ f_O \rho^{O\text{-}Si}(r) + f_{Si} \rho^{Si\text{-}O}(r) \}$$
$$= 4\pi r^2 g^{\frac{1}{2}} \{ f_O \rho_{Si} + f_{Si} \rho_O \}$$
$$+ \frac{r^2}{\pi} \int_0^\infty \alpha^2 i_1(\alpha) \cos \alpha r \, d\alpha \qquad (20)$$

and

$$\int_{r_1}^{r_2} G(r) \, dr = \text{area under Si-O peak}$$
$$= g^{\frac{1}{2}} \{ f_O N^{O\text{-}Si} + f_{Si} N^{Si\text{-}O} \} \qquad (21)$$

where $N^{O\text{-}Si} = 2$ is the number of Si atoms about an O atom near $r = 1.6$ Å. Using the triangle approximation method for measuring the area under the peak yields $N^{Si\text{-}O}$, the number of O atoms about an Si atom at a distance near 1.6 Å. The bound-isolated scattering cross section values used were 2.25 barns (silicon) and 3.8 barns (oxygen).

This procedure was followed for the first six peaks as shown by Fig. 2, and the results of the analysis are listed in Table 1. The experimental total neutron scattering values for the number of atoms at the various distances are approximate only since the triangle form of the peaks is determined by a few points only.

Satisfactory agreement of the experimental values, both of interatomic distances and of numbers of atoms located at these approximate distances, with corresponding values calculated from the Warren model is found.

Theoretical Calculation of Inelastic Scattering (Einstein Model)

Neutron Scattering in Non-crystalline Materials

The analysis presented in this section employs an Einstein model for neutron scattering by a crystal following the Finkelstein (1947) method, but summing over all possible transitions rather than merely those between the ground state and higher states. This procedure yields for the differential elastic coherent scattering cross section per atom, G_{coh},

$$G_{coh} = \frac{1}{N_T} \left(\frac{m_0}{\mu} \right)^2 a^2 \exp\left(-\frac{1}{2} g_1 q_0^2 \right) \sum_{m,n} \exp(i\mathbf{s} \cdot \mathbf{r}_{mn}) \qquad (1)$$

where $\mathbf{s} = \mathbf{K} - \mathbf{K}'$; $\mathbf{r}_{mn} = \mathbf{r}_m - \mathbf{r}_n$ and $\mathbf{r}_n$ is the position vector of the nth atom (monatomic substance).

Table 1

ATOMIC RADIAL DENSITY DISTRIBUTION RESULTS FOR CORNING SUPERPURE
VITREOUS SILICA (FIG. 2) COMPARED WITH WARREN'S MODEL

Semi-empirical Model for Inelastic Scattering

Proposed Interatomic Distance (first-noted atom is origin atom)	Warren Model		Total Neutron Scattering	
	Distance (Å)	No. of Atoms	Distance (Å)	No. of Atoms (exptl. values from areas under peaks of Fig. 2)
Si-O	1.60	4 O	1.6	4.3
O-O	2.65	6 O	2.6	6.6
Si-Si	3.20	4 Si	3.3	2.7
Si-2nd O	4.00	12 O	3.9	13.8
O-2nd O	4.50	6 O ⎱ [a] 18 O ⎰	4.5	6.9
Si-2nd Si	5.20	12 Si	5.1	12.0

[a] A three-dimensional model of SiO_2 tetrahedral units yields a total of 18 O atoms at the Si-2nd O spacing if a rigid radial orientation is followed; deviations from strict radial orientation, permitting a more compact filling of space, probably causes 1 O atom of each 3 basal O atoms to be nearer the origin atom, yielding 6 as the number of O atoms at the O-2nd O distance.

Defining

$$Y = \hbar^2 g_1 / 2mk \tag{2}$$

then

$$G_{\mathrm{coh}} = \frac{1}{N_T} \left(\frac{m_0}{\mu} \right) a^2 \exp\left(-Ys^2 \right) \sum_{m,n} \exp\left(i\mathbf{s} \cdot \mathbf{r}_{mn} \right) \tag{3}$$

where

$$s = |\mathbf{K} - \mathbf{K}'| = (4\pi/\lambda) \sin\left(\theta/2 \right) \tag{4}$$

In (1), (2), (3), and (4) the following symbols are defined as

$$g_1 = \frac{1 + w}{1 - w} \qquad w = \exp\left(-\Theta/T \right)$$

where Θ is the Einstein temperature;

$$q_0{}^2 = 8(m_0/m)\epsilon \sin^2\left(\theta/2 \right)$$

where m_0, m are the neutron and scattering atom masses, respectively, and

$$\epsilon = E/\hbar\omega$$

where E is the incident neutron energy; μ, reduced mass of neutron and scattering nucleus; N_T, the total number of atoms in the scattering volume; $\mathbf{K}$, $\mathbf{K}'$ are the incident and scattered neutron wave vectors ($2\pi/\lambda$, magnitude); and other symbols have the standard meanings.

In an experiment using polycrystalline material (monatomic), a radial density distribution about some origin atom may be obtained for a range of distances extending to the boundary of a crystallite. It is assumed that neutrons scattered by nuclei belonging to different crystallites do not contribute to the coherent scattering. In liquids, gases, and liquid-like materials, atoms are considered to occupy positions about an origin atom in an ordered fashion for short distances only. This distance from an origin atom may be taken as an effective radius r_1 beyond which the nuclei scatter the neutrons incoherently. Within the distance r_1 the distribution of atoms about an origin atom is given by a radial density distribution function $\rho(r)$.

Therefore the sum in (3) is assumed to be taken so that the atoms m and n are in the same crystallite. This immediately leads to an average over all crystallite orientations (assumed random) which gives

$$G_{\mathrm{coh}} = \frac{1}{N_c}\left(\frac{m_0}{\mu}\right)^2 a^2 \exp\left(-Ys^2\right) \sum_{m,n} \frac{\sin sr_{mn}}{sr_{mn}} \tag{5}$$

the summation being carried out over one crystallite; N_c is the number of atoms in a crystallite.

Equation (5) may be written

$$G_{\mathrm{coh}} = \left(\frac{m_0}{\mu}\right)^2 a^2 \exp\left(-Ys^2\right) + \frac{1}{N_c}\left(\frac{m_0}{\mu}\right)^2 a^2 \exp\left(-Ys^2\right) \sum_{m,n}' \frac{\sin sr_{mn}}{sr_{mn}} \tag{6}$$

where the prime on the summation sign denotes $m \neq n$.

The complete differential scattering cross section G_{sc} is given by

$$G_{\mathrm{sc}} = G^- + G^+ + G^0 + \left(\frac{m_0}{\mu}\right)^2 a^2 \exp\left(-Ys^2\right)$$

$$+ \frac{1}{N_c}\left(\frac{m_0}{\mu}\right)^2 a^2 \exp\left(-Ys^2\right) \sum_{m,n}' \frac{\sin sr_{mn}}{sr_{mn}} \tag{7}$$

where G^-, G^+, and G^0 are given by

$$G^- = \left(\frac{m_0}{\mu}\right)^2 a^2 \sum_{\lambda=1}^{\infty} \left(\frac{\epsilon + \lambda}{\epsilon}\right)^{\frac{1}{2}} \exp\left(-\frac{1}{2} g_1 q_{-\lambda}^2\right) w^{\lambda/2} I_\lambda(g_2 q_{-\lambda}^2) \quad \text{(7a)}$$

$$G^+ = \left(\frac{m_0}{\mu}\right)^2 a^2 \sum_{\lambda=1}^{k \leq \epsilon} \left(\frac{\epsilon - \lambda}{\epsilon}\right)^{\frac{1}{2}} \exp\left(-\frac{1}{2} g_1 q_\lambda^2\right) w^{-\lambda/2} I_\lambda(g_2 q_\lambda^2) \quad \text{(7b)}$$

$$G^0 = \left(\frac{m_0}{\mu}\right)^2 a^2 \exp\left(-\frac{1}{2} g_1 q_0^2\right) [I_0(g_2 q_0^2) - 1] \quad \text{(7c)}$$

In (7a), (7b), and (7c) the following symbols are defined.

$$g_2 = \frac{w^{\frac{1}{2}}}{1 - w}$$

$$q_{\pm\lambda}^2 = 2\frac{m_0}{m}[\epsilon + (\epsilon \pm \lambda) - 2\epsilon^{\frac{1}{2}}(\epsilon \pm \lambda)^{\frac{1}{2}} \cos\theta]$$

$I_\lambda(g_2 q_\lambda^2)$ is the modified Bessel function of order λ, defined by $J_\lambda(ix) = i^\lambda I_\lambda(x)$ in which $x = g_2 q_\lambda^2$ and $J_\lambda(ix)$ is the Bessel function of order λ
$I_0(g_2 q_0^2)$ is $I_\lambda(g_2 q_\lambda^2)$ with $\lambda = 0$

and all other symbols have been defined previously.

Noting that $Y s^2 = \frac{1}{2} g_1 q_0^2$, it is seen by (7c) that

$$G^{0\prime} = G^0 + \left(\frac{m_0}{\mu}\right)^2 a^2 \exp\left(-\frac{1}{2} g_1 q_0^2\right)$$

$$= \left(\frac{m_0}{\mu}\right)^2 a^2 \exp\left(-\frac{1}{2} g_1 q_0^2\right) I_0(g_2 q_0^2) \quad \text{(8)}$$

where $G^{0\prime}$ is the modified elastic incoherent differential cross section per atom; it is the elastic cross section which would exist if all the atoms scattered incoherently. Therefore

$$G_{sc} = G^- + G^+ + G^{0\prime} + \frac{1}{N_c}\left(\frac{m_0}{\mu}\right)^2 a^2 \exp\left(-Y s^2\right) \sum_{m,n}' \frac{\sin s r_{mn}}{s r_{mn}} \quad \text{(9)}$$

Defining

$$G_I = G^- + G^+ + G^{0\prime} \quad \text{(10)}$$

where G_I is the bound independent differential scattering cross section (the differential cross section which would be observed for a bound atom scattering independently of all other atoms), then

$$G_{sc} = G_I + \frac{1}{N_c}\left(\frac{m_0}{\mu}\right)^2 a^2 \exp\left(-Y s^2\right) \sum_{m,n}' \frac{\sin s r_{mn}}{s r_{mn}} \quad \text{(11)}$$

If it is now assumed that the atomic distribution about any one origin atom is the same as about any other, (11) may be written

$$G_{sc} = G_I + \left(\frac{m_0}{\mu}\right)^2 a^2 \exp\left(-Ys^2\right) \sum_m \frac{\sin sr_{m0}}{sr_{m0}} \tag{12}$$

where the sum is taken over all atoms within a distance of r_1 from the origin atom.

Assuming an atomic radial density distribution $\rho(r)$, (12) may be written

$$G_{sc} = G_I + \left(\frac{m_0}{\mu}\right)^2 a^2 \exp\left(-Ys^2\right) \int_0^{r_1} 4\pi r^2 \rho(r) \frac{\sin sr}{sr}\, dr \tag{13}$$

The observed total scattering cross section σ_{sc} is found by integrating over the whole solid angle except that subtended by the detector (Ω_{det}). Therefore

$$\sigma_{sc} = \int_{4\pi - \Omega_{det}} G_{sc}\, d\omega \tag{14}$$

Defining Ω_{det}, the solid angle subtended by the neutron detector,

$$s = \alpha \sin\left(\theta/2\right) \tag{15}$$

where

$$\alpha = 4\pi/\lambda \tag{16}$$

The solid angle of the detector can be approximately accounted for by permitting s to range over all values from s_0 to α, where

$$s_0 = \alpha \sin\left(\theta_0/2\right) \tag{17}$$

Then integrating (13) over all solid angles except that of the detector, the total scattering cross section is

$$\sigma_{sc} = \int_{4\pi - \Omega_{det}} G_I\, d\omega + \frac{8\pi}{\alpha^2}\left(\frac{m_0}{\mu}\right)^2 a^2 \int_{s_0}^{\alpha} \exp\left(-Ys^2\right) \int_0^{r_1} 4\pi r\rho(r) \sin sr\, dr\, ds \tag{18}$$

In the first integral on the right-hand side of (18) G_I does not increase sharply as θ approaches zero; therefore if $\Omega_{det} \ll 4\pi$, this first integral can be approximated by σ_I, which is the bound independent cross section found by integrating (10) over the whole solid angle.

Therefore (18) becomes

$$\sigma_{sc} = \sigma_I + \frac{2\sigma}{\alpha^2}\left(\frac{m_0}{\mu}\right)^2 \int_0^{\alpha} \exp\left(-Ys^2\right) \int_0^{r_1} 4\pi r\rho(r) \sin sr\, dr\, ds$$

$$- \frac{2\sigma}{\alpha^2}\left(\frac{m_0}{\mu}\right)^2 \int_0^{s_0} \exp\left(-Ys^2\right) \int_0^{r_1} 4\pi r\rho(r) \sin sr\, dr\, ds \tag{19}$$

where $\sigma = 4\pi a^2$.

In the third term on the right-hand side of (19), if

$$\rho(r) = \rho_0$$

for $r_0 \leq r \leq r_1$, where ρ_0 is the average atomic density of the material, and if $s_0 r_0$ is small compared to unity for the neutron energies of interest in this experiment, then the following approximations may be made. As r ranges from 0 to r_1, then, since sr will be small compared to unity, there will be little variation of sin sr as s varies from 0 to s_0; therefore in the third term on the right-hand side of (19) $\rho(r)$ is averaged over r for $0 \leq r \leq r_0$. This average value of $\rho(r)$ is assumed to be ρ_0. Therefore for both $0 \leq r \leq r_0$ and $r_0 \leq r \leq r_1$, $\rho(r)$ may be replaced by ρ_0 in the third term on the right-hand side of (19). This means that for forward scattering an average density would be seen experimentally.

With $\rho(r)$ replaced by ρ_0 in the third term, it may be integrated to show that this term yields predominantly forward scattering if r_1 is large. Therefore, making the assumption that r_1 is large compared to the wavelength of the scattered neutrons, the major contribution to the integration over s in the third term on the right-hand side of (19) comes from the region around $s = 0$. Consequently only a small error is made in the calculation of the total scattering cross section $\sigma_{\rm sc}$ if the upper limit for s in the third term of (19) is taken to be α rather than s_0. Equation (19) may be then written

$$\sigma_{\rm sc} = \sigma_I + \frac{2\sigma}{\alpha^2}\left(\frac{m_0}{\mu}\right)^2 \int_0^\alpha \exp\left(-Ys^2\right) \int_0^\infty 4\pi s[\rho(r) - \rho_0] \sin sr \, dr \, ds \quad (20)$$

in which the definition has been made that $\rho(r) = \rho_0$ for $r \geq r_1$.

Rearranging terms and defining

$$g(\alpha) = \alpha^2 \frac{\sigma_I - \sigma_{\rm sc}}{\sigma(m_0/\mu)^2} \quad (21)$$

there is obtained

$$g(\alpha) = -2\int_0^\alpha \exp\left(-Ys^2\right) \int_0^\infty 4\pi s[\rho(r) - \rho_0] \sin sr \, dr \, ds \quad (22)$$

Differentiating (22) and rearranging yields

$$\int_0^\infty 4\pi r[\rho(r) - \rho_0] \sin \alpha r \, dr = \tfrac{1}{2} \exp\left(Y\alpha^2\right) g'(\alpha) \quad (23)$$

Assuming

$$\lim_{\alpha \to \infty} \exp\left(Y\alpha^2\right) g'(\alpha) = 0 \quad (24)$$

a Fourier transform may be performed which yields

$$4\pi r^2[\rho(r) - \rho_0] = -\frac{r}{\pi} \int_0^\infty \exp(Y\alpha^2)\, g'(\alpha) \sin r\alpha \, d\alpha \qquad (25)$$

Integrating (25) by parts and assuming

$$\lim_{\alpha \to \infty} g(\alpha) \exp(Y\alpha^2) = 0 \qquad (26)$$

yields

$$4\pi r^2[\rho(r) - \rho_0] = \frac{r^2}{\pi} \int_0^\infty \exp(Y\alpha^2)\, g(\alpha) \cos r\alpha \, d\alpha$$

$$+ \frac{2Yr}{\pi} \int_0^\infty \alpha \exp(Y\alpha^2)\, g(\alpha) \sin r\alpha \, d\alpha \qquad (27)$$

Equation (27) may be used for structure analysis of liquid-like materials by performing a total neutron scattering cross section experiment to determine the σ_{sc} of (21). In (21) the σ_I must be calculated assuming a certain Einstein temperature for the material.

Neutron Scattering in a Diatomic Liquid-like Material

If a material contains two types of atoms denoted by i and j, (11) may be written

$$G_{sc} = G_I + \frac{1}{N_c} \exp(-Ys^2) \sum_{m,n}' a_m a_n \left(\frac{m_0}{\mu_m}\right)\left(\frac{m_0}{\mu_n}\right) \frac{\sin sr_{mn}}{sr_{mn}} \qquad (28)$$

where the same average Y is used for both types of atoms and G_I is assumed as averaged over both types of atoms.

Therefore, defining f_i, f_j, the fractions of i- and j-type atoms respectively, the differential scattering cross section becomes [following a procedure similar to that for (7) to (11) above]

$$G_{sc} = G_I + \exp(-Ys^2) \left[f_i a_i^2 \left(\frac{m_0}{\mu_i}\right)^2 \sum_{mi} \frac{\sin sr_{mini}}{sr_{mini}} \right.$$

$$+ f_i a_i a_j \left(\frac{m_0}{\mu_i}\right)\left(\frac{m_0}{\mu_j}\right) \sum_{mj} \frac{\sin sr_{mjni}}{sr_{mjni}}$$

$$+ f_j a_j^2 \left(\frac{m_0}{\mu_j}\right)^2 \sum_{mj} \frac{\sin sr_{mjnj}}{sr_{mjnj}}$$

$$\left. + f_j a_i a_j \left(\frac{m_0}{\mu_i}\right)\left(\frac{m_0}{\mu_j}\right) \sum_{mi} \frac{\sin sr_{minj}}{sr_{minj}} \right] \qquad (29)$$

Defining

$$\rho^{ii}, \text{ density of } i\text{-type atoms about an } i\text{-type atom}$$

$$\rho^{jj}, \text{ density of } j\text{-type atoms about a } j\text{-type atom}$$

$$\rho^{ji}, \text{ density of } i\text{-type atoms about a } j\text{-type atom}$$

$$\rho^{ij}, \text{ density of } j\text{-type atoms about an } i\text{-type atom}$$

(30)

yields

$$G_{sc} = G_I + \exp\left(-Ys^2\right)\left[f_i a_i{}^2 \left(\frac{m_0}{\mu_i}\right)^2 \int_0^{r_1} 4\pi r^2 \rho^{ii} \frac{\sin sr}{sr}\, dr \right.$$

$$+ f_i a_i a_j \left(\frac{m_0}{\mu_i}\right)\left(\frac{m_0}{\mu_j}\right) \int_0^{r_1} 4\pi r^2 \rho^{ij} \frac{\sin sr}{sr}\, dr$$

$$+ f_i a_j{}^2 \left(\frac{m_0}{\mu_j}\right)^2 \int_0^{r_1} 4\pi r^2 \rho^{jj} \frac{\sin sr}{sr}\, dr$$

$$\left. + f_j a_i a_j \left(\frac{m_0}{\mu_i}\right)\left(\frac{m_0}{\mu_j}\right) \int_0^{r_1} 4\pi r^2 \rho^{ji} \frac{\sin sr}{sr}\, dr \right] \quad (31)$$

Therefore, as for monatomic liquid-like materials and using the fact that for large interatomic distances

$$\rho^{ii} \longrightarrow \rho_i$$

$$\rho^{ij} \longrightarrow \rho_j$$

$$\rho^{jj} \longrightarrow \rho_j$$

$$\rho^{ji} \longrightarrow \rho_i$$

(32)

where ρ_i and ρ_j are average atomic densities of i- and j-type atoms, the total scattering cross section may be written

$$\sigma_{sc} = \sigma_I + f_i \frac{2\sigma_i}{\alpha^2}\left(\frac{m_0}{\mu_i}\right)^2 \int_0^\alpha \exp\left(-Ys^2\right) \int_0^\infty 4\pi r[\rho^{ii} - \rho_i]\sin sr\, dr\, ds$$

$$+ f_j \frac{2\sigma_j}{\alpha^2}\left(\frac{m_0}{\mu_j}\right)^2 \int_0^\alpha \exp\left(-Ys^2\right) \int_0^\infty 4\pi r[\rho^{jj} - \rho_j]\sin sr\, dr\, ds$$

$$+ f_i \frac{2(\sigma_i\sigma_j)^{1/2}}{\alpha^2}\left(\frac{m_0}{\mu_i}\right)\left(\frac{m_0}{\mu_j}\right) \int_0^\alpha \exp\left(-Ys^2\right) \int_0^\infty 4\pi r[\rho^{ij} - \rho_j]\sin sr\, dr\, ds$$

$$+ f_j \frac{2(\sigma_i\sigma_j)^{1/2}}{\alpha^2}\left(\frac{m_0}{\mu_i}\right)\left(\frac{m_0}{\mu_j}\right) \int_0^\alpha \exp\left(-Ys^2\right) \int_0^\infty 4\pi r[\rho^{ji} - \rho_i]\sin sr\, dr\, ds$$

(33)

In (33) the term $(\sigma_i \sigma_j)^{1/2}$ is positive if the scattering lengths of the atoms i and j carry the same sign, but negative if the scattering lengths have opposite signs (the scattering lengths are both positive for oxygen and silicon).

Defining

$$g = \frac{\sigma_j (m_0/\mu_j)^2}{\sigma_i (m_0/\mu_i)^2} \tag{34}$$

the total scattering cross section may be written

$$\sigma_{sc} = \sigma_I + f_i \frac{2\sigma_i}{\alpha^2} \left(\frac{m_0}{\mu_i}\right)^2 \int_0^\alpha \exp\left(-Ys^2\right) \int_0^\infty 4\pi r[\rho^{ii} - \rho_i] \sin sr \, dr \, ds$$

$$+ f_j g \frac{2\sigma_i}{\alpha^2} \left(\frac{m_0}{\mu_i}\right)^2 \int_0^\alpha \exp\left(-Ys^2\right) \int_0^\infty 4\pi r[\rho^{jj} - \rho_j] \sin rs \, dr \, ds$$

$$+ f_i g^{1/2} \frac{2\sigma_i}{\alpha^2} \left(\frac{m_0}{\mu_i}\right)^2 \int_0^\alpha \exp\left(-Ys^2\right) \int_0^\infty 4\pi r[\rho^{ij} - \rho_j] \sin sr \, dr \, ds$$

$$+ f_j g^{1/2} \frac{2\sigma_i}{\alpha^2} \left(\frac{m_0}{\mu_i}\right)^2 \int_0^\alpha \exp\left(-Ys^2\right) \int_0^\infty 4\pi r[\rho^{ji} - \rho_i] \sin sr \, dr \, ds \tag{35}$$

Again following a method analogous to that for the monatomic case, let

$$\rho(r) = f_i \rho^{ii} + f_j g \rho^{jj} + f_i g^{1/2} \rho^{ij} + f_j g^{1/2} \rho^{ji} \tag{36}$$

and

$$\bar{\rho} = f_i \rho_i + f_j g \rho_j + f_i g^{1/2} \rho_j + f_j g^{1/2} \rho_i \tag{37}$$

and

$$g(\alpha) = \alpha^2 \frac{\sigma_I - \sigma_{sc}}{\sigma_I (m_0/\mu_i)^2} \tag{38}$$

Then it can be shown that

$$4\pi r^2 [\rho(r) - \bar{\rho}] = \frac{r}{\pi} \int_0^\infty \exp\left(Y\alpha^2\right) g(\alpha)[r \cos \alpha r + 2Y\alpha \sin \alpha r] \, d\alpha \tag{39}$$

Equation (39) can then be used for the analysis of the structure of a diatomic liquid-like material.

Once $\rho(r)$ has been obtained from (39), a verification of a certain assumed model of the atomic structure of the material can be carried out in the following manner. Let

$$N^{ii} = \int_{r_a}^{r_b} 4\pi r^2 \rho^{ii} \, dr$$

= number of i-type atoms located in the volume
between two concentric spheres of radii r_a and
r_b with center at the position of an i-type atom

$$N^{jj} = \int_{r_a}^{r_b} 4\pi r^2 \rho^{jj} \, dr$$

= number of j-type atoms about a j-type atom
in the volume defined by r_a and r_b

$$N^{ij} = \int_{r_a}^{r_b} 4\pi r^2 \rho^{ij} \, dr \tag{40}$$

= number of j-type atoms about an i-type atom
in the volume defined by r_a and r_b

$$N^{ji} = \int_{r_a}^{r_b} 4\pi r^2 \rho^{ji} \, dr$$

= number of i-type atoms about a j-type atom
in the volume defined by r_a and r_b

Then, if $4\pi r^2 \rho(r)$ of (39) is plotted, a series of positive area peaks will appear with their maxima at various r values. The particular model of the material which is assumed will identify these peaks as corresponding to i-1st, j distances; i-1st, i distances; j-2nd, j distances; and so forth. Therefore, looking at any particular peak, the model will tell what types of atoms are involved. If now the area under the peak is found, it can be related to the numbers defined in (40). For example, if the first peak corresponds to the i-1st, j distance (and therefore also the j-1st, i distance), then $\rho^{ii} = \rho^{jj} = 0$. Therefore, by (36) and (40),

$$\text{area under 1st peak} = g^{\frac{1}{2}}[f_i N^{ij} + f_j N^{ji}]$$

Now it can be shown that

$$N^{ji} = \frac{f_i}{f_j} N^{ij} \tag{41}$$

for the i-1st, j distance; therefore

$$\text{area under 1st peak} = 2g^{\frac{1}{2}} f_i N^{ij} \tag{42}$$

Equation (39) was used to test the model proposed by Warren (1934, 1937) for high purity, crystalline-free Corning vitreous silica. In this model the basic unit structure consists of one silicon atom surrounded tetrahedrally by four oxygen atoms; each of these oxygen atoms is a corner of another tetrahedron—four tetrahedra in all surrounding one tetrahedron. This type of buildup continues for some distance; but the structure is not repeated at regular intervals, as for a crystalline material. It is also assumed that each oxygen atom is doubly bound between two silicon atoms, its location bisecting the line joining the two silicon atoms.

A three-dimensional model of the above proposed structure was built to scale, and from this model the various following distances and distributions were found to be important: Si-O; O-O; Si-Si; Si-2nd O; O-2nd O; and Si-2nd Si with O-3rd O. It is necessary to include the last of these because from the model it turned out that there were O-3rd O distances approximately the same as Si-2nd Si distances.

The experimental total cross section of Corning superpure vitreous silica is shown in Fig. 3. The data were obtained at the Argonne Na-

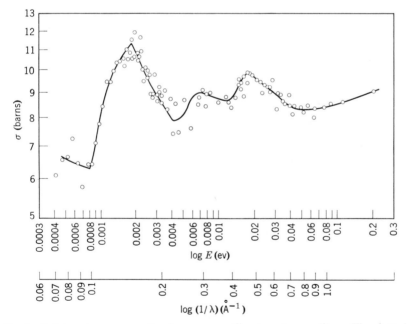

Fig. 3. Total neutron cross section for superpure Corning vitreous silica. The plotted points include the best data of Fig. 1 and additional data obtained with a spiral neutron velocity selector (chopper) which is superior in resolution and intensity to the original velocity selector used for the data of Fig. 1. Counting statistics, 2% probable error except for the very low energy data.

tional Laboratory using the mechanical slow neutron velocity selectors at the thermal column of the heavy-water reactor.

The bound independent cross section σ_I was computed by the Ballistic Research Laboratory, Aberdeen Proving Grounds, Maryland. An Einstein temperature of $313°K$ as computed from measurement of the Young's modulus of the vitreous silica was used. σ_I was calculated theoretically by the method of Delaney (1958).

Subtracting the capture cross section (as on page 99) from the total experimental cross section (Fig. 3) yields σ_{sc}, and so $g(\alpha)$ of (38) was calculated. The $4\pi r^2 \rho(r)$ was obtained by carrying out numerically the integration involved in (39). The resulting radial density distribution is plotted in Fig. 4. Distances between atoms were then read off the

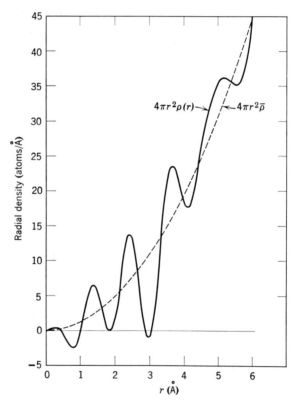

Fig. 4. Atomic radial density distribution for superpure Corning vitreous silica obtained by 702-type digital computer analysis of the data of Fig. 3. The inelastic scattering was calculated by the Einstein model theory and eliminated from the total scattering as described in the text.

radial distribution curve and compared with those given by Warren's model. These results are listed in Table 2.

Table 2

ATOMIC RADIAL DENSITY DISTRIBUTION RESULTS FOR CORNING SUPERPURE VITREOUS SILICA COMPARED WITH WARREN'S MODEL

Theoretical Einstein Model for Inelastic Scattering

Proposed Interatomic Distance (first-noted atom is origin atom)	Warren Model		Total Neutron Scattering	
	Distance (Å)	No. of Atoms	Distance (Å)	No. of Atoms (from areas under peaks of Fig. 4)
Si-O	1.60	4 O	1.38	1.87 Si, about 0 3.74 O
O-O	2.65	6 O	2.42	6.37 O
Si-Si	3.20	4 Si	—	
Si-2nd O	4.00	12 O	3.65	17.5 O
O-2nd O	4.50	6 O [a] 18 O		

[a] A three-dimensional model of SiO_2 tetrahedral units yields a total of 18 O atoms at the Si-2nd O spacing of a rigid radial orientation is followed; deviations from strict radial orientation, permitting a more compact filling of space, probably causes 1 O atom of each 3 basal O atoms to be nearer the origin atom, yielding 6 as the number of O atoms at the O-2nd O distance.

Areas under the peaks of Fig. 4 also were employed to verify the model, and these results appear in Table 2. The agreement of the first two peaks with the model is quite satisfactory. Table 2 shows that the Si-Si distance is uncertain from the neutron-determined atomic radial density distribution curve (Fig. 4). Either it does not show up or it is not resolved from the Si-2nd O peak. The latter possibility seems more probable in view of the number of atoms, 17.5, corresponding to the neutron peak at 3.65 Å. If this peak combines the effects due to the Si-Si and the Si-2nd O distances, the Warren model designates 16 atoms corresponding to these two distances, as may be seen from Table 2. Another possibility is that the neutron peak at 3.65 Å combines the Si-2nd O (12 O atoms) and the first set of O-2nd O (6 O atoms) distances, as indicated by Table 2.

An examination of Tables 1 and 2 shows that the data in Table 1 agree in a more satisfactory fashion with Warren's model for vitreous silica than do the data in Table 2. This is a rather anomalous result since the theoretical model for inelastic scattering using the Einstein model (Table 2) is exact, whereas the semiempirical method (Table 1) is approximate only. The Einstein model has been applied successfully (Delaney, 1958) to the calculation of the total scattering cross section for materials such as Mg, Be, and Al, so that this model must be accepted with some confidence. Hence it is concluded that the scatter of the experimental points (Fig. 3) must be responsible for the incomplete results obtained for the structure of vitreous silica using the neutron-scattering method. It is intended to continue these preliminary neutron-scattering experiments in an effort to remove the discrepancies and uncertainties in the experimental data and so achieve finally a structure determination for vitreous silica which will be free of the uncertainties both in the present neutron and the older x-ray determinations.

ACKNOWLEDGMENTS

It is a distinct pleasure to acknowledge the essential contribution to this work of Drs. M. Hamermesh and G. R. Ringo of the Argonne National Laboratory and of Dr. Paul J. Persiani of Saint Louis University. The abiding interest of Drs. Sherwood Githens, Jr., and Hermann Robl of the Office of Ordnance Research at Duke, of Dr. Louis A. Turner of the Argonne National Laboratory, and of O. G. Burch and H. H. Holscher of the Owens-Illinois Glass Company has been indispensable, and deep appreciation is here expressed.

REFERENCES

Bendt, P. J., and Ruderman, I. W., *Phys. Rev.* **77**, 575 (1950).

Brill, T., and Lichtenberger, H., *Phys. Rev.* **72**, 585 (1947).

Danielson, G. C., and Lanczos, C., *J. Franklin Inst.* **233**, 365 (1942); **233**, 435 (1942).

Delaney, R. M., Ph.D. Dissertation, "Einstein Model for Thermal Neutron Scattering," Saint Louis University, June 1958.

Finkelstein, J., *Phys. Rev.* **72**, 907 (1947).

Frisch, O. R., *Progress in Nuclear Physics*, Academic Press, New York, 1950, Vol. 1, p. 206.

"Nuclear Data," National Bureau of Standards Circular No. 499 (U. S. Government Printing Office, Washington, D. C., 1950).

Shull, C. G., and Wollan, E. O., *Phys. Rev.* **81**, 527 (1951).

Warren, B. E., *J. Am. Ceram. Soc.* **17**, 249 (1934); *J. Appl. Phys.* **8**, 645 (1937).

Weber, A. H., *Nucleonics* **7**, 31 (1950).

by

Jerzy Zarzycki

**Centre de Recherches de la Cie.
de St. Gobain**

High Temperature X-ray Diffraction Methods Applied to the Study of Non-crystalline Media. Structure of Molten Fluorides and Chlorides

The structure of non-crystalline solids appears to be intermediate between the structure of crystals and that of liquids. Glass, for instance, is often defined as "undercooled" or "frozen in" liquid, and its structure can be statistically described by using radial distribution functions in a way similar to that used for a liquid. Actually, if the structure of crystalline media has been worked out quite extensively, the structure of liquids, especially those obtained by fusion of solids at high temperatures, remains almost completely unknown.

A systematic study of structural changes induced by fusion in both crystalline and non-crystalline media should not only help in understanding the structure of disordered solids but should also provide a sound basis for a theory of fusion.

The diffraction of x-rays or of neutrons leads to a "static" description of the structure, the "dynamic" part being supplemented by infrared or Raman spectroscopy.

Unfortunately, in the case of non-crystalline solids, the theory of vibration of random lattices has not yet been worked out, so the experimental results obtained by these last two methods cannot be fully interpreted.

In the present study, therefore, we shall limit ourselves to the "static" side of the problem, showing the use that can be made of high temperature x-ray diffraction methods applied to the study of non-crystalline media.

Our initial investigations were concerned with the series of fluorides whose structure in the liquid state had not been studied until recently (Zarzycki, 1956, 1957a).

This investigation has an added interest if we take into account the isostructural connection which exists between certain fluorides and oxides (Goldschmidt, 1926).

Thus, for example, the fluorides LiF, NaF, KF, and CaF_2, which we are concerned with, can be regarded as isostructural correspondents of MgO, CaO, BaO, and ZrO_2. At the same time the study of the molten fluorides will give us some idea of the structure which the corresponding oxides would present in a molten state if it were possible under present technical conditions to determine their structure by high temperature x-ray diffraction methods.

A study of molten LiCl and KCl has already been attempted by Lark-Horovitz and Miller (1936; Miller and Lark-Horovitz, 1937).

At that time the Fourier inversion theory had not been extended to the field of heteroatomic amorphous bodies, so these authors were compelled to introduce certain simplifications for the atomic scattering factors ($f_{Li} = 0$ in the case of LiCl, and $f_K = f_{Cl}$ in the case of KCl).

We thought it of interest, therefore, to take up again the study of chlorides as a whole (Zarzycki, 1958), using the more elaborate methods of technique and interpretation now at our disposal. Thus, by completing the results we obtained previously for fluorides, we hope to give a more accurate picture of the structure of molten halides.

Experimental Method

The experimental apparatus has already been described elsewhere (Zarzycki, 1955, 1956). We shall simply mention here that it consists of a special focusing camera working in conjunction with a curved-quartz focusing monochromator (Fig. 1). All the exposures were made using

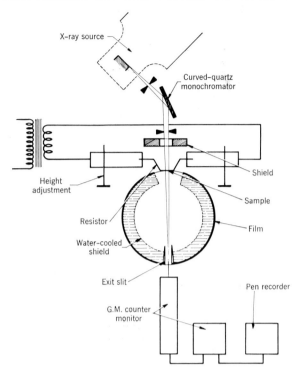

Fig. 1. High temperature x-ray diffraction camera for the study of molten salts (Zarzycki, 1956).

strictly monochromatic radiation. The sample studied *by transmission* consists of a thin film of liquid maintained in position by capillary forces in a slit made in a heating sample holder. This consists of a strip of Pt-20% Rh alloy fed by low voltage current. The maximum working temperature given by this furnace is 1600°C. The sample varied in thickness from 0.3 to 0.5 mm. The Geiger-Mueller counter monitor placed behind the camera on the transmitted beam permits the measurement of the absorption coefficient of the sample and of the air-scattering background. It also provides a means of controlling the thickness of the sample throughout the whole experiment.

The wavelength used for all these investigations was Mo Kα (45 kv, 6 ma), the times of exposure ranging from 6 to 12 hours.

The following compounds were studied in the liquid state:

LiF at 860°C	NaF at 1000°C	KF at 870°C
CaF$_2$ at 1500°C	LiCl at 620°C	NaCl at 820°C
KCl at 810°C	BaCl$_2$ at 1000°C	

Results

The intensity data obtained from microphotometric records are corrected for absorption in the sample, air-scattering background, polarization effect of the sample and the monochromator, camera form factor, and film shrinkage.

Figures 2 to 9 show the diffraction spectra obtained in this way. Intensity is expressed in electron units, the independent coherent scattering curve being calculated in each case for a totally ionized molecular unit.

The spectra of lithium compounds are seen to be particularly sharp. This is probably due to the considerable discrepancy between the structure factors of the constituent ions.

Generally speaking, the spectra of the chlorides are more "condensed" than those of the corresponding fluorides. This systematic decrease of the diameters of the diffraction halos can be explained by the general expansion of interionic distances, the F^- ions being replaced by the more voluminous Cl^- ions.

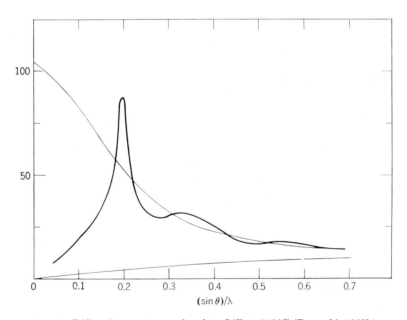

Fig. 2. Diffraction spectrum of molten LiF at 860°C (Zarzycki, 1957b).

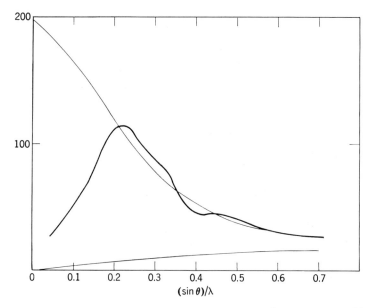

Fig. 3. Diffraction spectrum of molten NaF at 1000°C (Zarzycki, 1957b).

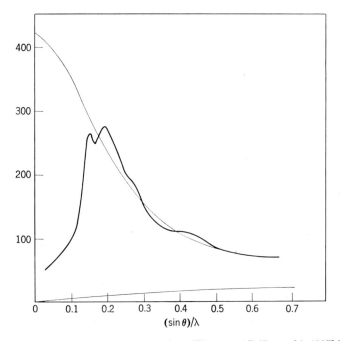

Fig. 4. Diffraction spectrum of molten KF at 870°C (Zarzycki, 1957b).

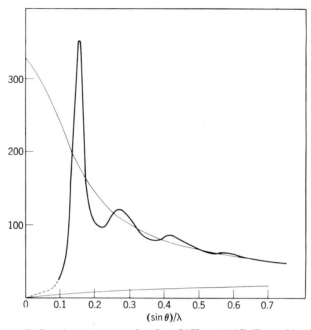

Fig. 5. Diffraction spectrum of molten LiCl at 620°C (Zarzycki, 1958).

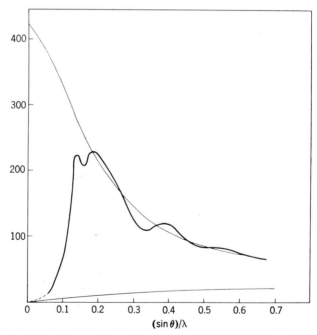

Fig. 6. Diffraction spectrum of molten NaCl at 820°C (Zarzycki, 1958).

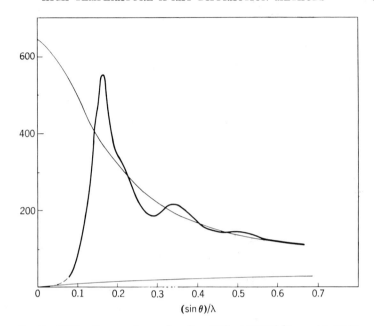

Fig. 7. Diffraction spectrum of molten KCl at 810°C (Zarzycki, 1958).

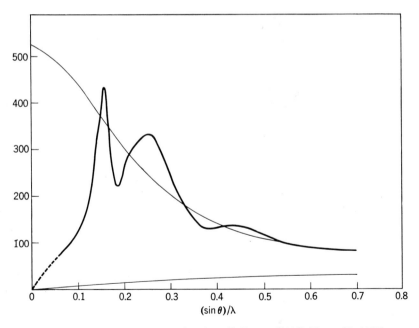

Fig. 8. Diffraction spectrum of molten CaF$_2$ at 1500°C (Zarzycki, 1958).

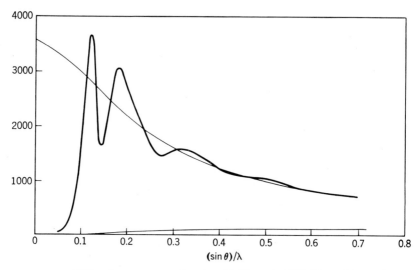

Fig. 9. Diffraction spectrum of molten $BaCl_2$ at $1000\,°C$ (Zarzycki, 1958).

The two alkaline earth halides, CaF_2 and $BaCl_2$, have been specially chosen because of the similarity of their anion radius to cation radius ratio:

$$\frac{r_{F^-}}{r_{Ca^{2+}}} = 1.37 \qquad \frac{r_{Cl^-}}{r_{Ba^{2+}}} = 1.34$$

We can see that a great analogy exists between the two spectra, the CaF_2 spectrum being simply a more expanded version of the $BaCl_2$ spectrum.

Analysis of the Spectra

The spectra previously described were analyzed by means of radial Fourier transform, after Warren, Krutter, and Morningstar (1936).

It is known that the radial distribution curve is defined by the formula

$$\sum_m K_m 4\pi r^2 \rho_m(r) = \sum_m K_m 4\pi r^2 \rho_0 + \frac{2r}{\pi} \int_0^\infty Si(S) \sin rS \, dS$$

where r is an interionic distance; $\sum_m$ is the summation extended to a molecular unit; K_m is the average effective electronic number of the atom m as defined by $K_m = f_m/f_e$, f_m being the structure factor of the atom m and f_e the average structure factor of an electron, which is defined by

$$f_e = \frac{\sum\limits_m f_m}{\sum\limits_m Z_m}$$

for a molecular unit made up of n atoms of atomic numbers

$$Z_1, Z_2, \cdots, Z_m, \cdots, Z_n$$

In addition,

$$S = (4\pi \sin \theta)/\lambda$$

$$i(S) = \frac{I_{\text{coh}} - \sum\limits_m f_m^2}{f_e^2}$$

ρ_0 is the average electron density:

$$\rho_0 = \frac{dN \sum\limits_m Z_m}{M}$$

where N is Avogadro's number, d is the macrosopic density of the fused salt, and M is the molecular mass.

The effective atomic numbers K_m being functions of s in the limited interval of integration $(0, S_0)$, the average values will be used:

$$\overline{K}_m = \frac{1}{S_0} \int_0^{S_0} K_m \, dS$$

The integral

$$\frac{2r}{\pi} \int_0^{S_0} Si(S) \sin rS \, dS$$

was calculated by a Mader-Ott harmonic analyzer.

Table 1 gives the numerical data used in analyzing each particular

Table 1

	$\overline{K}_C$	$\overline{K}_A$	d_t (°C)
LiF	2.8	9.2	$d_{860} = 1.79$
NaF	11.3	8.6	$d_{1000} = 1.94$
KF	20.0	8.0	$d_{870} = 1.89$
CaF$_2$	21.5	8.25	$d_{1500} = 2.75$
LiCl	2.4	17.6	$d_{620} = 1.49$
NaCl	10.3	17.7	$d_{820} = 1.54$
KCl	18.9	17.1	$d_{810} = 1.50$
BaCl$_2$	58.6	15.7	$d_{1000} = 3.12$

case, i.e., the average effective electronic numbers $\overline{K}_C$ and $\overline{K}_A$ of the cation and the anion as well as the density d_t of the molten salt at the temperature t of the experiment.

In the case of the alkali halides this density was calculated according to the data of Jaeger (1917), confirmed more recently by Van Artsdalen and Yaffe (1955).

The density of $BaCl_2$ is taken from Drossbach (1938) and that of CaF_2 from Bååk (1955).

Figures 10 to 17 show the radial distribution curves corresponding to the spectra given in Figs. 2 to 9.

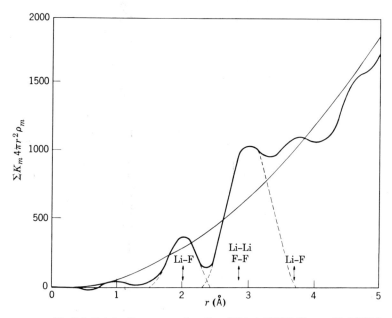

Fig. 10. Radial distribution curve of molten LiF at 860°C (Zarzycki, 1957b).

Interpretation of Structure

In Figs. 10 to 17 we have indicated by arrows the first interionic distances of the corresponding *crystallized* compounds. It can be seen that these distances correspond to the consecutive peaks of the radial distribution curves of the compounds in the molten state.

Thus, for example, in the case of LiF where three well-resolved maxima can be seen, these maxima correspond very closely to the three first interionic distances:

$$Li-F, \quad Li-Li \ (or \ F-F), \quad and \quad (Li-F)_{II}$$

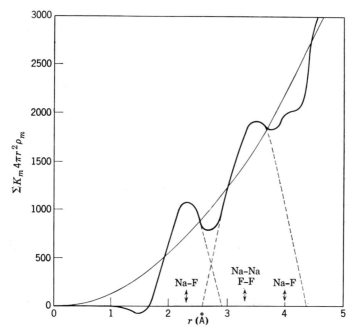

Fig. 11.   Radial distribution curve of molten NaF at 1000°C (Zarzycki, 1957b).

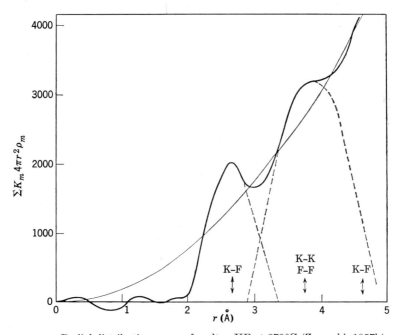

Fig. 12.   Radial distribution curve of molten KF at 870°C (Zarzycki, 1957b).

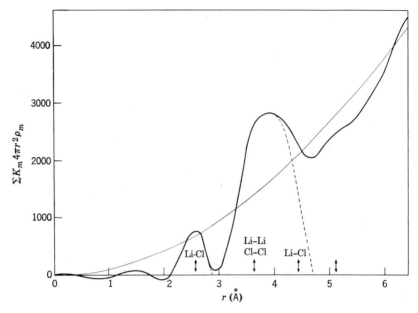

Fig. 13. Radial distribution curve of molten LiCl at 620°C (Zarzycki, 1958).

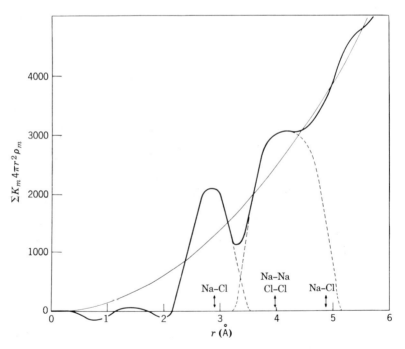

Fig. 14. Radial distribution curve of molten NaCl at 820°C (Zarzycki, 1958).

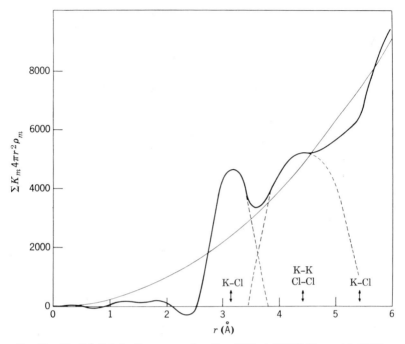

Fig. 15. Radial distribution curve of molten KCl at 810°C (Zarzycki, 1958).

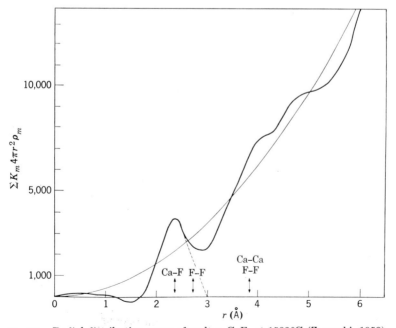

Fig. 16. Radial distribution curve of molten CaF_2 at 1500°C (Zarzycki, 1958).

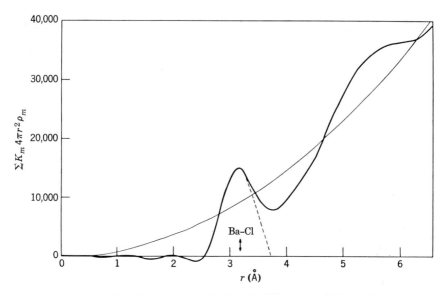

Fig. 17. Radial distribution curve of molten $BaCl_2$ at 1000°C (Zarzycki, 1958).

of the crystal, the small discrepancy being attributable to the thermal expansion of the crystal lattice before the melting point is reached. In a similar fashion, the radial distribution curves for other alkali halides show two or three more or less resolved maxima which also closely correspond to the first interionic distances of the crystalline compounds.

It can be seen that each time a maximum is well resolved it corresponds to an interionic distance in the solid state, and conversely no additional peaks occur between these maxima. This indicates that the short range order of the crystal is still maintained after fusion.

In the case of the alkaline earth halides CaF_2 and $BaCl_2$ only one peak is well resolved, corresponding to the contact anion-to-cation distance.

The information about the structure being far too incomplete in these cases, we shall limit ourselves in the following discussion to the structure of *alkali* halides only. As the interionic distances are the same in the liquid as in the solid, how can we explain the marked expansion which takes place when these compounds pass from solid to liquid state? The answer to the problem is given by the study of the coordination numbers calculated from the radial distribution curves in the classical way.

In Table 2 we have a comparison between the coordination numbers relative to the molten and the solid state, associated with the first interionic distances previously mentioned. Here $n_A{}^C$ represents the number

Table 2

	$n_A{}^C(\equiv n_C{}^A)$		$n_C{}^C(\equiv n_A{}^A)$	
	Molten	Solid	Molten	Solid
LiF	3.7	6	8	12
NaF	4.1	6	9	12
KF	4.9	6	9	12
LiCl	4.1	6	9	12
NaCl	4.7	6	9	12
KCl	5.2	6	10	12

	$n_A{}^C(\equiv 2n_C{}^A)$	
	Molten	Solid
CaF_2	6.8	8
$BaCl_2$	5.5	8

of ions A (anions) situated around a central ion C (cation) at a distance A-C. (In the liquid phase $n_A{}^C$ and A-C obviously represent only average values.)

We can see that *all the coordination numbers relative to the molten state are systematically much lower than those for the solid state.* For example, in the case of molten NaF, an ion would have an average of *four* neighboring ions as opposed to *six* in the crystal. This is important for the general understanding of the structure of molten halides.

The conservation in the molten state of the sequence of the first interionic distances accompanied by a pronounced decrease of the coordination number can only be accounted for by the existence of "holes" in the molten salt.

Any other interpretation of the decrease in the coordination numbers based, for example, on a general modification of the coordination scheme would not be in accord with the persistence in the molten state of the short range order of the crystal, this order in the case of alkali halides being characterized by a sequence of interionic distances which vary in the progression

$$I, \quad \sqrt{2}, \quad \sqrt{3}, \quad \cdots$$

We must therefore admit that the decrease in the coordination numbers is due to a formation of "holes" in the liquid "lattice," where the short range order is the same as that in the solid state.

The structure of the molten halides investigated is thus essentially lacunar in nature. Figure 18 gives a two-dimensional model of such a structure.

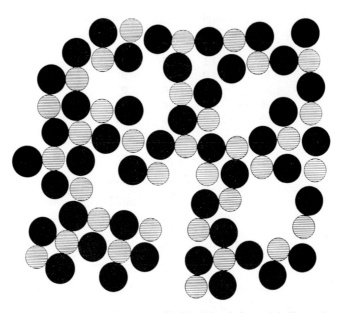

Fig. 18. Lacunar structure of molten alkali halides (schematic) (Zarzycki, 1957b).

We can now see the reason for the marked increase in volume observed on fusion of those salts; this expansion corresponds to the formation of cavities. Questions immediately arise as to the *form, size,* and *distribution* of these holes.

Using data taken from other sources, we shall now try to develop this model more quantitatively.

Total volume of the holes. The proportion of the holes formed in the molten salt can be expressed by the formula

$$x = (V_F - V_{PF})/V_F$$

which represents the ratio of the increase in volume on fusion to the volume of the fused salt at melting point. (V_F and V_{PF} are the molar volumes of liquid and solid at melting point.)

The results given in a recent work (Schinke and Sauerwald, 1956) enable us to calculate the value of x for the different halides. These values are given in Table 3. For the compounds in question, the *pro-*

Table 3

	LiF	NaF	KF	LiCl	NaCl	KCl
x	0.227	0.215	0.147	0.207	0.200	0.147
L cal/mole	6200	7900	6700	4970	6560	6100
t_F (°C)	844	980	856	614	801	768
σ (erg/cm²)	255.2	201.6	143.2	140.2	114.1	97.4
d_F (g/cm³)	1.79	1.95	1.91	1.49	1.55	1.53

portion of the holes amounts to as much as 15 to 23% of the total volume of the liquid.

Dimensions of the holes. Before one can calculate the dimensions of the holes, one needs an additional factor, for example, the *total surface* of the cavities. In order to obtain this, one can assume that the energy associated with the formation of holes is equal to the heat of fusion of the crystal:

$$L = S\sigma$$

where L is the heat of fusion of the crystal, σ is the surface energy of the liquid at melting point, and S is the total surface of the holes.

In actual fact, the effective surface energy of a hole of molecular size is *lower* than the surface energy of a free surface (Frenkel, 1955), but it is impossible to calculate it in the light of our present knowledge. The results obtained must therefore be regarded only as first approximation.

To carry the calculations further it is now necessary to formulate a hypothesis on the *form* of the holes.

Spherical holes. The simplest method consists in considering all the P cavities as spherical (Fig. 19a). The average radius r of the holes will then be determined by the following three relations:

$$V_F - V_{PF} = \tfrac{4}{3}\pi r^3 P$$

$$S = 4\pi r^2 P$$

$$L = S\sigma$$

from which we deduce that

$$r = \frac{3(V_F - V_{PF})\sigma}{L}$$

That is, for a molten salt of molecular weight M and the density d_F, the average radius is

$$r = 3M\sigma x / d_F L$$

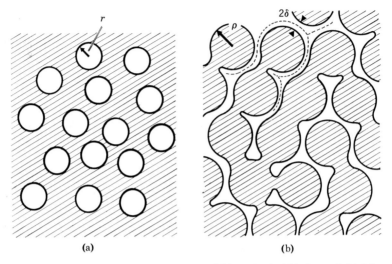

Fig. 19. Distribution of cavities in the case of (a) "spherical" holes and (b) "fluctuating fissures" (Zarzycki, 1958).

To obtain some idea of the number of "holes" thus formed in the lattice we shall consider the ratio of the number of the holes to the total number of ions contained in one mole of fused salt:

$$k = P/2N$$

where N is Avogadro's number. Using data contained in Table 3 (for references see Zarzycki, 1958), we calculated the values of r and k for the liquid salts at the temperature of fusion, t_F. The results are given in Table 4, from which it can be seen that the average radii of holes thus defined are smaller than the radii of the constituent ions. (In view of

Table 4

	LiF	NaF	KF	LiCl	NaCl	KCl
"Spherical holes"						
r (Å)	0.97	0.84	0.69	1.18	0.94	0.82
k	0.72	1.54	2.72	0.70	1.80	2.58
"Fluctuating fissures"						
ρ (Å)	3.22	3.00	3.95	4.35	3.70	4.70
2δ (Å)	0.65	0.56	0.46	0.79	0.63	0.55
	15.4	8.3	12.1	19.3	8.6	12.4

the previous approximations, these figures represent only orders of magnitude.) For a series of salts having the same anion it can, however, be seen that, passing from Li to Na and K, the holes tend to diminish in size, whereas they increase considerably in number. Thus in salts with heavy cation, there would be a large number of very small holes; in some, as many as three holes to each constituent ion.

We found it difficult to accept that such a proportion of holes would not lead to a complete disappearance of the short range order which we had proved to exist in these liquids by x-ray diffraction methods. This led us to formulate a second hypothesis, according to which the volume of cavities is distributed in a different manner.

"Fluctuating fissures." According to the second hypothesis the cavities are not uniformly distributed throughout the mass but tend to join together forming sheets, or, in other words, they constitute *fissures* or *cracks* between the *clusters* of ions, thus separating them more or less completely (Fig. 19b).

As result of thermal agitation, there is a transference of ions from one cluster to another, or, what amounts to the same thing, the fissures are displaced in the opposite direction, so the term "fluctuating fissures" seems to us appropriate for this phenomenon.

In this model the short range order characteristic of the crystal can be conserved in the clusters.

In our calculations ρ represents the average radius of the clusters, and 2δ the gap separating them. Assuming the clusters to be completely isolated from each other, we then have the four equations

$$V_F = \tfrac{4}{3}\pi(\rho + \delta)^3 Z$$

$$S = 4\pi\rho^2 Z$$

$$V_F - V_{PF} = S\delta$$

$$L = S\sigma$$

(where Z represents the number of clusters contained in a mole of fused salt) from which we can deduce

$$\delta = \frac{(V_F - V_{PF})\sigma}{L}$$

or

$$2\delta = \tfrac{2}{3}r$$

The gap separating the clusters is thus of the same order of magnitude as the radius of the holes in our first hypothesis. The value of ρ can then be calculated from the equation

$$(\rho + \delta)^3/\rho^2 = 3M\sigma/d_F L$$

The third characteristic value of the model will be m, the average number of ions in a cluster:

$$m = 2N/Z$$

Table 4 gives the values for ρ, 2δ, and m calculated from the data in Table 3. (Here, too, these figures give only orders of magnitude.)

A study of Table 4 shows that the clusters are composed, on an average, of 8 to 19 ions, i.e., one or, at most, two complete ionic shells (possessing the NaCl type of structure) surrounding a given central ion *There is very little variation in the size of the gaps between the clusters for all compounds studied, the gaps being of the order of 0.6 Å.* Thus it can be seen that the clusters are large enough for the short range order of the crystal to be retained in this type of structure.

The mutual orientation of the clusters must be completely random, because, in spite of the small gaps between the clusters (a fraction of the atomic radii), no additional maxima are to be seen on the radial distribution curves which we have previously described.

It now remains to study the *influence of the degree of dislocation of the lattice on the average coordination number* as obtained by x-ray diffraction studies. To calculate this we shall assume that the clusters *have an NaCl type of structure*, that they are all composed of the same number of ions, m, and that they are completely separated from each other.

In this case, the first average coordination number of the structure as a whole is identical with that of the first average coordination number N_m of the cluster. N_m is the weighted mean of all the first coordination numbers N_i attributed to the different ions compiling the cluster:

$$N_m = \frac{\sum\limits_{m} n_i N_i}{\sum\limits_{m} n_i}$$

This calculation was made for different values of m, on the assumption that successive ionic shells are added around a central ion.

The function $N_m = f(m)$ is plotted in Fig. 20. This corresponds to an ideal case where all the clusters are quite separated from each other. If the clusters were *partially joined together* (as in Fig. 19b), N_m would show an automatic *increase*.

The function N_m thus gives us the *lower limit* of the average coordination number for a lattice split into clusters but still retaining a certain amount of "bridge" formation.

On Fig. 20 are also marked the points corresponding to the various halides studied and defined by the coordinates ($n_A{}^C$, m). One can see that the points are well placed in the portion of the plane, which is

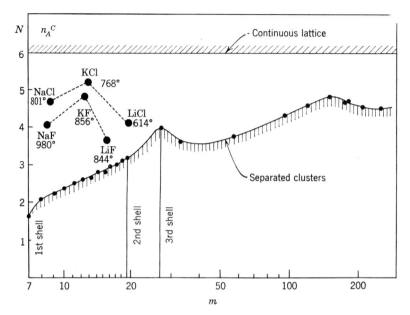

Fig. 20. Relation between the coordination number and the degree of dislocation of the lattice (Zarzycki, 1958).

limited, on the one side by the line $N = 6$, the upper limit corresponding to the continuous crystal lattice, and on the other side by the function $N = f(m)$, the lower limit which corresponds to the liquid composed of *isolated* clusters. One can see that our experimental results do not conflict with the hypothesis of "fluctuating fissures."

Moreover, from Fig. 20, the following conclusions can be deduced regarding the structure of molten halides.

1. The different clusters which make up the liquid are *not completely separated from each other*. In fact, the points corresponding to the different compounds under consideration are seen to be well above the limit $N = f(m)$ of a hypothetical case where the clusters are quite separated. (In reality, for experimental reasons, the values of n_A^C were obtained for temperatures slightly above the melting points indicated on the graph.)

2. Lithium salts are made up of larger clusters but they are *more separated* than those in sodium or potassium compounds.

3. For each group of compounds having the same anion, the size of the cluster is related to the melting point of the compound. Thus, for the sequences

$$\text{NaF } (980°) \;\; \rightarrow \;\; \text{KF } (856°) \;\; \rightarrow \;\; \text{LiF } (844°)$$
$$\text{NaCl } (801°) \;\; \rightarrow \;\; \text{KCl } (768°) \;\; \rightarrow \;\; \text{LiCl } (614°)$$

the average number m of ions compiling a cluster *increases* from 8 to 14 and from 8 to 19; i.e., the degree of dislocation of the lattice *decreases* with the melting point of the halides.

Conclusion

In this study we have attempted to show the possibilities offered by high temperature x-ray diffraction methods when applied to the study of molten halides.

We hope that a more extensive investigation of molten salts in general will lead to a better understanding of the structure of liquids at high temperatures and also aid in the determination of the structure of non-crystalline solids.

SUMMARY

High temperature x-ray diffraction studies of the molten fluorides, LiF, NaF, KF, CaF_2, and chlorides, LiCl, NaCl, KCl, $BaCl_2$, are reported. Analysis of the radial distribution curves deduced from the spectra by means of the spherical Fourier transform shows that for the alkali halides the short range order of the crystal is maintained in the molten state, whereas the coordination numbers are much *lower*. This confirms the existence of "holes" in these molten salts.

With the aid of supplementary data it is shown that these "holes" are actually "fluctuating fissures" between ion clusters consisting, on an average, of 1 to 2 ionic shells surrounding a central ion.

REFERENCES

Bääk, T., *Acta Chem. Scand.* **9**, 1406 (1955).
Drossbach, P., *Elektrochemie geschmolzener Salzen*, Springer, Berlin, 1938.
Frenkel, J., *Kinetic Theory of Liquids*, Dover, New York, 1955.
Goldschmidt, V. M., *Skrifter Norske Videnskaps-Akad. Oslo* (8) **7** (1926).
Jaeger, F. M., *Z. anorg. Chem.* **101**, 1 (1917).
Lark-Horovitz, K., and Miller, E. P., *Phys. Rev.* **49**, 418 (1936).
Miller, E. P., and Lark-Horovitz, K., *Phys. Rev.* **51**, 61 (1937).
Schinke, H., and Sauerwald, F., *Z. anorg. Chem.* **287**, 313 (1956).
Van Artsdalen, E. R., and Yaffe, I. S., *J. Phys. Chem.* **59**, 118 (1955).

Warren, B. E., Krutter, H., Morningstar, O., *J. Am. Ceram. Soc.* **19**, 202 (1936).

Zarzycki, J., *Compt. rend.* **241**, 480 (1955).

Zarzycki, J., *J. phys. radium* (Suppl. Phys. Appl.) **17**, 44A (1956).

Zarzycki, J., *Compt. rend.* **244**, 758 (1957) (a).

Zarzycki, J., *J. phys. radium* (Suppl. Phys. Appl.) **18**, 65A, (1957) (b).

Zarzycki, J., *J. phys. radium* (Suppl. Phys. Appl.) **19**, 13A (1958).

DISCUSSION

J. A. PRINS

I wish to compliment you on the experimental results which you reported, and I accept them at their face value, but I disagree with your interpretation. The point is that one may resolve these radial distribution peaks in a manner different from yours, as suggested in Fig. 1. Indeed, it is possible that the peaks

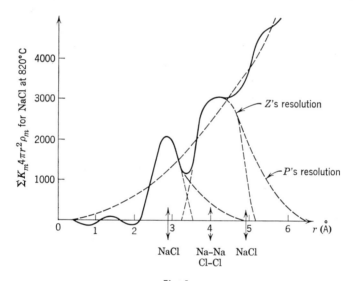

Fig. 1.

which represent the first and second coordination shells are considerably skewed toward the larger distances; actually, the average coordination numbers are really larger than the estimates based on your resolution of the radial distribution curve. This skewness is introduced by the randomness or fluctuations in the configurations of the first and second shells.

J. ZARZYCKI

I beg to disagree with your proposition, for the simple reason that there is no need to consider the coordination number in order to reach my conclusions. I have introduced it only for the sake of simplicity. Note that the same distances are observed in the liquid as in the solid and that the ratios of the locations of the peak maxima are *the same in the liquid as in the solid*, while *the density of the liquid is much lower*. Furthermore, I wish to call to your attention that the radial distribution curve for LiCl shows the first peak as completely resolved, with no skewness.

J. A. PRINS

The skewness in the radial distribution curve for individual coordination spheres may give one a false impression of the distance of closest approach and of the average distance of separation of the central atom from the centers of the surrounding shells. The distance of closest approach may appear unaltered, but the average value may well be larger. This type of diffraction experiment inherently cannot provide sufficiently precise data and sufficient information to allow a resolution of this question, because of the possibility that these curves are skewed.

There is one experiment which may provide new evidence to answer this question. Reliable small angle scattering data would prove whether the liquids which you have been working with consist of clusters or are indeed uniformly distributed as in other liquids. Your model should, I believe, lead to a considerable amount of small angle scattering.

M. L. HUGGINS

It may well be that the location of the first peak is not affected much by the change in coordination number. The second peak would be expected to vary considerably with change in coordination number, and the third peak even more so.

O. L. ANDERSON

I wish to clarify one point. Is it true, Professor Prins, owing to the possibility of skewness in the shapes of the individual radial distribution peaks, that location of the maximum may be smaller than the average bond length indicated by the curve? If that is correct, it suggests that some of the interpretations which have been given for x-ray diffraction data from glasses should be reconsidered.

S. H. BAUER

The radial distribution curves deduced by Dr. Zarzycki from x-ray diffraction patterns of molten alkali halides are very interesting. However, I believe they can be accounted for without the introduction of very complicated models involving holes or fissures in the structure of the liquids. I wish to call attention to the now well-established fact that the alkali metal halide vapors as present in equilibrium with the molten liquid consist not of single molecules (MX) but as dimers (M_2X_2). The dimerization energy is very large, being of the order of 60 kcal for LiF; it decreases to the order of 35 kcal for CsF, following a linear decline with the interionic distance. The structure of the dimer in the vapor phase has not been determined, but on the basis of electrostatic computations it is presumed to be diamond-shaped with interionic distances not so short as those determined by microwave measurements for the monomers, but presumably somewhat less than the interionic distances present in the crystal. Thus the dimers represent an intermediate stage of aggregation between the completely dissociated molecules and the well-crystallized material. It is, therefore, attractive to postulate that in the molten phase a variety of polymers are present. For example, dimers may be generated by the drawing together of four atoms (two positive and two negative ions) lying adjacent to each other in one (100) plane; tetramers can be made from ions in adjacent planes, etc. In this drawing together of ions away from the structures as present in the crystal, holes of a sort are introduced, and so the density goes down and the coordination number correspondingly decreases. One should, therefore, postulate a series of structural units ranging from dimers to tetramers to higher polymers which move about together and have transitory but still a finite lifetime. As would be predicted on the basis of this model, the higher the association energy for the dimer, the lower would be the average coordination number observed, as reported by Dr. Zarzycki for LiF; the lesser the dissociation energy for the dimer (for the heavier metal halides), the larger would be the average coordination number observed. Clearly, because these diffraction data were recorded only to a maximum of 0.7 in $(\sin/\theta)/\lambda$, the resolution available in the radial distribution curves is severely limited (see my discussion on the effect of maximum diffraction angle in Chapter 3). I maintain that the precise shape of the radial distribution peaks is at present not known. For this reason, one should be rather careful in attempting to account in too great detail for the individual areas as arbitrarily drawn in under these peaks.

J. ZARZYCKI

The results of Professor Kusch and co-workers (R. C. Miller and P. Kusch, *J. Chem. Phys.* **25,** 860, 1956) concerning the abundance of polymeric species of the alkali halides in the vapor phase show that trimers exist for LiF and that the abundance of dimers decreases from LiF to CsF. There is, I think, a striking analogy with our results concerning the liquid halides, the size of the clusters being maximum in the case of lithium compounds.

G. J. DIENES

Allow me to tell you about an interesting example of an artificial amorphous substance. When one records x-ray diffraction patterns from heavily irradiated diamond, he finds essentially a liquid-type pattern, although the diamond, of course, remains solid. One can interpret the radial distribution curve deduced from these data on the assumption that one has moved carbon atoms from their proper locations and placed them interstitially, leaving vacancies. Then one can ask for the change in the diffraction intensity due to the various radial distribution shells starting from any central carbon atom; he finds that the experimental data are fitted very nicely on the basis of this assumption. The amorphous nature of the pattern appears then from the strains which are introduced by the irradiation process and fits with the notion of interstitial atoms and vacancies.

J. A. PRINS

According to your model, I would not describe the irradiated diamond as a liquid structure but as an amorphous structure of a very different kind. As far as the radial distribution curve is concerned, there will be broadening of the first and second shells of the same order of magnitude as in a liquid, but that is not proof that it is liquid-like. By definition, in the case of a liquid, there should be very little small angle scattering, but, if one has small colloidal crystals, then very close to the central beam there ought to be considerable small angle scattering. This is an essential difference.

G. J. DIENES

We have observed small angle scattering from these samples, but the data are not quantitatively reliable.

A. B. LIDIARD

I favor Dr. Zarzycki's initial interpretation of the data, for there appears to be a very nice correspondence between these conclusions and results arrived at by several workers at Imperial College (Kitchener et al.) and at the University of Pittsburgh. They studied the conductivity and diffusion coefficients in molten salts, the latter deduced from the diffusion of tracers. One might at first assume that these two quantities would be related through the Einstein equation; but, in fact, the diffusion coefficients which one determines in the tracer experiment are greater than those calculated from the Einstein relation, using conductivity. On the basis of a quasi-lattice picture, this is interpreted by saying that one not only has vacant sites which give rise to normal ion conduction, but also pairs of vacant sites, with one of each sign. By being mobile such pairs aid diffusion, but by being electrically neutral they do not affect the conductivity. If one had a single vacancy per coordinate shell, he would get a reduction in coordination number of about 16% ($\frac{1}{6}$). If he had one vacant pair in a coordination shell, then the reduction would be 33%. Dr. Zarzycki's figures lie between these two. Therefore I think that the conductivity and diffusion data do favor the simple interpretation.

O. L. ANDERSON

Dr. Zarzycki discards the hole model because of a surface energy argument. I might raise the question as to how small a hole may be and still permit one the use of a macroscopic surface energy.

J. ZARZYCKI

I agree that we can only use the macroscopic surface energy to provide an order of magnitude. The real surface energy of a hole or a crack is possibly lower, but the difficulty is that, if we accept a lower figure for the surface energy, we must postulate a larger number of holes.

M. L. HUGGINS

It appears to me that one must settle this question unequivocally by means of another technique. The x-ray method appears to be insufficient by itself to determine the coordination number around individual atoms. Even the density plus the x-ray data are insufficient. Perhaps one should use nuclear magnetic resonance where it is possible, as well as other methods, to supplement these data.

J. H. CRAWFORD, JR.

There is one class of materials where the coordination number increases, and this is elements of group IV of the periodic table, germanium being an example. On fusion, the coordination number increases from 4 to something between 7 and 8, and along with that change the material assumes metallic properties. At the melting point the conductivity increases by several orders of magnitude. I raise the question whether it has been possible to determine the coordination number as a function of temperature by using x-ray diffraction techniques.

J. ZARZYCKI

O. Samoilov [*J. Fiz. Khim. U.R.S.S.* **30**, 244 (1956)] reported some results concerning the elements of group IV. The change in coordination number, $\Delta n = n_{liq} - n_{sol}$, amounts to $+4$ for Ge, 0 for Sn, and -1 for Pb.

M. J. BUERGER

Professor Prins suggested that the maxima do not give the correct average separations and that the resolution of the radial distribution curve into individual peaks is an arbitrary one and may indeed consist of skewed peaks. On this basis I propose another model. Suppose one considers an atom near a surface. That atom is supposed to have a coordination number of 6, but, being near the surface, it actually has a lower coordination number, perhaps 4. The checkerboard structure for NaCl is no longer the stable one under these circumstances, and indeed a lower coordination number would naturally follow. This type of mixed coordination is not an impossible model. We know of a number of structures which on heating transform from a larger to a smaller coordination number, unlike the situation in bismuth; CsCl is such an example. I might suggest that in a mixed collection of this sort which consists of a variety of sizes of rings and groups there could be a reduction in density.

P. J. W. DEBYE

I believe that one can conserve the relationship for the positions of the peaks and still reduce the coordination number. Let us start with a perfect NaCl lattice and remove at random chlorine atoms and sodium atoms. That, of course, makes the density smaller. The positions of the maxima in the interatomic distance and the radial distribution have not been changed, but the widths of the peaks have been made larger, owing to the increased thermal motions resulting from the presence of the holes and thus the formation of a somewhat irregular lattice.

G. J. DIENES

The wobbling of the atoms and the appearance of holes start in the solid well below the melting point; Professor Debye's model for the liquid is an extension of what we know occurs in the solid.

by

M. Lax

H. L. Frisch

Bell Telephone Laboratories, Inc.

Electronic Band Structure of One-Dimensional Disordered Arrays

In a number of solid state problems we are interested in the distribution of energy levels of an electron in an array of scattering centers possessing no long range order, for example a disordered crystal. The loss of translational periodicity can be accomplished in at least two characteristic ways.

1. The alloy problem can be thought of as the result of random replacement of a certain fraction of the solvent atoms on their lattice sites by solute atoms.

2. The impurity band problem in semiconductors can result from addition of a certain concentration of impurity atoms at random sites in the host crystal.

We shall be concerned primarily with models of the latter type of disorder which also arises if one deals with the electronic energy bands of liquid metals. The quantity of greatest physical interest is the density of states (which is essentially the number of states of energy less than the stated energy divided by the volume of the array) which we take in the limit as the number of impurity (or solute) atoms and the volume of the array become infinite in such a way as to maintain a definite, finite (number) concentration of impurity atoms. Thus we can dispense with the specification of boundary conditions on the wave function of the electron and obtain a bulk density of states which characterizes the energy band in a macroscopic array.

A number of different formal methods for calculating the density of states for such problems have been suggested; of these we shall discuss three. Only the last of these, which reformulates these problems in terms of a multiple scattering formalism, whose equations unfortunately can be dealt with only approximately, can, in principle at least, deal with realistic models in three dimensions. The other two approaches are strictly limited to apply only to one-dimensional arrays, for which both give numerically exact results. The second actually gives formally the exact analytical solution in that finding the density of states for one-dimensional arrays is reduced to the quadrature of a single linear second-order differential equation. These exact solutions for suitable one-dimensional models possess a certain amount of intrinsic interest. They vividly illustrate the expectation that the effect of the random distribution of the impurity scattering centers (atoms) of the array on the density of states is large in the low density or tight-binding limit and decreases as the density of scattering centers increases. Still, the primary interest in carrying out extended computations on the exactly solvable one-dimensional models is that, by specializing the results of the approximate three-dimensional multiple-scattering approach to one dimension, the computations can be compared and the validity of the approximations made can be ascertained (at least for the one-dimensional models).

We shall develop the formal methods of computation, keeping in mind that the results will be in general applicable to the impurity band problem, to a lesser extent to "one-dimensional liquid metals," and hardly at all to the alloy energy band problem. For simplicity we assume that we are dealing with impurities of a single kind, and the periodic structure of the host lattice will be largely neglected since we shall treat the electron in the effective mass approximation. This approximation is permissible since the relevant electron wavelengths in an impurity band are comparable to or larger than the mean separation between impurities (these are of the order of the cube root of the reciprocal number concentration of the impurities), and this separation is in general large compared to the lattice constant of the host crystal. This is usually not the case in an alloy. Furthermore, in this regard we shall assume that the localized potentials associated with the scattering centers are short range and that the spatial region of extreme curvature is small.

Another great simplification in constructing one-dimensional models of impurity bands is obtained by replacing the actual, deep, localized potential of the impurity scattering centers by a δ function potential. The strength of the scattering potential is thus characterized by a single parameter which can be chosen to be the range $1/\kappa_0$ of the bound state wave function associated with a single such scattering center, rather than two or more parameters as with other potentials. The fact that contacts between two bands cannot occur with this choice of potential plays no role here since we shall not deal with interband effects. This simplification is permissible if the width of the actual one-dimensional impurity potential is small compared to both the mean separation between impurities and $1/\kappa_0$.

One-Dimensional Impurity Bands

Adopting the simplified model discussed in the preceding section, we set the host crystal potential equal to zero and distribute at random along the x-axis the δ functions representing the impurity scattering centers with an average number density n. The distribution of these scattering centers thus obtained is a Poisson distribution with parameter n. The wave function $\psi(x)$ of an electron of energy E satisfies the Schrödinger equation

$$\left[\frac{d^2}{dx^2} + 2\kappa_0 \sum_n \delta(x - x_n) \right] \psi(x) = \kappa^2 \psi(x) \tag{1}$$

where $\kappa_0 > 0$ and

$$E = - \frac{\hbar^2 \kappa^2}{2m}$$

where κ is real if $E < 0$, imaginary $(= -ik)$ if $E > 0$, with m the (effective) mass of the electron and x_n the position of the nth scattering center, and

$$\psi(x_n + 0) - \psi(x_n - 0) = 0 \tag{2}$$

The wave function appropriate for a single δ function is $\psi_0(x) \sim \exp(-\kappa_0 |x - x_0|)$ of energy $E_0 = -(\hbar^2/2m)\kappa_0^2$. $(1/\kappa_0)$ is, as stated, the range of the bound state. Clearly, the only dimensionless parameters of the problem are a dimensionless energy $(\kappa/\kappa_0)^2$ and a dimensionless density of impurities $\epsilon = n/\kappa_0$.

The calculation of the density of states in one dimension is considerably simplified because, as first emphasized in connection with this problem by James and Ginzbarg (1953), the number of nodes of a solution of the wave equation with energy E determines how many states of the system possess energies less than E. Thus one can show that the desired density of states Nn is the average number of zeros of $\psi(x)$ per unit x. We shall now roughly sketch two techniques for computing the density of states:

Direct Counting Method

This simple method, most closely pursued by Lax and Phillips (1958), considers a suitable realization of the configurations of η randomly distributed δ functions generated by a Monte Carlo procedure and employs an IBM 650 machine to count in effect the nodes of $\psi(x)$ for this configuration. The law of large numbers and the central limit theorem of probability theory ensure that the expected (average) error in the density of states obtained by this procedure is of the order of $\eta^{-\frac{1}{2}}$ as $\eta \to \infty$. Considerable ingenuity is now required to simplify equation (1) so that the time required by the machine for the counting is not prohibitive for large η, e.g., to obtain accuracies of $\frac{1}{2}\%$ chains of 500–1000 impurity atoms are necessary. Previous machine calculations (James and Ginzbarg, 1953; Landauer and Phillips, 1954) were deficient in this regard and also were carried out only for very restricted impurity concentrations, at least for our purposes.

In order to study the nodes of $\psi(x)$ we need to consider only the ratio $\psi'(x)/\psi(x)$ at x_n and x_{n+1}. Setting

$$a_n = \frac{\psi'(x_n - 0)}{\kappa\psi(x_n - 0)}$$

$$b_n = \frac{\psi'(x_n + 0)}{\kappa\psi(x_n + 0)} \tag{3}$$

$$\bar{x}_n = x_{n+1} - x_n$$

one finds, on integrating equation (1) after some manipulation, that

$$a_{n+1} = \frac{b_n + \tanh \kappa\bar{x}_n}{1 + b_n \tanh \kappa\bar{x}_n} \tag{4}$$

while the δ function at x_n produces a jump in ψ'/ψ given by

$$b_n = a_n - 2\kappa_0/\kappa \tag{5}$$

Since the density of states may be large for $\kappa \simeq \kappa_0$ and at low densities

$\kappa \bar{x}_n \gg 1$ (tanh $\kappa \bar{x}_n \simeq 1$), one gains in the number of significant figures in the machine calculation by rearranging (4) and (5) into

$$b_n' = a_n' - 2(\kappa_0/\kappa - 1)$$

$$a_{n+1}' = -\frac{2(2 - b_n') \exp(-2\alpha u_n)}{b_n' + (2 - b_n') \exp(-2\alpha u_n)}$$

(6)

with $a_n' = a_n - 1$, $b_n' = b_n - 1$, and $\alpha = \kappa(\kappa_0 \epsilon)^{-1}$. The dimensionless parameter $u_n = x_n/\langle x \rangle = n x_n$ is a random variable, independent of density, so that the same set of u's can be used for different densities.

One now uses the machine to count nodes, i.e., sign changes of ψ occurring between δ functions using the condition

$$b_n < -1 \qquad \text{sign}(a_{n+1} b_n) < 0$$

(7)

which are both necessary and sufficient for one zero of ψ to have occurred in the interval. For positive energies the connection formulas are obtained from (4) and (5) by replacing κ by $-ik$. Setting $b_n = -\tan \phi_n$, $a_{n+1} = -\tan \chi_{n+1}$, one can show that the number of nodes of ψ (in the interval) is given by greatest integer contained in $(\chi_{n+1} + \pi/2)/\pi$ — greatest integer contained in $(\phi_n + \pi/2)/\pi$.

The results of these calculations will be discussed and presented below under "Numerical Comparisons."

Stochastic Process

Frisch and Lloyd (1958) obtain the average number of zeros of $\psi(x)$ per unit x (satisfying equation 1) by studying the two-dimensional Markov process constituted by $\psi(x)$ and $\psi'(x)$ (the underlying random element being the random distribution of scattering centers). The Markov property derives from the independent increments property of the distribution of scattering centers (i.e., in one dimension the distribution is a Poisson distribution). Once the stationary distribution of ψ'/ψ is known, the average number of zeros of $\psi(x)$ per unit x can be obtained from a formula due to Rice (1944, 1945), which originally arose in the analysis of the zeros of a random noise current.

Consider the random point $\xi = \psi(x)$, $\eta = \psi'(x)$ in a ξ, η space. Between scattering centers ($x \neq x_n$), ξ, η satisfies

$$\frac{d\xi}{dx} = \eta \qquad \frac{d\eta}{dx} = +\kappa^2 \xi$$

(8)

while at a scattering center (e.g., $x = x_n$)

$$[\eta] = \psi'(x_n + 0) - \psi'(x_n - 0) = -2\kappa_0 \xi(x_n)$$

$$[\xi] = \psi(x_n + 0) - \psi(x_n - 0) = 0 \tag{9}$$

by virtue of equations (3) and (5). The transformations given by equations (8) and (9) possess unit Jacobeans and state that, as x varies between the location of the scattering centers, the (ξ, η) moves along an ellipse or hyperbola according as $\kappa^2 < 0$ or $\kappa^2 > 0$, while at a scattering center the tangent of the angle of the radius vector of the point experiences a jump by an amount $-2\kappa_0$ (see Fig. 1).

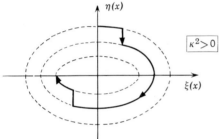

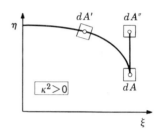

Fig. 1. Motion of the random point (ξ, η) for positive energies.

Fig. 2. Detail of the motion of the random point (ξ, η) for positive energies.

We assume that the (normalized) differentiable probability density of (ξ, η), $p(\xi, \eta; x)$ exists. Referring to Fig. 2, we see that the number of points in dA (centered at ξ, η) at $x + dx$, $p(\xi, \eta; x + dx)\, dA$ can arise either by (a) being in dA' (centered at $\xi - \eta\, dx$, $\eta - \kappa^2\xi\, dx$) at x and not being scattered in the interval dx with probability $1 - n\, dx + o\,(dx)$ or (b) being in dA'' (centered at $\xi, \eta + 2\kappa_0\xi$) at x and being scattered in the interval dx with probability $n\, dx + o\,(dx)$:

$$p(\xi, \eta; x + dx)\, dA = (1 - n\, dx)p(\xi - \eta\, dx, \eta - \kappa^2\xi\, dx; x)\, dA'$$

$$+ n\, dx\, p(\xi, \eta + 2\kappa_0\xi; x)\, dA'' + o\,(dx) \tag{10}$$

Expanding to terms $o(dx)$ (noting that $dA'/dA = dA''/dA = 1$), one obtains effectively the forward equation of the Markov process:

$$\frac{\partial p}{\partial x} = -\left(\kappa^2\xi \frac{\partial}{\partial \eta} + \eta \frac{\partial}{\partial \xi}\right) p + n[p(\xi, \eta + 2\kappa_0\xi; x) - p(\xi, \eta; x)] \tag{11}$$

Once p is given for some initial value of x, say x_0, p for any x can be obtained by solving this equation. From (11) the mth moments of p,

$$\langle \xi^r \eta^s \rangle = \iint_{-\infty}^{\infty} \xi^r \eta^r p(\xi, \eta; x)\, d\xi\, d\eta \qquad r + s = m, r, s \geq 0 \qquad (12)$$

satisfy m linear ordinary equations. Thus, for example, for the first moments ($\langle \xi \rangle$ and $\langle \eta \rangle$) the system is

$$\frac{d\langle \xi \rangle}{dx} = \langle \eta \rangle$$

$$\frac{d\langle \eta \rangle}{dx} = (\kappa^2 - 2n\kappa_0)\langle \xi \rangle \qquad (13)$$

$\langle \xi \rangle$ and $\langle \eta \rangle$ are of the form of free waves $e^{ik'x}$, where the "wave vector" k' satisfies the dispersion relation

$$k'^2 = 2n\kappa_0 - \kappa^2 \qquad (14)$$

This rigorous result will be useful subsequently in our discussion of the multiple scattering approach. In general, the first moments blow up as $|x| \to \infty$ for $\kappa^2 > 2n\kappa_0$ (the "band edge") unless the initial probability density is such that $[\langle \psi' + 2\kappa_0 \psi \rangle]_{x=x_0} = 0$, in which case $\langle \xi \rangle$ and $\langle \eta \rangle$ vanish. Such a choice is not possible for the second (and higher) moments, and these diverge as $|x| \to \infty$.

To calculate the distribution of $\psi'/\psi = \eta/\xi$ we need consider only the marginal angular probability density $R(\theta; x)$. Introducing polar coordinates,

$$\rho = (\xi^2 + \eta^2)^{\frac{1}{2}} \qquad \theta = \arctan(\eta/\xi)$$

so that

$$p(\xi, \eta; x) = p(\rho \cos \theta, \rho \sin \theta; x)$$

we find $R(\theta; x)$ by applying the integral operator $\mathcal{I}$ on p:

$$R(\theta; x) = \int_0^{\infty} p(\rho \cos \theta, \rho \sin \theta; x) \rho\, d\rho$$

$$= \mathcal{I}p \qquad (15)$$

This probability density approaches a stationary value as $x \to \infty$, $R(\theta)$. The equation for $R(\theta)$ is obtained by applying $\mathcal{I}$ to both sides of equation (11) and setting $\partial R/\partial x = 0$. The formula of Rice (1944, 1945) asserts that the number of zeros of $\xi = \psi(x)$ in the interval $(0, L)$ is given by

$$\int_0^L dx \int_{-\infty}^{\infty} |\eta| p(0, \eta; x) \, d\eta$$

Hence the desired density of states $nN(\kappa)$ follows as

$$nN(\kappa) = \lim_{L \to \infty} \frac{1}{L} \int_0^L dx \int_{-\infty}^{\infty} |\eta| p(0, \eta; x) \, d\eta$$

$$= R\left(\frac{\pi}{2}\right) + R\left(-\frac{\pi}{2}\right) = 2R\left(\frac{\pi}{2}\right) \tag{16}$$

since $R(-\pi/2) = R(\pi/2)$. Our final results are considerably simplified by considering the stationary probability density of $\eta/\xi = z = \tan\theta$, $T(z)$ with

$$2R(\theta) = (z^2 + 1)T(z) \tag{17}$$

which satisfies the linear difference differential equation, derived from the equation satisfied by $R(\theta)$,

$$\frac{d}{dz}[(z^2 - \kappa^2)T(z)] + n[T(z + 2\kappa_0) - T(z)] = 0 \tag{18}$$

with

$$\int_{-\infty}^{\infty} T(z) \, dz = 1$$

and

$$nN(\kappa) = \lim_{z \to \infty} z^2 T(z) \tag{19}$$

The Fourier transform of $T(z)$,

$$u(\omega) = \int_{-\infty}^{\infty} \exp\,(i\omega z) T(z) \, dz$$

exists and satisfies the ordinary, linear second-order differential equation,

$$u''(\omega) + \left[\kappa^2 - n\left(\frac{1 - e^{-2i\kappa_0\omega}}{i\omega}\right)\right] u(\omega) = 0 \qquad \omega > 0 \tag{20}$$

with

$$nN(\kappa) = -\frac{u'(0 + 0)}{\pi u(0)} \tag{21}$$

showing that the density of states is exhibited in terms of a quadrature as stated. Substitution of the first term of the WBJK expansion of the solution of (20) in (21) yields directly the optical model which will be discussed in connection with the multiple scattering approach. For details of the numerical solution and various series expansions of the solution of (20) we refer the reader to the original paper (Frisch and Lloyd, 1958); we list here only a number of properties of the density of states.

1. For positive energies,

$$\frac{1}{1 - e^{-n\pi/k} + \Delta} \leq N(+k) \leq \frac{1 + \Delta}{1 - e^{-n\pi/k} + \Delta}$$

$$\Delta = n \int_{-\infty}^{\infty} \frac{1 - \exp\left\{-(n/k)[\pi/2 + \arctan(z/k)]\right\}}{(z + 2\kappa_0)^2 + k^2} dz \qquad (22)$$

$$N(+k) = \frac{k}{n\pi} + \frac{1}{\pi}\arctan\frac{\kappa_0}{k} + 0\left(\frac{n}{k}\right) \qquad k \gg n$$

2. For negative energies,

$$N(\kappa) \leq (\tfrac{1}{2}\epsilon)^{m-1}/m! \qquad \epsilon = n/\kappa_0 \qquad (23)$$

where m is the largest integer contained in $(\kappa/\kappa_0 - 1)$. For $\kappa/\kappa_0 > 1$ and $nT \ll 1$,

$$N(\kappa) \approx \exp\left[(-nT)(nT)^m/m!\right]$$

where $nT = (n/\kappa)\log\left[(\kappa/\kappa_0) - 1\right]$.

The Multiple Scattering Approach

To reformulate this problem in terms of the multiple scattering formalism developed by Lax (1951, 1952), Lax and Phillips (1958) consider an external incident wave $\phi(x)$ impinging on an array of scatterers whose potential field is given by $2\kappa_0 \sum_j \delta(x - x_j)$. The resulting equation for the wave field $\psi(x)$ is, of course, equation (1), whose solution in terms of the Green's function corresponding to the operator $d^2/dx^2 - \kappa^2$, $(2\kappa)^{-1}$ $\exp\left(-\kappa|x - x'|\right)$ is

$$\psi(x) = \phi(x) + \frac{\kappa_0}{\kappa}\int \exp\left[-\kappa|x - x'|\right]\sum_j \delta(x' - x_j)\psi(x') \, dx'$$

$$= \phi(x) + \sum_j L_j(x) \qquad (24)$$

where

$$L_j(x) = (\kappa_0/\kappa)\exp\left[-\kappa|x - x_j|\right]\psi(x_j)$$

$$= \exp\left[-\kappa|x - x_j|\right]L_j(x_j) \qquad (25)$$

is the field emitted from scatterer j.

Adopting the language of the self-consistent field method, the effective field $\psi^i(x)$ impinging on scatterer i differs from the total field ψ by the field emitted by i; that is,

$$\psi^i(x) = \psi(x) - L_i(x) = \phi(x) + \sum_{j \neq i} L_j(x) \tag{26}$$

In particular, at $x = x_i$,

$$\psi(x_i) = \psi^i(x_i) + (\kappa_0/\kappa)\psi(x_i)$$
$$= \psi^i(x_i) + [\kappa/\kappa_0 - 1]^{-1}\psi^i(x_i)$$

so that, by equation (26),

$$L_i(x_i) = [\kappa/\kappa_0 - 1]^{-1}\psi^i(x_i) \tag{27}$$

and from (25), changing i into j,

$$L_j(x) = A(|x - x_j|)\psi^j(x_j)$$

with $$\tag{28}$$

$$A(|x|) = [\kappa/\kappa_0 - 1]^{-1} \exp\left[-\kappa|x|\right]$$

This equation asserts the expected result that the wave which leaves the scatterer is given by an operator $A(|x - x_j|)$ acting on the wave incident on the jth scatterer.

Substituting (28) into (26) and (24), we obtain the equation for the effective fields and the total field:

$$\psi^i(x_i) = \phi(x_i) + \sum_{j \neq i} A(|x_i - x_j|)\psi^j(x_j)$$
$$\psi(x) = \phi(x) + \sum_{j} A(|x - x_j|)\psi^i(x_j) \tag{29}$$

In the impurity band problem we are interested in the "self-sustained" solution for which $\phi(x) \equiv 0$, so that the equation for the effective fields reduces to the homogeneous system

$$c_i = \sum_{j} A_{ij} c_j \tag{30}$$

where $c_i = \psi^i(x_i)$ and $A_{ij} = A(|x_i - x_j|)$ and $A_{ii} = 0$. We shall now apply this result to obtain the density of states for two limiting cases, low and relatively high density of scattering centers.

Low Densities of Scatterers; Pair Theory

One expects, in analogy with the virial expansion of the statistical mechanical theory of imperfect gases, that at low densities (n) of scatterers the primary multiple scattering effect is due to pairs of scatterers.

In the pair theory one ascribes the broadening of the isolated bound level wholly to such pair interactions. If two scatterers located at x_m and x_n form a pair, then the appropriate solution of (30), which is localized about them, is obtained by neglecting all c_j, $j \neq n, m$ in (30), since $c_m, c_n \gg c_j$. Thus (30) reduces to

$$c_m = A_{mn}c_n \qquad c_n = A_{nm}c_m$$

or

$$A_{mn}A_{nm} = 1 = A_{nm}^2$$

so that

$$\kappa/\kappa_0 - 1 = \pm \exp\left(-\kappa|x_{nm}|\right) \qquad (x_{nm} = x_n - x_m) \qquad (31)$$

by virtue of (28).

But, because of the Poisson distribution of scatterers, the probability that the nearest neighbor of a scatterer located at x_n lies between x_{nm} and $x_{nm} + dx_{nm}$ is $2n \exp\left(-2n|x_{nm}|\right)$. Similarly the probability that the nearest neighbor distance is greater than x_{nm} is $\exp\left(-2n|x_{nm}|\right)$. Solving for $\exp\left(-2n|x_{nm}|\right)$ in terms of $\kappa/\kappa_0 - 1$ from (31) and using the definition of $nN(\kappa)$, we find that according to the pair theory the dimensionless (integral) density of states $N(\kappa)$ is given by

$$N(\kappa) = \begin{cases} \frac{1}{2}(1 + |\kappa/\kappa_0 - 1|^{2n/\kappa}) & \text{for } 0 \leq \kappa/\kappa_0 \leq 1 \\ \frac{1}{2}(1 - |\kappa/\kappa_0 - 1|^{2n/\kappa}) & \text{for } 1 \leq \kappa/\kappa_0 \leq 2 \end{cases} \qquad (32)$$

The differential density of states in the neighborhood of $\kappa/\kappa_0 = 1$ is approximately

$$\frac{dN(\kappa)}{d(\kappa/\kappa_0)} \simeq 2\epsilon |\kappa/\kappa_0 - 1|^{-1+2\epsilon} \qquad (33)$$

Equation (33) exhibits a long tail, leading to a first moment proportional to ϵ. Any fixed fraction of the states is confined to a neighborhood of $\kappa/\kappa_0 = 1$ of length of the order of $e^{-1/\epsilon}$. In this respect the results are quite comparable with those obtained for a periodic array, where the band width is proportional to the overlap and also varies as $e^{-1/\epsilon}$ (with n given by the reciprocal of the fundamental repeat distance). At low densities the introduction of randomness modifies the shape of the central region, introducing a singularity at $\kappa/\kappa_0 = 1$, and adds a long tail.

High Densities of Scatterers: The Optical Model

At high densities the fractional fluctuation in density of scatterers about a given one is small. This suggests that the properties of our scattering system are then described in excellent approximation by the properties of the averaged (over the random locations of the scatterers) waves. Thus as $\epsilon \to \infty$ we replace the c_i by the average c_i which are plane waves:

$$c_i \approx \langle c_i \rangle = \exp{(ik'x_i)}\, c \qquad c = |\langle c_i \rangle| \qquad (34)$$

We know that the plane wave form of $\langle c_i \rangle$ is rigorously correct in one dimension from the exact theory; cf. equations (13) and (14). Introducing this *Ansatz* (34) into (30), we find that

$$\frac{\kappa}{\kappa_0} - 1 = \sum_{j \neq i} \exp{[-\kappa|x_j - x_i| + ik'(x_j - x_i)]}$$
$$= -1 + \sum_{\text{all } j} \exp{[-\kappa|x_j - x_i| + ik'(x_j - x_i)]} \qquad (35)$$

At sufficiently high density ($\epsilon \gg 1$) we can, by virtue of the law of large numbers, replace the sum in (35) by its ensemble average,

$$\frac{\kappa}{\kappa_0} - 1 = 1 + \int_{-\infty}^{\infty} n \, dx \, \exp{(-\kappa|x| + ik'x)}$$

which gives us the previously found dispersion relation (14). Since the number of zeros in $\cos k'x$ in a length L is $k'L/\pi$, we find that the optical model (dimensionless) density of states, $N_{\text{op}}(\kappa)$, is given by

$$N_{\text{op}}(\kappa) = (2n\kappa_0 - \kappa^2)^{1/2}/\pi n$$
$$= [2\epsilon - (\kappa/\kappa_0)^2]^{1/2}/\pi\epsilon \qquad (36)$$

As we shall see, the actual density of states is approximated fairly well by (36) except at the band edge, where fluctuations produce a tail whose qualitative form can be obtained, at least for not too large κ/κ_0, by a "local density" model.

We should note that, except for the use of the δ function scattering potential, the results of the multiple scattering approach so far displayed have been obtained without using any special properties of the one-dimensional model used by the other two approaches. These special properties concern (a) the fact that the density of states is equal to the average number of zeros of $\psi(x)$ per unit x and (b) the fact that the random spatial distribution of scattering centers possesses the independent increments property which leads to the Markoffian processes explicitly exhibited or used in equations (4) to (7) or (10) and (11). Incidentally, while the use of the δ function potentials simplifies greatly the exact treatment in one dimension, one can replace this potential by an arbitrary short range potential. If this is done, one finds, for example, that the difference-differential equation for the marginal distribution of ψ'/ψ, equation (18), has to be replaced by a suitable integrodifferential equation, and so on.

Applications to Limiting Cases of Three-Dimensional Impurity Bands

The simplest problem that may be attacked in three dimensions is the point isotropic scatterer. Equations (29) remain valid if the Green's function $A(x_i - x_j)$ is replaced by $A(r_i - r_j)$ with

$$A(r) = (f/r) \exp(-\kappa r) \qquad (37)$$

where $f = f(\kappa)$ is the S wave scattering amplitude. If one applies the effective range theory used in describing nuclear forces (Blatt and Weisskopf, 1952) and takes the limit as the effective range goes to zero, one sees that a reasonable choice for the scattering amplitude is given by *

$$f = 1/(\kappa - \kappa_0) \qquad (38)$$

At low densities the success of the pair theory in one dimension (see "Low Densities of Scatterers: Pair Theory" above) suggests that we apply it in three dimensions. The condition $1 = A^2$ leads to the result

$$\kappa - \kappa_0 = \pm[\exp(-\kappa r)]/r \qquad (39)$$

so that, at a given r, two states are produced, one with $\kappa > \kappa_0$, one with $\kappa < \kappa_0$. The Hertz distribution of nearest neighbor distances (Hertz, 1909),

$$\text{Prob. } (r > r_1) = \exp[-(4\pi/3)n r_1^3] \qquad (40)$$

can now be translated into an integral density of states:

$$N(\kappa) = \tfrac{1}{2}[1 - \exp(-4\pi n r^3/3)] \qquad \kappa > \kappa_0$$
$$N(\kappa) = \tfrac{1}{2}[1 + \exp(-4\pi n r^3/3)] \qquad \kappa < \kappa_0 \qquad (41)$$

where $r = r(\kappa)$ is obtained by solving (39) with the upper sign for $\kappa > \kappa_0$ and the lower sign for $\kappa < \kappa_0$. The choice $N(\kappa_0) = \tfrac{1}{2}$ has been imposed, and $\exp[-4\pi n r(\kappa)^3/3]$ represents the probability that $r(\kappa) < r < r(\kappa_0)$ $\leq \infty$, i.e., that a shift from κ_0 of less than $|\kappa - \kappa_0|$ has taken place, in either direction (with probability $\tfrac{1}{2}$ for each direction).

The transcendental equation for $r(\kappa)$ cannot be solved explicitly, but we can investigate certain limiting cases. For $\kappa \gg \kappa_0$, we may neglect κ_0 in (39) and we find that

$$r \simeq \eta/\kappa \qquad (42)$$

---

* The choice of the scattering amplitude, off the energy shell, is obtained by applying analytical continuation to the results for f on the energy shell. The validity of such analytical continuation for a general class of potentials is discussed by Khuri (1957).

where η is a solution of

$$u = \ln (1/u) \tag{43}$$

Thus

$$N(\kappa) \simeq \tfrac{1}{2}\{1 - \exp\left[-4\pi n(\eta/\kappa)^3/3\right]\}$$
$$\rightarrow (2\pi/3)\, n\eta^3/\kappa^3 \tag{44}$$

Thus, in three dimensions, a longer tail is present for $\kappa \gg \kappa_0$, as contrasted to the one-dimensional case, for which $N(\kappa)$ goes to zero at $\kappa/\kappa_0 = 2$—because $\exp\left(-\kappa|x|\right)$ has a maximum value of unity whereas $[\exp\left(-\kappa r\right)]/r$ has no maximum.

If

$$\xi \equiv |(\kappa/\kappa_0) - 1| \ll 1 \tag{45}$$

then we have to a good approximation that $u = \kappa_0 r$ obeys

$$u = \ln (1/\xi) - \ln u \tag{46}$$

If we neglect $\ln u$ compared to $u \simeq \ln (1/\xi)$, then we obtain

$$N(\kappa) \simeq \tfrac{1}{2}\{1 \mp \exp\left[-\epsilon(\ln (1/\xi))^3\right]\} \tag{47}$$

where $\epsilon = (4\pi/3)\, n/\kappa_0^3$ is a dimensionless density representing the number of atoms within "range" of a given atom. Thus an appreciable fraction of the total density of states occurs within the range

$$|\kappa/\kappa_0 - 1| \lesssim \exp\left(-\epsilon^{-\frac{1}{3}}\right) \tag{48}$$

The differential density of states in the same approximation is given by

$$\frac{dN}{d\xi} = \frac{3}{2}\frac{\epsilon}{\xi}\left[\ln\left(\frac{1}{\xi}\right)\right]^2 \exp\left[-\epsilon\left(\ln\frac{1}{\xi}\right)^3\right] \tag{49}$$

In contrast to the one-dimensional case, $dN/d\xi$ does not approach ∞ as $\xi \rightarrow 0$, but instead vanishes there. This low density at $\kappa/\kappa_0 = 1$ arises from the small probability of large separations [going as $\exp\left(-r^3\right)$ in three dimensions and $\exp\left(-|x|\right)$ in one dimension].

As $\kappa \rightarrow 0$, $r(\kappa) \rightarrow 1/\kappa_0$, so that

$$N(0) = \tfrac{1}{2}[1 - \exp\left(-\epsilon\right)] = 1 - \tfrac{1}{2}\epsilon \tag{50}$$

is in qualitative agreement with the one-dimensional case.

At high densities ϵ, the integral density of states is given in good approximation by the optical model. For the three-dimensional case, we have

$$N(\kappa) = (2\pi)^{-3}\int d\vec{k}' = \frac{1}{6\pi^2}\, [k'(\kappa)]^3$$
$$|k'| \le k'(\kappa) \tag{51}$$

We anticipate from previous work (Lax, 1951, 1952) that

$$k'^2 = -\kappa^2 + 4\pi n f c \qquad (52)$$

where $f = (\kappa - \kappa_0)^{-1}$ and c is the ratio of the effective field to the average field.

Numerical Comparisons

The machine method for determining the density of states by counting zeros is essentially an exact method. The accuracy of the numbers quoted are limited only by the length of the chain of atoms used. For chains of 500–1000 atoms, used in the computation, random errors of about 0.5% occur, as may be seen by comparing results after 500 and after 1000 atoms in Table 1.

Table 1

INTEGRATED DENSITY OF STATES AT NEGATIVE ENERGIES, $\epsilon = 0.1$

κ/κ_0	Machine Results (%) (500 atoms)	Machine Results (%) (1000 atoms)	Pair Theory (%)	Schmidt's Formula (%)
0.001	89.6	89.2	91.0	90.8
0.67	84.6	84.6	85.7	86.4
0.92	78.6	77.9	78.8	79.4
0.99	70.6	69.7	70.0	71.0
0.997	65.6	—	65.6	66.9
0.999	62.6	—	62.6	64.1
0.9995	61.4	61.1	60.9	62.3
0.99968	60.2	59.9	60.0	61.3
0.99985	58.6	58.6	58.5	59.9
0.999995	53.8	53.2	54.4	54.7
0.999999	51.4	51.4	53.0	52.9
1.000000	42.8	—	50.0	44.4
1.000005	36.6	37.0	45.6	38.5
1.00032	32.8	33.4	40.0	33.8
1.0010	31.2	31.8	37.4	32.0
1.0030	29.0	—	34.6	28.6
1.01	25.4	25.9	30.0	26.0
1.078	18.6	18.2	18.9	17.2
1.33	6.4	7.7	7.9	7.3
2.00	0.4	0.5	0.0	0.0

Similarly the solutions based on the differential-difference equation (18), or the differential equation (20), are limited only by the accuracy of the quadrature formulas used in solving the equations. It should therefore be no surprise that, wherever calculations have been made at the same or neighboring energies, for the same ϵ, agreement is obtained within the accuracy of both computations (i.e., 1% or better); see, for example, Figs. 3 and 4.

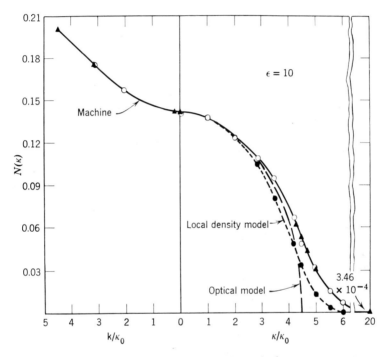

Fig. 3. Integrated density of states vs. the dimensionless square root energy κ/κ_0 for $\epsilon = 10$. The dark triangles correspond to values obtained from the numerical integration of equations (20) and (21).

Our primary purpose is to compare the numerically computed density of states with simple models like the pair model at low densities and the optical model at high densities. The accuracy of the models in one dimension will give some idea as to the possible validity of their extension to three dimensions.

At low densities, $\epsilon = 0.1$ and $\epsilon = 0.01$, we find in Tables 1 and 2 that the pair theory is an excellent approximation in the wings. For $|\kappa/\kappa_0 - 1| \sim \exp(-1/\epsilon)$, however, the pair theory has too high a differential

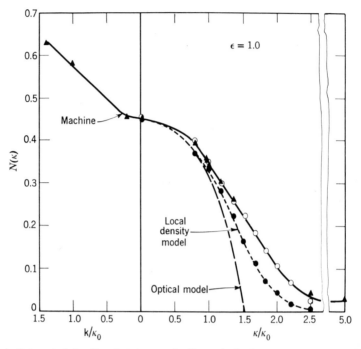

Fig. 4. Integrated density of states vs. the dimensionless square root energy κ/κ_0 for $\epsilon = 1.0$. The dark triangles correspond to values obtained from the numerical integration of equations (20) and (21).

density of states for $\kappa/\kappa_0 < 1$ and too low for $\kappa/\kappa_0 < 1$ (see, for example, the slopes in Fig. 5). The region $|\kappa/\kappa_0 - 1| < \exp(-1/\epsilon)$, of course, is so small that it has no influence on the moments of the distribution, these all being given correctly to order ϵ by the pair distribution.

A solution accurate to order ϵ even in the central region was obtained by Schmidt (1957). His result, which may also be obtained by solving an integral equation that parallels the procedure used in our machine calculation, is given in our notation by

$$1 \leq \frac{\kappa}{\kappa_0} \leq 2 : N(\kappa) = \frac{1 - y}{(\frac{3}{2} - \frac{1}{2}y)^2}$$

$$0 \leq \frac{\kappa}{\kappa_0} \leq 1 : N(\kappa) = (\tfrac{3}{2} - \tfrac{1}{2}y)^{-2}$$

(53)

where $y = |(\kappa/\kappa_0) - 1|^{\epsilon}$.

In these equations more accuracy will be obtained in the wings if ϵ is replaced by n/κ, and the latter value is used in all comparisons with

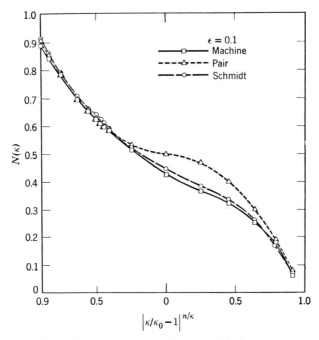

Fig. 5. Integrated density of states vs. the dimensionless square root energy κ/κ_0 for $\epsilon = 0.1$.

Schmidt (1957). Tables 1 and 2 show that Schmidt's result is indeed correct almost everywhere to order ϵ. The moments of both the pair and the Schmidt distribution to lowest order in ϵ are both given by

$$\langle (\kappa/\kappa_0 - 1)^n \rangle = 4\epsilon/n \tag{54}$$

for n even (and not zero), with a vanishing result for n odd. Yet even to lowest order in ϵ, the distribution is not symmetric in $(\kappa/\kappa_0 - 1)$. Indeed, the Schmidt result indicates that $N(\kappa_0) = \frac{4}{9}$ instead of $\frac{1}{2}$, so that more of the states are above $\kappa/\kappa_0 = 1$ than below.

The reason for the inaccuracy of the pair model near $\kappa/\kappa_0 = 1$ is that the density in this region is produced by pairs that are very far apart, and under these circumstances more distant atoms cannot be neglected. If one considers a triple of atoms, one can readily show that two-thirds of the states will have $\kappa/\kappa_0 < 1$ and one-third will have $\kappa/\kappa_0 > 1$, so that the corrections produced by a next nearest neighbor will push states upward, the direction indicated by the Schmidt result.

At high densities we see from Table 3 and Fig. 3 that the optical model fits the numerical data quite accurately except below the band edge. States appear in that region because of density fluctuations that are neg-

Table 2

INTEGRATED DENSITY OF STATES AT NEGATIVE ENERGIES, $\epsilon = 0.01$

$\kappa/\kappa_0 - 1$	Machine Results (%)	Pair Theory (%)	Schmidt's Formula (%)
-0.999	98.6	99.0	99.0
-10^{-4}	91.4	91.6	91.8
-10^{-5}	89.3	89.7	89.9
-10^{-6}	87.5	87.9	88.0
-10^{-11}	79.7	80.0	81.4
-10^{-20}	70.5	70.0	71.9
-10^{-35}	64.1	60.0	61.3
-10^{-40}	63.3	58.2	59.5
2×10^{-49}	30.6	44.6	36.6
10^{-35}	30.3	40.0	33.7
10^{-20}	26.6	30.0	25.9
10^{-11}	19.1	20.0	17.7
10^{-6}	12.2	12.1	11.4
10^{-5}	10.4	10.3	9.9
10^{-4}	8.3	8.4	8.1
1	0.0	0.0	0.0

Table 3

INTEGRATED DENSITY OF STATES AT NEGATIVE ENERGIES, $\epsilon = 10$

κ/κ_0	Machine Results (%)	Optical Model (%)	Local Density Model (%)
0.0 [a]	14.2	14.2	
0.00001	14.1	14.1	14.1
1.0	13.8	13.8	13.8
2.0	12.4	12.6	12.4
2.83	10.9	10.9	10.5
3.50	9.6	8.8	8.1
4.16	6.7	5.2	4.9
4.272 [a]	6.3	—	—
4.47	4.85	0.0	3.4
4.472 [a]	5.4	0.0	—
4.672 [a]	4.4	0.0	—
4.97	3.2	0.0	1.3
5.00 [a]	3.15	0.0	
5.50	1.5	0.0	0.3
6.00	0.7	0.0	0.0
20.00 [a]	0.0346	0.0	—

[a] Obtained from equations (20) and (21).

lected in the optical model. If one considers a periodic lattice with fluctuations in the lattice constant so chosen as to give the variable

$$F = \sum_{i \neq j} \exp\left[-\kappa |x_i - x_j|\right] \tag{55}$$

the same fluctuations as it takes for a random distribution, one generates a density of states shown in Figs. 3 and 4 and Tables 3 and 4 as the local

Table 4

INTEGRATED DENSITY OF STATES AT NEGATIVE ENERGIES, $\epsilon = 1.0$

κ/κ_0	Machine Results (%)	Optical Model (%)	Local Density Model (1) (%)	Local Density Model (2) (%)
0.001	45.6	45.0	45.0	45.0
0.02 [a]	45.1	—	—	—
0.8 [a]	39.3	—	—	—
0.8	39.8	37.0	37.0	37.0
0.98 [a]	35.2	—	—	—
1.00 [a]	34.5	—	—	—
1.00	34.3	31.8	31.7	33.5
1.002 [a]	33.49	—	—	—
1.02 [a]	33.5	—	—	—
1.18 [a]	29.8	—	—	—
1.18	30.2	24.8	27.4	28.0
1.37 [a]	25.8	—	—	—
1.37	26.8	11.0	21.9	22.3
1.53	22.3	0.0	17.1	16.6
1.69	18.3	0.0	12.7	11.1
1.84	14.0	0.0	9.1	7.0
2.00	10.3	0.0	5.8	4.4
2.20	6.4	0.0	3.1	1.8
2.50 [a]	4.3	—	—	—
2.50	2.5	0.0	1.1	0.6
5.00 [a]	2.7	—	—	—

[a] Obtained from equations (20) and (21).

density (L.D.) model. The local density can be seen to fit the tail below the band edge qualitatively, although the total density in the tail is underestimated. The total density below the band edge N_0 is plotted against ϵ in Fig. 6 and is seen to vary as $\epsilon^{-2/3}$. This differs slightly from

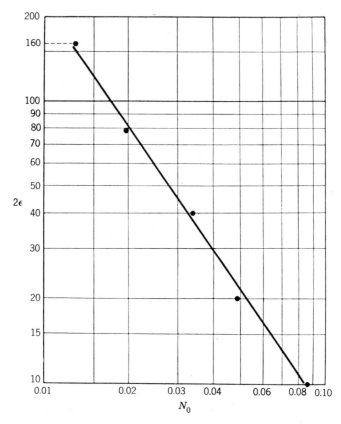

Fig. 6. Density variation of N_0, the fraction of states below the optical band edge.

an $\epsilon^{-5/8}$ dependence predicted by the local density model. An approximate treatment of the difference-differential equation (Frisch and Lloyd, 1958) in the region of high density yields

$$N(\kappa) = [2 \cdot 3^{1/6} \cdot \pi^{1/2} \epsilon^{2/3} \int_0^\infty \exp\left[-t^6 - \mu t^2\right] dt]^{-1} \tag{56}$$

when

$$\mu = (3/\epsilon^2)^{1/3}[2\epsilon - (\kappa^2/\kappa_0^2)]$$

At the band edge $\mu = 0$, so that

$$N_0 = [2 \cdot 3^{1/6} \pi^{1/2} \Gamma(\tfrac{7}{6}) \epsilon^{2/3}]^{-1} = 0.2532 \epsilon^{-2/3} \tag{57}$$

in remarkable agreement with Fig. 6. A comparison of equation (56) with the numerical results for $\epsilon = 10$ is shown in Fig. 7.

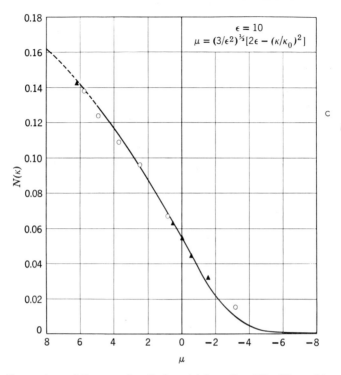

Fig. 7. Comparison of the second optical model (equation 56) with machine results for $\epsilon = 10$.

REFERENCES

Blatt, J. M., and Weisskopf, V. F., *Theoretical Nuclear Physics*, Wiley, New York, 1952.

Frisch, H. L., and Lloyd, S. P., *Bull. Am. Phys. Soc.* **Ser. II, 3,** 31 (1958); and further results to be published shortly.

Hertz, P., *Math. Ann.* **67,** 387 (1909).

James, H. M., and Ginzbarg, A. S., *J. Phys. Chem.* **57,** 840 (1953).

Khuri, N. N., *Phys. Rev.* **107,** 1148 (1957).

Landauer, R., and Helland, J. C., *J. Chem. Phys.* **22,** 1655 (1954).

Lax, M., *Revs. Mod. Phys.* **23,** 287 (1951).

Lax, M., *Phys. Rev.* **85,** 621 (1952).

Lax, M., and Phillips, J. C., *Phys. Rev.* **110,** 41 (1958).

Rice, S. O., *Bell System Tech. J.* **23** (1944) and **24** (1945), reprinted in N. Wax, *Noise and Stochastic Processes*, Dover, New York, 1954, pp. 189 ff.

Schmidt, H., *Phys. Rev.* **105,** 425 (1957).

DISCUSSION

P. DEBYE

I am wondering whether you really are doing everything you should be taking your scatterers as distributed completely at random. There might be a correlation, which should be considered.

H. L. FRISCH

For the purposes of the one-dimensional model the assumption of a Poisson distribution of scatterers probably suffices. The problem of introducing a significant correlation between the scatterers for our one-dimensional model, as well as a distribution in the value of κ_0, has been considered by Dr. S. P. Lloyd. I believe that in the range where the optical model begins to apply (i.e., high density of scatterers) the effect of such correlations is small; this certainly need not be the case at low densities, where significant changes could be produced in the energy spectrum.

I have thought about this problem in three dimensions in the pair approximation. The random Hertz distribution of nearest neighbors must, among other things, be replaced by suitable generalization, which at least in the case of "hard sphere correlations" I know.

P. DEBYE

There is a useful analogy. If the physicist talks about polymers and talks about the average square distance from beginning to end, and he takes the formal mathematical formula of random walk, then he can step on one point just as many times as he likes. In the actual case, it is impossible to occupy a place which is already occupied. There is the same problem here because these impurities are allowed to fall on top of each other in this calculation.

Now, one other point. You make distinctions between two kinds of disturbance. You say, "I have a fine lattice and I make holes in it, you see, or I distort a lattice." Now, as soon as you allow thermal motion, then the two are not so distinct.

H. L. FRISCH

In connection with your last point, Prof. M. Kac was a summer visitor at the Bell Telephone Laboratories last year. During that time he was interested in a one-dimensional impurity band problem where two kinds of scatterers were randomly distributed on a strict linear lattice. Incidentally and more in connection with your first point, the principal ergodic theory underlying the one-dimensional model has been worked out.

J. A. KRUMHANSL

Would it be reasonable to say that there are really two quite different directions in which the effects of randomness lead—one having to do with metals, and the other with non-metals. The tail in the distribution of energy levels is particularly important in the case of non-metals, for example.

H. L. FRISCH

Yes. The positive energy behavior is quite important when we are dealing with "liquid metals."

J. A. PRINS

I should like to ask a related question. When you have that irregular arrangement of scatterers, then you may suppose that a scatterer not only scatters the wave but also absorbs it. This may be handled by taking a complex constant potential in the well, or some other complex expression. Of course, you can treat this case as you have done here; it is a little bit more complicated, but you are able to treat it. If you are able to do that, you may perhaps answer this question: If I have such an arrangement and I inject an electron in some point, what happens to the electron? How far does it go? What is its wave function in that small region it can reach? This would be a perfect answer to Mr. Van Nordstrand, who wants to know the fine structure of the x-ray absorption edge. Couldn't you apply your calculations to this problem?

H. L. FRISCH

Possibly. A machine calculation in one dimension can certainly be attempted on a more realistic model.

S. H. BAUER

The one-dimensional model is well worth considering as a problem of inherent chemical interest. A conjugated polyene, $\left(\begin{smallmatrix} H & H \\ -C = C- \end{smallmatrix}\right)_n$, is a one-dimensional metal, in the same sense as a single layer of graphite is a two-dimensional metal. Could your computational method be extended, so that one might predict the change in the positions of ultraviolet absorption bands in such polyenes as a function of random replacement of H atoms by more electronegative atoms or groups?

H. L. FRISCH

Right.

7

by

Robert A. Van Nordstrand

Sinclair Research Laboratories, Inc.

X-ray Absorption Edge Spectroscopy of Compounds of Chromium, Manganese, and Cobalt in Crystalline and Non-crystalline Systems

X-ray absorption spectra showing fine structure associated with the K absorption edge of an element are well understood only in two widely separated energy ranges, the Kossel structure within 2 or 3 volts of the edge, and the Kronig structure in the range 100–500 volts above the edge. Kossel structure appears to be due to transitions of the K electron to bound atomic states belonging to the atom of origin. Kronig structure appears due to transitions of the electron into the continuum of the energy level diagram of a crystal, in which range there is a non-uniform density of states resulting from interactions of the electron wave with the periodic crystal lattice. Between these two charted spectral ranges lies an important intermediate energy range.

Although a number of spectra in these intermediate energies have been reported, the range has not been clearly defined and the fine structure patterns have not been clearly explained.

This intermediate energy range, roughly 3–100 volts above the K edge, is the subject of the study described in this chapter. Spectra are compared for a wide variety of compounds of chromium, manganese, and cobalt in different physical states. In this range, and for compounds of these elements, the fine structure appears related solely to factors in the immediate neighborhood of the atom excited.* These factors include locations and types of the neighbor atoms. This region of influence extends 4–5 Å from the center of the atom being excited.

Ultimately this form of x-ray spectroscopy may provide, for noncrystalline solids, liquids, and adsorbed phases, some of the details regarding atomic arrangement previously available only for crystalline solids and for gases.

Experimental Methods

The data were all obtained using a geiger counter diffractometer (Philips) with a quartz crystal ($d = 3.343$ Å) as a monochromator. The line focus on a copper target x-ray tube was used with $\frac{1}{12}$ degree divergence slits and a 0.003-inch receiving slit. Distances from target to crystal and crystal to receiving slit were both 17 cm. The x-ray tube was operated at 25 ma; at 11 kv for chromium and manganese, at 15 kv for cobalt.

The sample was supported between the crystal and the receiving slit. Special effort was taken to prepare sample mountings of optimum and uniform thickness. Intensity readings were obtained as times required for 10,000 counts. The readings were taken at 0.01 degree intervals, corresponding roughly to 2 ev steps. A standard set of incident intensity readings was determined for each element and used throughout the study of that element. No peaks or edges were observed in the incident intensity curves within the spectral ranges required for the three elements.

Absorption edge patterns shown here are all normalized so as to have a value zero below the edge and a value unity about 200 volts above the edge. This normalization puts all patterns on a comparable amplitude scale. The normalized absorption coefficients describe absorption only by the K shell of the atoms.

---

* A similar subdivision of these spectra was prepared previously (Kiestra, 1950), but somewhat different energy ranges were recognized. According to Kiestra, K edge spectra for these first transition series elements include fine structure extending up to 40 ev which is related to the atom in question; fine structure in the range 40 to 150 ev related to the first one or two coordination spheres; and fine structure above 150 ev related to the whole crystal lattice.

The absorption coefficients are plotted as a function of the energy of the photon minus the energy of the first part of the K edge for the corresponding metal. These metal K edge values (Cauchois and Hulubei, 1947) are 5988 ev for chromium, 6537 for manganese, and 7709 for cobalt. This excess energy of the incoming photon is considered equal to the energy of the resultant electron. The curves may thus be considered, alternatively, as absorption coefficients plotted as a function of the energy of the ejected electron.

Results

The spectra have been grouped in thirteen figures. Figures 1 through 7 cover manganese compounds. Five contrasting spectra are presented in Fig. 1, primarily to show the wide range of fine structure obtained from various forms of this element. More closely related spectra are grouped in the following six figures. Figures 8 and 9 contain cobalt compounds, Fig. 8 showing contrast and Fig. 9 comparing spectra of divalent cobalt. Figure 10 presents miscellaneous chromium spectra. Figures 11, 12, and 13 show cross comparisons among the three elements. Cubic oxides of cobalt and manganese are compared in Fig. 11, tetrahedral ions such as the chromate in Fig. 12, and hexacyanides and related complexes in Fig. 13.

Four types of curves occur so frequently throughout this study that an arbitrary numerical classification is convenient. These are illustrated by reference to specific spectra. Because they resemble curves describing a vibrating system with varying degrees of damping, terms such as *amplitude, cycle, period*, and *damping* have been found useful in describing the curves.

The type I spectrum consists of a curve which, as the energy becomes positive, rises in a simple manner from zero to give a single major peak well above 1, drops to a single minimum somewhat below 1, rises to a second weak maximum, and drops then to a stable value of unity; one and a half cycles of fluctuation are seen. Spectra of type I (and II) are conveniently coded by adding after the Roman numeral the values in volts at which the successive extrema occur. An illustration of type I is shown in Fig. 13, the spectrum of $K_3[Co(NO_2)_6]$; it may be coded as I-27-46-74.

The type II spectrum is similar to that of type I but shows an additional cycle, having three well-resolved maxima and two minima, or two and a half cycles. The hexacyanide spectra in Fig. 13 are of type II.

The type III spectrum rises from zero to the value unity and remains

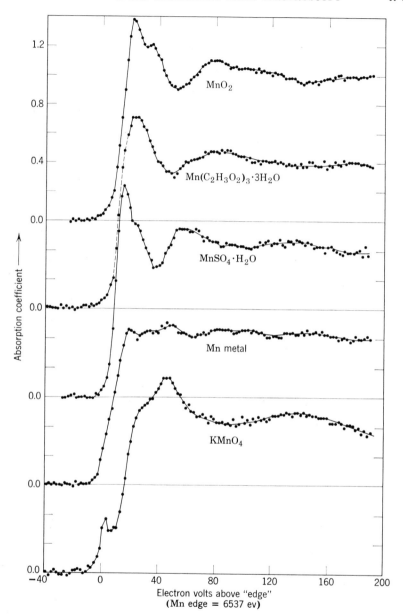

Fig. 1. Five distinctive x-ray K absorption edge spectra of manganese in various chemical combinations.

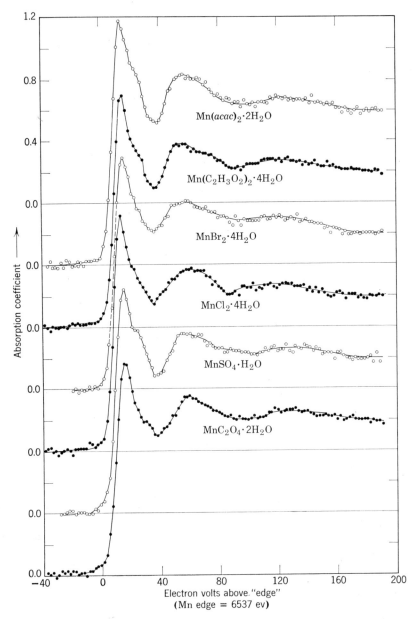

Fig. 2. Absorption spectra of six crystalline manganese salts. Spectra are type I (I-15-38-60).

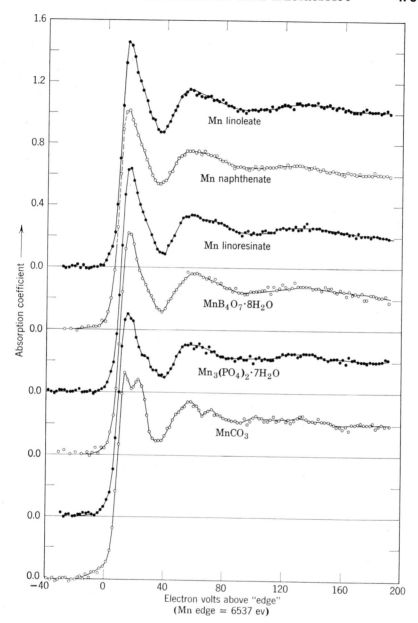

Fig. 3. Spectra of three non-crystalline compounds and two crystalline salts of divalent Mn, all type I (I-15-38-60). $MnCO_3$ sample contained MnO_2, which caused second maximum.

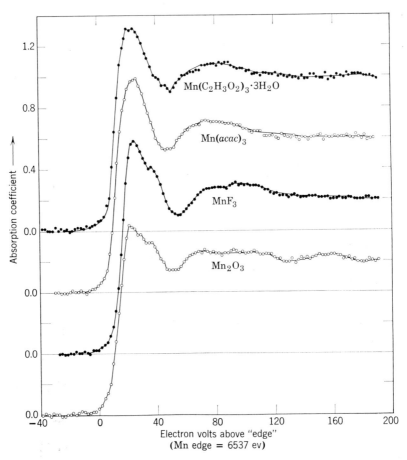

Fig. 4. Absorption edge spectra of manganic compounds, all of type I. Top two are I-25-45-80, MnF₃ is I-25-55-X, and Mn₂O₃ is I-21-50-X.

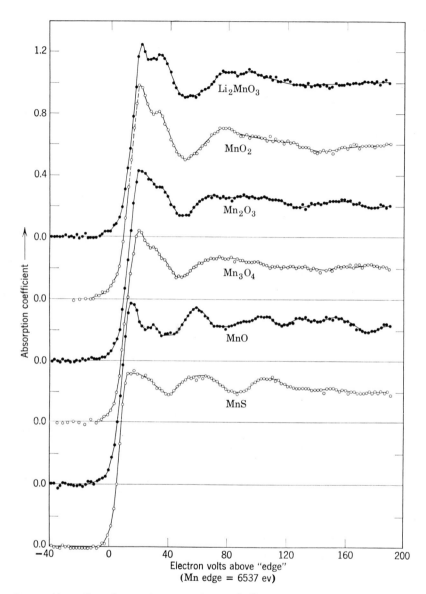

Fig. 5. Absorption edge spectra comparing two halite structure compounds, MnO and MnS; oxides of increasing oxygen content; and MnO_2 with Li_2MnO_3.

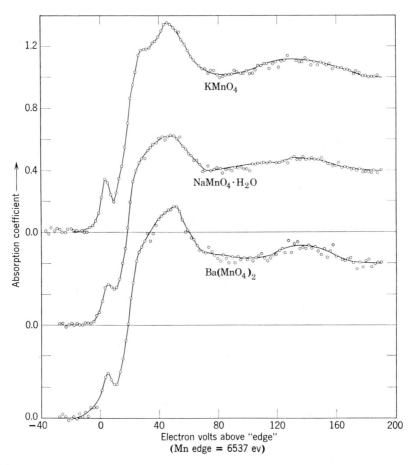

Fig. 6. Absorption edge spectra of crystalline permanganates; type IV, characteristic of the tetrahedral complexes.

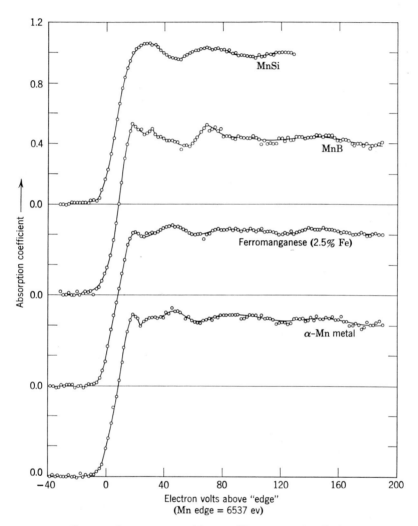

Fig. 7. Spectra of manganese and its metallic compounds, all of type III.

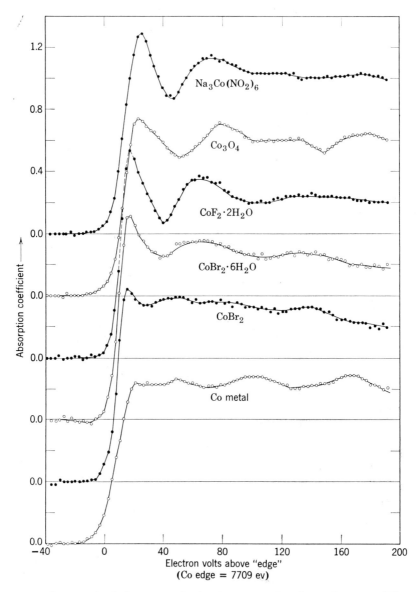

Fig. 8. Spectra of cobalt compounds showing progressive change from type III to type I; also two compounds of higher valence.

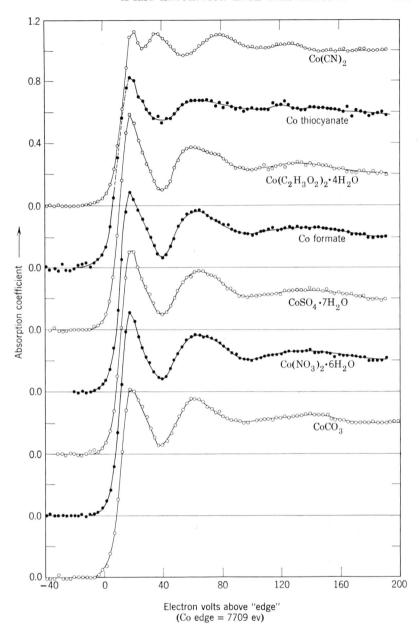

Fig. 9. Spectra of cobaltous compounds; five are of type I (I-20-40-65).

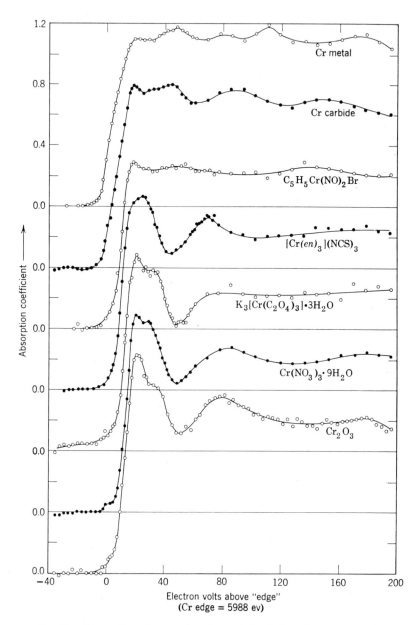

Fig. 10. Absorption edge spectra of a variety of chromium compounds.

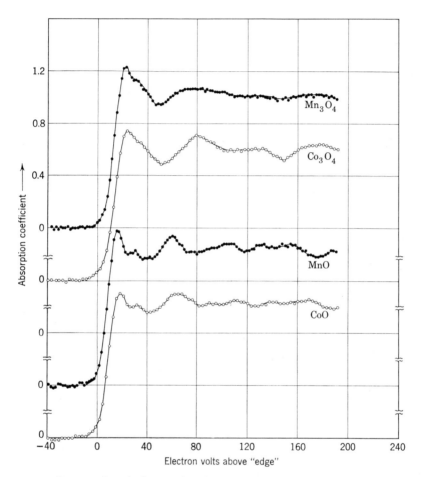

Fig. 11. Spectra of equivalent oxides of cobalt and manganese. MnO, CoO, and Co_3O_4 are cubic, Mn_3O_4 is tetragonal.

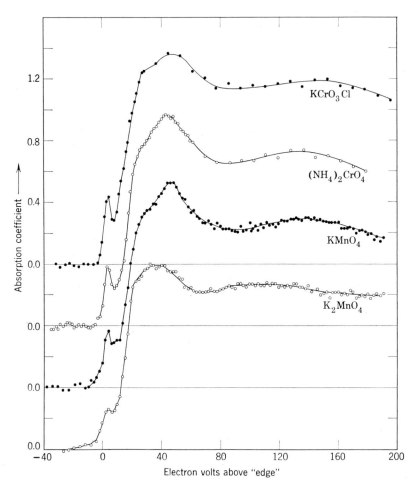

Fig. 12. Spectra of tetrahedral groups, all type IV; manganate, permanganate, chromate, and chlorochromate.

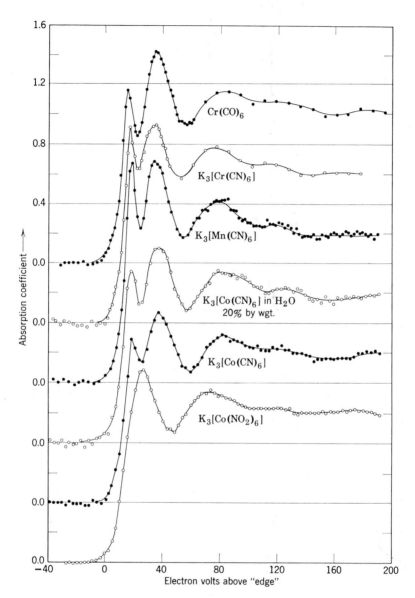

Fig. 13. Spectra of three crystalline and one aqueous hexacyanides and a hexacarbonyl, all type II. $K_3Co(NO_2)_6$, type I, shown for comparison.

at that value with further fluctuations of only minor amplitude. The spectrum for manganese metal in Fig. 1 is a good illustration. Whereas type II and type I curves represent two successive stages in the approach to critical damping, the type III curve is the stage referred to as critically damped.

The type IV spectrum has a sharp absorption peak at rather low energies, 4 or 5 ev. The main rise to unity occurs at an appreciably higher energy. At higher energies this curve is complex, as seen in the example of type IV, the $KMnO_4$ spectrum in Fig. 1.

The following correlations have been found to date between these types of fine structure and the arrangement of atoms in the immediate vicinity of the atom being excited. When spectra of types I, II, and IV are obtained, atoms from the group C, N, O, F constitute the first coordination sphere. Type IV spectra are associated with a tightly bonded tetrahedral configuration of oxygen atoms; type I, with octahedral configurations; and type II, with a specific type of octahedral coordination in which double atom groups, CN or CO, form linear arrays along each of the three axes in the manner: N-C-Cr-C-N. Certain compounds with octahedral coordination show instead of the expected type II, a damped, atypical spectrum. These compounds are usually either metallic or have a form of bonding which may provide considerable electronic mobility about the atom being excited. Type I spectra show systematic differences related to ion charge or valence. These differences may be caused by changes in ionic radii which accompany changes in charge. The spectra do not appear to be sensitive to the nature of the atom being excited so long as the configuration remains unchanged within the region of influence, i.e., out to 4 or 5 Å from the atom.

Type IV Spectra

The permanganate ion has been studied in a variety of forms. In Fig. 6 are shown the spectra of three crystalline salts, Ba, Na, and K. The spectra are almost identical, yet the compounds have different crystal structures. Also giving the same spectra but not included in the figures are the crystalline $Ca(MnO_4)_2$, an aqueous solution of $NaMnO_4$, and a silica gel on which $NaMnO_4$ was adsorbed. Although the type IV spectra appear to be defined wholly by the permanganate tetrahedron, the first coordination sphere outside the permanganate tetrahedron has not been varied sufficiently to eliminate it as a factor.

In contrast to the case of permanganate adsorbed on silica gel, an analogous experiment on activated carbon gave a curve showing no trace of the type IV spectrum of permanganate. Instead it gave the spectrum of MnO_2, as would be predicted from the known ability of activated carbon to reduce permanganate to MnO_2. The application of this branch of spectroscopy to problems concerning the adsorbed state constitutes one of its most promising uses.

A second group of type IV spectra is shown in Fig. 12, which includes the permanganate, manganate, chromate, and chlorochromate ions. The chromate and the permanganate spectra are identical, probably because of identical size and shape of the two ions. The spectrum shifts when the permanganate is reduced one step to the manganate ion. The shift is explained on the basis of an expected expansion of the tetrahedral ion upon gaining the additional electron. The chromate spectrum does not change much upon substitution of one chlorine for one oxygen.

Type I Spectra

The three elements studied here usually exhibit octahedral coordination in the common salts, hydrates, complexes, and oxides. The type I spectrum is associated with this coordination.

Figure 2 shows spectra of hydrated crystalline salts of divalent manganese. The curves are essentially the same, I-15-38-60. A weak, poorly resolved peak is shown on the high energy side of the main peak in some of these spectra, specifically for those compounds in which the oxygen coordination is not supplied exclusively by water. Figure 3 shows additional curves of divalent manganese salts. The upper four spectra are identical and do not show this extra peak. The spectrum (not shown) of an aqueous solution of manganous nitrate is identical with the top four curves of Fig. 3. The linoleate, naphthenate, and linoresinate, whose spectra are shown in this figure, are in a non-crystalline, resinous condition.

A spectrum not typical of manganous salts is shown in Fig. 3, labeled manganous carbonate. The atypical strong second peak is also shown in a published (Hanson and Beeman, 1949) spectrum of this carbonate. The sample used here was found to contain considerable MnO_2, which accounts for the second peak in the curve. Spectra obtained with purer manganous carbonates show only the single major peak characteristic of the manganous salts, including the weak unresolved satellite.

The shift of the entire type I spectrum to higher energies with increase in valence or ionic charge on the manganese is shown in the top three spectra in Fig. 1. Trivalent manganese in various compounds is shown in Fig. 4.

Cobalt salts (see Figs. 8 and 9) show the same type I spectra and the same sensitivity to valence or ionic radii as manganese.

In spectra of the cobalt salts the weak unresolved peak noted in spectra of partially hydrated manganese salts does not appear. On the other hand, spectra of the chromic salts show even stronger peaks developing on the high energy side of the main peak.

Type II Spectra

Spectra of the hexacyanides and a hexacarbonyl, shown in Fig. 13, are of type II. The spectrum of a similar complex, $Co(NO_2)_6^{3-}$, also in Fig. 13, is of type I. These and other comparisons indicate that the key feature of compounds giving type II spectra is an octahedral coordination shell comprised of the linear ligands CN or CO.

The persistent association of type II spectra with this configuration of ligand atoms is seen throughout the following sequence of hypothetical conversions, in which almost identical spectra are obtained from each preparation.

(a) Make a solution of potassium cobalticyanide in water.

(b) Crystallize to form the anhydrous $K_3[Co(CN)_6]$.

(c) Transform Co to Mn to form $K_3[Mn(CN)_6]$, which has a crystal structure different from its predecessor.

(d) Transform Mn to Cr to form $K_3[Cr(CN)_6]$, which has the same crystal structure as its predecessor.

(e) Transform nitrogen to oxygen and eliminate the potassium to form $Cr(CO)_6$, which has a crystal structure different from any of its predecessors.

Thus these spectra depend neither on the identity nor on the electronic state of the central atom, nor on the crystal structure, but only on the coordination shell.

The type II spectra provide a means of establishing the upper limit of the intermediate energy range. The complex spectra of both crystalline and dissolved potassium cobalticyanide are identical out to 100 ev; beyond this, both crystal and solution spectra are fully damped. Thus, as these spectra do not depend on crystallinity, there is no Kronig structure, and the entire type II fine structure, extending out to 100 ev, is within the intermediate energy range. Similar considerations based upon type I and type IV spectra give the same upper limit.

The lower limit to the range may be deduced from the type IV spectra. In these curves peaks occur at energies as low as 3 ev. They appear to be fixed not by the crystal structure nor by the electronic state of the central atom, but they change and disappear in step with the rest of the type IV spectral features when changes occur in the coordination shell.

The apparent limits to this spectral range are, therefore, roughly 3–100 ev. Although Kronig structure features may occur in this energy range, they would be obscured by spectra of type I, II, or IV. These energy limits do not show a trend with atomic number of the excited atom within the narrow range studied, 24 through 27.

Type III Spectra and Damping

The spectra of metals and metallic phases, after the single rise from zero to unity, have very weak fluctuations. The rise contains details which have been described in the literature (Beeman and Friedman, 1939) but which cannot be shown on the scale used here.

Spectra of the metals manganese, cobalt, and chromium are shown in Figs. 7, 8, and 10, respectively. Fluctuations appear to be confined to ±5%. Figure 7 compares spectra of various metallic phases containing manganese. The ferromanganese, containing only about 2.5% iron, has a spectrum indistinguishable from that of metallic manganese. The metallic compounds MnB and MnSi have type III spectra, clearly distinguishable, however, from that of the pure metal.

The crystalline elements cobalt, manganese, and chromium give type III spectra, whereas crystalline argon and krypton give spectra (Shaw, 1956) resembling type I. Therefore the type III spectrum can be attributed neither to the elemental state, nor to the absence of ions, nor to the relatively large interatomic distances found in metals; but, perhaps, to the presence of relatively free electrons within the region of influence around the atom being excited.

The open sandwich compound, cyclopentadienyl chromium dinitroso bromide, $C_5H_5Cr(NO)_2Br$ (see Fig. 10), has a type III spectrum. This compound has such a multitude of geometric parameters that superposition of all effects may wipe out detail from the spectrum. However, the mobility of the electrons in this sandwich molecule may cause the type III spectrum, by analogy with the metal.

The spectra of MnS and $CoBr_2$ are almost as devoid of structure as that of the metal; possibly there is some relation to the polarizability of the sulfide and bromide ions.

The transition, referred to as damping, from a spectrum of type I to one of type III may be seen in various stages in the oxides shown in Fig. 5. The MnO_2 spectrum is of type I. As oxygen is removed, the average separation of the manganese atoms is reduced. The sequence of MnO_2, Mn_2O_3, Mn_3O_4, MnO, and manganese metal give spectra with successively increased damping. A similar damping sequence is shown in spectra of Co_3O_4, CoO, and cobalt metal. In both cases the damping is attributed to the increased proximity of metal atoms and the related increased freedom for exchange in the electronic system.

A third damping sequence is shown in Fig. 8, starting with the strong type I spectrum of $CoF_2 \cdot 2H_2O$, proceeding through $Co \cdot 6H_2O \cdot Br_2$, $CoBr_2$, and cobalt metal.

Period Changes

The spectra shown here, and published spectra covering the 0–30 ev range with higher resolution (Hanson and Beeman, 1949; Böke, 1957), indicate that very sharp peaks occur only at the lowest energies, with increasingly broad peaks at higher energies. This trend is apparent within a type II spectrum (Fig. 13) where successive maxima are increasingly far apart; it is also shown in comparisons between spectra as in Fig. 1. If a type II spectrum is plotted as a function of the wavelength of the ejected electron, rather than of its energy, the period becomes constant, as seen in Fig. 14. With increased valence, the major maximum in type I spectra not only shifts to higher energies but also broadens. Again, taking as the independent variable the wavelength instead of the energy of the ejected electron eliminates the broadening. The meaning of this will be discussed.

Kronig Structure

Many of the spectra shown here exhibit fine structure which appears within the scope of Kronig's treatment of crystalline substances. The spectrum of metallic cobalt (Fig. 8) is a clear example.

This Kronig-type fine structure is distinguished from types I, II, and IV by:

1. Extension, often, to several hundred electron volts above the principal edge.

2. Amplitude of fluctuations low, less than 5%.

3. Restriction to crystal systems of high symmetry having few atoms in the primitive unit cell.

Of the metals, the face-centered cubic cobalt and the body-centered cubic chromium give distinct Kronig structure. The more complex crystal structure of the α-manganese is probably responsible for the absence of distinct Kronig structure in the manganese spectrum. Similarly, patterns of the cubic oxides (Fig. 11), CoO, MnO, and Co_3O_4, show Kronig structure in the 100–200 ev range, whereas that of the tetragonal Mn_3O_4 does not. The spectra of MnS and $MnSi$ show what

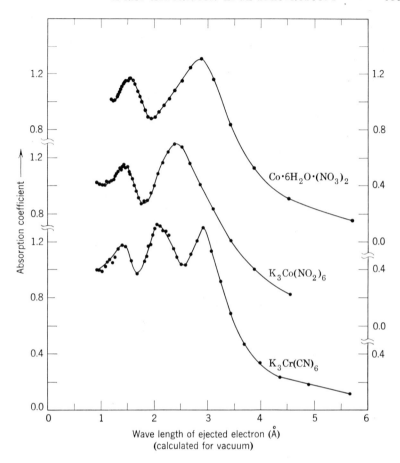

Fig. 14. Spectra of three compounds shown as a function of wavelength of the ejected electron. Preceding figures all represent spectra as a function of energy of ejected electron.

appears to be Kronig structure extending throughout the 0–200 ev energy range examined.

General Remarks

Electrons ejected from the K shell with an energy in the range 3–100 ev must be considered as traveling through the medium surrounding the excited atom, not in any bound state associated with the excited atom and its immediate neighbor atoms. However, the fine structure is not determined by the surrounding medium; hence it is not explained, as is the Kronig structure, by considering density of energy states in the medium. Thus it appears necessary to rely solely on transition probability considerations.

Electrons ejected from the K shell with 3–100 ev energy have wavelengths of 7–1.2 Å, respectively, calculated from the formula $\lambda = (150/\text{ev})^{1/2}$, which gives the wavelength λ of the electron in vacuum. These wavelengths correspond to distances from the atom being excited to the first and second nearest neighbors. These are just the atom neighbors which have been shown here to determine the absorption edge fine structure.

In view of the preceding two paragraphs, the assumption is made that the transition probability is affected primarily by factors which the electron encounters within a distance out from the K shell corresponding to 1 wavelength.

The absorption data, when plotted as a function of wavelength of the ejected electron, may be expected to have maxima at wavelengths corresponding roughly to a distance from the excited atom at which electrical potentials are correct (positive) for the enhancement of the transition leading to the ejection of this electron. Minima occur at wavelengths corresponding to radii at which electrical potentials discourage the transition.

The K electron may thus serve as a probe to describe conditions at varying distances from the atom of its origin. The sensitivity to structure would be expected to disappear for wavelengths shorter than about 1.5 Å (70 ev), as the first cycle of such a wave is completely within the atom of origin. Therefore, for shorter wavelengths (higher energies), the absorption coefficient is sensitive only to density of states, and Kronig structure is the only fine structure possible. For longer wavelengths, i.e., within the first 1 or 2 volts, the Kossel structure due to bound states is a source of fine structure. Also, wavelengths greater than 7 Å may sample such a variety of potentials that the resultant transition probability is averaged out.

Figure 14 presents the absorption coefficients plotted as a function of wavelength of the ejected electron as calculated for vacuum, for the three compounds $K_3Cr(CN)_6$, $K_3Co(NO_2)_6$, and $Co \cdot 6H_2O \cdot (NO_3)_2$. In one method of assigning maxima to the various coordination shells the 1.5 Å maximum in each spectrum is ignored, being attributed to second order effects. The hexacyanide spectrum displays two distinct equivalent maxima at 2.1 and 2.9 Å, corresponding to the two octahedral coordination shells of about 2.3 and 3.4 Å radii. The cobaltinitrite and the hexahydrate spectra show only a single maximum, at 2.4 and 2.9 Å, respectively, corresponding to the single octahedral coordination shell of about 2.1 Å radius for both compounds. In a second method of assigning maxima the 1.5 Å maximum is attributed to the first coordination shell; the longest wavelength maximum is attributed to the first coordination shell external to the $Co \cdot 6H_2O$, the $Co(NO_2)_6$, and the $Cr(CN)_6$ groups. Agreement between distances and wavelengths is poor, possibly resulting from difficulties in determining the proper values of wavelength to use within the crystal or the molecule, difficulties in defining wavelength in a region within a molecule, and difficulties in defining the first cycle of an electron wave emanating from the K shell of an atom. However, since the energies of the ejected electrons involved in these spectra, 3–100 ev, bear no relationship to electron energy levels available in the small group of atoms which define the spectra, and since the wavelengths of these electrons do match the dimensions of this group of atoms, there is some justification for considering the spectra a function of wavelength of the ejected electron.

A treatment closely related to the present model is the theory presented by Kronig (Kronig, 1932; Hartree, Kronig, and Petersen, 1934) to explain the spectra of molecular gases like $GeCl_4$. Kronig treated the problem as an interference between the wave representing the direct ejected electron and that representing the electron scattered by the ligand atoms. He considered that such interference effects determined the transition probabilities, and hence the absorption coefficients.

In the present model the electrical fields provided by the ligand atoms are assumed to affect the transition probability if they fall within the range of 1 wavelength of the ejected electron.

In this model there may be some explanation of the damping of the spectra by free electrons; these electrons possibly shield the excited atom from the field of the ligand, or may randomize this field, or may couple with the ejected electron.

SUMMARY

The fine structure spectra in the range 3–100 ev above the x-ray K absorption edge, in compounds of chromium, manganese, and cobalt, appear related solely to factors within a shell surrounding the atom being excited. This shell extends from a radius about 1.5 Å, out to about 4 or 5 Å, from the center of this atom. These factors include the geometry and nature of the atoms present in this coordination shell and a factor apparently involving presence of free electrons.

Classification of spectra into four types provides some order within this spectral range. All tetrahedral complexes, as permanganate, manganate, chromate, and chlorochromate, are of one type. Most octahedral complexes are of a second type. Octahedral complexes having double linear ligands, such as CO or CN, are of a third type. Metals and some other compounds fall in a fourth type.

The discussion of these spectra as a function not of energy of the ejected electron but of its wavelength may have some utility. A model is described here which is similar to the theory of Kronig for fine structure in molecular gases in that it relates geometric parameters of the molecule and wavelength of the ejected electron to the fine structure.

The empirical correlations developed here from crystalline systems of known structure are shown to be applicable to non-crystalline solids, adsorbed phases, and liquid solutions.

ACKNOWLEDGMENTS

I am indebted to many persons for assistance: to Professor S. H. Bauer and the late Mr. J. W. Teter at the inception of the study; to Mr. R. D. Duncan and Drs. G. R. Mitchell, R. R. Chambers, and J. A. Perry at critical stages in the study; to Professor F. Basolo for his interest and his compounds; and to the several experienced workers in the field of x-ray spectroscopy who have given advice.

REFERENCES

Beeman, W. W., and Friedman, H., *Phys. Rev.* **56,** 392 (1939).

Böke, K., *Z. physik. Chem.* **10,** 45, 59 (1957).

Cauchois, Y., and Hulubei, H., *Tables de constantes et données,* Numérique I, Hermann et Cie., Paris, 1947.

Hanson, H. P., and Beeman, W. W., *Phys. Rev.* **76,** 118 (1949).

Hartree, D. R., Kronig, R. de L., and Petersen, H., *Physica* **1,** 895 (1934).

Kiestra, S., in "Conference on the Application of X-ray Spectroscopy to Solid State Problems," Madison, Wis., Oct 23–25, 1950; Report NAVEXOS P. 1033, p. 36.

Kronig, R. de L., *Z. Physik* **75,** 468 (1932).

Shaw, C. H., in *Theory of Alloy Phases,* American Society for Testing Materials, Philadelphia, 1956, pp. 13–62.

DISCUSSION

S. H. BAUER

The method proposed by Van Nordstrand, which is at this point empirical but eventually may be based on a sufficiently developed theory, provides a measure of the coordination around a given element in an amorphous system as well as in a crystalline system. It is probably true that when the resolution is increased one finds much more detail in the structure of the absorption edges, all of which cannot be explained. Perhaps the virtue of this experiment is its somewhat limited resolution, so that one can interpret the dominant features of the pattern and not be worried about the finer details.

R. A. VAN NORDSTRAND

Yes, I think there is justification in working with this level of resolution. When one works with the best resolution which can be attained at present, there is a tendency to study only the first 30 ev above the principal edge, and it is probable that only in the first 10 ev is there fine structure requiring this resolution. However, to use the correlations developed here, spectra should extend to 100 or 200 ev above the edge, a fantastic feat if points are recorded at 0.1 volt intervals with a spectrometer of 0.1 volt resolving power.

ROMAN SMOLUCHOWSKI

Has any x-ray work been done on the shape of emission lines for non-crystalline solids?

LYMAN G. PARRATT   (contributed after the meeting)

Precision work on x-ray emission line shapes from non-crystalline materials has not been done; precision data have been obtained from target materials presumed to be in the crystalline state, but their true state had never been determined. Many materials when bombarded by electrons become amorphous in the immediate region of bombardment which is, of course, the emitting region, even though the bulk is crystalline. Also, many evaporated materials which have been used for tube targets were shown by electron diffraction to be amorphous, when their melting points are not very much higher than room temperature.

The shapes of x-ray lines from supposedly crystalline metals in the transition group are known to depend upon their chemical and physical states, but precision work on x-ray line shapes of elements other than the transition group metals has not been extensively pursued. It is believed by some of the workers in this field that the shape of an x-ray line is determined by the electronic configuration of the valence electrons. This is the case when the valence electrons have s-type symmetry, and this is why the sensitivity to physical and chemical states for the transition elements is so marked. It is my opinion that very little dependence of x-ray line shape on the physical state or on the crystallinity of the target material would be found except in those elements for which valence electrons have a definite type of symmetry. For reference, see L. G. Parratt [*Revs. Mod. Phys.* **31,** 616 (1959)].

ALVIN COHEN

In a soda silica glass matrix, what amount of middle transition elements such as cobalt, nickel, or iron would be needed to detect and study these K edge structures?

R. A. VAN NORDSTRAND

In our first attempt, we were able to obtain spectra with 0.5% of cobalt in aluminum oxide. This is probably the lower limit for the elements you named in a soda-silica glass matrix. We can probably use as little as 0.1% in a water solution.

ALVIN COHEN

This technique might offer the possibility of settling some of the arguments about the coordination number of various transition elements in glasses. About the only technique currently used is electron spin resonance, and this is very difficult to interpret unless analogous crystalline systems are studied concurrently.

O. L. ANDERSON

Have you derived a set of rules, or do you merely empirically group common coordination cases?

R. A. VAN NORDSTRAND

On most of the figures, I have grouped common coordination cases to show the similarities upon which the empirical correlations are based. In Fig. 1, contrasting spectra are shown resulting from widely differing types of coordination.

N. J. KREIDL

Referring to Dr. Cohen's remarks about the possibilities of investigating the coordination number in glasses, where they are not too well known, I propose the possibility of using the lack of order in glass reversely to answer some of these questions. In the case of manganese, two species which resemble the divalent and the trivalent states can be obtained in glass in the following completely different ways:

(a) One of them is to melt under reducing or oxidizing conditions, or alternatively to electrolyze the melt.

(b) If one pairs the manganese with some other transition elements (for instance, vanadium), one obtains more of the species resembling divalent manganese.

(c) When one heats glass which appears to possess divalent manganese to a high temperature and quenches it, one gets more of the species which resembles trivalent manganese.

(d) In the fourth experiment, irradiation with sunlight or ultraviolet light on manganese paired with another transition element increases the concentration of the species resembling trivalent manganese.

(e) Finally, if high energy radiation is used, one gets a change from something which looks like divalent manganese to something that looks like trivalent manganese.

In the last two examples, the coordination remains unchanged because the transformations are induced at room temperature, and one would not expect a change in configuration. It would prove very interesting to determine by the use of such samples whether in those cases where two peaks appear the correct interpretation should follow the electronic change or whether the interpretation should be based on the distances between the surrounding atoms. What do you think of the feasibility of such experiments?

ALVIN COHEN

I think there are probably several key structures here which could be analyzed. Suppose one takes an isoelectronic sequence, in which the central atoms apparently have the same coordination number even though it has not been determined, and solves the structure for one; then he might get all of them. For example, use Ti^{4+}, V^{5+}, and Cr^{6+}, which are isoelectronic; by solving one key structure, one might deduce the correct structures for all three.

ROMAN SMOLUCHOWSKI

Weiss (Weiss, R. J., and DeMarco, J. J., International Conference on Current Problems in Crystal Physics, M.I.T., July, 1957) has shown recently that, while the number of $3d$ electrons in metallic nickel is about 9, i.e., just what one would expect, the corresponding number for α-iron is only 2 to 3, the rest being hybridized s-p states. If these results are confirmed, it will appear that one has to be very careful in using atomic electronic shell structures for solid state considerations.

R. A. VAN NORDSTRAND

A few isoelectronic cases are included in the chapter. For example, the permanganate spectrum is identical with the chromate spectrum, but not with the manganate spectrum (Fig. 12). Also, the Cr_2O_3 spectrum matches that of MnO_2, but not that of Mn_2O_3.

On the other hand, the hexacyanides and the hexacarbonyl of Fig. 13, which were suggested and provided by Professor F. Basolo of Northwestern University for the specific purpose of testing the relative significance of configuration, valence, and isoelectronic nature, show that isoelectronicity plays a secondary role. Comparisons of CoO and MnO and of Co_3O_4 and Mn_3O_4 spectra (Fig. 11) suggest a geometric rather than an electronic energy level interpretation.

J. E. GOLDMAN

It is not clear to me in what form your sample is. In what state is manganese, and is it supported?

R. A. VAN NORDSTRAND

The sample is either powder, foil, or liquid solution. Metallic manganese has been studied as an evaporated film, as evaporated whiskers, and as finely ground powder. All were α-manganese; all gave the same spectrum. The spectra shown in Figs. 1 and 7 were obtained using a powder which was ground to pass a 300-mesh sieve, then air-elutriated to collect the lightest 10% fraction. Optimum thickness for manganese metal is about 10 μ. Some catalyst samples studied have been so dilute that optimum sample thickness was 1 or 2 mm.

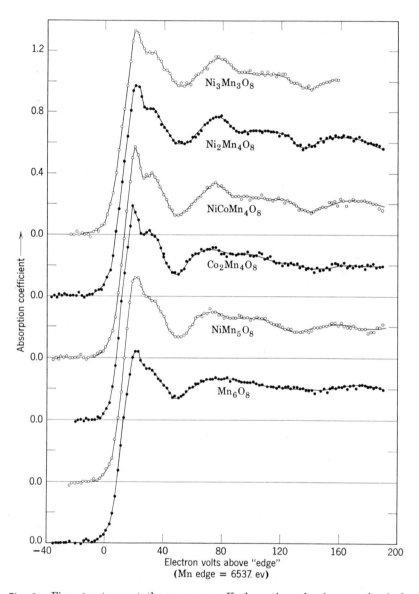

Fig. 1. Fine structures at the manganese K absorption edge in several spinels.

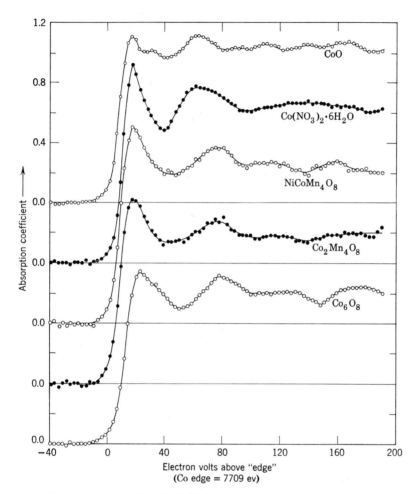

Fig. 2. Fine structures at the cobalt K absorption edge in several spinels and in two divalent reference compounds.

M. L. HUGGINS

It is possible to obtain different spinels in which the same element (e.g., manganese) is in one case in a tetrahedral site and in another case in an octahedral site. One can obtain other spinels in which the same element (for example, iron) is in a given kind of site but is divalent in one case and trivalent in the other. Studies of these would give very direct comparisons for your correlations.

R. A. VAN NORDSTRAND

A study of spinels is being carried out currently. Some of the results, obtained with samples of mixed spinels provided by Dr. L. V. Azároff, are shown here. Figure 1 shows the fine structure at the manganese K edge. Figure 2 shows the fine structure at the cobalt K edge in two of the same spinels, plus some reference spectra. At this time, no detailed discussion of these spectra can be offered except to remark that the manganese appears to be trivalent, the cobalt divalent.

by

W. P. Slichter

Bell Telephone Laboratories, Inc.

Magnetic Resonance
Studies of Glasses

Spectroscopy is one of the key fields of physical measurement, for it allows determinations of the energy levels of molecules, atoms, and nuclei. The classic examples come from studies of the visible and ultra-violet regions of the electromagnetic spectrum, regions which are still under active study. More recently, other portions of the spectrum have attracted attention, both at shorter and at longer wavelengths. In many circumstances, energy levels become altered when the substance is placed in a magnetic field. The fashion in which the levels change commonly involves not only the applied field but also detailed factors such as crystalline force fields, chemical bonding, and molecular motion. The branch of spectroscopy dealing with these effects is given the broad term "magnetic resonance." It is a new field of experiment, involving electronic techniques which were largely developed during and after World War II. One broad category is electron paramagnetic resonance (EPR), which is concerned with the energy levels of molecules, atoms, or ions containing unpaired electrons.

The second broad category is nuclear magnetic resonance (NMR). The measurement of the feeble magnetism in many species of nuclei has been of keen interest in nuclear physics. However, a different aspect of NMR is of interest in this chapter, namely, the use of magnetic nuclei to study local fields in the sample, with the special aim of studying structure and chemical bonding.

There are several features common to the two kinds of magnetic resonance, electronic and nuclear. For convenience, we shall use the word "particle" to mean either an electron or a magnetic nucleus. In addition to the fundamental properties of mass and charge, such particles possess angular momentum (spin). This angular momentum is accompanied by a magnetic moment. That is to say, the particle behaves as if it were a little magnet whose axis coincides with the spin axis.

Consider an imaginary experiment in which a solitary particle is placed in a laboratory magnet of field strength H_0. Then it is a fundamental fact of quantum mechanics that each energy level possessed by the particle in the absence of the applied field now becomes split into $(2I + 1)$ sublevels. Here I is the spin number, and it is a half-integer, 0, $\frac{1}{2}$, 1, $\frac{3}{2}$, 2, $\cdots$.* That is to say, application of a magnetic field causes the energy of the particle to be altered, the new values of the energy being discrete quantities above and below the value for the field-free particle. The energies which the particle may possess in the presence of field H_0 are

$$E = -m\mu H_0/I \tag{1}$$

Here m is the magnetic quantum number, and it has any of the $(2I + 1)$ values in the series $I, I - 1, I - 2, \cdots, -(I - 1), -I$. The parameter μ is the magnetic moment of the particle. Note that the sublevels are equally spaced, and that the interval between them is

$$\Delta E = \mu H_0/I \tag{2}$$

A quantum of energy can excite a transition between energy levels if it has the value ΔE. Or, expressed in terms of radiation frequency, ν, the quantum absorbed or emitted during a transition between energy levels is given by

$$h\nu_0 = \mu H_0/I \tag{3}$$

Note that either ν_0 or H_0 can be the independent variable. Thus, if we choose an explicit field H_0, there is just one frequency ν_0 for which the particle will absorb or radiate electromagnetic energy. Conversely, if the radiation frequency is set, electromagnetic energy is absorbed by the particle only when the field assumes the value H_0. Because only the right value of ν or else of H corresponds to transitions between energy states split by the magnetic field, the experiment is termed *magnetic resonance.*

Both I and μ are characteristic properties of the particle. The ratio μ/I is often written $g\beta$. Here g is the so-called "spectroscopic splitting factor," "Landé factor," or simply "g-factor." It is a basic quantity for each species of particle. The quantity β is the *magneton,* either elec-

---

* Althought the treatment here is intended to point out features common to both NMR and EPR, it should be emphasized that the spin number of the electron is $\frac{1}{2}$, and that it is only among nuclei that other values of the spin number may occur.

tronic or nuclear, and is a constant. In terms of fundamental constants of nature the magneton is given by

$$\beta = eh/4\pi Mc \tag{4}$$

where e is the electronic charge, h is the Planck constant, c is the speed of light, and M is the mass of the electron in the case of the electronic (Bohr) magneton or is the mass of the proton in the case of the nuclear magneton.

Equation (3) for the radiation frequency associated with a transition in the field H_0 may be rewritten

$$h\nu_0 = g\beta H_0 \tag{5}$$

Note that, although the form of the expression is the same for both electronic and nuclear resonances, the values of ν_0 (or H_0) are quite different for the two categories of resonance. With a typical laboratory electromagnet, operating at a field strength of 10,000 gauss, ν_0 for the free electron is 28,025 mc/sec, while for the proton the resonance is 42.577 mc/sec, and for other nuclei it is in the range 1–45 mc/sec.

What we have already said, in our imaginary experiment on a solitary particle, implies that the resonance should consist of a sharp line the width of which would be set by the Heisenberg uncertainty principle (Fig. 1a). In practice, the resonances may consist of a broad envelope (Fig. 1b), or perhaps a fine structure consisting of a series of narrow envelopes (Fig. 1c). We shall consider later some of the factors which lead to these more complicated structures.

Experimental Methods

As we have just seen, magnetic resonance experiments with typical laboratory magnets involve microwave frequencies for EPR and radiofrequencies for NMR. Although the detailed electronic methods are different, it is common to both techniques that the apparatus consists of a magnet, a source of radiation (transmitter), a specimen cell, and a system for detecting the absorption or emission of radiation by the sample (i.e., a receiver).

We have noted that it makes no difference in principle whether we hold the magnetic field constant and scan the resonance by varying the radiofrequency or hold the frequency constant and vary the magnetic field. Each method has been used with great success in NMR. The stability of crystal-controlled transmitters and the development of well-regulated electromagnets have both caused the fixed-frequency method to become

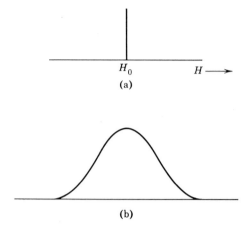

H_0 $H \longrightarrow$

(a)

(b)

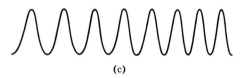

(c)

Fig. 1. (a) Hypothetical NMR spectrum for single paramagnetic particle. (b) Envelope of a multiplicity of resonances. (c) Fine structure in a resonance curve (hyperfine structure of divalent cobalt ion in cobalt bismuth nitrate). (After Bleaney and Stevens, 1953.)

somewhat favored over the fixed-field method. With EPR it is distinctly preferable to operate at fixed microwave frequency.

Nuclear Magnetic Resonance

A typical apparatus for NMR measurements is shown schematically in Fig. 2 (Bloch, Hansen, and Packard, 1946). The transmitter coil, its axis perpendicular to the direction of the applied magnetic field, supplies radiofrequency energy to the sample. The magnetic field is varied slowly and steadily, and when it reaches the resonant value the energy from the transmitter induces transitions to higher states. The return of nuclei to lower states releases energy which is picked up by the receiving coil, situated with its axis perpendicular to the axis of the transmitting coil and also to the direction of the applied field. A great gain in performance is achieved by using a system of modulation. In this

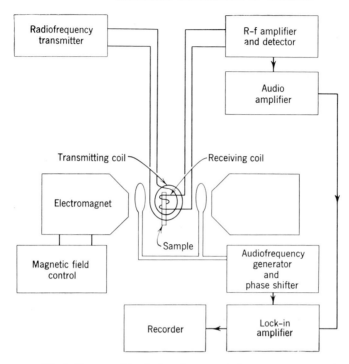

Fig. 2. Block diagram of typical nuclear magnetic resonance apparatus.

method the slowly changing magnetic field is augmented by an alternating field at low audiofrequency and with an amplitude which is small compared with the resonance width (Figs. 1b and 1c). When the magnetic field passes through the resonance region, the signal emitted by the resonating nuclei contains an audio component which is detected and then amplified. The use of narrow band amplification at this audiofrequency, synchronized or "locked in" with the phase of the modulation, greatly enhances the ratio of signal to noise. The output of the amplification is plotted on a recording potentiometer. As a consequence of this system of modulation and detection, it is not the resonance envelope itself which is recorded, but rather the derivative of the envelope with respect to the magnetic field. Usually the interpretation of the data can be made directly in terms of the derivative curve, without integration to obtain the absorption curve itself.

There are other circuits for NMR involving only a single coil for the sample (Pound and Knight, 1950; Watkins and Pound, 1951; Gutowsky, Meyer, and McClure, 1952). Radiofrequency bridges have also been used (Bloembergen, Purcell, and Pound, 1948; Anderson, 1949). However, these circuits are not especially different from the one outlined above, and each category of circuit has some advantages.

Electron Paramagnetic Resonance

The microwave frequencies involved in EPR demand electronic methods which are quite different from those of NMR, though the technique of sweeping with a modulated magnetic field is essentially the same as that just given. Conventional circuits and wiring applicable at radio-frequencies are inappropriate for microwaves, since such circuits entail stray inductances and capacitances which become troublesome at very high frequencies. Furthermore the transit time of the current is a significant fraction of the high frequency cycle. These difficulties, which interfere with establishment of the proper phase relationships in the vacuum tube, are avoided by using the *klystron* as the generator of microwave power. For a detailed description of the klystron the reader is referred to a specialized source, such as the highly readable account given by Pollard and Sturtevant (1948). The device itself produces microwave power, which is then conveyed to the sample through the wave guide. Figure 3 shows schematically a typical EPR spectrometer. The sample is held in a resonant cavity which has the property that, by virtue of its carefully chosen dimensions, it can store a considerable amount of microwave energy. The sample therefore experiences electromagnetic field strengths many times larger than those in the wave guide feeding the cavity. This gain permits the study of resonances in small samples. An output wave guide from the cavity is connected to a bolometer which measures the power transmitted by the cavity. When the modulated magnetic field passes through the resonance region, the sample absorbs power from the cavity in the magnet gap. The power transmitted to the bolometer therefore changes. The change contains an audiofrequency component from the field modulation and is amplified by a circuit synchronized with the modulation, as in the NMR apparatus.

NMR in Solids

Nuclear Magnetic Moments

Extensive studies in recent years have yielded values of magnetic moment and spin for over 130 isotopes, representing more than 80 elements. The excellent reviews by Andrew (1955) and Pake (1956) list nuclear magnetic moments and describe their measurement. Table 1

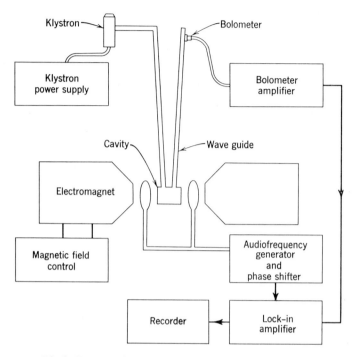

Fig. 3. Block diagram of typical electron magnetic resonance apparatus.

Table 1 [a]

Isotope	Magnetic Resonance Frequency (mc/sec) in 10,000 gauss	Natural Abundance (%)	Spin I (units of $h/2\pi$)
H[1]	42.577	99.984	½
H[2]	6.536	0.0156	1
B[10]	4.575	18.83	3
B[11]	13.660	81.17	3⁄2
C[13]	10.705	1.108	½
O[17]	5.772	0.037	5⁄2
Na[23]	11.262	100	3⁄2
Si[29]	8.460	4.70	½
P[31]	17.235	100	½
K[39]	1.987	93.08	3⁄2
K[41]	1.092	6.91	3⁄2

[a] From Pake (1956).

gives examples of nuclei, including those of particular interest, present or potential, in the study of non-crystalline solids. It is found empirically that nuclei have zero magnetic moment when both the atomic number and the mass number are even. Consequently, the isotopes C^{12}, O^{16}, and Si^{28} have no magnetic moment and cannot be used in NMR studies, despite their obvious importance.

Broadening of the Resonance

Let us return to our hypothetical experiment in which a solitary particle is situated in the field of a laboratory magnet. Suppose now that we have two particles instead of one, and for convenience consider them to be protons ($I = \frac{1}{2}$). Then the magnetic field felt by each proton consists of the field from the laboratory magnet augmented by the field caused by the magnetic moment of the other proton. Equation (3) then becomes, for the proton,

$$h\nu = 2\mu(H_0 \pm H_{loc}) \tag{6}$$

Here H_{loc}, the local field, adds to the applied field if the two magnetic moments are parallel and subtracts from the applied field when the moments are opposed. The magnitude of H_{loc} depends upon the spatial array of the protons with respect to the field direction H_0 and upon the separation between the nuclei. If r is the distance between the two nuclei and θ is the angle between the internuclear vector and the applied field, equation (6) becomes explicitly (Pake, 1948)

$$h\nu = 2\mu[H_0 \pm \tfrac{3}{2}\mu r^{-3}(3\cos^2\theta - 1)] \tag{7}$$

Thus the single resonance attributable to an isolated proton (Fig. 4a) becomes split into a pair of fixed lines, equally spaced about H_0 by an amount depending upon the relative positions of the nuclei and the orientations of the magnetic moments (Fig. 4b). Typically, this splitting is about 5 gauss when the nuclei are about 1 Å apart.

Although we have been discussing a hypothetical experiment on a single pair of protons, there are actual systems which approximate this situation. For example, studies of polycrystalline hydrated salts (Pake, 1948) and 1,2-dichloroethane (Gutowsky, Kistiakowsky, Pake, and Purcell, 1949) yielded resonances which resemble the schematic view of the pair resonance. In these non-hypothetical cases, the interactions between neighboring pairs are small but still are not negligible. The effect of these interactions is to cause each of the split resonances to be supplemented, positively and negatively, so that each contains a multiplicity of lines. Evidence of the pair splitting still remains, however, as is shown in Fig. 4c. Similarly, more complicated absorptions have been

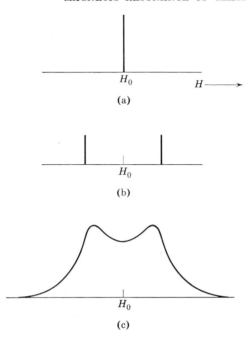

Fig. 4. (a) Hypothetical NMR spectrum of a single proton. (b) Hypothetical spectrum for a pair of protons. (c) Absorption envelope for a solid composed of pairs of protons.

observed for systems of three nuclei (Gutowsky, Kistiakowsky, Pake, and Purcell, 1949). The shapes to be expected in resonances from several types of simple arrays of nuclei have been calculated (Pake, 1948; Andrew and Bersohn, 1950).

Ordinarily, though, the solid system contains such a range of interactions that the absorption lacks detailed features such as those shown in Fig. 4c. The envelope is experimentally reproducible, but it generally is not described by any convenient function. One cannot readily calculate the contour of such a resonance on the basis of a structural model, but, as we shall see presently, there are calculations which relate the shape of the resonance curve, or "line" as it is often called, to models of the molecular structure.

The Effect of Motion

So far we have tacitly supposed that the nuclei are stationary. When molecular motion carries nuclei from one point in the lattice to another, a given nucleus encounters a number of different local fields, some of which add to and some of which subtract from the applied field. When the motion is rapid enough, the effect is to average out the deviations of magnetic field from the value H_0. Accordingly the resonance envelope becomes narrower. For protons the typical reorientation frequencies responsible for the onset of narrowing lie in the range 10^4 to 10^5 cps (Bloembergen, Purcell, and Pound, 1948; Gutowsky and Pake, 1950). Such motion is commonly observed in solids. Higher frequencies are still more effective in narrowing the resonance. The chaotic motion found in most liquids leads to very narrow resonances, a thousandth or less of the width in rigid solids. The frequencies responsible for the on-set of narrowing are, of course, small compared with those associated with familiar thermodynamic processes. For example, they make only a minor contribution to the heat capacity even at quite low temperatures, unless it happens that they are associated with a transition of some sort. The frequencies of motion responsible for the heat capacity of most sub-stances lie in the range 10^{12} to 10^{13} cps, but the displacements are only a small fraction of a lattice dimension and therefore are not effective in averaging out the local magnetic fields which broaden the resonance.

We should anticipate later discussions by remarking that care must be taken in comparing transitions described by the onset of NMR line narrowing and transitions seen by other techniques, for example, the methods of dynamic mechanical relaxation or dielectric absorption. For such comparisons to be valid, they must relate to the same frequency range and the same temperature interval.

The Second Moment of the Resonance Curve

We have already remarked that the line shape can be calculated ex-plicitly for certain simple cases. In general, though, calculation of the line shape on the basis of a structural model is too difficult. More than that, the result would be rather unprofitable, for the multiplicity of in-teractions erases the fine structure in the resonance. Instead, one ordi-narily seeks comparisons between model and experiment by making use of the *second moment* of the resonance line shape (Van Vleck, 1948; Gutowsky, Kistiakowsky, Pake, and Purcell, 1949).

$\Delta H_2{}^2$, the second moment expressed in terms of magnetic field, is de-fined as

$$\Delta H_2{}^2 = \frac{\int_{-\infty}^{\infty} (H - H_0)^2 f(H)\, dH}{\int_{-\infty}^{\infty} f(H)\, dH} \tag{8}$$

Here $f(H)$ is the line shape as a function of the magnetic field. Even though $f(H)$ is usually not a convenient analytic function, equation (8) can, of course, be solved numerically. From the form of that equation, we see that $\Delta H_2{}^2$ is the mean value of $(H - H_0)^2$, the square of the deviation of the magnetic field from the resonant value, with the average being taken over the symmetrical line shape $f(H)$. The denominator is a normalizing factor.

Van Vleck (1948) has shown that $\Delta H_2{}^2$ can be explicitly calculated from a model of the structure. The treatment, which is quantum mechanical, will not be reviewed here. The variables are the magnitudes and orientations of the internuclear vectors. $\Delta H_2{}^2$ is shown to be proportional to a sum involving these vectors,

$$\Delta H_2{}^2 \sim \sum_{j>k} r_{jk}^{-6}(3 \cos^2 \theta_{jk} - 1)^2 \tag{9}$$

Here r_{jk} is the separation between the jth and the kth nucleus, and θ_{jk} is the angle between the vector $\mathbf{r}_{jk}$ and the applied field H_0. Suppose that one internuclear spacing is abundant and furthermore is small enough to make an important contribution when reckoned in terms of its inverse sixth power. The contribution of water molecules in hydrates is an example of such a situation (Pake, 1948). The second moment is then dominated by these interactions, or, conversely, the experimental second moment can be used to fix the size of the internuclear separation. Even when there is not a dominant internuclear separation, the second moment can be used, at least in principle, for crystallographic determinations (McCall and Hamming, 1959). In non-crystalline substances, on the other hand, there is a distribution of r_{jk}'s which is usually broad and indeterminate. The NMR measurement is then unlikely to predict a unique possibility for a distribution of r_{jk}'s and hence offers little help in specifying structures of non-crystalline solids.

Even so, measurement of the second moment is a valuable adjunct to the study of motion in solids, non-crystalline as well as crystalline. The onset of motion causes a narrowing of the resonance, as we have remarked, and it also causes a decrease in the second moment. Indeed, one may calculate the decrease resulting from certain types of motion in crystalline solids (Gutowsky and Pake, 1950; Andrew, 1950; Powles and Gutowsky, 1953; Andrew and Eades, 1953a, 1953b). Such calculations can only be gross approximations when applied to non-crystalline solids. Still, the measured second moment acutely reflects changes in the shape of the resonance curve and hence is quite sensitive to the onset of motion. Since $\Delta H_2{}^2$ depends upon the square of the deviation from the center of the resonance, as may be seen from equation (8), it particularly describes changes in the larger splittings, i.e., in the interactions between closely spaced nuclei.

The line width is an easier quantity to measure than the second moment. Moreover, since the experimental second moment is especially affected by the shape of the outer portions of the resonance curve, where the absorption is small and somewhat ambiguous, the value of $\Delta H_2{}^2$ is rather uncertain. This is especially true for solids at elevated temperatures, where the sensitivity tends to fall off and the signal-to-noise ratio deteriorates. Despite these disadvantages, the onset of motion is commonly to be seen more acutely in measurements of $\Delta H_2{}^2$ than in measurements of the line width.

The Glass Temperature in High Polymers

Nuclear resonance studies on non-crystalline solids have dealt with organic high polymers. To my knowledge, there have been no studies of structure and motion in inorganic glasses by NMR. A most important class of non-crystalline solids is represented by certain high polymers. We ordinarily distinguish between the glassy polymers and the rubber-like substances. Compounds normally thought of as rubber-like are simply those long chain polymers which exhibit the familiar characteristics of softness and elasticity at room temperature. Glassy polymers are those which show rigidity, brittleness, and transparency at ordinary temperatures. Many polymers are capable of partial crystallization, but we shall not dwell upon these substances. It is likely that nearly all chain polymers composed of extremely long molecules pass through a rubber-like region as we raise the temperature, provided of course that decomposition does not occur.

A central feature in the behavior of rubber-like substances is the random thermal motion of the molecular segments. Plainly, this motion falls off progressively at lower temperatures. For some compounds, crystallization occurs when the motion becomes sufficiently reduced. If the rubbery material is cooled too rapidly to permit crystallization, or if there are structural features which inhibit the orderly alignment of the chain segments, the loss in thermal motion leads to a change from rubber-like elasticity to glassy rigidity. The transformation is also seen in the supercooling of some simple liquids, such as glycerol. The temperature at which this change occurs is called the *glass temperature* or the *second-order transition temperature*.

The glass transition in polymers is not a true thermodynamic transition, for it depends upon the time scale of the experiment. However, it recalls order-disorder transformations of some alloys and the onset of rotational motion of small molecules in some crystalline solids. The transition involves no discontinuity in a primary thermodynamic quantity, but rather a change in the slope of the graph of the primary thermodynamic variable as a function of temperature. That is, a discontinuity occurs not in the volume, but in the expansion coefficient; and not in the heat content, but in the heat capacity. In general, tests requiring shorter times tend to give higher values of the glass temperature, and often more abrupt and pronounced transitions (Boyer and Spencer, 1946). Conversely, in tests which are conducted very slowly there is often no evidence of an explicit glass temperature. Rather, there is merely a gradual trend from the glassy condition to the rubbery, or the reverse. However, even though the glass temperature lacks thermodynamic meaning and suffers from ambiguity, it is a useful quantity for comparison of materials. Since the transformation is evidently associated with changes in the extent of molecular motion, it is appropriate for investigation by NMR.

NMR in Amorphous Polymers

Nuclear resonance studies of structures in amorphous polymers have had little to offer. Whether one supposes that a high degree of randomness exists in the array of chain segments, or whether there are in fact short sequences of chain segments which possess regularity, the NMR method is not a highly sensitive test. It may conceivably be useful in deciding between a few discrete possibilities for structures, but when the solid contains a distribution of structures the NMR method is not at all explicit in describing the distribution. However, it offers unique measurements of motion.

Polystyrene

Holroyd, Codrington, Mrowca, and Guth (1951) have noted that NMR line narrowing occurs in glassy polystyrene in the temperature range 380–400°K. Similar results have been reported by Odajima, Sohma, and Koike (1955, 1957). The transformation seen by NMR corresponds closely with the glass transition seen in dilatometric studies (Fox and Flory, 1950). However, this change occurs at much higher temperatures than in familiar elastomers or in many semicrystalline polymers. For example, motion in non-crystalline regions begins at about 240–250°K in natural rubber (Gutowsky and Meyer, 1953), at about 250–260° in polyethylene (McCall and Slichter, 1957), and near room temperature in polypropylene (Slichter and Mandell, 1958). In polystyrene, evidently the bulkiness of the substituents, the phenyl groups, offers sizable constraint to chain motion.

The familiar form of polystyrene is glassy, but the substance also exists in crystalline form (Natta and Corradini, 1955a, 1955b). The ability of some polymers to crystallize (and the failure of others to crystallize) involves a number of considerations (Bunn, 1954; Mandelkern, 1956). It is almost a definition to say that the most important feature of the crystalline state is three-dimensional regularity. Those polymers which show a regular repetition of the same chemical grouping along the chain, and which possess regularity in shape, are usually able to crystallize to a large extent. Conversely, polymers which possess chemical or geometrical irregularities are likely not to crystallize. The glassy character of polystyrene and some other polymers comes about because the repeating units possess large side groups which occur indiscriminately in left- and right-hand positions along the chain. In the new form of polystyrene, the methods of catalysis used in the synthesis are able to direct succeeding monomer units preferentially into left-hand dispositions along the chain, or else into right-hand dispositions. The resulting chains are still bulky, because of the size of the phenyl group, but the molecules are regular enough that they can crystallize.

One would expect the crystalline structure to exhibit closer spacings between atoms, on the whole, than the glassy structure. This expectation is borne out in Fig. 5. Here the second moments of the two kinds of polystyrene are compared over a wide temperature range. The greater values of $\Delta H_2{}^2$ for the crystalline compound come about because of the more orderly structure.

Attempts to calculate $\Delta H_2{}^2$ for glassy polystyrene have so far been highly approximate (Odajima, Sohma, and Koike, 1957). The calculation of $\Delta H_2{}^2$ for the crystalline form should be more gratifying, since there is already explicit information from x-ray diffraction (Natta and Corradini, 1955a). Although the intricacies of the structure will make the calculation something of a chore, the result will be of crystallographic interest with respect to the ordered compound and will serve as a comparison standard for the amorphous compound.

Even without calculation of $\Delta H_2{}^2$, we may discuss qualitatively some features of the molecular behavior. The very gradual decrease of $\Delta H_2{}^2$ with rising temperature, shown in Fig. 5, points out that motion develops with difficulty. The decrease in $\Delta H_2{}^2$ is more rapid for the glassy material than for the crystalline. One would expect this difference, for the glassy structure must possess numerous defects which offer some freedom to the motion of chain elements. However, for both the glassy and the crystalline polystyrenes, the development of motion occurs much

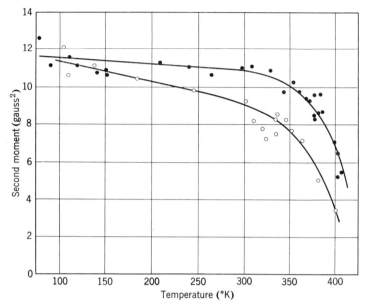

Fig. 5. Variation of second moment with temperature for polystyrene (unpublished studies by Slichter). Closed circles, crystalline; open circles, amorphous.

less readily than in the other systems cited below, and indeed less readily than with most linear polymers. This comparative constraint to motion doubtless stems from the hindrances imposed by the bulky phenyl groups. Parenthetically, when crystallizable polystyrene is quenched from the melt, it too is glassy and it shows the same temperature dependence of ΔH_2^2 as does the amorphous compound in Fig. 5.

We have already noted that the narrowing of the resonance in both forms of polystyrene (decrease in ΔH_2^2) in the interval 380–400°K corresponds closely to the glass transition as seen by other measurements. However, the transformation occurs at a much lower temperature than the melting point of the crystalline form of the polymer (Natta, 1956). Although the nature of the motion responsible for the glass transition has not been specified for polystyrene, or indeed for any polymer, it is plainly much less drastic than the motion which causes the crystalline substance to melt.*

* The motions responsible for narrowing of the resonance are nearly always quite complex, but still it is possible to gauge the extent of motion in a solid by calculating ΔH_2^2 for simple models of the motion (Andrew, 1950; Andrew and Eades, 1953a, 1953b; Powles and Gutowsky, 1953; Slichter, 1955). It should be possible to develop instructive models for polystyrene, too, invoking simple motions such as rotation of the phenyl groups about the twofold axis or small amplitude oscillation of the main chain.

Polymethyl Methacrylate (PMMA)

The excellent optical properties of polymethyl methacrylate make it an important polymer of commerce. Until quite recently it occurred only as a glassy substance. The proton resonance in PMMA has been studied by Holroyd, Codrington, Mrowca, and Guth (1951), by Odajima, Sohma, and Koike (1955, 1957), and by Powles (1956). All these studies were made on glassy samples of PMMA, but recently it has been found that this polymer can be made in crystalline form (Fox et al., 1958; Stroupe and Hughes, 1958). The difference between the glassy and the crystalline types depends on the disposition of the repeating unit which, like styrene, possesses a bulky substituent and is capable of assuming either a left- or a right-hand position in the molecule. As with polystyrene, a regular sequence of either left- or right-handed units leads to a structure which is capable of crystallizing.* When there is randomness

$$
\left[\begin{array}{c} CH_3 \\ | \\ -CH_2-C- \\ | \\ C=O \\ | \\ O-CH_3 \end{array} \right]_n
$$

in the sequence, the chains fail to pack in orderly fashion, and the familiar glassy substance results.†

PMMA has features which differ from those of polystyrene. In PMMA the ester side chains are bulky enough to lead to glassy structures. However, the methyl group on the ester is presumably more capable of motion than is the phenyl group. Moreover, the methyl group attached to the main chain in PMMA is also capable of motion.

The NMR studies of PMMA to date all show a marked narrowing of the resonance near 340°K, corresponding in temperature to glass transi-

* Depending upon the conditions of polymerization, crystalline PMMA may exhibit regularity in two forms. In one form, sequences of repeating units in the molecules may be either predominantly left-handed or predominantly right-handed. In the other form, the chain consists of an orderly alternation of the left-handed and the right-handed segments. Natta has given the names "isotactic" and "syndiotactic," respectively, to these two classes of regular polymer structure.

† In a paper at the 1958 Gordon Research Conference on Polymers, W. E. Goode reported that the familiar glassy PMMA of commerce contains appreciable sequences of repeating units arrayed in orderly fashion. These sequences elude detection by x-ray diffraction but are discernible in infrared studies. It will be interesting to learn what differences, if any, can be discerned in NMR between the molecular motion possessed by such compounds and the motion occurring in the glassy compounds which have virtually no sequences of ordered units.

tions seen by other methods (Würstlin, 1955; Rogers and Mandelkern, 1957). Furthermore, the NMR transition occurs in the same temperature region as that associated with dielectric loss maxima at frequencies of 10^4 to 10^5 cps (Deutsch, Hoff, and Reddish, 1954). Since the dielectric dispersion must be caused by motion of the ester groups, one concludes that the NMR narrowing and also the glass transition correspond to motions involving these groups.

Powles (1956) has measured the second moment of the resonance in PMMA over a broad temperature range (Fig. 6). He finds a decrease in

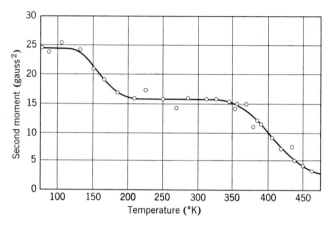

Fig. 6. Variation of second moment with temperature for polymethyl methacrylate (Powles, 1956).

$\Delta H_2{}^2$ with rising temperature in the region 130–200°K. This is the temperature region in which methyl group rotation begins in some methyl-substituted methanes (Powles and Gutowsky, 1953). It seems proper to ascribe this change to CH_3 rotation in PMMA, too, for the hindrances to such motion should be much smaller than those related to motion of the main chain.

Powles has made an approximate calculation of $\Delta H_2{}^2$ for motionless PMMA. The chain configuration is too ambiguous for a detailed calculation. Therefore Powles has combined the values of $\Delta H_2{}^2$ for isolated CH_2 and CH_3 groups (Gutowsky and Pake, 1950; Andrew and Bersohn, 1950), with proper statistical weights, and has augmented these quantities by a figure estimated to describe the interactions among proton groups within the molecule and between molecules. This approximate result agrees well with the experimental value at 77°K, suggesting that at this temperature the motion has indeed become quenched.

Powles has also computed ΔH_2^2 for the case in which motion consists of rapid rotation of the methyl groups about the three-fold axis. The measured ΔH_2^2 from 200° to 340°K (Fig. 6) agrees closely with the value predicted for rotation of just half of the methyl groups. Powles suggests that the two types of methyl groups, those attached to the main chain and those in the ester groups, have different but essentially uniform environments throughout the solid, so that they commence rotation at distinctly different temperatures. He has tried to distinguish between the two types of methyl groups by studying polymethyl α-chloroacrylate, in which chlorine atoms replace the methyl groups attached to the main chain in PMMA. For reasons which apparently were instrumental* the results are ambiguous, but the problem is intriguing and merits further attention.

Polypropylene

Widely different constraints to motions of groups are found in polypropylene. This polymer exists as a crystalline substance (Natta and Corradini, 1955c) and as an amorphous, rubbery compound at ordinary temperatures. Again, the crystalline substance is that which shows a high degree of regularity in the sequence of right- or left-handed monomers, while the amorphous substance shows great irregularity in the sequences.

$$\left[CH_2 - \begin{array}{c} CH \\ | \\ CH_3 \end{array} \right]_n$$

Measurements of the NMR line width of the amorphous material show that considerable motion sets in somewhat below room temperature (Slichter and Mandell, 1958). This is the temperature region associated with the glass transition (Natta, 1955; Reding, 1956). The resonance narrows rapidly as the temperature is raised, tending even at room temperature toward the small widths found with true liquids. This liquid-like behavior is in accord with the rubbery nature of the non-crystalline polymer.

Figure 7 shows the temperature dependence of ΔH_2^2 for the two types of polypropylene. As with polystyrene, the non-crystalline form has a lower value of ΔH_2^2 than the crystalline form at every temperature, as one would expect from the difference in the regularity of the structures.

There are two temperature regions in which narrowing of the resonance occurs. In the low temperature region (77–110°K), the motion is pre-

---

* Private communication from Dr. Powles.

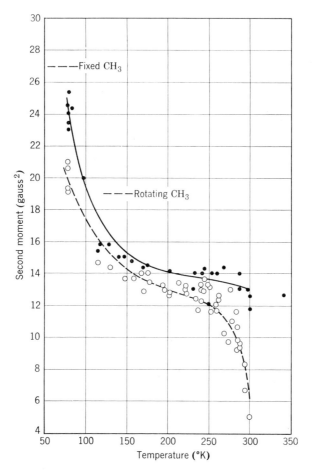

Fig. 7. Variation of second moment with temperature for polypropylene (Slichter and Mandell, 1958). Solid circles, crystalline; open circles, amorphous.

sumably comparatively easy. It seems likely that this is the motion of the methyl groups about the three-fold axis. Plainly, the narrowing near room temperature must require greater energy. It is attributed to motion of the main chains. These assignments are in keeping with dynamic mechanical data (Sauer, Wall, Fuschillo, and Woodward, 1958), which show dispersion occurring near room temperature but none at low temperature. Presumably fairly sizable motion is needed to produce mechanical loss. Motion of the main chain would suffice, but simple rotation of the methyl groups would not be expected to couple with mechanical excitation.

Although $\Delta H_2{}^2$ cannot be accurately calculated for the glassy solid, some insight into the low temperature motion can be gained by comparison with values of $\Delta H_2{}^2$ calculated for the crystalline compound. Figure 7 shows (upper dashed line) the value computed for completely motionless chains, and also (lower dashed line) the value computed for the structure when the motion consists solely of rotation of all the methyl groups. Evidently, most of the narrowing of the resonance at low temperature is accounted for in terms of methyl group rotation.

A salient feature of Fig. 7, in contrast with the graphs for the two prior examples, is that $\Delta H_2{}^2$ continues to broaden as the temperature is lowered. There is no sign that the motion has been quenched in polypropylene, as it apparently has been in the other polymers discussed. Clearly, there are major differences among the glassy polymers with respect to the ease of motion of substituent groups.

High Resolution NMR

Electronic Effects in NMR

We have already mentioned some of the interactions experienced by nuclear magnetic moments. An important class of interactions yet to be mentioned consists of those associated with the electronic environment of the nuclei. The most important of these are (a) the so-called "chemical shift" and (b) the indirect coupling between nuclear spins. These interactions are small compared with the line broadening couplings which occur within solids. Therefore, ordinarily they can be observed only in liquids or solutions, where the molecular motion is active enough to average out the broadening contributions between molecules. Their study also requires highly homogeneous magnetic fields. The term "high resolution NMR" is applied to these experiments.

Matter is ordinarily diamagnetic; that is, the application of an external magnetic field causes a circulation in the electrons which produces a magnetic field partially canceling the applied field. Hence the effective magnetic field seen by the nucleus, H_{eff}, is slightly altered from the applied field, H_0. The nucleus is thus somewhat shielded from the applied field by the presence of the electrons. The shielding is described by the relation

$$H_{\mathrm{eff}} = H_0(1 - \sigma) \tag{10}$$

Here σ, the shielding constant, is about 10^{-5} for protons and as great as 10^{-3} for some nuclei.

The electronic configuration around a given nucleus, of course, depends upon details of the chemical bond. Hence the shielding seen by magnetic nuclei varies, and the NMR resonance line has correspondingly different components, or "chemical shifts." The shifts are spoken of as being paramagnetic or diamagnetic, depending upon whether, from the viewpoint of the nucleus, the electronic configuration aids or opposes the applied field. Actually, we cannot measure this relation in an absolute sense, since we never study the bare nucleus. The paramagnetism or diamagnetism of the shift is therefore only comparative and is ordinarily expressed in terms of some convenient reference compound. A negative value of σ, then, means that the nucleus in question sees an environment which is more paramagnetic than the environment within the reference. The more paramagnetic nucleus is, of course, the one which is less shielded magnetically. An interesting set of examples occurs in a series of fluorine compounds, in which the shielding around the F^{19} nucleus is found to decrease with increasing electronegativity of the atom to which the fluorine is bonded, i.e., with increasing covalency in the character of the bond (Gutowsky and Hoffman, 1951; Saika and Slichter, 1954).

The general theory for the chemical shift (Ramsey, 1950, 1952, 1953) is quite complex, and the results depend acutely on the choice of wave functions. Therefore only isolated examples of the chemical shift have been calculated, notably the shift for the fluorine nucleus (Saika and Slichter, 1954). The situation is especially difficult for the proton, for which the electron density near the nucleus and the associated shielding are quite small. However, the proton shift is of obvious interest in chemistry, and has been investigated theoretically with some success (e.g., Pople, 1956; Bernstein, Schneider, and Pople, 1956; McGarvey, 1957; McConnell, 1957). These studies are only a beginning. It is fair to hope, though, that further studies will refine the theories and will enhance our understanding of chemical bonding.

The effect of indirect coupling, mentioned above, is seen as a multiplet structure in the resonance. The interaction comes about because one nucleus in the molecule induces a magnetic moment in the electron distribution in the molecule, and the induced moment interacts with a second nucleus, splitting its resonance (Gutowsky, McCall, and Slichter, 1953). As it is expressed by Pake (1956), the interaction between nuclear moments is "telegraphed" from one to the other by the bonding electrons of the molecule. These splittings offer promise of giving detailed information about chemical bonding, though again we are handicapped by inadequacies in wave functions.

Chemical Shifts in Glasses

Holzman, Lauterbur, Anderson, and Koth (1956) have measured the Si^{29} resonance in various materials, including silica, quartz, and some multicomponent glasses. The Si^{29} isotope occurs in a natural abundance of only 4.7%, and so the nuclear spin-spin interactions in the solid are small. With respect to silicone oil, $[(CH_3)_2SiO]_x$, the chemical shifts of the glasses are diamagnetic, more so than those of either metallic silicon or silicon carbide. In these terms, $(CH_3)_3SiF$ has a paramagnetic shift, and furthermore the resonance is split by indirect coupling. However, these examples are all merely observations and have yet to be interpreted.

Electron Paramagnetic Resonance

Electronic Interactions

We have already considered some of the fundamental features common to both NMR and EPR. There are important formal similarities between the two, but it must be added that nuclear paramagnetism is the simpler. The difference in complexity comes in part from the fact that interactions among nuclear magnetic moments are small compared with those among electronic magnetic moments; and, furthermore, from the fact that the nuclei are shielded by the electron shells from other than magnetic interactions.*

As we have already remarked, the phenomenon of electron paramagnetic resonance is shown only by molecules having electronic angular momentum, either from unpaired electron spin or from non-zero orbital momentum. In a full shell of electrons the orbital and spin angular momenta of the individual electrons compensate to give a zero resultant, and so the substance is diamagnetic. This kind of compensation occurs in most substances. There are two categories, though, which are exceptions to this general rule: (a) atoms having unfilled orbits lying inside the valency shell, and hence always having unpaired electrons; (b) substances in which some of the bonds have been altered so as to yield unpaired electrons. The first category includes the transition and rare earth elements. There is much interest in the study of the energy levels

---

* The last statement is strictly true only for nuclei for which $I = \frac{1}{2}$, among which are numbered many of the most important isotopes. When I exceeds $\frac{1}{2}$ the nucleus possesses an electric quadrupole moment which interacts with the electrons.

of these atoms, and the perturbation of the levels by the surrounding lattice, though so far this category has played little part in the examination of non-crystalline solids.   The second category is of particular interest here: it includes specialized aspects such as the study of the effect of irradiation in producing dislocations or broken bonds.

We have already mentioned g, the spectroscopic splitting factor; cf. equation (5).   In effect, it measures the rate at which the energy levels diverge with application of a magnetic field.   For the free electron spin, the spectroscopic splitting factor is 2.0 (or 2.0023, taking account of relativistic effects).   However, an electron in a paramagnetic ion sees not only the applied magnetic field but also the field due to its own orbital motion.   That is, there is a "spin-orbit coupling."   This coupling causes the g-value to depart from 2.0, and the size of the departure is a measure of the coupling.

The orbits may become quite distorted from those characteristic of free paramagnetic ions, in the electric fields occurring within crystals. The magnetic field associated with the orbital motion will then have directional properties, and so the spin-orbit coupling will show anisotropy.* A measurement of the g-value therefore shows anisotropy as the orientation of the applied field H_0 is changed with respect to the axes of the crystal.

The positions, splittings, and intensities of the resonances can be analyzed to give information on the nature of chemical binding of the paramagnetic ion.   The theory has been developed in some detail.   However, the maximum information is to be had only when the experiment includes variation of the angle between H_0 and the crystal axes.   A single crystal is therefore required.   Even so, much can be learned from polycrystalline and glassy materials.

Factors Affecting Line Shape

The shape of the resonance is affected by several kinds of interactions.

Spin-lattice relaxation.   The resonance is broadened by interaction between the paramagnetic centers and the thermal vibrations of the lattice.   Evidently, thermal motion of the lattice causes fluctuations in the crystalline fields, and, acting through the spin-orbit coupling, the motion spreads out the energy levels, making them diffuse.   Decrease in spin-lattice broadening comes with reduction in temperature.

---

* For example, cupric salts normally show a variation in g-value from 2.1 to 2.4, depending upon the orientation. The anisotropy is still greater in some other ions (see below).

Spin-spin coupling. The interaction between nearby paramagnetic ions in the rigid lattice produces a broadening analogous to that which we discussed earlier in the sections on NMR. The effect is substantially independent of temperature in EPR, but the broadening is reduced if the distance between paramagnetic ions is increased by dilution.

Exchange interaction. The resonance is often much narrower than would be expected from the interactions just discussed. The phenomenon is termed "exchange narrowing." In classical terms, the effect occurs because electrons in adjacent paramagnetic centers exchange places moderately frequently and therefore see an "average" magnetic environment. The process is formally reminiscent of the motional narrowing which occurs in NMR.*

Nuclear hyperfine interaction. If the electron circulates about a nucleus having a magnetic moment, the electron spin engaging in transition interacts with the magnetic field from the nucleus. Each electronic state therefore has $(2I + 1)$ components, corresponding to the $(2I + 1)$ orientations of the nuclear moment in the applied magnetic field.

The breadth of the resonance is important on several counts. First, a study of the factors affecting the breadth tells something about the nature of the interactions. Moreover, one's ability to observe fine structure may depend on control of line broadening. Indeed, if exchange of energy between spin and lattice is extremely rapid, the resonance may be too broad to be observable.

Studies of Irradiated Glasses

The effects of high energy irradiation upon solids are complex. One important process is the formation of ions. Another process is the displacement of atoms from their positions in the lattice. The former process is particularly associated with γ-rays, x-rays, electrons, and ions; the latter occurs especially with fast neutrons. It is not possible to make a sharp distinction between the mechanisms, since any practical radiation experiment ordinarily contains contributions from each. It is not surprising that irradiation should bring about paramagnetism. In insulating materials, paramagnetism presumably comes about because a small fraction of the electrons ejected by the bombardment fail to return to ordinary positions in the lattice. Instead they are captured by defects of some sort, for example, structural dislocations or impurity atoms. The trapping of an electron by a defect implies the existence elsewhere of a defect with an electron deficiency, i.e., a hole.

---

* Under some circumstances, exchange processes produce broadening of the resonance instead of narrowing. This effect occurs if the magnetic elements are unlike, i.e., if they have different g-factors.

Electron paramagnetic resonance studies of irradiated glasses have been reported by Yasaitis and Smaller (1953), Combrisson and Uebersfeld (1954), Weeks (1956), and van Wieringen and Kats (1957).

Yasaitis and Smaller (1953) have found that a strong resonance develops in a number of glasses after bombardment with γ-rays. The paramagnetic resonance absorption in a series of glasses varies in intensity with the irradiation dose, and the resonance absorption is proportional to the optical density. Conversely, annealing at 475°K causes a loss in resonance amplitude which is proportional to bleaching. In boron-free glasses, the absorption occurs in simple fashion near a g-value of 2. In glasses containing boron, there are four resonances which are attributed to nuclear hyperfine splitting with B^{11} $(I = \frac{3}{2})$. In all the glasses studied, except for vitreous silica, a strong resonance also occurs at $g = 4$, even in the absence of irradiation. It is attributed to impurities (see "Paramagnetic Resonance Absorption in Unirradiated Glass" below).

Weeks (1956) has studied the paramagnetic resonance spectra in high purity quartz, both fused and crystalline, after irradiation with fast neutrons at temperatures of about 525°K. In silica glass the irradiation produces asymmetric resonance envelopes, after doses typically amounting to 2×10^{19} neutrons/cm². The envelope evidently consists of a pair of resonances, one with a g-value of 2.0013 and a half-width of about 2 gauss, the other with a g-value of 2.0090 and a half-width of 40 gauss (Fig. 8). In a quartz single crystal which had been irradiated somewhat less, 3×10^{18} neutrons/cm², two groups of lines are found.

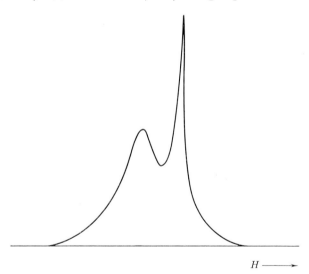

$H \longrightarrow$

Fig. 8. Resonance observed in neutron-irradiated fused quartz (schematic view adapted from Weeks, 1956).

The fine structure of these lines depends on the orientation of the crystal with respect to the field. The groups correspond in g-value to the two structureless resonances found in the irradiated glasses. Hence the resonances in the glasses appear to be the resultants of the resonances in the crystals when these are averaged over all orientations with respect to the magnetic field.

After more severe irradiation, 3×10^{20} neutrons/cm^2, the resonances in crystalline quartz lose their orientation dependence and assume the g-values and widths found in the glasses. This finding recalls the observations of Wittels and Sherrill (1954), comparing crystalline and fused quartz after intense irradiation (10^{20} neutrons/cm^2): after such treatment the two kinds of quartz have the same density and yield the same x-ray diffraction patterns.

Weeks has examined the possibility that the resonances come from the ionization of impurities by the intense γ-ray flux in the reactor. However, he finds from spectrochemical analysis that no impurity is common to all the samples, even though the resonances themselves are comparable. Furthermore, there is no evidence of nuclear hyperfine splitting of the resonances, even though most of the detected impurities have nuclear magnetic moments.

Since impurity effects seem to be ruled out, the resonances must originate with defects in the basic SiO$_4$ tetrahedra in the crystals and glasses. Weeks suggests three possible kinds of defects: (a) oxygen and silicon vacancies, which may be ionized; (b) interstitial oxygen and silicon; (c) broken Si-O bonds. The apparent g-values in the glasses, 2.0013 and 2.0090, lie above and below the free electron value of 2.0023. Weeks suggests that the two resonances may come from paramagnetic centers, one being an electron and the other a hole.

Van Wieringen and Kats (1957) have made EPR and optical investigations of silicate glasses and fused silica which had been irradiated with x-rays. The glasses contained alkali oxides, or mixtures of alkali and alkaline earth oxides, in known proportions. The resonance spectrum here, as in the studies by Weeks, consists of a pair of peaks, unlike in width and intensity. In glasses of different composition the shapes of the envelopes are similar, although differing somewhat in strength, g-value, and width. For a glass of a given composition, the intensities in the spectra depend on the temperature and duration of irradiation, but the shapes are the same.

After irradiation, the two peaks gradually diminish in intensity, but they do so at different rates. Hence the two peaks are ascribed to different kinds of paramagnetic centers. The two resonances occur on either side of the g-value expected for the free electron. The width of the resonance curves is too great to be due to interaction between separate paramagnetic centers, and the separation between the peaks is proportional to the applied magnetic field. Van Wieringen and Kats adduce that one resonance belongs to an electron and the other to a hole. They conclude that the electron (or hole) in the defect center must move in an electric field of low symmetry. These authors make some tentative correlations between the occurrence of paramagnetic centers and the optical behavior of the glasses.

Paramagnetic Resonance Absorption in Unirradiated Glass

Sands (1955) has observed EPR absorption in unirradiated specimens of glass. The resonance curves are asymmetric, and they seemingly correspond to two envelopes, centered respectively about $g \cong 4$ and $g \cong 6$. He has computed the absorption curve to be expected from paramagnetic centers of such anisotropy, distributed over all spatial orientations, and has found good agreement with experiment. He concludes that the observed absorption comes from an impurity which has anisotropic g-values in its lattice site in the glass. The viewpoint is borne out by measurements of cobalt glass: the cobalt ion is known from other systems to have anisotropic g-values in this range (Bleaney and Ingram, 1951; Bleaney and Stevens, 1953). Sands has also calculated the resonance envelope to be expected for cupric ions situated in the vitreous matrix. He has assumed the existence of electric fields characteristic of short range order. The result, which includes nuclear hyperfine interactions, compares quite well with experiment. Further studies of the nature of lattice positions in the vitreous state seem promising.

Studies of Free Radicals in Non-crystalline Solids

The techniques of EPR are among the most powerful in the detection of free radicals. The basis for the detection is that the free radical possesses an unpaired electron. Because of the importance of free radicals to a vast number of chemical processes, in both synthetic and natural systems, and especially in biological systems, the EPR method of detection is of keen interest. With reasonable refinements in technique, it is to be expected that 10^9 to 10^{11} radicals should be detectable in typical samples (Ingram, 1955).

It is inappropriate to undertake here a survey of the broad and active literature on EPR studies of free radicals, though brief mention may be made of some studies of free radicals in non-crystalline solids as an indication of the scope of the field.

The effect of irradiation upon inorganic glasses has already been mentioned. In certain organic glasses made from high polymers, high energy irradiation produces free radicals. Schneider (1955) has studied the effect of x-ray bombardment upon polymers such as polymethyl methacrylate and has interpreted the fine structure of the resonances in terms of models of the electronic configurations produced in the chain fragments.

In certain polymers, controlled pyrolysis produces structures which, in the large, are quite reproducible (Winslow, Baker, Pape, and Matreyek, 1955). Depending upon the temperature of pyrolysis, these structures show varying degrees of semiconductivity (Winslow, Baker, and Yager, 1955). At low temperatures of pyrolysis the semiconductivity is small, but there is a progressive increase in the concentration of unpaired electrons as the pyrolysis temperature is increased. Then, as pyrolysis continues, the EPR absorption falls off drastically and the semiconductivity increases markedly, corresponding to the development of free radical centers into conjugated systems.

Fraenkel, Hirshon, and Walling (1954) have verified the presence of free radicals during vinyl polymerization. Ingram, Symons, and Townsend (1958) have found radicals occluded in glassy solids during polymerization. These observations are of significance in kinetic studies of polymerization. The hyperfine patterns of these radicals, and those formed by chain fracture (above), offer information on radical structure.

Conclusion

In this incomplete survey of magnetic resonance, we have seen some examples of the application of resonance methods to studies of structure, motion, chemical bonding, and kinetics. As with other techniques, a great gain in the detail and rigor of the information is to be had from the use of single crystals. When applied to non-crystalline substances, it loses much of its force. Despite this disadvantage, though, magnetic resonance obviously offers information which would be difficult or impossible to find in other ways. The use of magnetic resonance to study glasses has merely begun.

REFERENCES

Anderson, H. L., *Phys. Rev.* **76**, 1460 (1949).

Andrew, E. R., *J. Chem. Phys.* **18**, 607 (1950).

Andrew, E. R., *Nuclear Magnetic Resonance*, University Press, Cambridge, 1955.

Andrew, E. R., and Bersohn, R., *J. Chem. Phys.* **18**, 159 (1950).

Andrew, E. R., and Eades, R. G., *Proc. Roy. Soc. (London)* **A216**, 398 (1953) (a).

Andrew, E. R., and Eades, R. G., *Proc. Roy. Soc. (London)* **A218**, 537 (1953) (b).

Bernstein, H. J., Schneider, W. G., and Pople, J. A., *Proc. Roy. Soc. (London)* **A235**, 515 (1956).

Bleaney, B., and Ingram, D. J. E., *Proc. Roy. Soc. (London)* **A208**, 143 (1951).

Bleaney, B., and Stevens, K. W. H., *Repts. Progr. Phys.* **16**, 108 (1953).

Bloch, F., Hansen, W. W., and Packard, M., *Phys. Rev.* **70**, 474 (1946).

Bloembergen, N., Purcell, E. M., and Pound, R. V., *Phys. Rev.* **73**, 679 (1948).

Boyer, R. F., and Spencer, R. S., *Advances in Colloid Sci.* **2**, 1 (1946).

Bunn, C. W., *J. Appl. Phys.* **25**, 820 (1954).

Combrisson, J., and Uebersfeld, J., *Compt. rend.* **238**, 572 (1954).

Deutsch, K., Hoff, E. A. W., and Reddish, W., *J. Polymer Sci.* **13**, 565 (1954).

Fox, T. G., and Flory, P. J., *J. Appl. Phys.* **21**, 581 (1950).

Fox, T. G., Garrett, B. S., Goode, W. E., Gratch, S., Kincaid, J. F., Spell, A., and Stroupe, J. D., *J. Am. Chem. Soc.* **80**, 1768 (1958).

Fraenkel, G. K., Hirshon, J. M., and Walling, C., *J. Am. Chem. Soc.* **76**, 3606 (1954).

Gutowsky, H. S., and Hoffman, C. J., *J. Chem. Phys.* **19**, 1259 (1951).

Gutowsky, H. S., Kistiakowsky, G. B., Pake, G. E., and Purcell, E. M., *J. Chem. Phys.* **17**, 972 (1949).

Gutowsky, H. S., McCall, D. W., and Slichter, C. P., *J. Chem. Phys.* **21**, 279 (1953).

Gutowsky, H. S., and Meyer, L. H., *J. Chem. Phys.* **21**, 2122 (1953).

Gutowsky, H. S., Meyer, L. H., and McClure, R. E., *Rev. Sci. Instr.* **24**, 644 (1953).

Gutowsky, H. S., and Pake, G. E., *J. Chem. Phys.* **18**, 168 (1950).

Holroyd, L. V., Codrington, R. S., Mrowca, B. A., and Guth, E., *J. Appl. Phys.* **22**, 696 (1951).

Holzman, G. R., Lauterbur, P. C., Anderson, J. H., and Koth, W., *J. Chem. Phys.* **25**, 172 (1956).

Ingram, D. J. E., *Spectroscopy at Radio and Microwave Frequencies*, Butterworths, London, 1955, pp. 294–295.

Ingram, D. J. E., Symons, M. C. R., and Townsend, M. D., *Trans. Faraday Soc.* **54**, 409 (1958).

Kittel, C., *Report of the Conference on Defects in Crystalline Solids*, Physical Society, London, 1955, p. 33.

McCall, D. W., and Hamming, R. W., *Acta Cryst.* **12**, 81 (1959).

McCall, D. W., and Slichter, W. P., *J. Polymer Sci.* **26**, 171 (1957).

McConnell, H. M., *J. Chem. Phys.* **27**, 226 (1957).

McGarvey, B. R., *J. Chem. Phys.* **27**, 68 (1957).

Mandelkern, L., *Chem. Revs.* **56**, 903 (1956).

Natta, G., *J. Polymer Sci.* **16**, 143 (1955).

Natta, G., *Angew. Chem.* **68**, 393 (1956).

Natta, G., and Corradini, P., *Rend. Accad. nazl. Lincei* **Ser. 8, 1**, 19 (1955) (a).

Natta, G., and Corradini, P., *Makromol. Chem.* **16**, 77 (1955) (b).

Natta, G., and Corradini, P., *Atti Accad. nazl. Lincei Mem.* **Ser. 8, 4,** 61 (1955) (c).
Odajima, A., Sohma, J., and Koike, M., *J. Chem. Phys.* **23,** 1959 (1955).
Odajima, A., Sohma, J., and Koike, M., *J. Phys. Soc. Japan* **12,** 272 (1957).
Pake, G. E., *J. Chem. Phys.* **16,** 327 (1948).
Pake, G. E., *Solid State Physics*, Vol. 2, Academic Press, New York, 1956, pp. 1–91.
Pollard, E. C., and Sturtevant, J. M., *Microwaves and Radar Electronics*, Wiley, New York, 1948.
Pople, J. A., *J. Chem. Phys.* **24,** 1111 (1956).
Pound, R. V., and Knight, W. D., *Rev. Sci. Instr.* **21,** 219 (1950).
Powles, J. G., *J. Polymer Sci.* **22,** 79 (1956).
Powles, J. G., and Gutowsky, H. S., *J. Chem. Phys.* **21,** 1695 (1953).
Ramsey, N. F., *Phys. Rev.* **78,** 699 (1950).
Ramsey, N. F., *Phys. Rev.* **86,** 243 (1952).
Ramsey, N. F., *Nuclear Moments*, Wiley, New York, 1953, p. 71.
Reding, F. P., *J. Polymer Sci.* **21,** 548 (1956).
Rogers, S. S., and Mandelkern, L., *J. Phys. Chem.* **61,** 985 (1957).
Saika, A., and Slichter, C. P., *J. Chem. Phys.* **22,** 26 (1954).
Sands, R. H., *Phys. Rev.* **99,** 1222 (1955).
Sauer, J. A., Wall, R. A., Fuschillo, N., and Woodward, A. E., *Bull. Am. Phys. Soc.* **Ser. II, 3,** 131 (1958).
Schneider, E. E., *Discussions Faraday Soc.* **19,** 158 (1955).
Slichter, W. P., *J. Appl. Phys.* **26,** 1099 (1955).
Slichter, W. P., and Mandell, E. R., *J. Chem. Phys.* **29,** 232 (1958).
Stroupe, J. D., and Hughes, R. E., *J. Am. Chem. Soc.* **80,** 2341 (1958).
Van Vleck, J. H., *Phys. Rev.* **74,** 1168 (1948).
Van Wieringen, J. S., and Kats, A., *Philips Research Repts.* **12,** 432 (1957).
Watkins, G. D., and Pound, R. V., *Phys. Rev.* **82,** 343 (1951).
Weeks, R. A., *J. Appl. Phys.* **27,** 1376 (1956).
Winslow, F. H., Baker, W. O., Pape, N. R., and Matreyek, W., *J. Polymer Sci.* **16,** 101 (1955).
Winslow, F. H., Baker, W. O., and Yager, W. A., *J. Am. Chem. Soc.* **77,** 4751 (1955).
Wittels, M. C., and Sherrill, F. A., *Phys. Rev.* **93,** 1117 (1954).
Würstlin, F., *Die Physik der Hochpolymeren*, Springer, Berlin, 1955, pp. 639–672.
Yasaitis, E. L., and Smaller, B., *Phys. Rev.* **92,** 1068 (1953).

DISCUSSION

D. A. VERMILYEA

From the temperature at which narrowing of the resonance occurs as a result of molecular motions in crystals, one can deduce a diffusion coefficient. Can this be done for amorphous solids as well?

W. P. SLICHTER

Self-diffusion seems to be indicated in many solid systems by a narrowing of the resonance line from the value expected for a wholly motionless lattice. An explicit measurement of the diffusion coefficient, in solids or liquids, depends in essence upon observing the relaxation of nuclei which have been elevated into a non-equilibrium distribution of excited states. In such studies, one observes the exchange of energy by nuclei with their environment after they have been "heated" to a temperature greater than that of the lattice. The relaxation processes leading to the energy exchange may include both rotation and translation and may involve other processes such as interaction with conduction electrons. When it can be adduced that the relaxation process primarily stems from translation, it is possible to calculate a diffusion coefficient. This can be measured by steady state methods similar to those just described, using different levels of radiofrequency power, but such a procedure proves very tedious. It is much easier to utilize the transient ("spin-echo") method of nuclear resonance, which was omitted from the foregoing treatment. However, most of such studies have been made on liquids, and rather few have been done on solids, since in solids the pertinent relaxation times tend to be inconveniently short.

A. B. BESTUL

It might be appropriate to mention pertinent experiments which have not been described, the NMR work done by Professor Bray at Brown University on glasses. He found it possible to do what one should call high resolution spectroscopy on B^{11} and Li^7 nuclei. By observing quadrupole effects in B^{11}, he has convinced himself and possibly me that he has essentially settled the coordination problem in the voids.

W. P. SLICHTER

The study of quadrupole spectra which you mentioned is potentially a powerful tool. Nuclei possessing spins other than $\frac{1}{2}$ possess quadrupole moments. This can be troublesome at times in that it introduces complexity in the usual nuclear resonance pattern, but this complexity is removed in a completely symmetric structure, in which the electric fields contributed by the surrounding groups are symmetrically disposed. Any dissymmetry in the surroundings reintroduces the splittings; these are, therefore, a measure of the dissymmetry present.

N. J. KREIDL

I would like to mention that phosphorus has been found quite useful by our group (at Bausch and Lomb Optical Company) and by other groups in electron paramagnetic resonance studies in associating the effects of radiation with trapped electrons. The phosphorus nucleus is used as a probe for determining the electron distribution, by observation of the splitting factor for phosphorus ion.

J. E. GOLDMAN

I wish to cite here some work carried out in our laboratory (Ford Motor Company) in which nuclear magnetic resonance coupled with x-ray measurements of radial distribution functions has yielded significant information on coordination in glasses. Dr. Milberg of our laboratory has been interested to learn what happens when water is introduced into a B_2O_3 glass and to determine the consequent coordination. He has been able to show from the radial distribution function that the hydrogen atoms enter to form BOHOB linkages. This can be seen quite clearly from the x-ray data, but very careful procedures had to be developed from compensating for the Compton scattering of the radiation and for other sources contributing to the background. Corrections for sample transparency and Compton scattering intensity have recently been published [Milberg, *J. Appl. Phys.* **29**, 64 (1958); Milberg and Brailsford, *Acta Cryst.* **11**, 672 (1958)].

Within the accuracy of the x-ray and infrared measurements, the three-fold coordination of the boron atoms with oxygen is not altered by the presence of 25 mole % H_2O. On the other hand, NMR work by Dr. Silver suggests of the order of 5% four-fold coordination—well within the accuracy of the x-ray and infrared measurements. This, of course, refers to the $B_2O_3 \cdot \frac{1}{3}H_2O$ as prepared by us in our laboratory. However, it is conceivable that alternative structures can be prepared by other methods of preparation.

Nuclear magnetic resonance studies have been made on boron oxide glasses by Silver and Bray [A. H. Silver and P. J. Bray, "Nuclear Magnetic Resonance Absorption in Glass. I. Nuclear Quadrupole Effects in Boron Oxide, Soda-Boric Oxide and Borosilicate Glasses," *J. Chem. Phys.* **29**, 984 (1958)]. Through measurement of the nuclear quadrupole interaction of the isotope B^{11}, it has been confirmed that boron has three (nearly) planar oxygen neighbors in boron oxide glasses. Measurement of a uniform quadrupole interaction gives strong support to the network former idea of glass and indicates a large covalent contribution, of the order of 50%, to the B-O bonds. Addition of a glass modifier, such as Na_2O or Li_2O, produces a reduction in the quadrupole interaction for some boron atoms. This is interpreted as a change in coordination and environment of some boron atoms to BO_4 tetrahedra. The remaining boron atoms have their local environment unchanged. Similar studies on "wet" boron oxide glass of approximate composition $B_2O_3 \cdot \frac{1}{3}H_2O$ show that, although BO_4 tetrahedra are formed with the presence of water, the relative number formed is much lower than with the alkali oxides. The implications of this in terms of glass structure and the influence of water upon its properties are interesting but beyond the scope of the present discussion.

Finally, I would like to mention some recent work by Knight and his associates using nuclear magnetic resonance techniques to examine the liquid state in metals which is the subject of a forthcoming survey (W. Knight, A. G. Berger, and V. Heine, "Nuclear Resonance in Solid and Liquid Metals: A Comparison of Electronic Structure"). Two techniques lend themselves to examination of liquid structure. One is the Knight shift, which is simply the shift of the magnetic resonance frequency of the nucleus due to the interaction with the conduction electrons which are polarized in the presence of a magnetic field and thus provides an additional effective field at the nucleus. The magnitude of this shift depends upon the density of energy states at the Fermi level and the nature of the wave functions at the Fermi level being greater when the latter are predominantly s in character. The other technique is to observe relaxation effects, e.g., quadrupolar broadening, which are sensitive to such factors as local symmetry and the like. Knight et al. have studied both these effects in several metals through the melting point and have come to the conclusion that there is a significant amount of zone structure remaining above the melting point. In only two of the ten metals examined (Ga, Bi) does an abrupt change appear at the melting point. In the other metals (Li, Na, Rb, Cs, Hg, Sn, In, Al) the Knight shift remains virtually unchanged through the melting point. This is a highly significant result in terms of understanding the electron structure of liquids. Its interpretation in terms of Brillouin zone structures are discussed by the authors in their paper, but the significant point in their conclusion is that the transition to the liquid state does not alter to any appreciable extent some of the long range symmetry characteristics of the wave functions of the banded (conduction) electrons.

EDGAR F. WESTRUM, JR.

I thought the application of NMR to the substituent group on the poly-ethylene-type plastics was very interesting, but I would like to inquire whether or not it is possible to learn something of the more subtle, larger scale motions of the chain in polyethylene. Has the comparison between the crystalline and amorphous states been studied by NMR?

W. P. SLICHTER

Yes, there have been a number of such studies. Perhaps one of the most conclusive ones was presented by McCall and Douglass, using a spin-echo experiment, in which they measured the self-diffusion of a variety of liquid hydrocarbons, including polymeric linear and branched chains, and were able to discern differences depending upon molecular configuration. They were also able to discern differences arising from branching. They demonstrated that in a linear polymer, such as fairly low molecular weight linear polyethylene, there occurs above the melting point a two-fold scale of relaxation processes, suggesting two different extents of order, i.e., a rather chaotic motion and a comparatively non-chaotic motion.

In elastomers, work was done by Gutowsky and his students at Illinois. They examined the flexibility of natural rubber and a number of synthetic elastomers which had been subjected to various degrees of cross-linking at different temperatures. One can also utilize a transient technique to examine these differences and thus determine the scale of relaxation times.

by

R. O. Davies

Queen Mary College, London

The Use and Limitations of Irreversible Thermodynamics in the Study of Relaxation Processes

What Is a Relaxation Process?

Since the term "relaxation" is notoriously slippery, it is as well to start by defining our use of it. We consider uniform homogeneous material systems in the neighborhood of equilibrium. Thermodynamically we may describe such systems by a set of "stimuli" or "thermodynamic forces" (such as pressure, electric and magnetic field, temperature) together with their corresponding "responses" or "thermodynamic co-ordinates" (dilatation, electric and magnetic polarization, energy). The correspondence lies, of course, in the fact that the (force) × (co-ordinate) products give contributions to an appropriate free energy.

If we start from an equilibrium state and make a *slow* small alteration in the forces, then the coordinates will change proportionately, the constants of proportionality being the thermodynamic coefficients—compliances or moduli as the case may be. If on the other hand we make a *sudden* change in the forces, then the coordinates will go through a transient period of time dependence before settling down to their new values. The system is exhibiting relaxation, in our sense of the word, and the phenomenon is a relaxation process. The time-dependent behavior can evidently be described by one or more two-terminal admittance or impedance functions. As is the case for electrical circuits, there are "realizability" conditions imposed on the impedance functions (see, for example, Guillemin, 1957) which take account of the passive, non-retroactive nature of physical systems.

There is one other condition which we wish to impose in order to complete our definition of relaxation: it is essential that the poles and zeros of the "driving point" impedance functions lie on the imaginary frequency axis. (The realizability conditions then ensure that poles and zeros are interlaced.) The effect of this is to make the system non-oscillatory; that is, the behavior in time involves exponentials and not sines. The electrical analogs of relaxing systems are therefore pure R-C or pure R-L circuits.

Some systems are oscillatory (e.g., resonant absorption of electrical energy, paramagnetic resonance, and nuclear resonance), and, surprisingly enough, they can be treated as thermodynamic systems (Onsager and Machlup, 1953; Hashitsume, 1956). We exclude them from the present remarks by the above definition of relaxation.

At first sight it seems as if we have a natural and useful classification of relaxation processes ready to hand: we can label systems according to the forces involved, i.e., "mechanical," "electrical," or "thermal," as the case may be. This is experimentally convenient but potentially misleading in condensed phases because there are always cross-effects and they are often important.

It is less precise but more valuable to adopt a classification based on the mechanism responsible for the relaxation process. Let us use the word "structure" to denote the relations *between* the basic particles of a system, e.g., space correlations and spin correlations. We then make the broad distinction between: (A) "chemical" mechanisms in which structural changes are unimportant but in which the "particle" changes its state, and (B) "physical" mechanisms which are dominated by structural changes. For example:

Type A. Chemical Mechanisms.
  (a) Isomeric changes in a molecule (e.g., rotational isomerism).
  (b) Molecular excitation (e.g., vibrational excitation).
  (c) Magnetic polarization (electronic or nuclear).
  (d) Electric polarization of dipoles in dilute solution or the gas phase; or of ions in a rigid framework.
  (e) Chemical reactions in (non-ionic) solution.
Type B. Physical Mechanisms.
  (a) Electric polarization in associated liquids and most ionic materials.
  (b) Chemical reactions in ionic solution.
  (c) "Pure" structural changes in liquids, high polymers, and glasses.

It is perhaps obvious that the distinction made here is not complete: all the chemical mechanisms involve some structural change, except in dilute gases. However, it is worth making for this reason: whereas fundamental microscopic theories about *physical* mechanisms will be of extraordinary complexity and are by no means in sight at present (consider the state of theories on liquid argon!), there is reasonable hope of some prompt progress with chemical mechanisms. Indeed, the most useful contributions to the theory of physical-type mechanisms have come either by forcing the mechanism into a chemical model or by making a "semimicroscopic" theory in which particles are treated macroscopically. As an example of the former procedure we have a discussion of volume changes in a glass by Orson Anderson (1956) in which the distribution of bond lengths in a silicate glass is arbitrarily divided into two, the fractions in each being treated as mole fractions of a two-state isomeric reaction. A recent and remarkable example of a semimicroscopic theory is the damped harmonic model of polymers due to Rouse (1953), Bueche (1954), and Zimm (1956). Vintage examples of the same approach are to be found in the dielectric theories associated with Debye, Onsager, and Fröhlich (see Fröhlich, 1949). A common feature of these semimicroscopic theories is that they do not fit readily into the thermodynamic framework, which is to be our main concern.

Consider, then, the role of irreversible thermodynamics in elucidating the behavior of chemical-type relaxations. We may suppose—a tall order, this—that the experimenter can obtain the impedance functions connecting thermodynamic forces and coordinates. (Let us mention here that there is an enormous and repetitive literature devoted to the theory and practice of presenting this information in different ways: relaxation spectra, impedances and admittances, their real and imaginary parts, indicial and step function responses, etc., can all be related to one another; and have been. Convenient reviews of this topic are given by Gross (1953), Macdonald and Brachman (1956), and Leaderman (1957). The experimenter's objective is now to relate his data to microscopic mechanisms in the system. He must first decide on the *number* of chemical mechanisms involved in the process. The theory of irreversible thermodynamics will then enable him to predict the *form* of his impedance functions, involving, it is to be hoped, a small number of parameters. This can be checked against his results and the parameters fitted to them. He could, of course, have got as far as this by an intelligent guess and would have done so in the days before irreversible thermodynamics became fashionable. Nevertheless, it is satisfying to have a generally applicable method for getting the time-dependent behavior of a system. Sometimes (see "Thermodynamic Equations of Motion for an Isotropic,

Viscoelastic Medium" below) the method gives results which are not quite easy to guess.

The next step is crucial: if he can now think of a chemical reaction mechanism appropriate to his system, our investigator may express the parameters obtained from his experiments in terms of the thermodynamic and kinetic *chemical* parameters of his reaction mechanism, i.e., in terms of heat and volume changes of the reaction on the one hand and the chemical rate constants or transition probabilities on the other. This is as far as thermodynamics can take him. It is generally felt, especially by chemists, that the latter "reaction" quantities are more accessible to a microscopic discussion than the original parameters and so real progress has been made.

To sum up: the thermodynamic theory of relaxation starts from an assumed chemical-type relaxation mechanism and aims to find: (a) appropriate forms for the macroscopic equations of motion, (b) methods of obtaining chemical reaction coefficients (like ΔH_0 and ΔV_0) from the observable parameters, (c) methods of obtaining transition probabilities or chemical rate constants from the observable parameters.

The first step does not involve the chemistry explicitly. In the remainder of this chapter we consider the thermodynamics of relaxation and its aims in more detail. In the next two sections we give a sketch of the thermodynamic theory of relaxation, the broad outlines in the first of them, and a more detailed part which takes in chemistry in the second. In the section following these two we discuss aims (a), (b), and (c) (above) by trying to carry them out for selected cases. Then we briefly assess the current situation.

The Thermodynamics of Relaxation: Basic Ideas

The essential idea needed to construct a thermodynamic theory is this: the relaxation mechanisms are described by one or more internal ordering variables z^r ($r = 1, \cdots, n$) which are added to the ordinary independent and controllable thermodynamic variables of the problem (e.g., entropy and volume) to complete the thermodynamic specification of the system. We shall suppose that there are ν ordinary independent variables x^α ($\alpha = 1, \cdots, \nu$). (Where appropriate, we use a summation convention with Roman letters in the second half of the alphabet running from 1 to n and Greek letters from 1 to ν.) The simplest internal variable arises from a single chemical reaction and can be taken to be the degree of reaction. In this section we shall not restrict outselves to the chemical case and shall thus leave the ordering variables undefined, although of course it is sometimes convenient to use the language of chemistry. It is obvious that, in a sense, the idea of using ordering variables dates from the time of Gibbs. Systematic study is, however, more modern. Eminent contributors include de Donder (1936), Frenkel (1946), Prigogine and Defay (1954), and particularly Meixner (1943, 1953, 1954). The present writer's interest in the subject originated in an attempt to understand some measurements on glasses made with Jones (Davies and Jones, 1953a, 1954a); a more detailed account of irreversibility on lines similar to this essay is available (Davies, 1956).

Let the forces conjugate to the chosen thermodynamic coordinates be X_α (e.g., temperature and pressure), and the affinities conjugate to the ordering parameters be A_r. Then changes in an appropriate free energy F are given by

$$-dF = X_\alpha \, dx^\alpha + A_r \, dz^r \tag{1}$$

The free energy is appropriate in the sense that, if the coordinates x^α are held fixed, then F necessarily decreases. Hence in equilibrium we must have $A_r = 0$, since F is a minimum at fixed x^α. We choose an equilibrium state as a fixed reference state and reckon X_α, x^α, and z^r as zero there. For small departures from the reference state it is reasonable to assume linear laws expressing X_α and A_r in terms of the independent variables of the system:

$$\begin{aligned} X_\alpha &= c_{\alpha\beta}x^\beta + \lambda_{\alpha s}z^s \\ A_r &= \lambda_{r\beta}x^\beta + \beta_{rs}z^s \end{aligned} \tag{2}$$

Since dF is a complete differential, then (Maxwell's relations) $c_{\alpha\beta} = c_{\beta\alpha}$, $\lambda_{r\beta} = \lambda_{\beta r}$, $\beta_{rs} = \beta_{sr}$. The significance of the constants here should be noted:

(a) The $c_{\alpha\beta}$ are "glassy," "frozen," or "instantaneous" moduli; they include elastic moduli, expansivities, heat capacities, etc.

(b) The $\lambda_{\alpha r}$ give the change in force per unit change in ordering variables; in the chemical case they may be the heat of reaction and volume change of reaction, and in any case they reflect the links between the mechanism of the relaxation and the external variables. We call them "reaction coefficients."

(c) The least familiar of these coefficients is the set $\beta_{rs} = \partial A_r/\partial z^s$, which can be called "ordering coefficients"; in the chemical case they involve the variation of chemical potential with composition, and in any case they give a measure of the force tending to push the system back to equilibrium when z^r is displaced. Except in the degenerate case of neutral equilibrium, β_{rs} is negative definite.

Equation (2) with its Maxwellian appendage implies all that is to be said about the static theory of thermodynamic relaxation. However, the modern theory of irreversibility yields also a dynamic account. The rate of irreversible dissipation of energy is, from the foregoing, given by

$$P_{\text{irr}} = -(dF/dt)_{\text{irr}} = A_r \, dz^r/dt \tag{3}$$

Since this is a bilinear form in the "forces" A_r and "flows" dz^r/dt, it is assumed that the appropriate kinetic law for the system is

$$dz^r/dt = L^{rs} A_s \tag{4}$$

in which the Onsager symmetry principle requires that

$$L^{rs} = L^{sr} \tag{5}$$

Eliminating A_r and z^s from (2) and (4), we have for the thermodynamic equations of motion

$$X_\alpha = \left\{ c_{\alpha\beta} - \lambda_{\alpha r} \left(I + \tau \frac{d}{dt} \right)^{-1} z_s{}^r (\beta^{-1})^{st} \lambda_{t\beta} \right\} x^\beta \tag{6}$$

in which we have written

$$\tau_s{}^r = -(\beta^{-1})^{rt} L^{-1}{}_{ts} \tag{7}$$

for the matrix of relaxation times. This use of the differential operator can easily be justified by Fourier methods.

If the change in state described by (6) be carried out sufficiently slowly, then the bracketed coefficient on the right side takes its limiting, equilibrium form which we denote by $\bar{c}_{\alpha\beta} \equiv c_{\alpha\beta} + \delta c_{\alpha\beta}$ where

$$\delta c_{\alpha\beta} = -\lambda_{\alpha r} (\beta^{-1})^{rs} \lambda_{t\beta} \tag{8}$$

The part $\delta c_{\alpha\beta}$, which is, by (8), connected to the reaction coefficients and the ordering coefficients, forms the relaxing part of the thermodynamic coefficients (sometimes $\delta c_{\alpha\beta}/\bar{c}_{\alpha\beta}$ is called a "relaxation strength"). Equation (8) does not depend on the dynamic assumption (4) and could have been obtained directly from (2). The relaxing components on the left side are measurable by doing "very fast" and "very slow" measurements and forming the difference. Unfortunately, there are too many unknowns on the right side to permit us to get reaction coefficients from such measurements, and the best we can do is to provide certain restrictions on the possible values of $\delta c_{\alpha\beta}$. Meixner points out that, thanks to the Schwarz inequality, we have

$$\delta c_{\alpha\alpha} \delta c_{\beta\beta} \geq (\delta c_{\alpha\beta})^2 \quad \text{(no summation)} \tag{9}$$

For the case of a single ordering parameter the equality sign is required in (9), and for a simple fluid system one then finds

$$\delta C_p \, \delta \kappa = TV(\delta\alpha)^2 \tag{10}$$

in which the new symbols refer to the heat capacity, compressibility, and expansivity of the system. Equation (10) has been used to test whether the system can be described by a single ordering parameter by Davies and Jones (1953b) and by Anderson (private communication). The results are not encouraging for glass-forming systems.

Turning now to the dynamical equation (6), it is instructive to see the form it takes for a one-parameter fluid system. Using p and T as independent variables, it can easily be thrown into the shape

$$\Delta S = \left\{ C_p + \frac{\delta C_p}{1 + \tau \, d/dt} \right\} \Delta T - V \left\{ \alpha + \frac{\delta\alpha}{1 + \tau \, d/dt} \right\} \Delta p$$

$$\Delta V = V \left\{ \alpha + \frac{\delta\alpha}{1 + \tau \, d/dt} \right\} \Delta T - V \left\{ \kappa + \frac{\delta\kappa}{1 + \tau \, d/dt} \right\} \Delta p \tag{11}$$

At constant temperature, for example, we find that the dilatation $\epsilon (\equiv \Delta V/V)$ and the pressure deviation $\pi (\equiv \Delta p)$ are related by

$$\epsilon + \tau\dot{\epsilon} + \bar{\kappa}\pi + \tau\kappa\dot{\pi} = 0 \tag{12}$$

Equation (12) is the well-known formula for simple relaxation, and its emergence illustrates once more how irreversible thermodynamics tends to produce the obvious. Let us remember, however, that for many years applied mathematicians have followed Stokes and written (if not used) a version of (12) in which the last term is suppressed. This implies that the "glassy" compressibility is zero and is hardly acceptable for liquids, except of course at low frequencies. It is indeed the advance of high frequency techniques that has made us think again.

In the general case of n ordering parameters it can be shown that the right side of (6) can be represented by the impedance function

$$Z_{\alpha\beta}(i\omega) = c_{\alpha\beta} + \sum_{r=1}^{n} \frac{\delta_r c_{\alpha\beta}}{1 + i\omega\tau_r} \tag{13}$$

and that, thanks to the Onsager relation (5), $Z_{\alpha\beta} = Z_{\beta\alpha}$. The total relaxing parts of the thermodynamic coefficients are now resolved into contributions from "normal" ordering variables:

$$\delta c_{\alpha\beta} = \sum_r \delta_r c_{\alpha\beta}$$

with

$$(\delta_r c_{\alpha\alpha})(\delta_r c_{\beta\beta}) = (\delta_r c_{\alpha\beta})^2 \quad \text{(no summation)} \tag{14}$$

These procedures are carried out by using a set of "normal" ordering variables chosen so as to make $\tau_s{}^r$ and β_{rs} simultaneously diagonal. The quantities τ_r are the eigenvalues of the τ matrix and constitute the spectrum of relaxation times of the system *relative to the chosen independent variables* x^α. The last point is frequently overlooked although one case of it, viz., the difference between retardation and relaxation times in viscoelasticity, is well known.

It is clear that one can extend the *results* of the theory by admitting linear, time-dependent operators with a continuous spectrum and letting (13) take a limiting form:

$$Z_{\alpha\beta}(i\omega) = c_{\alpha\beta} + \int_0^\infty \frac{f_{\alpha\beta}(\tau)\, d\tau}{1 + i\omega\tau} \tag{15}$$

It is the function $f(\tau)$ which is usually called the relaxation (or retardation) spectrum of a system. It should be observed that, regarded as a limit of (13), this function contains distributions of *both* the relaxation strengths $\delta_r c_{\alpha\beta}$ *and* the relaxation times τ_r. Therefore it should not be associated only with the time spectrum of (13). It can give only very crude indications about microscopic mechanisms.

There are other ways of introducing dynamical laws into the theory than by assuming equation (4). The most interesting of these considers the parameters z^r as undergoing Brownian motion in a harmonic force field with large damping (or small inertia). Thus z^r is assumed to be a Gaussian Markoff process. Equation (4) appears on the left side of a Langevin equation or alternatively as the equation governing the mean decay of a fluctuation. The inspiration behind theories of this type is undoubtedly the feeling that the concepts of Brownian motion are nearer to the microscopic realities and hence more likely to form a springboard for the jump. Without being churlish, one should perhaps recall that the chemical reaction theory of Kramers (1940) and the liquid theories of Kirkwood and his collaborators still need macroscopic friction constants. They are thus semimicroscopic, in the sense of our first section.

The Thermodynamics of Relaxation: A Treatment of the Chemistry

The main result of the general theory of the preceding section has been to exhibit the observable impedances in equation (13) in terms of relaxation strengths $\delta_r c_{\alpha\beta}$ and relaxation times τ_r which are eigenvalues of the matrix $\tau_s{}^r$. The relaxation strengths come from (8)—which involves the ordering coefficients β_{rs} and the reaction coefficients $\lambda_{\alpha r}$—and the relaxation matrix is defined by (7) in terms of β_{rs} and the rate constants L^{rs}.

To carry out the program of our first section, we now suppose that the ordering parameters z^r are the degrees of n independent chemical reactions such that a change in mole numbers N^i of the species i in the system is given by

$$dN^i = \nu_r{}^i \, dz^r \tag{16}$$

where $\nu_r{}^i$ are stoichiometric coefficients which can be regarded as fixing the choice of the z's. The corresponding affinities are

$$A_r = -\sum_i \nu_r{}^i \mu_i \tag{17}$$

where μ_i are the chemical potentials. Hence, by definition,

$$\beta_{rs} = -\sum_i \sum_j \nu_r{}^i \nu_s{}^j \frac{\partial \mu_i}{\partial N^j} \tag{18}$$

Let us now specialize the theory further by assuming that (a) the independent thermodynamic variables are p and T; (b) the reaction mechanisms are isomeric shifts between $(n + 1)$ states of a particle (there are therefore n independent reactions or ordering parameters); (c) the $(n + 1)$ species present form an ideal solution:

$$\mu_i = \mu_i{}^0 + RT \ln (N^i/N) \quad \text{where} \quad N \equiv \sum_i N^i$$

(Let Roman letters in the first half of the alphabet run from 1 to $n + 1$.)

A possible choice of independent reaction mechanisms for the system of (b) is obtained by setting

$$\nu_r{}^i = \delta_r{}^i - \delta_{n+1}^i \qquad i = 1, \cdots, n + 1 \tag{19}$$

$$r = 1, \cdots, n$$

It follows from (18), (19), and assumption (c) that

$$\beta_{rs} = -RT(1/N^{n+1} + \delta_{rs}/N^r) \quad \text{(no summation)} \tag{20}$$

The inverse of this, which is what appears in the crucial formulas (7) and (8), can be shown to be

$$(\beta^{-1})^{rs} = -\frac{1}{RT} \left(N^r \delta_{rs} - \frac{N^r N^s}{N} \right) \quad \text{(no summation)} \tag{21}$$

It is often desirable to express the mole numbers N^r appearing in these formulas in terms of the thermodynamic properties of the solution. Since they are the equilibrium mole numbers, the result comes by setting $A_r = 0$ in equation (17). This yields

$$N^i = (N/z) \exp\left(-\mu_i{}^0/RT\right) \tag{22}$$

where

$$z = \sum_i \exp\left(-\mu_i{}^0/RT\right)$$

The simplest case covered by the present formalism is the popular two-state reaction ($n = 1$) for which it can be shown from (20) and (22) that

$$\beta = -\frac{N}{RT} \frac{\exp\left(\Delta G_0/RT\right)}{\left[1 + \exp\left(\Delta G_0/RT\right)\right]^2} \tag{23}$$

where $\Delta G_0 = \mu_2{}^0 - \mu_1{}^0$.

In this case also, which we shall discuss below under "The Problem of Finding the Chemical Reaction Parameters (ΔH_0 and ΔV_0) from Ultrasonic Measurements of the Relaxation Strength," the two reaction parameters are essentially ΔH_0 and ΔV_0, the molar enthalpy and volume changes in going from one pure state to the other.

Some Applications of the Thermodynamic Theory of Relaxation

Thermodynamic Equations of Motion for an Isotropic, Viscoelastic Medium

In order to show how the theory outlined under "The Thermodynamics of Relaxation: Basic Ideas" can be used to obtain suitable forms for the equations of motion of a system, consider the problem of finding thermodynamically reasonable expressions for a simple viscoelastic material showing relaxation in shear as well as in bulk behavior. This problem, although old, is not trivial.

We wish to make the simplest hypothesis about ordering parameters. The obvious idea is to try to obtain with a single parameter equations analogous to (12) for shearing motion as well as bulk motion. It is easy to see that, thanks to equation (9)—which becomes an equality for a single parameter—it is impossible to have a *relaxing* shear modulus in this case. The easiest generalization is to suppose that the internal ordering variable is a symmetric cartesian tensor z^{ij}. Since the material is isotropic, we must have (Jeffreys, 1931) β^{-1} of the form

$$(\beta^{-1})^{rs,kl} = -A\,\delta_{rs}\,\delta_{kl} - B(\delta_{rk}\,\delta_{sl} + \delta_{rl}\,\delta_{sk}) - C(\delta_{rk}\,\delta_{sl} - \delta_{rl}\,\delta_{sk}) \tag{24}$$

Now Maxwell's relation in this case is $(\beta^{-1})^{rs,kl} = (\beta^{-1})^{kl,rs}$, so that $C = 0$ in equation (24). By a similar argument, using the Onsager symmetry of (5), we have

$$(L^{-1})_{kl,mn} = L\,\delta_{kl}\,\delta_{mn} + M(\delta_{km}\,\delta_{ln} + \delta_{kn}\,\delta_{lm}) \tag{25}$$

and hence, using (7) for the τ matrix, we have

$$\tau_{mn}{}^{rs} = \tau_1 \, \delta_{rs} \, \delta_{mn} + \tau_2(\delta_{rm} \, \delta_{sn} + \delta_{rn} \, \delta_{sm}) \tag{26}$$

with $\tau_1 = 3AL + 2AM + 2BL$ and $\tau_2 = 2BM$ as the *two* relaxation times associated with the problem.

The thermodynamic equations of motion are now given by substituting (24) and (26) in the general expression (6):

$$X_\alpha = \left\{ \bar{c}_{\alpha\beta} - \frac{\delta_1 c_{\alpha\beta}\tau_1 \, d/dt}{1 + \tau_1 \, d/dt} - \frac{\delta_2 c_{\alpha\beta}\tau_2 \, d/dt}{1 + \tau_2 \, d/dt} \right\} x^\beta \tag{27}$$

where $\delta_1 c_{\alpha\beta} = (3A + 2B)\lambda_{\alpha,mm}\lambda_{\beta,nn}$
$\delta_2 c_{\alpha\beta} = 2A\lambda_{\alpha,mm}\lambda_{\beta,nn} + 4B\lambda_{\alpha,mn}\lambda_{\beta,mn}$

These rather formal expressions are actually full of interest when applied to find the thermoelastic response of an isotropic medium. The thermodynamic coordinates can be taken as temperature ($x^0 \equiv \Delta T$) and strain ($x^{ij} \equiv e_{ij}$, $i, j = 1, 2, 3$), Owing to isotropy, the reaction coefficients (λ) can be written

$$\lambda_{ij,mn} = l \, \delta_{ij} \, \delta_{mn} + m(\delta_{im} \, \delta_{jn} + \delta_{in} \, \delta_{jm})$$
$$\lambda_{0,mn} = c \, \delta_{mn} \tag{28}$$

Introduce (28) into the relaxing parts of (27) and write, for brevity, $3l + 2m = n$, $3A + 2B = C$. We find

$$\delta_1 c_{ij,kl} = n^2 C \, \delta_{ij} \, \delta_{kl}$$
$$\delta_2 c_{ij,kl} = (\tfrac{2}{3}n^2 C - \tfrac{16}{3}m^2 B) \, \delta_{ij} \, \delta_{kl} + 8m^2 B(\delta_{ik} \, \delta_{jl} + \delta_{jk} \, \delta_{il}) \tag{29}$$

$$\delta_1 c_{0,ij} = 3ncC \, \delta_{ij}$$
$$\delta_2 c_{0,ij} = 2ncC \, \delta_{ij} \tag{30}$$

$$\delta_1 c_{0,0} = 9c^2 C$$
$$\delta_2 c_{0,0} = 6c^2 C \tag{31}$$

The physical significance of these equations is immediate: they give the relaxing parts (associated respectively with the two relaxation times τ_1 and τ_2) of the (negative) isothermal elastic moduli (29) of the thermodynamic coefficient $-(\partial S/\partial V)_T$ (30) and of the heat capacity $(1/V)(\partial S/\partial T)_V$ (31).

We shall not discuss the kinetic implications of these results beyond observing that it is only pure shearing motion which has a single relaxation time (τ_2); any bulk effect involves both the relaxation times.

Consider now the total contributions to the relaxing thermodynamic coefficients. They are

$$\delta\lambda = -\tfrac{5}{3}n^2C + \tfrac{16}{3}m^2B$$

$$\delta\mu = -8m^2B$$

$$\delta\left(\partial S/\partial V_T\right) = -5ncC \tag{32}$$

$$\frac{1}{V}\,\delta\,\frac{\partial S}{\partial T_V} = 15c^2C$$

where λ and μ are Lamés moduli (μ is the shear modulus G). Since the bulk modulus is $K = \lambda + \tfrac{2}{3}\mu$, it follows that

$$\delta K = -\tfrac{5}{3}n^2C \tag{33}$$

Hence from (32) and (33) we have

$$-\frac{1}{V}\,\delta K\,\delta\left(\frac{\partial S}{\partial T}\right)_V = [\delta(\partial S/\partial V)_T]^2$$

or

$$-\delta K\,\delta C_v = TV[\delta(\alpha K)]^2 \tag{34}$$

where α is the expansivity.

(Notice that $\delta\mu$ and δK are negative.) The conclusion (34) is remarkable because *it is in fact equivalent to the result (10)*. Hence the introduction of a tensorial ordering parameter, while permitting a shear relaxation which is not possible in the scalar theory, still yields the same static relation as that theory. The relaxing part of the shear modulus is quite independent of the relaxing part of the bulk modulus and is not restricted by any thermodynamic relation.

The Problem of Finding the Chemical Reaction Parameters ΔH_0 and ΔV_0 from Ultrasonic Measurements of the Relaxation Strength

Over the last few years there has been considerable interest in using ultrasonic absorption measurements to get information about relaxation mechanisms whose relaxation times lie in the range 10^{-6} to 10^{-9} sec (reviewed by Davies and Lamb, 1957). In the case of a single mechanism, which we take to be an isomeric, two-state reaction in ideal solutions, measurements over a reasonable range of frequency at a given pressure and temperature yield two parameters: a relaxation strength (r) and a relaxation time (τ). We are concerned here with the former property, which can be shown to be proportional to the relaxing part of the adiabatic compressibility; in fact, $r = \delta\kappa_s/\bar{\kappa}_s$. Now, by the theory of the two preceding sections (especially equations (8) and (22)), one can express $\delta\kappa_s$ in terms of the reaction parameters of the system. The result can be written

$$\left\{\frac{\bar{C}_p}{R}\frac{r}{\bar{\gamma}-1}\right\}^{\frac{1}{2}} \equiv F(p,\,T) = \left\{\frac{\Delta H_0}{RT} - \frac{\bar{C}_p}{\bar{\alpha}V}\frac{\Delta V_0}{RT}\right\}\frac{\exp{(\Delta G_0/2RT)}}{1 + \exp{(\Delta G_0/RT)}} \qquad (35)$$

The left-hand side of this equation is, in principle, an observable function of pressure and temperature. The question is: how can knowledge of it lead to information about the *three* unknown reaction parameters on the right side, viz., ΔH_0, ΔV_0, and ΔG_0? It is obvious that some additional information must be brought to bear on the problem.

Since one wishes to use the variation of absorption with pressure and temperature, it is natural to introduce *derivatives* of F as fresh experimental quantities. Let us use the dimensionless combinations

$$\mathbf{G} = \frac{\Delta H_0}{RT} \qquad \mathbf{H} = \frac{\Delta H_0}{RT} \qquad \mathbf{V} = \frac{\bar{C}_p}{\bar{\alpha}V}\frac{\Delta V_0}{RT}$$

$$\mathbf{C} = \frac{\Delta C_{p0}}{R} \qquad \mathbf{A} = \frac{\bar{C}_p}{R}\cdot\frac{\Delta\alpha_0}{\bar{\alpha}} \qquad \mathbf{K} = \frac{\bar{C}_p}{R}\frac{\gamma}{\gamma-1}\frac{\Delta\kappa_0}{\bar{\kappa}} \qquad (36)$$

and let us assume that $(\bar{\alpha}V/\bar{C}_p)$ is constant so as to linearize the problem in terms of the dimensionless pressure, $P \equiv (\bar{\alpha}V/\bar{C}_p)p$. One then finds by differentiating equation (35) that

$$\mathbf{H} - \mathbf{V} = 2F \sec\gamma$$

$$\mathbf{C} - \mathbf{A} = 2\left(1 + \frac{\partial\ln F}{\partial\ln T}\right)F(\sec\gamma) - \mathbf{H}F\tan\gamma \qquad (37)$$

$$\mathbf{K} - \mathbf{A} = 2\frac{\partial\ln F}{\partial P}F(\sec\gamma) + \mathbf{V}(1 + \mathbf{F}\tan\gamma)$$

where $\mathbf{G} = 4\tanh^{-1}\tan\frac{1}{2}\gamma$.

The awful truth is now revealed: there are *three* accessible experimental parameters $[F, (\partial\ln F)/(\partial\ln T), \text{ and } (\partial\ln F)/\partial P]$ and no less than *six* unknowns ($\mathbf{G, H, V, A, C, K}$) with only three relations between them. So we must make at least *three* more assumptions before being able to get anything from the data!

In all existing discussions the assumptions are (or imply) that $\mathbf{V} = \mathbf{A} = \mathbf{C} = \mathbf{K} = 0$. Hence

$$\frac{\partial \ln F}{\partial P} = 0$$

$$\mathbf{H} = 2 \left\{ F^2 + \left(1 + \frac{\partial \ln F}{\partial \ln T} \right)^2 \right\}^{1/2}$$

(38)

The first of equations (38) has rarely been tested, except by Litovitz and Carnevale (1958), who are wise enough not to press the interpretation too far. The second equation often gives "reasonable" values for ΔH_0, but the external checks are precarious. The assumption $\Delta V_0 = 0$ is a very strong one, even for the isomeric reactions under consideration. The point is that $\Delta V_0 / V$ must be compared with $\bar{a}(\Delta H_0/\bar{C}_p)$. Putting in reasonable values ($\alpha = 10^{-3}$ deg^{-1}, $\Delta H_0 = 2$ kcal mole^{-1}, $C_p = 50$ cal mole^{-1} deg^{-1}), one finds that the terms are comparable for a volume change of only 4%. This is not a large volume change for isomeric changes in a liquid.

Other attempts to deal with the equations (37) have not been very successful.

The Problem of Finding the Transition Probabilities from Ultrasonic Measurements of a Relaxation Time

It will be recalled that the relaxation times are introduced into the theory (in equation 7) by an expression involving the solution properties (β) and a set of macroscopic friction constants (L^{ij}) defined in equation (4) by a method characteristic of the Onsager theory. The L^{ij} seem to be far removed from anything that we think we understand. For the $(n + 1)$-state process of equations (19) to (23) we can do rather better: let us introduce a set of macroscopic parameters $p_i{}^j$ and assume, instead of equation (4), that the kinetics of the system is governed by

$$\frac{dN^i}{dt} = \sum_j N^j P_j{}^i \qquad (39)$$

with

$$\sum_j P_i{}^j = 0$$

Clearly, $P_i{}^j$ ($i \neq j$) can be interpreted as the probability per unit time that a particle in state i goes over to state j. It should be noticed that the $P_i{}^j$ are functions of the thermodynamic variables (x^α) and the ordering variables (z^r).

Expand equation (39) about an equilibrium state for which

$$\sum_j \bar{N}^j P_j{}^i = 0 \qquad (40)$$

and we find, with the help of (16), that

$$\frac{d \,\Delta N^i}{dt} = \sum_s \left\{ \sum_j \bar{N}^j \frac{\partial P_j{}^i}{\partial z^s} + \sum_j P_j{}^i \nu_s{}^i \right\} z^s + \sum_\alpha \left\{ \sum_j \bar{N}^j \frac{\partial P_j{}^i}{\partial x^\alpha} \right\} x^\alpha \quad (41)$$

On the other hand, the original kinetic equation involving the L^{rs} (4) yields, with (2), the expression

$$\frac{dz^r}{dt} = - \sum_s W_s{}^r z^s - \sum_\alpha W_\alpha{}^r x^\alpha \quad (42)$$

where

$$W_s{}^r = (\tau^{-1})_s{}^r = - \sum_t L^{rt} \beta_{ts}$$

and

$$W_\alpha{}^r = \sum_t L^{rt} \lambda_{t\alpha}$$

Comparing (41) and (42) [with the help of the stoichiometric representation (19) chosen for the $(n + 1)$-state process] now gives for the matrix of inverse relation times the formula

$$(\tau^{-1})_s{}^r = W_s{}^r = P^r_{n+1} - P_s{}^r - \sum_j \bar{N}^j \frac{\partial P_j{}^r}{\partial z^s} \quad (43)$$

Since the $P_i{}^j$ are intensive properties of the system, one has also a Gibbs-Duhem type of formula expressing homogeneity:

$$\sum_k N^k \frac{\partial P_i{}^j}{\partial N^k} = 0 \quad (44)$$

Equations (43) and (44) give more surveyable expressions for the relaxation times than the original expression (7).

There are two important conclusions to be drawn from this result.

(a) Let us write the form taken by (43) for the simplest and commonest case of a 2-state process. We find

$$\tau^{-1} = P_1{}^2 + P_2{}^1 + x \frac{\partial P_2{}^1}{\partial x} - (1 - x) \frac{\partial P_1{}^2}{\partial x} \quad (45)$$

where $x = N^2/N$. The first two terms in this expression are well known and have been used many times in discussions of rate processes. The second two terms are new, and there is no *a priori* reason why they should be small compared with the first two terms. Hence

In order to calculate relaxation times we need both the transition probabilities and their dependence on concentration.

(b) In the earlier rate expressions, an essential condition for the reality of relaxation times and the operator manipulations of the section titled "The Thermodynamics of Relaxation: Basic Ideas" was the Onsager symmetry of equation (5): $L^{rs} = L^{sr}$. In the transition probability approach one requires

$$\sum_r \beta_{tr} W_s{}^r = \sum_r \beta_{sr} W_t{}^r$$

Using (20) and (43), this condition is

$$\sum_j \left\{ \frac{1}{N^s N^{n+1}} \sum_r (N^s \alpha_s{}^{jr} - N^r \alpha_r{}^{js}) \right.$$

$$+ \frac{1}{N^t N^{n+1}} \sum_r (N^r \alpha_r{}^{jt} - N^t \alpha_t{}^{js})$$

$$\left. + \frac{1}{N^t N^s} (N^s \alpha_s{}^{jt} - N^t \alpha_t{}^{js}) \right\}$$

$$+ \frac{1}{N^s N^{n+1}} \sum_r (N^s P_s{}^r - N^r P_r{}^s)$$

$$+ \frac{1}{N^t N^{n+1}} \sum_r (N^r P_r{}^t - N^t P_t{}^r)$$

$$+ \frac{1}{N^t N^s} (N^s P_s{}^t - N^t P_t{}^s) = 0 \qquad (46)$$

for all t, $s \leq n$. [Here we have written $\alpha^{ij} = -\alpha^{ji} = \bar{N}^i P_i{}^j - \bar{N}^j P_j{}^i$ (no summation)—an expression which satisfies $\sum_k N_k \alpha_k{}^{ij} = 0$ because of (44); also $\alpha_r{}^{ij}$ means $\partial \alpha^{ij}/\partial N^r$.]

It is obvious that *sufficient* conditions for this to be true are

$$N^s P_s{}^t = N^t P_t{}^s \quad \text{(no summation)} \qquad (47)$$

together with

$$\sum_j N^s \alpha_s{}^{jt} = \sum_j N^t \alpha_t{}^{js} \qquad (48)$$

Condition (47) is usually said to be the condition for "microscopic reversibility." Equation (48) is a new condition which has no obvious physical interpretation.

We are thus led to conclude:

In order for the Onsager reciprocal relations to be true we need to impose on the transition probabilities conditions other than those given by the microscopic reversibility principle.

Conclusion

To what extent does the thermodynamic theory of relaxation achieve the objects outlined in the first section? I think that the work in equations (24) to (34) shows that it is moderately successful in providing reasonable macroscopic equations of motion. In contrast, the work in equations (35) to (48) shows that even the "pointers" toward microscopic information (ΔH_0, ΔV_0, transition probabilities) are very difficult to obtain in practical cases. Here, I think, the theory must at present be judged a moderate failure.

ACKNOWLEDGMENT

The work summarized in the section titled "The Problem of Finding the Chemical Reaction Parameters ΔH_0 and ΔV_0 from Ultrasonic Measurements of the Relaxation Strength" was done in collaboration with Dr. John Lamb, whose demands for usable results have been an enormous stimulus to me.

REFERENCES

Anderson, O. L., *J. Appl. Phys.* **27**, 943 (1956).
Bueche, F., *J. Chem. Phys.* **22**, 603 (1954).
Davies, R. O., *Repts. Progr. Phys.* **18**, 326 (1956).
Davies, R. O., and Jones, G. O., *Proc. Roy. Soc. (London)*A **217**, 26 (1953) (a).
Davies, R. O., and Jones, G. O., *Advance in Phys.* (Phil. Mag. Suppl.) **2**, 370 (1953) (b).
Davies, R. O., and Lamb, J., *Quart. Revs. (London)* **11**, 134 (1957).
de Donder, T., *Affinity*, University Press, Stanford, 1936.
Frenkel, J., *Kinetic Theory of Liquids*, University Press, Oxford, 1946.
Fröhlich, H., *Theory of Dielectrics*, University Press, Oxford, 1949.
Gross, B., *Mathematical Structure of Theories of Viscoelasticity*, Hermann, Paris, 1953.
Guillemin, E. A., *Synthesis of Passive Networks*, Wiley, New York, 1957.
Hashitsume, N., *Progr. Theoret. Phys. (Kyoto)* **15**, 369 (1956).
Jeffreys, H., *Cartesian Tensors*, University Press, Cambridge, 1931.
Kramers, H., *Physica* **7**, 284 (1940).
Leaderman, H., *Lecture Notes on High Polymer Physics*, Tokyo, 1957.
Litovitz, T., and Carnevale, E. H., *J. Acoust. Soc. Am.* **30**, 134 (1958).
Macdonald, J. R., and Brachman, M. K., *Revs. Mod. Phys.* **28**, 393 (1956).
Meixner, J., *Ann. Physik* (5) **43**, 470 (1943).
Meixner, J., *Kolloid-Z.* **134**, 3 (1953).
Meixner, J., *Z. Naturforsch.* **9a**, 654 (1954).
Onsager, L., and Machlup, S., *Phys. Rev.* **91**, 1505 (1953).

Prigogine, I., and Defay, R., *Chemical Thermodynamics*, Longmans, Green, London, 1954.

Rouse, P. E., *J. Chem. Phys.* **21**, 1272 (1953).

Zimm, B. H., *J. Chem. Phys.* **24**, 269 (1956).

DISCUSSION

R. W. DOUGLAS

Some recent observations of Van Zee and Noritake [Van Zee, A. F., and Noritake, H. M., *J. Am. Ceram. Soc.* **41**, 164 (1958)] make possible the evaluation of the volume viscosity and the shear viscosity in soda-lime-silica glasses. In these experiments specimens of the glass which had been previously brought to equilibrium at the temperature of the experiment were subjected to bending stresses and the decay of stress was measured photoelastically. This system of stress is uniaxial, and the results were therefore analyzed in terms of the simple spring and dashpot system of Fig. 1. As shown in this figure, the volume relaxa-

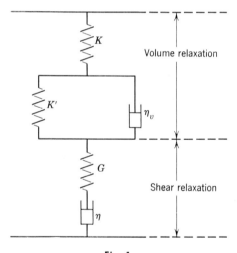

Fig. 1.

tion is represented by K, which represents the bulk modulus, the relaxing part of the modulus by K', and the volume viscosity by η_v. The shear modulus and the shear relaxation are represented by G and η.

Solution of the equations representing this system for the decay of stress under constant strain leads to the equation

$$S = Ae^{-\lambda_{-1}t} + Be^{-\lambda_{-2}t}$$

The roots of this equation, λ_{-1}, λ_{-2}, are given by

$$2 = \lambda \left(\frac{K^1}{\eta_v} + \frac{E}{9\eta_v} + \frac{E}{3\eta} \right) \pm \left[\left(\frac{K}{\eta_v} + \frac{E}{9\eta_v} + \frac{E}{3\eta} \right)^2 - \frac{4K'E}{3\eta_v\eta} \right]^{\frac{1}{2}}$$

Van Zee and Noritake's results were expressed in the form shown in Fig. 2, where τ_1 and τ_2 correspond to $1/\lambda_1$ and $1/\lambda_2$ in the equation given above.

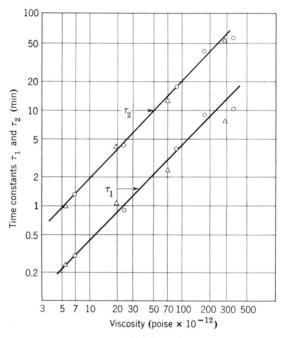

Fig. 2.

It is seen that both τ_1 and τ_2 are directly proportional to the viscosity; that is, the ratio λ_1/λ_2 is independent of the viscosity and therefore of the temperature. Inspection shows that this will be so if K' and E are constant and if the ratio η_v/η is constant and independent of temperature. As τ_1/τ_2 is constant, η and η_v vary with temperature in precisely the same way.

If $E = 6.2 \times 10^{11}$, $G = 2.6 \times 10^{11}$, it is found that $\eta_v/\eta = 0.49$ and $K' = 0.6 \times 10^{11}$. The relaxation times at $\eta = 5 \times 10^{12}$ are, volume, 27.2 sec and, shear, 19.3 sec.

Simple extension of the analysis shows that, if product $GE = 11.61 \times 10^{22}$, the relaxation times will be equal; that is, if $E = 5.4 \times 10^{11}$ and $G = 2.15 \times 10^{11}$, which values are within 20% of the values given by Morey, the bulk relaxation is equal to the shear relaxation time.

The similarity of η_v and η for a silicate glass is in accord with the observations of Litovitz on organic glass-forming liquids, although his observations were made at much lower viscosities.

R. O. DAVIES

What I should like to know is whether an experiment on pure shear shows a single relaxation time whereas one involving bulk motion shows two. Your experiment used a uniaxial stress and was therefore a combination of bulk and shear motion.

S. H. BAUER

A relaxation process which is occurring at a sufficiently rapid rate may not have a definable temperature. In particular, the transition probability between translational and vibrational levels may be sufficiently low (10^{-3} to 10^{-5} for some gases) to raise the question whether in any given system local temperature equilibrium had been attained.

R. O. DAVIES

The situation varies with the sort of process of interest. For processes on a time scale of, for example, 10^5 to 10^9 inverse seconds, one can reasonably assume that the nuclear motions in the material are such that you can define dynamic temperature corresponding to the mean kinetic energies being proportional to kT.

The temperature in this context is the one which the system would have in equilibrium with its surroundings, and this normally means the nuclear motion. I daresay one could devise cases where, let us say, there was magnetic coupling between nuclear spins and undefined external forces but where you allow only mechanical couplings between the atoms themselves and not their surroundings. Then this temperature definition is not satisfactory. It is a kinetic temperature, not a structural temperature. Structural temperature is characterized by the structure of the medium, but this is not; this is the dynamical temperature which is transmitted to surroundings.

S. H. BAUER

I am not so sure that this can be satisfactorily explained in this way.

R. O. DAVIES

Perhaps you are right.

J. A. KRUMHANSL

I would like to ask if there is any reason why the concept of a tensor ordering parameter and the necessity, for example, for two relaxation times should not apply in a crystalline or well-ordered crystalline structure?

R. O. DAVIES

None whatever. It is very likely. I should also add that one can also have vectorial ordering parameters. For example, paramagnetic relaxation is dealt with by such a technique.

10

by

Theodore A. Litovitz

Catholic University of America

Liquid Relaxation Phenomena and the Glass State

The physical properties of a liquid differ from those of an amorphous solid mainly because the liquid structure can change with pressure and temperature. The specific heat, thermal expansion coefficient, and compressibility are larger in a liquid than in the solid state because of the structural change contributions. It has been suggested by many investigators that the glass transition is simply a structural relaxation phenomenon where the time necessary for the molecular processes contributing to structural rearrangement becomes larger than the time duration of a normal experiment. Thus, in the glassy state, the structural rearrangements do not contribute to the properties of the substance.

Comparison of measurements above and below the glass transition temperature, T_g, shows that as much as one-half of the specific heat, thermal expansion, and compressibility of a liquid is due to structural rearrangements. Actually, one does not need to study the substance in the glassy state to investigate these structural relaxation properties. By drastically reducing the time scale of the experiment one can measure certain glass-like properties of a liquid at temperatures higher than the normal glass transition temperature.

It is very difficult to decrease the time scale of an experiment measuring either the specific heat or volume expansion to less than several minutes. However, by using sonic and ultrasonic waves one can measure sound velocity and thus compressibility or elasticity from very long times or "static" measurements down to times as short as $\frac{1}{100}$ of a microsecond or less. Using these short times, one can make a "pseudo" glass transition occur at temperatures above the normal glass transition. This "pseudo" glass transition occurs when the period of the ultrasonic wave is shorter than the relaxation time associated with structural changes.

Using these high frequency ultrasonic waves, one can measure the shear rigidity and compressibility of the non-crystalline liquid lattice and compare these properties with the values found in normal solids.

Because of the intimate connection between the kinetics of the glass transition and viscous relaxation effects an understanding of relaxation phenomena in liquids is useful in explaining certain aspects of the glass transition. For example, it was at first thought that the temperature at which the normal glass transition occurs is determined by the value of the shear viscosity, but more recently it has been realized that the volume viscosity and volume relaxation effects play the more important role. Ultrasonic absorption data serve as a useful means of determining the volume viscosity of liquids. Using ultrasonic data, the relationships between shear and volume viscous processes have been investigated, with a resultant better understanding of the role of shear viscosity in determining the glass transition temperature.

Use of Ultrasonic Data to Calculate Volume Viscosity

Over 100 years ago, Stokes (1845) recognized the possible existence of a volume (or compressional) viscosity in liquids. However, at that time no method was available to measure this viscosity. As a result, volume viscosity was completely neglected in theoretical calculations and assumed to be zero. Since about 1940, with the development of techniques for the accurate measurement of dynamic mechanical properties of liquids at high frequencies, it has become evident that this assumption is incorrect.

The most striking demonstration of the existence of a volume viscosity is found in the results of the measurements of ultrasonic absorption in liquids. When a sound wave passes through a liquid, it applies a longitudinal stress to the liquid. The theory of elasticity shows one that a longitudinal stress is composed of the sum of a pure shear stress and a pure compressional (or volume) stress. Because of this, the absorption of an ultrasonic wave is related to both shear and volume (or compressional) viscous processes.

The observed absorption coefficient α_{obs} (in a frequency region where no dispersion exists) can be written in terms of both the shear viscosity

η_s and the volume viscosity η_v. This relation is given by

$$\alpha_{obs} = \frac{2\pi^2 f^2}{\rho v^3}\left(\frac{4}{3}\eta_s + \eta_v\right)$$ (1)

Or, if $\eta_v = 0$, one gets the shear viscous loss predicted by Stokes:

$$\alpha_{shear} = \frac{8\pi^2 f^2}{3\rho v^3}\eta_s$$ (2)

where f is the frequency of the ultrasonic wave, ρ is the density of the medium, and v is the ultrasonic velocity. One sees that the total absorption is simply a sum of the two viscous effects.

The difference between the calculated value of α_{shear} and the observed absorption coefficient α_{obs} is usually referred to as the "excess" absorption, that is to say, all absorption in excess of that due to shear viscosity. The values of α_{shear} are easily calculated. Then, using experimental values for α_{obs}, η_v can be calculated from

$$\eta_v = \frac{4}{3}\eta_s\left(\frac{\alpha_{obs} - \alpha_{shear}}{\alpha_{shear}}\right)$$ (3)

Since, to this day, there are no viscosimeters available which measure the volume viscosity of a liquid, the measurements of ultrasonic absorption play a unique role in the study of volume viscosity.

The results of ultrasonic studies indicate that most polyatomic liquids exhibit a volume viscosity. If one asks what is the mechanism or cause of this volume viscosity, the answer is not simple. Unlike the shear viscosity, there are many different mechanisms of volume viscosity.

Consider, for example, the relation of η_v to η_s. In Table 1 the ratio η_v/η_s is tabulated for several liquids which are divided into two groups,

Table 1

COMPARISON OF THE RATIO OF VOLUME TO SHEAR VISCOSITY (η_v/η_s)

Associated Liquids		Non-associated Liquids	
Water	2.5	Carbon disulfide	≈ 1300
Glycerol	1.1	Benzene	100
Methyl alcohol	3.2	Carbon tetrachloride	35
n-Propyl alcohol	1.2	Toluene	13
Ethylene glycol	1.0	Nitrobenzene	6.4

associated and non-associated liquids. It can be seen that in the non-associated liquids the ratio η_v/η_s varies from a value of 5 or 6 up to about 1000. Furthermore, in these liquids it is found that the temperature dependence of η_v is completely different from η_s. It appears that in these liquids η_v is in no way related to η_s.

In the associated liquids the situation is different for η_v is always roughly equal to η_s. The ratio η_v/η_s is rarely higher than 3 or less than $\frac{1}{2}$ or $\frac{1}{10}$. Furthermore, the temperature dependence of η_v is very closely the same as that of η_s. Thus one finds that the volume viscosity of associated liquids is closely related to the shear viscosity.

It is now known that the volume viscosity in non-associated liquids is related mainly to thermal relaxation processes, which involve, for example, the lag in equilibration of energy between internal and translational degrees of freedom. In associated liquids the volume viscosity is caused by a structural relaxation effect. The concept here is that the molecules of the liquid, when under an acoustic pressure, will "flow" into lattice positions of closer packing, filling up holes in the liquid. This "flow" or structural rearrangement process takes a finite time, and thus the volume changes are out of phase with the pressure. When the acoustic pressure and change in volume are out of phase, the result is absorption.

The word "flow" used here is perhaps the clue to why the shear and compressional viscosities appear so closely related. Eyring's theory of shear viscous flow involves a translational "jump" of a molecule from one lattice site to another in the direction of shear flow. The structural or compressional rearrangement process also appears to involve a "jump" of one or more molecules from one site to another. This time, however, the "jump" is in the direction of closer packing. In both the shear and compressional processes a molecule changes its lattice position, and it is therefore not surprising that the same bonds must be broken in both processes and thus the activation energies are closely related.

It should be emphasized that the mechanisms involved in the volume viscosity of the non-associated liquids have nothing to do with the structural relaxation process causing the glassy state. It is clear that the "structural" volume viscosity found in the associated liquids is important when one considers the kinetics of stabilization of structure, in a glass or other amorphous substance.

In this connection it is of interest to note that those substances which tend to form a glass always exhibit a "structural" type of volume viscosity in a liquid state. The "association" in these liquids is due to directed forces between molecules (such as hydrogen bonding); the presence of these forces enhances greatly the degree of order in the liquid and makes structural relaxation an important effect in volume viscosity. On the other hand, these forces tend to allow the liquid to supercool and vitrify since the energy of orienting a molecule during crystallization involves the breaking of bonds. The effect of this is to increase the activation energy for crystallization and to slow up the rate of crystallization.

Frequency Dependence of Compressibility

Because of structural relaxation, the normal compressibility of a liquid,[*] κ_0, is made up of two parts:

$$\kappa_0 = \kappa_\infty + \kappa_{\text{relax}} = \frac{1}{v}\left(\frac{\partial v}{\partial p}\right)_{\substack{\text{change in} \\ \text{lattice} \\ \text{spacing}}} + \frac{1}{v}\left(\frac{\partial v}{\partial p}\right)_{\substack{\text{structural} \\ \text{rearrangement}}} \tag{4}$$

The first term, κ_∞, is the high frequency compressibility; it involves mainly a decrease in the liquid lattice spacings and is for most purposes instantaneous. The second term, κ_{relax}, involves the flow or structural rearrangement of molecules and has associated with it a relaxation time.

Because of this relaxation phenomenon, the compressibility is complex (pressure and volume changes are out of phase) and frequency-dependent. For sinusoidal stress, single relaxation theory gives the following expression for κ_c, the complex compressibility:

$$\kappa_c = \kappa_\infty + \frac{\kappa_{\text{relax}}}{1 + i\omega\tau_p} \tag{5}$$

The real part of the compressibility, κ, is given by

$$\kappa = \kappa_\infty + \frac{\kappa_{\text{relax}}}{1 + \omega^2\tau_p{}^2} \tag{6}$$

where τ_p is the structural relaxation time at constant pressure. τ_p is related to the structural relaxation time at constant volume, τ_v, by $\tau_v = (\kappa_\infty/\kappa_0)\tau_p$.

The imaginary part is related to the volume viscosity discussed in the preceding section by the relation

$$\eta_v = (\kappa_{\text{relax}}/(\kappa_\infty)^2)\tau_p \tag{7}$$

[*] Note that all the compressibilities discussed here are those values calculated from ultrasonic data and are therefore the adiabatic values.

In Fig. 1 we see a plot of κ versus frequency for n-propyl alcohol.*
The data in Fig. 1 follow only roughly the predictions of single relaxation theory as given in equation (6). In all the associated liquids measured it was found necessary to assume a distribution of relaxation times in order to fit the data. The distribution found to fit the struc-

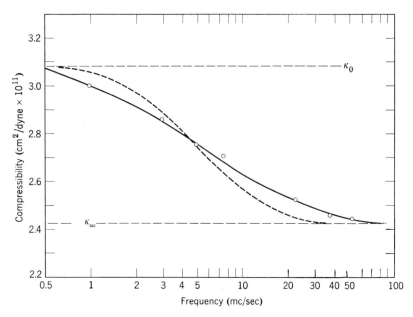

Fig. 1. Compressibility of n-propyl alcohol plotted as a function of frequency at $-130°C$. Solid lines are the values calculated from ultrasonic data. The dashed curve is the frequency dependence predicted using a single relaxation time (equation 6). Data taken from Lyon and Litovitz (1956).

tural relaxation data best is an asymmetric one used by Davidson and Cole (1951) to fit dielectric data and is different from that found in the shear relaxation effects below.

It can be seen that the compressibility drops from a low frequency

---

* The magnitude of the velocity dispersion measured in a viscous liquid is related to both shear and compressional effects. The velocity at low frequencies ($\omega\tau \ll 1$) is given by $v_0{}^2 = \kappa_0/\rho$.

At high frequencies ($\omega_t \gg 1$) the velocity v_∞ is given by $v_\infty{}^2 = 1/\rho\kappa_\infty + G_\infty/\rho$, where G_∞ is the high frequency shear modulus of the liquid.

To calculate κ one must separately measure G_∞, v_∞, and v_0. Combining equations, one gets

$$\kappa_{\text{relax}} - \frac{1}{\rho v_0{}^2} - \frac{1}{\rho v_\infty{}^2 - \frac{4}{3}G_\infty}$$

value of 3.1×10^{-11} cm^2/dyne to 2.4×10^{-11} cm^2/dyne at higher frequencies. Using the ultrasonic data, one can calculate the fraction of the compressibility of a liquid due to structural rearrangements or relaxation. In Table 2 the data on κ_{relax}/κ_0 for several liquids are listed.

Table 2

RELAXATIONAL PART OF THE COMPRESSIBILITY OF LIQUIDS

Calculated from Ultrasonic Data [a]		Calculated from Data [b] above and below T_g	
Water	0.61	Polystyrene	0.76
Glycerol	0.375	Rubber	0.58
1,2,6-Hexanetriol	0.43	Glucose	0.40
2-Methyl-2,4-pentanediol	0.28	Colophonium	0.29
n-Propyl alcohol	0.23		

[a] Litovitz (1957).   [b] Davies and Jones (1953).

It can be seen that anywhere from about 30% to 60% of the compressibility of a liquid is due to structural relaxation.

Also, in the same table, isothermal values of $(\kappa_{liquid} - \kappa_{glass})/\kappa_{liquid}$ as measured by static means are tabulated. Since, presumably, the glass transition removes structural contributions the values of $(\kappa_{liquid} - \kappa_{glass})/\kappa_{glass}$ should be in agreement with κ_{relax}/κ_0. Unfortunately, in no liquids have both quantities been measured, but it can be seen that the range of values is the same in both columns.

Temperature Dependence of Compressibility

In Fig. 2, κ is plotted as a function of temperature for Arochlor (biphenyl pentachloride). The temperature range of 75° to −46°C corresponds to a viscosity change from 0.25 poise to an estimated 10^{15} poise.

At the high temperatures, κ is frequency-independent (in the frequency range measured), and its behavior is typical of all liquids, e.g., slowly decreasing with decreasing temperature. As the temperature of the liquid is lowered, the rate of any molecular diffusion process which is necessary to accomplish structural rearrangements becomes increasingly diminished. When the structural relaxation time is of the order of the

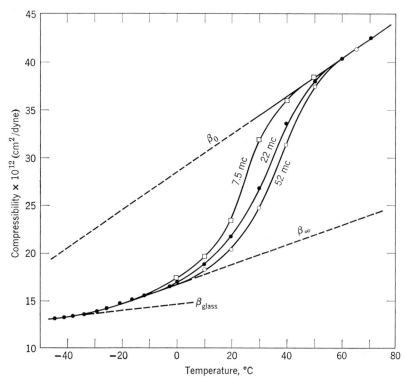

Fig. 2. Compressibility of Arochlor plotted as a function of temperature for three different ultrasonic frequencies. Data taken from Litovitz and Lyon (1958).

time duration of a normal experiment, perhaps 30 minutes, the liquid exhibits glass-like properties; this is the normal glass transition temperature. For the ultrasonic measurement this transition occurs in the temperature region where the structural relaxation time is of the order of the period of the ultrasonic wave. For the frequencies used in Fig. 2, the temperature of this transition is about 60°C above the normal glass transition temperature. As the temperature of the liquid is lowered, the adiabatic compressibility at a given frequency drops rather sharply and levels off at a somewhat lower value, which is again independent of frequency. This lower value is the high frequency compressibility of the liquid, κ_∞. Of course, the temperature of this transition is frequency-dependent. The sharpness of this transition is not so great as at the normal transition temperature, T_g. This is so because the temperature dependence of the structural relaxation times increases as the temperature is lowered. Near T_g a change of 1°C may change this relaxation time by a factor of ten. At the higher temperatures a

1°C change may change the relaxation time by less than a factor of two. It is this large dependence of volume relaxation time upon temperature near T_g which makes the formation of the glass appear to be a real transition even though it is not.

The value of κ_∞ is determined purely by the elastic behavior of the liquid lattice. When measuring κ_∞, no liquid flow takes place during a sonic compression. The structural contributions to the compressibility have been removed.

It is of interest to compare the temperature dependence of κ_∞ and κ_0 in Arochlor. It can be seen that the temperature dependence of the glass-like compressibility is about the same as that for the liquid compressibility. One normally expects glass or solid-like compressibilities to be less temperature-dependent than the liquid values.

The explanation of this lies in the fact that we have not gone through a glass transition in the usual sense at 20°C. The liquid behaves like a glass to the sound wave for a given measurement because of the short time duration of the wave. However, when one changes the external temperature this is a long time experiment, in *changing the liquid structure*. Lowering the liquid temperature in the normal times necessary to lower a bath temperature allows increases in the amount of order, decreases in the number of holes, and increases in the number of nearest neighbors. The ultrasonic wave "sees" the order present at the external temperature. When one changes the temperature of a crystal or glass, these effects do not occur. The degree of order in a solid is very much less temperature-dependent than in a liquid.

Thus we must conclude that the changes in lattice structure which occur in our pseudo-glass causes the relatively large temperature effects noted in the high frequency compressibility measurement. To prove this, one simply lowers the temperature until the time for structural rearrangement of the lattice is longer than the time necessary to change the temperature, i.e., below the normal T_g. Below this temperature the elastic constants should take on a solid-like temperature dependence, typical of the glass state. This should occur at the ordinary glass transition temperature, where the time for structural rearrangement becomes longer than normal cooling times. In Fig. 2 one sees that the only change in going through the glass transition is that the slope decreases and becomes more typical of the glass state. The value of $(1/\kappa)\,(\partial\kappa/\partial T)_{\text{glass}}$ is less than one-half the liquid value.

Note that the concept of a "second-order transition" (often applied to glass formation) obviously does not hold here. Here we have a derivative property of our liquid $(1/v)\,(\partial v/\partial p)$, which does not show an abrupt change in value on passing through the glass transition temperature. This is, of course, evidence that the glass transition is simply a relaxation effect.

The liquid which we study with ultrasonics between T_{rel} and T_g can be termed, in a sense, an *equilibrium glass*. For these values of κ, if extrapolated below T_g, give the equilibrium value of the instantaneous elasticity which the glass will exhibit if given sufficient time in cooling.

From comparison of the temperature dependence of κ_∞ and κ_0, it can be seen that $\kappa_\infty - \kappa_0$, or (κ_{rel}) decreases as the temperature is lowered. The decrease of κ_{rel} indicates that the component of κ_0 which is due to structural rearrangement is decreasing. This is a consequence of the fact that, as the temperature is lowered, the amount of order in our liquid increases. As a result there are fewer possibilities for structural rearrangements. For example, if at a lower temperature there are fewer holes in the liquid, then under compression the number of molecules which can jump into a closer packing must decrease. When there are no more holes in the liquid (e.g., a crystal type of lattice) then κ_∞ must approach κ_0 in value. Of course, the point at which these two quantities approach each other cannot be reached because at the glass transition temperature the number of holes or degree of order is frozen in.

Comparison of Structural and Shear Relaxation

An apparent relation between T_g and the shear viscosity has been noted by several investigators (Davies and Jones, 1953; Kauzmann, 1948). For example, in many liquids T_g occurs at the temperature where the shear viscosity is about 10^{13} poise. This fact can be understood if one compares the data on structural and shear relaxation.

A liquid exhibits a shear rigidity if stressed at sufficiently high frequencies (i.e., when the period of ultrasonic shear wave is shorter than the shear relaxation time). When a single relaxation time exists, the complex shear rigidity can be expressed as follows:

$$G_c = G_\infty \frac{\omega^2 \tau_s^2}{1 + \omega^2 \tau_s^2} + i G_\infty \frac{\omega \tau_s}{1 + \omega^2 \tau_s^2} \tag{8}$$

where G_∞ is the value of the modulus of shear rigidity at high frequencies $(\omega \tau_s \gg 1)$ and τ_s is the shear relaxation time. The shear viscosity is given in terms of these quantities * by

$$\eta_s = G_\infty \tau_s \tag{9}$$

* When a distribution of relaxation times is present, equation (8) is still valid if the value of τ_s used is the average relaxation time.

Table 3

SHEAR AND COMPRESSIONAL MODULI FOR SEVERAL LIQUIDS

(dynes/cm^2 × 10^{-10})

	G_∞	K_∞	G_∞/K_∞
Sodium chloride	12.6	48.5	0.26
Nickel	73.5	37.3	0.20
Glycerol	2.3	7.4	0.31 (Piccirelli and Litovitz, 1957)
1,2,6-Hexanetriol	2.0	5.7	0.35 (Miester, 1957)
1,3-Butanediol	0.74	3.3	0.22 (Cotter, 1957)
Polyisobutylene	0.58	2.7	0.17 (Mason, 1948)

In Table 3 the value of the high frequency shear modulus is listed for several liquids and compared to those of a crystalline and amorphous solid. The magnitude of G_∞ for the organic liquids is less than one-tenth the values found for the typical solids. For the one polymer listed, the value is about one-hundredth that found for nickel. Also listed in Table 3 are values for K_∞, the high frequency compressional modulus of these liquids. (Note that the modulus of compression is simply the reciprocal of the compressibility.) It can be seen that not only the shear modulus, but also the compressional modulus, in these liquids is considerably less than that in crystalline solids. Even though the magnitudes of G_∞ and K_∞ vary by a factor of 10 to 100 in going from solids to liquids, the ratio G_∞/K_∞ remains much more constant. This indicates that factors such as random lattice structure and holes which cause the "solid-like" compressibility of a liquid to be greater than a crystalline solid affect the shear modulus in much the same manner.

Consideration of the temperature dependence of the shear rigidity of liquids further emphasizes the difference between the "solid-like" behavior of our liquid and ordinary solids. In Table 4, one can see that the temperature dependence of G_∞ in glycerol is 10 times and 100 times greater than that found for the elastic moduli of aluminum and soft glass respectively. This result is explained in the same way as was the temperature dependence of compressibility. The increase in the number of holes and randomness in the liquid structure as the temperature rises decreases the rigidity of the liquid lattice.

The data on frequency dependence of rigidity demonstrate the exist-

Table 4

TEMPERATURE DEPENDENCE OF ELASTIC MODULI

(Soft) glass	$\frac{1}{E}\left(\frac{\partial E}{\partial T}\right)^{*}$	0.067×10^{-3}
Aluminum	$\frac{1}{G}\left(\frac{\partial G}{\partial T}\right)$	$0.72 \ \times 10^{-3}$
Glycerol	$\frac{1}{G_{\infty}}\left(\frac{\partial G}{\partial T}\right)$	$4.5 \ \ \times 10^{-3}$

* E is Young's modulus.

ence of a distribution of relaxation times, as was found in structural or volume relaxation experiments. A significant difference exists in the type of distribution function necessary to fit the shear data was found to be symmetric on a logarithmic scale as opposed to the asymmetric type needed to fit the compressional data. At this time there is no explanation for this difference in behavior.

If one wishes to compare the shear and compressional relaxation times, the most meaningful comparison is between the average values. The ratio τ_v/τ_s is compared in Table 5. It can be seen that the average

Table 5

COMPARISON OF AVERAGE STRUCTURAL AND SHEAR
RELAXATION TIMES (τ_v/τ_s)

Glycerol	0.81	(Piccirelli and Litovitz, 1957)
1,3-Butanediol	0.79	(Cotter, 1957)
2-Methyl-2,4-pentanediol	2.70	(Sciamanda, 1958)
1,2,6-Hexanetriol	4.60	(Meister, 1957)

shear and compressional relaxation times are very close in value. Furthermore, it has been found that the temperature dependence of τ_v and τ_s are the same, indicating that activation energies for the two processes are close in value.

Thus there appears to be little doubt that the molecular mechanisms involved in shear and compressional flow are very closely related.

Because of this close relation of τ_s and τ_v, one can understand the reasons why T_g can so often be located in terms of the value of the shear viscosity. Recalling that $\eta_s = G_\infty \tau_s$ and noting in Table 3 that G_∞ is of the order of 10^{10} dynes/cm^2, one finds that when $\eta_s \approx 10^{13}$ poise τ_s is 10^3 sec or about 15 min. This, of course, means that τ_v is of the order of 15 min. Thus, even though the glass transition is a structural relaxation phenomenon, the shear viscosity is often a useful indicator.

Comparison of Structural and Dielectric Relaxation

It has been generally accepted that a similarity exists in the dielectric and viscous behavior of a liquid. A correspondence between dielectric relaxation time and the shear viscosity was long ago predicted by Debye (Debye, 1929) on the basis of a hydrodynamic model. That a relaxation exists between shear viscosity and the dielectric relaxation time, τ_D, is shown by the fact that τ_D has the same temperature dependence as the shear viscosity in many liquids. To compare these phenomena further, both the viscous and dielectric relaxation times should be considered. One wonders if the molecular motions performed by the dipoles as they rotate from one equilibrium site to another are similar to the processes occurring in viscous flow where a "translational" jump occurs.

A comparison of the dielectric and structural relaxation times is given in Table 6. In all the liquids listed, the ultrasonic behavior indicates that a distribution of relaxation times exist. In the dielectric case only the higher alcohols show this distribution. In these higher alcohols it has been shown that the distribution function necessary to fit the dielectric data is asymmetric and (though not so broad) is quite similar to that found for the structural relaxation data. In no case listed was the distribution of dielectric relaxation times similar to the symmetric function found for shear viscous relaxation.

In Table 6 the comparison is between the average relaxation times. In every case the temperature dependences of τ_D and τ_v were found to be the same, indicating that the activation energies for the two processes are close in value.

It can be seen that, when the number of carbon atoms and OH groups are equal, τ_D and τ_s are close in value. However, as the number of OH groups becomes smaller than the number of carbon atoms, τ_D systematically diverges in value from τ_v.

In these liquids the OH groups make up the dipole. In glycerol the dipole is essentially the whole molecule: however, when considering n-butyl alcohol, it can be seen that the dipole (OH group) is at one end and is a small part of the molecule. The dipole motion in this case can

Table 6

COMPARISON OF DIELECTRIC AND STRUCTURAL RELAXATION TIMES

τ_D/τ_v

Glycerol	C—C—C | | | O O O H H H	1.0	(Litovitz and Sette, 1953)
1,2-Propanediol	C—C—C | | O O H H	3.5	(Pilon, 1957)
1,2-Butanediol	C—C—C—C | | O O H H	6.1	(Cotter, 1957)
n-Propyl alcohol	C—C—C | O H	19.0	(Lyon and Litovitz, 1956)
n-Butyl alcohol	C—C—C—C | O H	169.0	(Davidson and Cole, 1951)

simply involve rotation about a C-C bond and need not involve reorientation of the whole molecule.

Hirai and Eyring (1958) have suggested that in structural relaxation the process of rearrangement of molecules is a combined process which consists of the cooperative movement of many (around 6 to 12) molecules around a hole. For this cooperative motion, there is an entropy increase in the activated state owing to the increased structural randomness possible inside the flowing molecules. It is this entropy which can explain the difference between τ_D and τ_v.

According to the Eyring rate process theory (Eyring, 1936) the relaxation time for either case is given by the expression

$$\tau = \frac{\hbar}{kT} \exp\left(\frac{\Delta F}{kT}\right) = \frac{\hbar}{kT} \exp\left(\frac{\Delta H - T\,\Delta S}{kT}\right)$$

where $\hbar$ is Planck's constant, ΔF is the free energy of activation, ΔH is the activation enthalpy, and ΔS is the activation entropy. Since $\partial \tau/\partial T$ is the same for both dielectric and viscous processes, ΔH must be the same. The difference in the values of τ is due to the greater entropy in the activated state of the structural relaxation process. This effect makes $(\Delta F)_{\text{structural}}$ less than $(\Delta F)_{\text{dielectric}}$ and, thus, τ_v less than τ_D.

In liquids like glycerol, where the whole molecule is involved in dielectric rotation, one would expect about the same structural randomness to occur in the activated states of both dielectric and structural relaxation processes and thus τ_D should be close in value to τ_v.

These results explain the significant differences between the value of T_g measured by ordinary means (i.e., specific heat, thermal expansion, etc.) and that estimated by dielectric relaxation. It has been found that the temperature at which τ_D is 30 minutes can be as much as 30–40° above T_g. The "lattice" structural relaxation time determines T_g, and only in those liquids where $\tau_D = \tau_v$ should the dielectric experiment agree with other methods of determining τ_g. Since in many liquids τ_D can be expected to be longer than τ_v, one would expect dielectric relaxation effects at a higher temperature.

REFERENCES

Cotter, L. E., Master's Dissertation, Catholic University of America, Washington, D. C., 1957.

Davidson, D. W., and Cole, R. H., *J. Chem. Phys.* **19**, 1484 (1951).

Davies, R. O., and Jones, G. O., *Proc. Roy. Soc. (London)* **A217**, 26 (1953).

Debye, P., *Polar Molecules*, Dover Publications, New York, 1929.

Eyring, H., *J. Chem. Phys.* **4**, 283 (1936).

Hirai, N., and Eyring, H., *J. Appl. Phys.* **29**, 810 (1958).

Kauzmann, W. J., *Chem. Revs.* **43**, 219 (1948).

Litovitz, T. A., and Sette, D., *J. Chem. Phys.* **21**, 17 (1953).

Litovitz, T. A., *J. Acoust. Soc. Am.* **210** (1957).

Litovitz, T. A., and Lyon, T., *J. Acoust. Soc. Am.* **30**, 856 (1958).

Lyon, T., and Litovitz, T. A., *J. Appl. Phys.* **27**, 129 (1956).

Mason, W. P., Baker, W. O., McSkimin, H. J., and Heiss, J. H., *Phys. Rev.* **73**, 1074 (1948).

Meister, R. M., Ph.D. Dissertation, Catholic University of America, Washington, D. C., 1957.

Piccirelli, R., and Litovitz, T. A., *J. Acoust. Soc. Am.* **29**, 1009 (1957).

Pilon, P. E., Master's Dissertation, Catholic University of America, Washington, D. C., 1957.

Sciamanda, R. J., Master's Dissertation, Catholic University of America, Washington, D. C., 1958.

Stokes, G. G., *Cambridge Trans.* **8**, 287 (1845).

DISCUSSION

P. L. KIRBY

The important distinction which the author draws between the dipole relaxation of part of a molecule and the cooperative relaxation of several molecules leads me to remember a similar important distinction in the case of mechanical relaxations in inorganic glasses. It is quite valid to represent the mechanical relaxation of modifying ions by the movement of such ions within the relatively static framework of the network-forming ions. The dielectric relaxation, in such a case, is a very similar process. However, relaxations which involve the main glass-forming network itself are more complex. It is utterly futile to consider the movement of a single ion or even a group of ions against a background which is composed of similarly mobile units. Thus the dependence of the probability of an ionic movement on the occurrence of similar movements by neighboring ions illustrates the cooperative aspect of this process. The associated parameters of activation energy and entropy are thus less easily identified with any features in the structure which may be measured under more static conditions.

J. A. PRINS

I understand the general argument that, for high frequencies, the liquid behaves almost like a glass. But the peculiar aspect of Table 1 was that η_v/η_s was of the order of one for the liquids you called associated and which also have a glass-forming tendency, even without considering a very high frequency; and that η_v/η_s was a much higher number, say of the order of 100, for many other simpler liquids, such as carbon tetrachloride. But are not all these simpler liquids on the right side of your Table 1 molecular liquids? Then I thought (and I hope I am making a mistake and so learning something) that the shear viscosity of these molecular liquids is simply much too low, since the forces between carbon tetrachloride molecules, for example, are rather weak; while in the associated liquids on the left side of your Table 1 the forces between the different molecules are of the same order as the intramolecular forces; if you shear against intermolecular forces in the associated liquids you simultaneously get intramolecular movement, while in the simpler liquids on the right-hand side of the table you do not and so cannot lose energy inside the molecules. This, I thought, is the reason for the big difference in η_v/η_s.

T. A. LITOVITZ

I should like to say that in a few minutes you have come to the conclusion we have reached over years as to why the thermal relaxation process really cannot occur in water and other liquids with a strong coupling between molecules. This is not important in polymers, for example, because it is easy to obtain energy out of a vibrational degree of freedom, if the molecule is really tangled up with its neighbor, or has some kind of polar or directed force; and, if the energy transfer is easy, the relaxation time is short and is an unimportant effect.

R. W. DOUGLAS

Litovitz referred to the distribution of bulk relaxation times as being skew while the shear relaxation times were said to be distributed symmetrically. Did he really mean relaxation times, or was it the distribution of the product of each relaxation time and its contribution to the elastic process?

T. A. LITOVITZ

By distribution function I mean that function which gives the fractional number of relaxation times which have a value lying in the interval between τ and $\tau + d\tau$.

P. DEBYE

You know that in liquids with very simple molecules, for instance mercury, there is x-ray evidence for a definite structure around each molecule (or atom). I wonder whether you have observed any relaxation concerned with this structure.

T. A. LITOVITZ

Structural relaxation has not been measured in the simple liquids such as mercury. The reason for this is that the relaxation times are too short for the range of present-day ultrasonic equipment. The times in these liquids would be less than 10^{-12} seconds, which would involve ultrasonic frequencies of the order of 10^{11} cps. In the more complicated associated molecules, the forces between molecules tend to slow their movement, and this results in much longer relaxation times.

R. O. DAVIES

The real reason why we cannot look at the bulk relaxation of liquid argon is that it is not easy to make ultrasonic experiments in the frequency range where relaxation may be expected. Such experiments would enable us to separate out instantaneous moduli which could be estimated theoretically. They would therefore be very important.

T. A. LITOVITZ

In order to detect a structural volume viscosity it is not necessary to measure ultrasonic absorption in a region where the period of the ultrasonic wave is of the order of the relaxation time. This is shown, for example, by the measurement of η_v in water at frequencies of the order of 10 megacycles, whereas the relaxation frequency is 10^{11} cps. The decisive factor is simply the numerical question of whether the value of η_v is large enough compared to η_s to be detected. If η_s is 1 poise and η_v is 10^{-3} poise, its contribution to the absorption will be within experimental error.

R. O. DAVIES

One can define bulk viscosity in a number of ways. In particular, the experimental facts that you cite can be interpreted—as you have done—as indicating a zero value for the *adiabatic* bulk viscosity. This, however, tells us nothing about the *isothermic* bulk viscosity. The high frequency experiments would be needed to show this up [Davies, *Proc. Roy. Soc. (London)* **A226**, 24 (1954)].

11

by

P. L. Kirby

Welwyn Electrical Laboratories Ltd., Bedlington

Kinetics
of Mechanical
Relaxation Processes
in Inorganic Glasses

The vitreous state has come to be accepted as a definitive form of matter, and it is certainly appropriate to consider it as a non-crystalline type of structure. However, the rather "negative" idea implied in the description of the glassy state as involving a random array of atoms is unsatisfactory. In the first place, and particularly if one shrinks from the idea of "absolute" irregularity in a condensed system, it becomes pertinent to consider the degree of randomness which prevails over any given range within the structure. Secondly, it by no means follows that a continuous structure can be built up from existing types of glass-forming units in which a degree of short range order leads smoothly to a long range irregularity, and in which known facts regarding density and interatomic spacing are reconciled. It has already been suggested (Tilton, 1957) that a vitreous material may possess some type of order repeated over a module of many atomic dimensions. We must hope that the deployment of improved radiographic techniques and related methods of analysis will reveal details of glass structure to the degree of precision required.

It is our intention now to comment on the possibilities and limitations of an approach to this problem from considerations of mechanical relaxation effects which can be observed in inorganic glasses. The final sections include a critical consideration of the usefulness of results obtained from relaxation experiments.

Rate-Controlled Processes in Glass

There are a number of experimentally observable rate-controlled processes which may be capable of throwing light on glass structure: self-diffusion, gas permeation, surface reactions, crystal growth, development of irradiation defects, electrical conductivity, dielectric relaxation, fracture, viscous flow, retarded elasticity, and so on. Retarded elasticity may be approached from the realm of rheology and can be regarded as a relaxation process.

A mechanical relaxation is defined as a macroscopic manifestation of a kinetic reaction within a material which has resulted from some change in the internal stress, and during which the stress/strain relationship is not unique but involves some function of time.

Inorganic glasses behave neither as ideal viscous fluids nor as ideal elastic solids. One noteworthy instance of this imperfect behavior is in the manifestation of an anelastic behavior (see Zener, 1948) which can be of considerable magnitude. This type of behavior exists phenomenologically between elastic and viscous effects and suggests a combination of these two mechanisms. In a simple spring (G) and dashpot (η) model an important parameter is the relaxation period, $\tau = \eta/G$, the combination of the latter two coefficients being representative of the expression "viscoelasticity."

It may well be that the very existence of a retarded elastic effect (time-dependent but completely reversible) between the two otherwise extreme phenomena of elasticity and viscous flow masks any complete distinction between the three. Thus it may not be possible to ascribe any atomic event uniquely to one phenomenon. Empirically, however, the three effects, although they may coexist, are distinguishable to a satisfactory degree, at least over certain temperature ranges.

Any type of mechanical relaxation depends ultimately on the probability of a structural element proceeding through an activated state to a new configuration. Kinetically the effect of a number of such events is to endow the process with a reaction velocity. Alternatively, a consideration of the probability of the transition being made in a given time endows the system with a characteristic relaxation period.

The progress of rate-controlled reactions may be described in terms of the mean value of parameters in the rate equation; however, such practice may not provide the detailed picture required when we are seeking details concerning the randomness of the glass structure. In the case of the mechanical relaxations it is found that the experimental pattern cannot be explained in terms of a unique relaxation period. If a range of such periods exist, then there must be a range of possible reaction curves whose coordinates vary in shape and in magnitude. It is, perhaps, not surprising that such a condition does prevail for a relaxation which involves mass transport in an irregular condensed structure.

The basis of the present approach is to identify parameters in the rate equation, activation energy and activation entropy, with physical features of the structure. This can be done with the aid of potential energy diagrams which are associated with the interatomic forces in the structure. It is finally hoped that the range of variation of such parameters as relaxation period and the energy and entropy of activation can be used to indicate the degree to which the structure deviates from perfect regularity. This analysis is widened by a consideration of the conditions which exist over a range of temperatures.

Relaxation Effects in Glass

The application of stress to a glass results in one or more of three types of deformation. There is an instantaneous elastic strain which completely disappears on removal of the load. Another reversible effect is the development of a retarded elastic deformation, small in magnitude at room temperature, but increasing with temperature and equaling the first effect in prominence in the transformation range. The third effect is the irreversible flow, also of very small magnitude at room temperature, but increasing so rapidly with temperature that it practically swamps the previous two effects above the transformation range.

A number of experimental methods are available which are directed toward producing some manifestation of the delayed elastic relaxation in glass. These are listed in Table 1 in three groups, one from each of which (designated by asterisks) will be considered in more detail in the later sections.

Table 1

Group 1. Unidirectional
  *I. Deformation under constant stress
  II. Stress relaxation at constant strain
  III. Annealing of internal stresses

Group 2. Transient
  *IV. Impact methods

Group 3. Cyclic
  *V. Natural decay of free vibrations
  VI. Forced vibrations—Q from resonance curve

Methods of type I have been applied successfully at temperatures up to the transformation range, utilizing both transverse and torsional deformation. A load is applied to the glass and the deformation is measured at intervals over the required period of time. It is necessary to eliminate from the observations the effects of the initial instantaneous deformation and the continuously increasing irreversible deformation, which is a result of the viscous flow. A further delayed elastic curve can be obtained from the recovery which follows the removal of the load. From the retarded deformation curve two types of information relating to (a) the magnitude and (b) the time rate of the effect can be deduced. The former is usually denoted by the relaxation ratio Δ, defined as the ratio of the total delayed to the instantaneous strain:

$$\Delta = \frac{\epsilon_R}{\epsilon_I} \qquad \text{whence also} \qquad \Delta = \frac{E_0 - E_\infty}{E_\infty} \tag{1}$$

In the assessment of this parameter, elastic and viscous effects having been eliminated, it is mainly a matter of ensuring that the retarded effect has run to completion. That this is not perhaps a very simple matter is stressed in a later section.

The time rate of the retarded strain occurring in a simple single spring and dashpot system can be described uniquely by the retardation period τ. This parameter governs the exponential variation of strain (ϵ) with time (t).

$$\epsilon = \epsilon_\infty[1 - \exp(-t/\tau)] \tag{2}$$

It has been found that the delayed elastic effect observed in glasses cannot be represented by a single relaxation period τ, but that a range of such periods is required. Thus a smooth distribution function $\Delta(\tau)$ is used to express the variation in magnitude of the delayed elastic effect over all possible time values for τ. This function is represented by $\Delta(\tau)$ (it is more correctly described as $\Delta(\ln \tau)$, as it is convenient to express the large range of τ values concerned on a logarithmic basis), and the total relaxation ratio at any given temperature is

$$\Delta = \int_{-\infty}^{\infty} \Delta(\tau)\, d(\ln \tau) \tag{3}$$

It would be proper to refer to the term $\Delta(\tau)$, obtained from experiments mentioned above concerning retarded elastic strain measurements, as a "retardation spectrum." A similar distribution function from stress relaxation measurements would give a "relaxation spectrum." In the particular case of glasses, both functions vary so slowly with the time value of τ that they can be regarded as identical, and no distinction is drawn between the strain retardation period and the stress relaxation period. The generalized distribution function $\Delta(\tau)$ is then conveniently referred to as the "relaxation spectrum" of the material.

From a complete strain retardation curve we can evaluate Δ, and, if the curve follows some known analytic function of time, an inversion can be performed and the form of $\Delta(\tau)$ evaluated. Errors of observation are always magnified in this process and if, as is the case with glasses, the experimentally observed curve is not that of a known function, approximate methods must be used to compute $\Delta(\tau)$. Some methods of higher approximation have been published (Roesler and Pearson, 1954; Schwarzl, 1953). Results obtained from retarded elastic experiments are described below.

Returning to Table 1, it is certainly possible to make use of method II in the case of glasses, for the internal stress can generally be measured conveniently by optical means. It is, of course, necessary to ascertain the nature of any thermal dependence of the stress-optical coefficient.

Method III, the relief of internal stress by an annealing process, is a subject of very great importance in the field of glass technology. It is not, however, ideally suited to the present needs; because the study must necessarily involve the decay of a system of balanced stresses (i.e., stresses which vary in both magnitude and direction within the sample) and there is no direct consideration applied to any associated dimensional changes. Thus both the internal stresses and strains may vary, and neither are generally homogenous throughout the specimen.

We return now to the thought that the total relaxation of a glass is a result of the individual relaxation of elements within the structure whose natural relaxation periods vary over many decades. We have suggested that, at least in principle, careful experimentation and analysis of a delayed elastic deformation curve could yield information concerning the entire relaxation spectrum. It is not difficult to imagine that the two limitations which appear respectively at long and at short relaxation times are (a) the ordinary difficulty of proceeding with a single experiment for periods of months and years, and (b) the difficulty of eliminating the effects of transients at the very beginning of the retarded curves and the fact that the so-called "instantaneous" elasticity, involving the movement of bulk matter, is an effect which does require a finite period for its completion.

It is, therefore, a most welcome discovery that a very different phenomenological approach gives direct indication of the basic anelastic effect at very fast time rates. This effect is the phenomenon of the damping or decay of cyclic vibrations and forms the basis of methods V and VI.

Elementary consideration of the decay of vibration, wherein is implied a continuous loss in energy by the vibrating system, shows that (if loss to external objects is eliminated or accounted for) there is an internal transformation of the oscillatory energy (into heat) if the stress and the strain (two cyclic variations) are not in phase. This immediately suggests a similarity to the time lag which occurs in the case of delayed elasticity between the applied unidirectional stress and the resulting strain. In the case of oscillatory stress a convenient measure of the amount of energy absorbed per cycle is tan δ, where δ is the phase angle between stress and strain. This expression has come to be known as the "internal friction."

If we were to explore the anelastic behavior of a simple relaxing system (relaxation period τ, relaxation ratio Δ) by examining the internal friction at some variable frequency $\nu(= \omega/2\pi$; ω is the angular frequency in radians per second), the following relation would be established.

$$\tan \delta = \Delta \frac{\omega\tau}{1 + \omega^2\tau^2} \tag{4}$$

Thus the internal friction (a dimensionless quantity) has a maximum value of $\Delta/2$ at the frequency $\nu = 1/(2\pi\tau)$, where a type of "resonance" is established with the internal relaxation effect. At frequencies below and above this value, the internal friction decreases according to equation (4) ("Debye" curve).

If, on the other hand, a system is used which has a large number of relaxing elements whose natural speeds of response vary over a wide range, then the largest effect will be felt from those elements whose relaxation period is close to the reciprocal of the applied frequency. The total effect experienced will then be integrated from all the partial effects due to individual elements,

$$(\tan \delta)_\omega = \int_{-\infty}^{\infty} \Delta(\tau) \frac{\omega\tau}{1 + \omega^2\tau^2} \, d(\ln \tau) \tag{5}$$

and it is seen that this equation combines the influence of a Debye curve with that of the distribution function $\Delta(\tau)$ (controlling the *maximum* height of the Debye curve for any particular value of τ), and summing both effects over all values of τ for a given applied frequency $\nu(= \omega/2\pi)$.

It is possible to carry out experiments to determine the internal friction tan δ at varying frequencies. It is then tempting to synthesize a particular form for $\Delta(\tau)$ which accounts for all the observed values of $(\tan \delta)_\omega$.

Which of methods V or VI is chosen to investigate the internal friction is mainly a question of experimental convenience and devolves mainly on the frequency concerned. At low frequencies, particularly in the subsonic range, there is no reason why the decay of free vibrations should not be utilized. The internal friction is found from the logarithmic decrement (λ), by $\tan \delta = \lambda/\pi$.

At higher frequencies the forced vibration method is to be preferred. There is no fear that the *small* excursion in frequency carried out around the resonant frequency (dependent on sample size, mode of vibration, and temperature) will invalidate the results, for the rate of variation of $\tan \delta$ itself with frequency is found to be very slow.

The two basic methods mentioned, viz., the unidirectional delayed effects and the cyclic damping effects, are limited at higher temperatures by the onset of viscous flow. This limitation is absolute in the former case, in that the irreversible flow (which may be corrected for) swamps the reversible deformations and makes the "correction" a ludicrous process. In the second case, although the use of higher frequencies might lead to a possible exploration of the relaxation at higher temperatures the limitation is practical. Here it becomes impossible to maintain the shape of the sample in such a way that vibrations may be imposed upon it.

In the case of cyclic damping effects, one immediately thinks of the transformation of the glass into the liquid state which occurs as the temperature increases. The parallel measurement would then be that of the absorption of sonic waves in the liquid. With this effect the absorption coefficient is generally proportional to the viscosity in the absence of anomalous effects. Then, at high "fluid-like" temperatures, one would expect that an increase of temperatures would bring about a *decrease* in the absorption of longitudinal waves at sonic frequencies.

As will be shown below, the internal friction, measured at sonic frequencies, is continually *increasing* as the temperature rises toward the transformation range. We can imagine the whole relaxation spectrum undergoing a shift toward shorter periods as the temperature is increased. The maximum absorption of the cyclic energy will occur as the peak of the distribution (i.e., the mean relaxation period) passes the period of the applied oscillation. This will occur at a temperature above the transformation range. It would be most interesting to be able to follow the variation in cyclic absorption with temperature and observe a continued increase to a maximum and then a decrease as the rising temperature moves the peak of the relaxation spectrum past the applied frequency. At the present time there is no report of such an experiment having been performed for the general viscoelastic relaxation of an inorganic glass.

We have shown how results from internal friction and retarded elastic experiments can be combined. Method IV, involving the application of transient stresses to the glass, can also give a smaller amount of information which is in accord with the other results. The method is utilized to overcome some limitations of the other methods. In this case the glass can be taken to such a temperature that it assumes the flow characteristics of the liquid state and yet, under the action of a short duration transient stress pulse, a partially elastic reaction is observed.

Variation of Internal Friction with Temperature

Using Pyrex chemical glass (Corning 7740), for which information on retarded elastic behavior is also available, internal friction has been measured at temperatures up to the transformation range, at frequencies between 1 cps and 37 kc/sec (Kirby, 1954a; Marx and Sivertsen, 1953).

At frequencies at the lower part of this range a measurement of the internal friction can be obtained from the rate at which natural vibrations of a specimen decay. In the work referred to, Pyrex glass rods held vertically in an electric muffle furnace underwent torsional oscillation. The upper end was clamped and inertia disks, attached to the lower end, were used to vary the frequency of the oscillation. At higher frequencies measurements have been made by exciting longitudinal vibrations in glass bars. Figure 1 illustrates the type of result available from measurements made at the extreme limits of this frequency range and shows the variation of the cyclic energy loss with temperature from 0° to 550°C.

This variation of tan δ with temperature is similar to that shown by a number of inorganic glasses, and at very low temperatures another peak has been observed in the case of fused silica (Anderson, 1955).

Prominent features would thus appear to be:

1. A low temperature peak for fused silica. This is probably a structural relaxation due to a sideways movement of the oxygen ions to a nearby alternate position, a feature peculiar to the random network of Si-O ions.

2. Peaks due to the relaxation of network-modifying ions, such as alkali ions. Such peaks (see Fig. 1) have been observed at 100–200°C lying above the general background of energy loss which is believed to be due to

3. The general increase in internal friction as the transformation range is approached. This is ascribed to the same mechanism of gen-

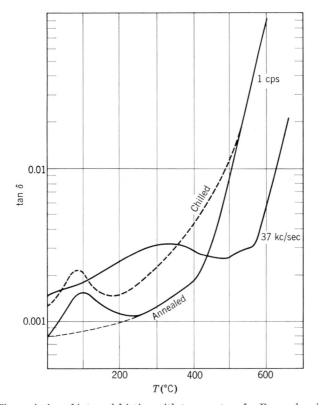

Fig. 1. The variation of internal friction with temperature for Pyrex chemical glass.

eral relaxation on the part of the network-forming ions which gives rise to the retarded elastic effect.

Another point to note is that, as the curve for chilled glass (Fig. 1) suggests, the thermal history of the sample has some bearing on the internal friction observed at temperatures below the transformation range.

Both the "alkali ion" peaks and the low temperature "Si-O bond" peaks have been resolved from the background of general relaxation and their relaxation spectrums analyzed.

It remains to be seen the information that can be extracted from the curves in Fig. 1 which will have bearing on a computation of the relaxation spectrum for the general relaxation of the network. At subsonic frequencies a value for tan δ attributable to the general network relaxation would appear to be available at temperatures above 300°C. However, at ultrasonic frequencies the alkali ion peak is displaced to higher temperatures and obscures this region; thus at these frequencies a value for the general relaxation could be obtained only for a temperature of about 550–650°C.

Retarded Elastic Deformations

Confining ourselves to the same inorganic glass for which internal friction results have been quoted, measurements on the delayed extension and recovery effects have been carried out at temperatures between 250° and 450°C (Kirby, 1954b). Samples in the form of thin rods have been examined under both flexural and torsional deformation while held in a furnace at the required temperature. The retarded deformation under load and the recovery on the removal of the load both exhibited similar variations with time in the two methods of deflection. Also, over the range of temperatures used, the curves illustrated the same general effects. There is an instantaneous deformation on application of the load, a further delayed increase in strain merging into a final constant flow rate. The magnitude of the instantaneous deformation varies little with temperature, the general order of time rate of the retarded process shows some temperature variation, and the irreversible viscous flow increases very rapidly with temperature particularly at the higher temperatures used. The permanent deformation remaining after the completion of the recovery process is a measure of the net flow of the specimen and is used to correct the form of the extension curves to eliminate the irreversible part of the deformation. The curve now exhibits a time variation similar to that shown by the retarded recovery on removal of the load.

It should be stressed that in the course of these experiments observations were continued for a time sufficiently long for the final readings of deformation to show no apparent further change. The final daily variation in readings showed no statistical significance compared with the experimental error. Thus, as every reasonable precaution had been taken regarding the stability of the sample supports, the provision of vibration-free mountings, temperature control, etc., it was genuinely felt that no great improvement would result unless quite elaborate improvements were made to the apparatus. From this it was deduced that the "delayed" effect, while still approaching an asymptotic value, should be at least well within, say, 10% of completion. On this basis, measurements, not only of the time rate characteristics, but also of the total magnitude of the delayed elastic deformation, were made. The results are summarized in Figs. 2 and 3, which show the variation with tem-

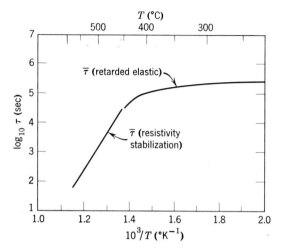

Fig. 2. The variation of the mean relaxation period with temperature for Pyrex chemical glass.

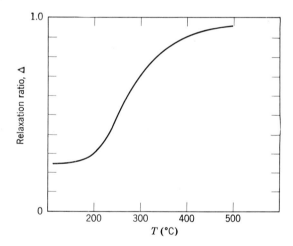

Fig. 3. The apparent variation of the relaxation ratio with temperature for Pyrex chemical glass.

perature of the *mean* relaxation period ($\bar{\tau}$) and of the relaxation ratio (Δ) respectively. The results are then used in a consideration of the total structural relaxation which is being studied.

The major aim is now to correlate the work on internal friction with that on the unidirectional delayed elastic effect. Data from the former experiments are available over the widest range of frequencies (1 cps to

37 kc/sec) at a temperature of 550°C. At this temperature there is less confusion due to other relaxation effects. Unfortunately, however, the delayed elastic measurements cannot be made on this glass at such a high temperature, owing to interference from the irreversible viscous flow. Nevertheless, as will be emphasized later, there is good reason for being more confident of the absolute validity of the retarded elastic results at higher temperatures, because the main danger stems from the possibility that the delayed process was not observed to completion— a danger more likely to materialize at lower temperatures. For this reason there is some suspicion of the apparent low values of Δ at lower temperatures and also the apparent lack of variation of $\bar{\tau}$ with temperature below the transformation range.

What is to be attempted now amounts to an addition of results from the slow delayed elastic measurements, which can be regarded as information on energy loss occurring at a frequency of, say, 10^{-3} cps. The latter value corresponds to a mean relaxation period of about 166 sec (which appears to be the value for Pyrex chemical glass at about 550°C).

If, as in this case, we are exercising a preference to perform this analysis at as high a temperature as possible, an extrapolation will have to be made to the experimental values for the mean relaxation period $\bar{\tau}$. The associated extrapolation for Δ is of very small magnitude. To ascertain the value for $\bar{\tau}$ at 550°C, for example, resort will be made to another series of "relaxation" periods, namely, those associated with time-dependent changes in electrical resistivity of the same glass during stabilization at a given temperature. The values for these periods are given in Fig. 2, and they run on smoothly from the delayed elastic relaxation periods. The overlap is not coincidental but is thought to be due to a dependence of both effects on the same structural changes, and it is fully supported by a further measurement of a mean mechanical relaxation period at a much higher temperature made during impact experiments and illustrated in Fig. 10.

Combination of Internal Friction and Delayed Elastic Results

Experimental values for tan δ at 550°C are plotted on logarithmic scales in Fig. 4. Ideally we would now like to add the equivalent quantity for the very low "frequency" concerned in the delayed elastic experiment. Although tan $\delta = \Delta/2$ for a *simple* relaxing system, we must be careful not to use the measured value for Δ from our experiments in this manner. Our value of Δ in the unidirectional loading experiments is derived from the relaxation of *all* elements in the system, those with relaxation periods both below and above $\bar{\tau}$. It is not possible to determine experimentally the value for $(\tan \delta)_{\omega = \bar{\tau}^{-1}}$, which involves only the elements whose relaxation period is close to $1/\omega$ and which is the point required for plotting on the graph in Fig. 4.

However, remembering that the measured relaxation ratio gives a value for relaxation attributable to the summed effect of all elements in the system, a further step is possible. By trial, a point (at the "apex" of the energy loss curves in Fig. 4) is determined which completes the

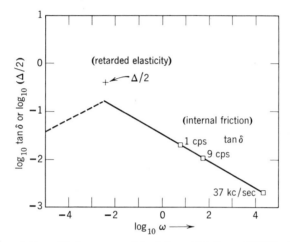

Fig. 4. The variation with frequency of the internal friction at 550°C. The straight line is not purely extrapolated; it represents a system whose combined relaxation is represented by the parameter equivalent to tan δ, viz., Δ/2.

required curve for the variation of tan δ with frequency. (N.B. At frequencies even lower than $\omega = \bar{\tau}^{-1}$ which are quite beyond experimental observation, the curve drops away at the same slope as on the high frequency side. On linear coordinates the curve would be a "broad" Debye curve; here it is represented by two straight lines with a fairly sharp intersection.) The requirement to be met in the establishment of the point $(\tan \delta)_{\omega = \bar{\tau}^{-1}}$ is that the series of staggered (single value τ) Debye curves, which on summation make up the experimental energy loss spectrum, have ordinate maxima which add up to give the known total value for Δ/2. The energy loss spectrum at both sides of the mean period must be considered.

For convenience, the staggered Debye curves can be taken at unit intervals of log ω (equivalent to −log τ). The maximum ordinate of each curve now represents the value of Δ/2 for that particular single τ value. This process is represented in Fig. 5.

The maximum ordinates are actually representing the *half-values* of the true relaxation spectrum [they represent the function $\Delta(\tau)/2$]. The simple summation of all these points gives the total value for $\Delta/2$, by the operation of equation (3) at "half-value" and because we have chosen $d(\log \tau)$ to be equal to unity.

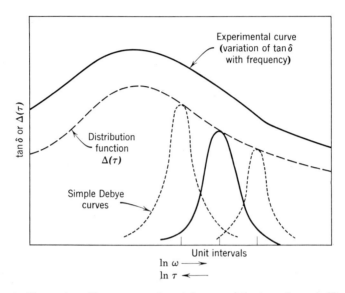

Fig. 5. An illustration of how an experimental curve of the type shown in Fig. 4 can be broken down into a series of Debye curves. The peaks of the latter represent the locus of the distribution function, and the sum of all the ordinates of the peaks gives the total $\Delta/2$ for the system.

It is found that a straight line curve in Fig. 4 does, in fact, meet the requirement of giving a total relaxation equal to the observed value of the relaxation ratio Δ. This trial straight line is not a unique solution, but it has the advantage of a single representation of the facts. Plotted on linear coordinates, the distribution function obtained has the form in Fig. 6.

The analysis given is not capable of giving accurate data of the form of this function near the peak. The latter are preferably obtained from the type of approximate analysis of a retarded deformation curve mentioned earlier. The curve in Fig. 6 has been produced in a combined manner, using retarded elastic data alone for the shape of the peak and using both retarded elastic and internal friction data to produce the tail of the curve. The curve in Fig. 6 is the normalized relaxation spectrum of the glass concerned, at 550°C.

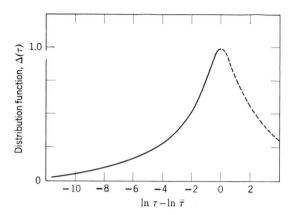

Fig. 6. The normalized distribution function for the mechanical relaxation in Pyrex chemical glass at 550°C.

Form of the Relaxation Spectrum

If a description of the relaxation spectrum at any given temperature had to be given in words, it would not be possible to overemphasize two particular aspects:

1. In the region of the "mean" relaxation period there is a very pronounced "peak."

2. At periods far removed from the mean there is a very long flat "tail" to the distribution.

We find that we can explain most of the observed effects of mechanical relaxation in glass on this picture, and there is no reason to believe that the *true* relaxation spectrum varies in form, to any significant extent, at temperatures below the transformation region. Whether or not *observation* of the total spectrum is possible is, however, another matter.

By utilizing methods similar to those described in the previous section, the relaxation spectra at other temperatures can be ascertained, and they conform to the general shape given in Fig. 6. It is not, however, intended to stress these results here, owing to the uncertainty, mentioned above, concerning apparent observations of $\bar{\tau}$ and Δ at lower temperatures.

In carrying the conclusions relating to the relaxation of the glass forward to consider the structural implications, the idea of the "peak plus tail" characteristic of the relaxation spectrum must be to the forefront of our thoughts.

Relaxation of Modifying Ions

Measurements of the variation of internal friction with temperature (Fig. 1) suggest that there exists within the glassy structure a relaxation mechanism in addition to that ascribed to the ions forming the vitreous network. This effect is observed in the appearance of a peak, or maximum value of tan δ, at temperatures varying from room temperature up to a few hundred degrees centigrade. The width of the peak is wider (on a temperature axis) than would be expected for a process with a unique relaxation period. From the magnitude of the shift in the temperature at which the peak occurs when the frequency is changed, it is possible to calculate an activation energy which is presumed to represent the mean behavior of the complex relaxing system concerned. In the graph in Fig. 7 the straight line indicates an activation energy of

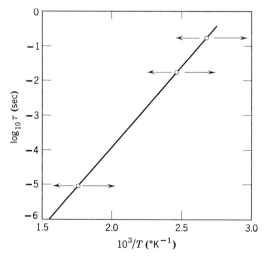

Fig. 7. Variation with temperature of the mean relaxation period of the alkali ions. The horizontal arrows indicate half-maximum widths for the "peak" and imply loci for the half-maximum limits of the distribution function on the vertical axis.

23 kcal/mole for Pyrex chemical glass (annealed). Measurements of electrical conductivity, which is due to the biased migration of sodium ions, show that this process is controlled by an activation energy of similar value. Additional evidence to suggest that, generally, alkali ions are responsible for this peak is that glasses free from alkali do not give a peak in the internal friction curve at these temperatures.

It is possible to estimate the form which the curves of internal friction versus temperature would have in the absence of the alkali ion peak, and then to assess the extent to which the tan δ for this particular effect rises above the background level. We can thereby evaluate a measure of the relaxation attributable solely to the action of the alkali ions. The final aim is to obtain the form of the distribution of relaxation periods (on a ln τ axis). However, we must be careful not to transpose from a temperature to a ln τ axis by the application of a *single* activation energy E, i.e., by means of the Arrhenius equation, $\tau = \tau_0 \exp(E/RT)$. At this stage it seems likely that a *range* of activation energies may be involved. The difficulty can be resolved by making use of a graphical method. Also, to simplify the procedure, instead of building up a series of staggered Debye curves to represent the observed loss, the width of the distribution will be represented by a single quantity. We shall consider the width at the half-maximum positions. These widths are added to Fig. 7 at the three frequencies available, and it is seen that the loci of half-maximum limits also imply limits on the vertical ln τ axis.

The result is surprising, for the half-maximum limits appear in the form of parallel lines. This suggests that all the relaxing elements which contribute to the peak of the effect are controlled by very similar activation energies. Apparently the range of values of τ which is required to account for the width of the peak is not due to variations in E, but in τ_0. In terms of reaction rate theory, this implies a distribution in activation entropy.

It is not possible to analyze the "tail" of the alkali ion relaxation spectrum. This is the region where the experimental values for tan δ are merging into the background, owing to the network relaxation. It is important to point out that it may well be that variation in activation energy from the above mean does control those elements concerned with the long τ and short τ tails of the distribution. Taylor (1956), analyzing the dielectric loss peaks due to alkali ions, was also led to conclude that the width of the spectrum could not be explained in terms of the variation in activation energy.

The analysis of the alkali ion relaxation in chilled glass shows that the relaxation spectrum has a narrower peak and that the activation energy is lower (about 16 kcal/mole for Pyrex chemical glass).

Suppose, then, that some of the structural elements vary, one from another, by requiring a variation in the activation entropy controlling their mechanical relaxation. This implies a variation in the shape and size of the potential well, as distinct from the intervening barriers. This does not, of course, rule out the very likely possibility that the "tails" of the relaxation spectrum relate to other elements which are concerned with a range of potential barrier heights. With this picture it is quite reasonable to accept that, in the case of chilled glass where the activation energy and hence the barriers are lower, there is less facility for the structure to show the same degree of randomness, with regard to variation in well shape and size, as in the case of annealed glass.

Short Period Transient Stresses

All measurements of elastic, delayed elastic, and internal friction effects in glass become impracticable at temperatures above the transformation range. It has already been pointed out that for retarded elasticity the limitation is absolute, in the sense that for any conceivable form of experiment the irreversible viscous deformation is of greater magnitude than the reversible effects. With internal friction, the difficulty is more practical, and, although the use of higher frequencies should carry one outside the range of interference from viscous flow, problems arise regarding the maintenance of sample shape. In addition, however, an analytic difficulty does arise in that, if the damping becomes very large, it can no longer be expressed accurately by the phase angle tan δ. Nevertheless, and particularly at high frequencies, the absorption of mechanical energy should still be observable in glass, if valid methods could be employed.

One such method is to apply a single unidirectional transient stress to the glass. This has been done by the adaption of very simple impulse techniques. A steel ball is dropped onto the surface of the heated glass and the relative height of rebound is observed. The absorption of kinetic energy is thereby calculated, and the assumption is made that this process approximates a single "half-cycle" of the equivalent cyclic event. Internal friction of magnitude tan δ is equal to an energy loss of $2\pi \tan \delta$ per cycle. Thus the fractional energy loss $\Delta E/E$ observed in the impact experiments is equivalent to $2\pi \tan \delta$, while the time of contact T (see measurements by Kirby, 1956) is equivalent to a frequency ν, where $\nu = 1/2T$.

The curve for the cyclic energy loss for Pyrex chemical glass is given in Fig. 8 and compared with internal friction curves.

It is seen that we now have measurements of energy absorption above the transformation range. In the case quoted it would also appear that with an impact time of 18 μsec ($\nu = 27.8$ kc/sec; $\omega = 175 \times 10^3$ rad/sec; equivalent $\tau = 5.72 \times 10^{-6}$ sec) complete absorption appears to occur at about 1000°C. It is reasonable to deduce that the mean

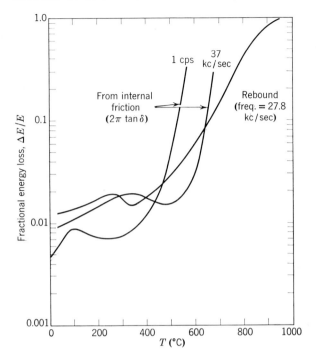

Fig. 8. Variation with temperature of cyclic energy loss from internal friction and impact rebound measurements.

relaxation period in the glass is about 5×10^{-6} sec at 1000°C. This point can be added to the graph in Fig. 10.

Structural Picture of Delayed Elasticity

The experimental evidence suggests that the mechanical relaxation effect associated with the main vitreous network possesses a relaxation spectrum with a pronounced peak and, in addition, a very long, flat tail. It is now appropriate to consider what implications this has on a picture of atomic events. Whatever "units" are properly described by a potential energy diagram (energy plotted against a configuration co-ordinate), these are the units which possess the wide range of relaxation periods. We should certainly avoid the use of a potential diagram which purports to describe the movement of a single ion against a rela-tively immobile background of stationary ions. This device might be most useful for the consideration of the electrical conduction or the mechanical relaxation of, for example, alkali ions within the network of a silicate glass. But, if the process being studied is the movement of the network ions themselves, then a more generalized potential diagram must be considered.

At this stage it is as well to point out that there is only one possible feature of the potential diagram which describes the process which the relaxing unit is to undergo as a delayed but reversible process; this is that the adjacent potential "well" must be of higher absolute level than the initial well. The passage of a system between wells of similar level is illustrative of the irreversible viscous flow. This is the essential distinction between the two processes: it is not a matter of the height of the intervening barrier, but a question of the "floor" level of adjacent wells.

It may be felt that at certain temperatures there is a greater "quantity" of delayed elastic deformation compared with the amount of viscous flow occurring. This is a difficult point to settle quantitively because, of course, the latter deformation increases linearly with time without limit. But a picture which one can bear in mind is that the system may traverse a succession of the "reversible" types of wells, before it falls down into a deeper well of irreversible type. Thus at lower temperatures the majority of the units would surmount only the reversible barriers, whereas, as the temperature is raised and more energy is made available, unit systems will begin to move over sufficient barriers to experience the "equal floor level" criterion to a larger extent.

With what features, then, must the randomness of the structure be associated? Certainly there must be a very large number of different potential diagrams covering all the variety of relaxing elements in the glass. We have seen that in the case of the relaxation alkali ions within the general network, those elements which predominate around the mean relaxation period differ more in terms of activation entropy than of activation energy. This has been interpreted as a variation in the shape and size of potential wells, as distinct from barrier heights, and it is a characteristic which may also be possessed by the main network. However, it would be unreasonable to try to assess *all* the randomness in the structure, with variations in the form of the well, with the exclusion of the barrier variation. Over the many decades of log τ concerned with the "tail" of the relaxation spectrum there must be a considerable variation in the height of barriers on the potential diagrams and therefore of the corresponding activation energy.

The final picture is therefore one of a large collection of potential energy diagrams whose characteristics vary considerably. From the very low barriers which are mounted, generally at the early stage of a delayed elastic process, the collection ranges to the enormously high barriers where statistically the chance of their being surmounted, during the course of even a "long" experiment, is quite negligible. Some barriers will lead to a well whose floor level is the same as that of the preceding well, and the passage over this barrier will correspond to an irreversible process.

It is interesting to conjecture that, if at least part of the randomness of a vitreous structure is a manifestation of variation in the shape of a potential well, then this implies a variation of the actual elastic coefficients controlling movements within a well. There is, however, no obvious macroscopic event which would seem capable of demonstrating the existence of a range of microelastic coefficients, and all observation leads only to an evaluation of a mean value.

Temperature Variation of Relaxation Periods

By lumping the characteristics of the observed elasticity, delayed elasticity, and viscosity, the average values of these events at any temperature can be represented by a simple model, G_1, G_2, η_2, and η_3 (Fig. 9). Because the instantaneous elasticity G_1 and the irreversible viscosity η_3 can be described completely by single coefficients, their representation is quite satisfactory. The combination G_2 and η_2 to represent the delayed elasticity suffers from the serious drawback that only one relaxation period ($\tau_2 = \eta_2/G_2$) is represented.

Alfrey (1948) has considered the idea that G_1 and η_3 combined may form a "series" or Maxwellian type of relaxation. There is insufficient evidence to say whether a separate relaxation effect can be observed in glass. The picture is clouded because of the existence of a wide range of $G_2 + \eta_2$ elements and by variations in η_3 with time, at constant temperature, during a stabilization process.

Nevertheless, from experimental observation of values for G_1 and η_3 over a range of temperatures, the values for a calculated Maxwellian relaxation coefficient can be plotted against temperature. These are

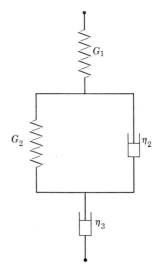

Fig. 9. A simple four-element model.

shown in Fig. 10 with the available data for the *mean* delayed elastic relaxation period $\bar{\tau}$.

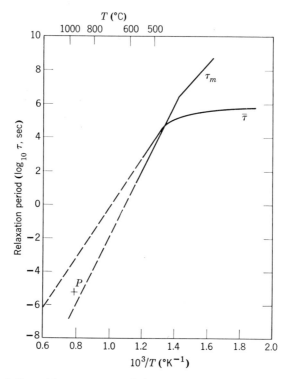

Fig. 10. Variation with temperature of the mean mechanical relaxation period and a calculated Maxwellian relaxation period.

On this diagram is also the point P, which denotes full energy absorption during the impact tests at the appropriate equivalent relaxation period. It is seen that this point bears some resemblance to the extrapolated values of $\bar{\tau}$ and τ_m.

It would be wrong to overemphasize any distinction between $\bar{\tau}$ and τ_m. In the first place the horizontal part of the $\bar{\tau}$ versus $1/T$ curve at low temperature has already been questioned. At elevated temperatures a structural consideration of the matter makes it difficult to see a clear distinction between the two component types of viscosity coefficient η_2 and η_3. For example, one aspect of this difficulty is that the earlier idea that delayed elasticity involves passage across a barrier into a higher-floor-level well becomes increasingly difficult to picture as the temperature is raised. A particular transition in the structure may at one moment come into this category, but, before the reverse change has had time to occur, the continuous change in surrounding conditions might make the first disposition very stable. Thus the system is at the bottom of quite a deep well. There is the feeling that there must be a continual reaction between the viscous and the reversible transitions, owing to an essential self-dependence of any movement within the structure. Particularly at high temperatures it is difficult not to conclude that the irreversible effects exert a full domination over the reversible effects, not only in magnitude but also in absolute priority.

Full Picture of Time-Dependent Strain

A consideration of this matter will be made in the light of two previous experimental results. On the one hand, at temperatures from about 300°C up to and including the transformation range, the delayed elastic strain versus time curve has a smooth curvature which very roughly approximates an exponential function (Kirby, 1954b). Thus the curve approximates very loosely the form

$$\log (S/S_0) = at \tag{6}$$

We shall also say that the over-all magnitude of the complete delayed strain *appears* to increase with temperature (Fig. 3), but the general order of time rate, i.e., the constant a ($\equiv 1/\tau$), does not vary very greatly with temperature (Fig. 2).

The second fact is that observation of delayed but reversible effects at room temperature indicates apparently quite a different form (Murgatroyd and Sykes; Murgatroyd, 1948). To a very *close* approximation, although for a very short duration compared with that for which the effect could run, the strain varies with time in the following manner:

$$S/S_0 = b \log t \tag{7}$$

We simply want to know on which side of the equation *should* the logarithm be? An answer is to be found as follows. Express the variation in strain in linear units against the logarithm of time. Then the first equation (6), giving the simple exponential approach to an asymptotic value, takes on the form of a sigmoidal curve (Fig. 11a). We do know that, if the system is really made up of units possessing a range of relaxation periods (compared with the unique value for the simple exponential system), then a wider sigmoidal curve is obtained (Fig. 11b).

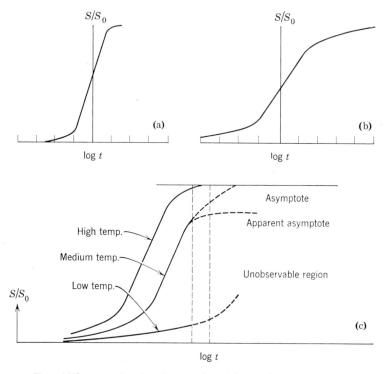

Fig. 11. Sigmoidal curves showing the complete delayed elastic deformation process for (a) simple and (b) complex relaxing systems. The curves in (c) illustrate the suggested behavior for glasses at various temperatures.

We now suggest that at every temperature the delayed elastic effect in glass is of such a nature that the strain/time variation is described by a wide sigmoidal curve. These curves are, however, displaced along the time axis according to the temperature, by time periods which are, by normal standards, quite considerable. This situation is represented in Fig. 11c, and two vertical lines are added to represent an indefinite, but quite inevitable, distinction on this logarithmic time scale, between what can be and what cannot be observed in human experience.

It is now clear that the universal sigmoidal curve representing quite constant behavior at all temperatures is capable of a variety of different manifestations. At low temperatures a result, very close indeed to a linear relationship between S/S_0 and log t, and therefore in accord with equation (7) is found.

At high temperatures the full effect can be observed, and the relaxation spectrum is found to have the usual "peak plus tail" characteristic, which gives a behavior, as is found experimentally, of which equation (6) is a "rough" representation. At intermediate temperatures a very important point is brought out. The curve obtained will, no doubt, be quite smooth (although lacking in symmetry when plotted in this manner) and, aided by the investigator's imagination, will appear to have run very close to an asymptotic value. One can imagine the situation where an experiment lasting for days, weeks, and months would actually need to be protracted for decades of years before the evidence was clearly available to show that the process had not, after all, been nearly complete at the six-month stage!

This understandable human error thus leads to two incorrect assumptions: (a) the magnitude of the whole process is underestimated, giving too small a value for Δ, and (b) the τ value representing the *mean* relaxation period is *shorter* than the true mean and there is a surprising lack of sensitivity of $\bar{\tau}$ to temperature.

Our final conclusion is, then, that at lower temperatures the true mean relaxation period $\bar{\tau}$ continues the variation it possessed with $1/T$ °K in the transformation range and that the true relaxation ratio Δ does not decrease with decreasing temperature. Some limited, but carefully controlled, experiments carried out by the author at temperatures close together *within* the transformation range have in fact suggested that Δ does not exhibit the large variation with temperature suggested by Fig. 3. In view of the structural picture put forward to explain retarded elasticity, it would be very difficult to explain why, at temperatures below the transformation range, the total amount of *possible* delayed elasticity should vary.

Finally, however, the point should be made that the results quoted in Figs. 2 and 3, on the delayed elastic effects in the range of temperatures up to 450°C, are, without doubt, a representation of the behavior of glass which would be found in any type of practical experiment. It is only in the unqualified incorporation of this work in a complete picture of the structural implications of viscoelasticity that a serious error may be made.

REFERENCES

Alfrey, T., *Mechanical Behavior of High Polymers*. Interscience Publishers, New York, 1948.

Anderson, O. L., and Bömmel, H. E., *J. Am. Ceram. Soc.* **38** (4), 125 (1955).

Kirby, P. L., *J. Soc. Glass Technol.* **38**, 383T (1954) (a).

Kirby, P. L., *J. Soc. Glass Technol.* **38**, 548T (1954) (b).

Kirby, P. L *Brit. J. Appl. Phys.* **7**, 227 (1956).

Marx, J. W., and Sivertsen, J. M., *J. Appl. Phys.* **24**, 81 (1953).
Murgatroyd, J. B., *J. Soc. Glass Technol.* **32**, 291T (1948).
Murgatroyd, J. B., and Sykes, R. F. R., *J. Soc. Glass Technol.* **31**, 17T (1947).
Roesler, F. C., and Pearson, J. R. A., *Proc. Phys. Soc. (London)* **B67**, 338 (1954).
Schwarzl, F., *Proc. 2nd Intern. Congr. Rheol. 1953*, 197 (1954).
Taylor, H. E., *Trans. Faraday Soc.* **52**, 873 (1956).
Tilton, L. W., *J. Research Natl. Bur. Standards* **59** (2), 139 (1957).
Zener, C., *Elasticity and Anelasticity of Metals*, University Chicago Press, 1948.

DISCUSSION

M. L. HUGGINS

We should be interested in relating the relaxation energy spectra of glasses to their chemical composition, to the types and distribution of the structural units present, and to changes of these types and their distribution as the temperature changes. It seems obvious that progress on this problem will be easiest if the glasses studied are of simple chemical composition and especially if the number of these types is small [Huggins, *J. Am. Ceram. Soc.* **38**, 172 (1955); *J. Phys. Chem.* **58**, 1141 (1954); Huggins and Abe, *J. Am. Ceram. Soc.* **40**, 287 (1957)].

Similar remarks are applicable to studies of many other properties of glasses.

I suggest also that studies of relaxation processes such as those discussed by Kirby might profitably be made using glasses or glass-like materials which, unlike ordinary silicate glasses, do not have "unobservable regions," owing to processes having very long relaxation times.

G. E. RINDONE (submitted in writing)

We have used internal friction measurements in our laboratories [at The Pennsylvania State University] as a means of studying structural problems in glass. Our approach has been to study simple glasses of widely varied compositions. For example, in $Na_2O \cdot 3SiO_2$ glass, Weyl and Hoffman [*Glass Ind.* **38**, 81 (1957)] found a low temperature peak at about $-40°C$ and another, less resolved, peak between 200° and 300°C. Forry [*J. Am. Ceram. Soc.* **40**, 90 (1957)] was able to obtain a better resolution of the high temperature peak. Recently, Ryder (Ph.D. Thesis, Dept. of Ceramic Technology, The Pennsylvania State University) and Rotger [*Glastech. Ber.* **31**, 54 (1958)] have observed two peaks for lithia and potassia as well as for soda-silica glasses. Both peaks shift to higher temperatures as the alkali progresses from Li to Na to K (Ryder, *loc. cit.*).

	Low Peak	High Peak
$Li_2O \cdot 3SiO_2$	$-43°C$	147°C
$Na_2O \cdot 3SiO_2$	$-38°$	177°
$K_2O \cdot 3SiO_2$	$-31°$	185°

The low temperature peak has been attributed by many investigators to the oscillation of alkali ions. The high temperature peak has been associated with the motion of non-bridging oxygen ions. This suggests that any compositional changes which influence the mobility of the alkali ions, and the movement of the non-bridging oxygen ions, should also influence these two peaks.

We are studying, for this reason, the influence of alkaline earths gradually substituted for silica in such a fashion as to keep the sodium-to-oxygen ratio constant. In the case of CaO substituted for SiO_2 in $Na_2O \cdot 3SiO_2$ (Fig. 1) the low temperature peak gradually diminishes in height and shifts to higher tem-

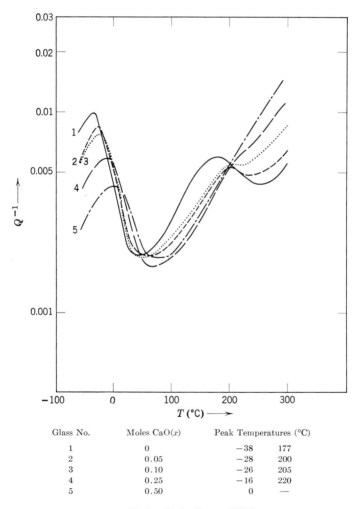

Glass No.	Moles CaO(x)	Peak Temperatures (°C)	
1	0	−38	177
2	0.05	−28	200
3	0.10	−26	205
4	0.25	−16	220
5	0.50	0	—

Fig. 1. $Na_2O \cdot xCaO \cdot (3 - x/2)SiO_2$.

peratures. The high temperature peak shows a similar shift, but, in addition, the peak becomes an inflection and finally disappears.

These observations can be understood on the assumption that the calcium ion surrounds itself with the non-bridging oxygen ions when introduced in a glass. The calcium ion which needs to be surrounded by 6 to 8 oxygen ions will co-ordinate 4 to 6 of the non-bridging oxygen ions already present in the glass. Not only will this restrict somewhat the movement of an equal number of sodium ions which are associated with these oxygen ions, but also the movement of the non-bridging oxygen ions themselves will be greatly restricted. This "tightening" of the glass structure by introducing CaO for SiO_2 is also evidenced by changes in other properties such as chemical durability. Soda-silica glasses are water-soluble, even with SiO_2 contents of 85%. However, a substitution of only a few percent CaO for SiO_2 is sufficient to make a durable glass.

12

by

Sang Joon Hahn

Taikyue Ree

Henry Eyring

University of Utah

Non-Newtonian Relaxation in Amorphous Solids

There are many known examples of relaxation in amorphous solids. The annealing of glass, however, has long posed interesting problems of great importance in engineering. Stress relaxation in high polymeric systems is also an important phenomenon with paramount significance for the plastic industry. In this chapter we shall discuss these relaxation phenomena as examples of reaction rate theory.

Many articles and monographs have been published concerning the annealing of glass, and theories have been proposed in explanation (cf. Morey, 1954; Stanworth, 1950; Weyl, 1951; Condon, 1953). The theory of "fictive temperature" proposed by Tool has been widely accepted (Tool, 1945, 1946), but it still lacks a clear theoretical formulation. As early as 1936, Eyring explained the annealing of glass (Eyring, 1936), applying rate theory (Eyring, 1935; Glasstone, Laidler, and Eyring, 1941 *). Cagle and Eyring studied the stress relaxation in glass, applying the well-known hyperbolic sine law (Cagle and Eyring, 1951). These authors successfully explained the observed fact that glass annealing is a second-order reaction with respect to internal stress for

---

* This reference will be abbreviated as GLE (1941) hereafter.

low stress (Adams and Williamson, 1920). Lillie (1936), however, proved experimentally that the second-order law holds only for special cases. Tool (1945) also arrived at the same conclusion by examining the Adams-Williamson data, there being certain cases which do not follow the second-order law. He showed that the fictive temperature theory holds better than the second-order law.

We have (Ree, Hahn, and Eyring, 1955; Ree, Fava, Higuchi, and Eyring, 1956; Fava and Eyring, 1956) recently proposed a general equilibration theory of transient phenomena and showed that this theory explains the stress relaxation in wool and high polymeric systems very well (Ree, Hahn, and Eyring, 1955). We now treat the glass problem from this more general point of view. It will be also shown that the fictive temperature theory is a special case of the general theory.

Equilibration Theory of Transient Phenomena

A system in a non-equilibrium condition transforms toward equilibrium at its characteristic rate. Here the system is under internal stress, and a transformation occurs to release this stress. Accompanying the relaxation, certain properties of the system change with time. Let q be such a property at time t. q may be the birefringence, the specific volume, the viscosity, the concentration, and so on. Of course, the change of the properties is due to an atomic or molecular rearrangement relieving the internal stress on the strained relaxation sites. Let n_f be the *effective* number of these relaxation sites per unit volume. n_f is assumed to be given by the equation

$$n_f = c(q - q_e)/(q_0 - q_e) \equiv c\phi \qquad (1)$$

Here q_e and q_0 are the properties at equilibrium and at the time zero, respectively, c being a proportionality constant. The internal stress on the relaxation site, F, is assumed to be

$$F = \sigma(n_f - n_{fe}) = \sigma n_f = \sigma c\phi \qquad (2)$$

σ being another proportionality constant having the dimensions of stress times volume. The second equality of (2) results from (1), since the value of n_f at equilibrium, n_{fe}, is equal to zero, because $q = q_e$ at equilibrium.

We now consider the rate of the relaxation process. The rate is given by

$$-\frac{dn_f}{dt} = k_f' n_f - k_b' n_b \qquad (3)$$

Here k_f' and k_b' are the specific rates of the forward and backward reactions, and are related (GLE, 1941) to the internal stress F by the relations

$$k_f' = k_f \exp [\mu\lambda\lambda_2\lambda_3 F/kT]$$

$$k_b' = k_b \exp [-(1 - \mu)\lambda\lambda_2\lambda_3 F/kT]$$

$$(4)$$

In (4), k_f and k_b are the specific rates of the two reactions when F is zero; λ, λ_2, λ_3 are the molecular dimensions in Eyring's theory of viscosity (GLE, 1941); and μ is $\frac{1}{2}$ when the barrier is symmetrical (GLE, 1941). The quantity n_b in (3) is the effective number of the sites per unit volume participating in the backward reaction. If the relaxation site acts also as the back-reaction site, n_f equals n_b. Assuming a symmetrical barrier and introducing (4) into (3), one obtains the equation

$$-\frac{d \ln n_f}{dt} = 2k_f \sinh \alpha F \tag{5}$$

where

$$\alpha = \lambda\lambda_2\lambda_3/2kT \tag{6}$$

Because of the relation of (1) and (2), equation (5) is represented as

$$-\frac{d \ln \phi}{dt} = 2k_f \sinh \alpha'\phi \tag{7}$$

where $\alpha' = \alpha\sigma c$. Especially if the condition, $\alpha'\phi \gg 1$, is satisfied, equation (7) may be written

$$-\frac{d \ln \phi}{dt} = k_f \exp (\alpha'\phi) \tag{8}$$

Equations (7) and (8)* are integrated, respectively, as follows:

$$k_f t = \sum_{n=0}^{\infty} [Ei(-\alpha'(1 + 2n)) - Ei(-\alpha'(1 + 2n)\phi)] \tag{9}$$

$$k_f t = Ei(-\alpha') - Ei(-\alpha'\phi) \tag{10}$$

Here, $Ei(x)$ is the exponential integral function; that is,

$$-Ei(-x) = \int_x^\infty \frac{\exp (-\xi)}{\xi} d\xi \qquad \text{for} \quad 0 < x < \infty$$

The values of the exponential integrals are found in mathematical tables (Jahnke and Emde, 1945; Lowan, 1940).

---

* Equation (8) is also derived from (3), if $k_f'n_f \gg k_b'n_b$, i.e., the potential barrier is unsymmetrical.

Stress Relaxation

In the annealing of glass the birefringence decreases with time, approaching zero value at equilibrium; the quantity q in this case is the birefringence (cm/cm). For most glasses a load of 1 kg/cm^2 produces a birefringence of about 3×10^{-7} (Morey, 1954, p. 167). Using this conversion factor, the observed birefringence (usually expressed in mμ/cm) is readily converted to the internal stress. ϕ in this case is given by the equation

$$\phi = r/r_0 \tag{11}$$

Here, r and r_0 are the birefringence at time t and zero, respectively, the birefringence at equilibrium, r_e, being zero.

When a fiber is stretched and kept at a constant length, the applied stress decreases with time and approaches zero stress. In this case, q is the applied stress f and ϕ is expressed by

$$\phi = f/f_0 \tag{12}$$

since $f_e = 0$.

Change of the Density and Viscosity

Density and viscosity change during the annealing of glass. Thus the measurements of density and viscosity are often used for studying the annealing process. In these cases ϕ is given by the equations

$$\phi = (v - v_e)/(v_0 - v_e) \tag{13}$$

$$\phi = (\eta - \eta_e)/(\eta_0 - \eta_e) \tag{14}$$

Here v and η are the specific volume and viscosity, respectively, the subscripts 0 and e indicating that the attached quantities belong to the states at time zero and at equilibrium.

Heterogeneity of the Sites

We have considered above only one kind of relaxation site. But it has been clear from the viscosity studies of high polymeric systems (Ree and Eyring, 1955; Powell and Eyring, 1944) that the relaxation sites are not uniform, but composed of various kinds of sites differing in relaxation time, β. Therefore we now introduce the idea of heterogeneity of relaxation sites.

For the ith kind of site, the following relaxation equations hold:

$$-\frac{d \ln \phi_i}{dt} = 2k_{fi} \sinh \alpha_i' \phi_i \qquad (15)$$

$$-\frac{d \ln \phi_i}{dt} = k_{fi} \exp (\alpha_i' \phi_i) \qquad (16)$$

Here ϕ_i, k_{fi}, and α_i' belong to the ith kind of site. Integrating the above equations, we obtain the equations corresponding to (9) and (10), which give the relation ϕ_i versus t. In the case of stress relaxation, ϕ_i equals f_i/f_{i0} as in (12). Thus the decay of stress, due to the ith kind of site, is obtained. Let us assume that there is no interaction between different kinds of sites and that for simplicity there are only two kinds of sites. Site 2 decays faster than site 1, as shown in Fig. 1a, where the decay of stress on sites 1 and 2 are shown as a function of time. From Fig. 1a, one understands that after a long time interval the stress relaxation is due to site 1 only, while in the initial period it is due to both sites.

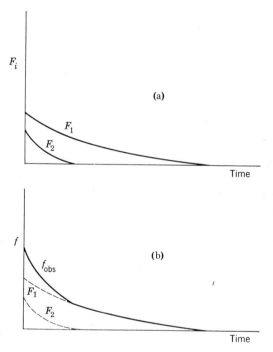

Fig. 1. Stress vs. time. (a) Two kinds of relaxation sites participate in a stress decay. Site 2 decays faster than site 1. (b) The observed stress decay curve, f_{obs}, is composed from the two stress decay curves, F_1 and F_2.

Suppose that we have the stress relaxation curve, f_{obs}, in Fig. 1b brought about by the relaxation sites shown in Fig. 1a. Applying (15) or (16) with (12) to the final part of the f_{obs} curve, we obtain the parameters, k_{f1} and α_1'/f_{10} (cf. the latter part of the chapter for the determination of the parameters). Substituting these parameters into the integrated equation, (9) or (10), one obtains the curve of F_1 versus t (cf. Fig. 1b). Subtract the F_1 versus t curve from the f_{obs} curve. The remainder is represented by curve F_2 in Fig. 1b. Applying (15) or (16) again to curve F_2, one obtains k_{f2} and α_2'/f_{20}. The theoretical curve for F_2 versus t is calculated from (9) or (10) by using these parameters. Thus the observed curve, f_{obs} versus t, is reproduced by superposing the two theoretical curves, F_1 versus t and F_2 versus t.

The aforementioned procedure is represented by a mathematical formula, if the stress relaxation follows equation (8). In this case, we obtain from (10) the equation

$$f = \sum_{i=1}^{2} f_i = \sum_{i=1}^{2} -\frac{f_{0i}}{\alpha_i'} Ei^{-1}[k_{f_i}t - Ei(-\alpha_i')] \tag{17}$$

Here, the function $y = Ei^{-1}(-x)$ indicates an inverse exponential integral function, i.e., $-x = -Ei(-y)$. When the relaxation follows the hyperbolic sine law, the equation is complicated; it is not given here.

Application of the Theory

Determination of the Parameters

The following is the customary procedure for determining the parameters occurring in (7) and (8). Since the latter is a special case of the former, the procedure for (7) includes that for (8). From the experimental curve of q versus t the logarithmic rates, $-d \ln (q - q_e)/dt$, which equal $-d \ln \phi/dt$, are obtained. Next the values of $\ln (-d \ln \phi/dt)$ are plotted against ϕ. If we approximate $\sinh \alpha'\phi$ by $\frac{1}{2} \exp (\alpha'\phi)$ in (7), a straight line is obtained in the initial stage of the experiment. From the slope and intercept on the y-axis of the straight line, one obtains α' and k_f, respectively. Using α' and k_f thus obtained and the experimental values of $-d \ln \phi/dt$, the values of Φ, which equals $d \ln \phi/dt + k_f \exp \alpha'\phi$, are calculated over the entire range of the experiment. From the plot of $\ln \Phi$ versus ϕ, which is a straight line with a negative slope, one obtains again the values of k_f and α'. If the values of k_f and α' found by the latter procedure agree with those previously found, equation (7) is justified.

Decrease of the Birefringence and Specific Volume in Glass

Daragan measured the birefringence and density of glass as a function of time over the temperature range 490–539°C (Daragan, 1952). The sample was an ordinary crown glass. We apply equation (8) to his results. The parametric values of k_f and α' are summarized in Tables 1 and 2. Using these parametric values, the curves f versus t and density versus t are calculated from equation (10) and are shown in Fig. 2. The

Table 1

PARAMETRIC VALUES FOR THE STRESS RELAXATION IN GLASS [a]

Temperature (°C)	$k_f \times 10^3$ (min^{-1})	α'	f_0[b] (mμ/cm)
500	1.73	4.50	150
511	3.00	6.21	138
519	11.00	4.60	115
528	45.3	2.14	107
539	50.0	3.00	100

$$\Delta H^{\ddagger} = 114 \text{ kcal/mole} \qquad \Delta S^{\ddagger} = 79.1 \text{ eu/mole}$$
$$\text{Average of } \alpha' = 4.09$$

[a] The composition of the glass (in %): SiO_2, 72.00; Na_2O, 14.00; CaO, 12.00; MgO, 0.10; Al_2O_3, 1.00; Fe_2O_3, 0.05; SO_3, 0.55. Total = 99.70%.

[b] These values are obtained from the original data (Daragan, 1952) by extrapolation.

Table 2

PARAMETRIC VALUES FOR THE VOLUME CONTRACTION IN GLASS [a]

Temperature (°C)	$k_f \times 10^4$ (min^{-1})	α'	$(v_0 - v_e) \times 10^3$ [a] (cc/g)
490	0.230	6.00	1.60
500	0.625	7.89	2.06
510	1.70	5.12	1.28
530	36.9	2.58	0.678

$$\Delta H^{\ddagger} = 108 \text{ kcal/mole} \qquad \Delta S^{\ddagger} = 78.5 \text{ eu/mole}$$
$$\text{Average of } \alpha' = 5.14$$

[a] Refer to the footnotes in Table 1.

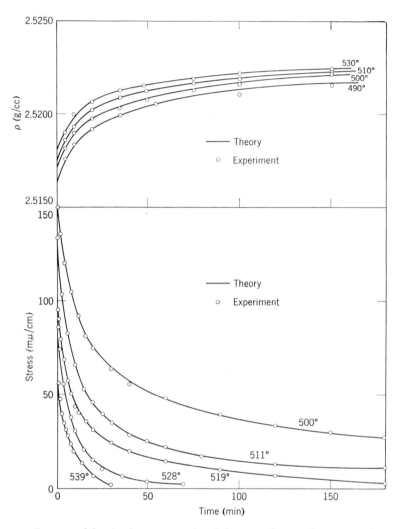

Fig. 2. Increase of density (upper curves) and decrease of stress (lower curves) with time during the annealing of the crown glass. Experimental data from Daragan (1952). Theoretical curves calculated from equation (10).

agreement between theory and experiment is perfect. By plotting $\ln k_f$ against $1/T$, the values of $\Delta H^{\ddagger}$ and $\Delta S^{\ddagger}$ are obtained; they are tabulated in Tables 1 and 2. One sees that the values of $\Delta H^{\ddagger}$ and $\Delta S^{\ddagger}$ obtained from the decreases of birefringence and specific volume with time are practically the same. This is natural, since the two properties reflect the same molecular process. We also recognize that the values of

$\alpha'(= \alpha\sigma c)$ are about constant, independent of temperature, and that the average value of α' for the stress relaxation ($\alpha' = 4.09$) and that for the volume contraction ($\alpha' = 5.14$) are nearly equal. The independence of temperature of α is found in various cases (Ree and Eyring, 1955, 1958). The factor σc is considered to be constant for a given sample. Thus the values of α' obtained from the stress decay and the volume contraction must be the same, since α is a function of the molecular dimensions of the relaxation site only (cf. equation 6).

The values of $\Delta H^{\ddagger}$ for viscous flow of glasses are usually found in the range of 100–150 kcal/mole (Stanworth, 1950, pp. 180, 184). From the viscosity data for glass No. 35 * (Robinson and Peterson, 1944), we found the values $\Delta H^{\ddagger} = 117$ kcal and $\Delta S^{\ddagger} = 65.7$ eu in the temperature range 500–600°C. (In the calculation of $\Delta S^{\ddagger}$ the molecular volume of the glass was estimated as 100 cc.) Our values, $\Delta H^{\ddagger} = 108 - 114$ kcal and $\Delta S^{\ddagger} = 78.5 - 79.1$ eu, seem thus very reasonable. The high values of $\Delta H^{\ddagger}$ and $\Delta S^{\ddagger}$ as in our case occur very frequently at near glass temperature not only for inorganic glasses but also for organic glasses (Hirai, Ree, and Eyring, 1958). According to these authors, the high values of $\Delta H^{\ddagger}$ and $\Delta S^{\ddagger}$ are apparent only, and are due to transitions of the second kind occurring at near glass temperature.

Effect of Thermal History on Viscosity

Lillie found that the viscosity of a sample of soda-lime-silica glass, at a temperature in the transformation range, increased with time toward an equilibrium value if previously treated at a higher temperature, and that the same glass had a viscosity decreasing with time toward the same final equilibrium value if previously treated for a sufficiently long time at a lower temperature. The experimental points in Fig. 3 are due to Lillie. We apply equations (8) and (14) to the Lillie data and find the parametric values summarized in Table 3. The theoretical curves in Fig. 3 are calculated from equation (10) by introducing these parametric values. The results are satisfactory. From the parametric values one may see that the two samples subjected to different heat treatments behave as though they were different materials, because different structures are impressed on the glass by the different heat treatment. In glass, not only viscosity but also other properties, such as specific heat, specific volume, and index of refraction, are functions of the thermal history (Stanworth, 1950; Morey, 1954).

* The composition is: SiO_2, 71.7%; Na_2O and K_2O, 15.9%; CaO, 9.2%; MgO, 0.52%; Al_2O_3, 1.58%; BaO, 0.26%; B_2O_3, 0.83%; Fe_2O_3, 0.06%. Thus this glass has about the same composition as the crown glass under consideration.

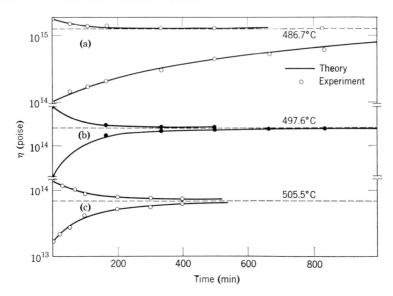

Fig. 3. Effect of thermal history on viscosity of soda-lime-silica glass. Three sets of experiments (Lillie, 1933) at different temperatures are shown: (a) 486.7°C, (b) 497.6°C, and (c) 505.5°C. The upper curve of each set was obtained for the sample treated previously at a higher temperature, while the lower curve was obtained for the sample treated previously for a long time at a lower temperature. The theoretical curves are calculated from equation (10).

Table 3

EFFECT OF THERMAL HISTORY ON VISCOSITY OF GLASS [a]

Temperature (°C)	$k_f \times 10^3$ (min^{-1})	$\eta_0 \times 10^{-14}$ (poise)	$\eta_e \times 10^{-14}$ (poise)	α'
	Chilled Glass			
505.5	6.71	1.30	0.830	1.36
497.6	5.80	5.86	2.63	2.10
486.7	4.31	26.3	12.6	2.06
	Heated Glass			
505.5	4.00	0.220	0.830	1.53
497.6	1.97	0.537	2.63	1.36
486.7	1.11	1.00	12.6	1.16

[a] The composition of the glass (in %): SiO_2, 69.73; Na_2O, 20.96; CaO, 9.05; K_2O, trace; R_2O_3, 0.18. Total = 99.92% (cf. Lillie, 1933).

The effects of thermal history on viscosity are also found for organic substances (Davies and Jones, 1953). Thus a figure similar to Fig. 3 has been found for the curve of viscosity of lubricating oil versus time and has been explained along these same lines (Ree, Fava, Higuchi, and Eyring, 1956).

Stress Relaxation in High Polymers

The stress relaxation in isobutylene polymers has been studied by Tobolsky and his associates (Andrews, Hofman-Bang, and Tobolsky, 1948; Brown and Tobolsky, 1951; Andrews and Tobolsky, 1951; Tobolsky, Dunell, and Andrews, 1951; Tobolsky and McLaughlin, 1952; Mark and Tobolsky, 1950). These authors stretched rings of polyisobutylene at a constant length and measured the decay of stress with time. The experimental points in Fig. 4 are from their results. The ordinate represents f/s_0, where f is stress (tensile force per cross-sectional area of the sample), and s_0 is the initial strain impressed on the sample. We found that in this case the hyperbolic sine law (equation 7) holds exactly, where $\phi = (f/s_0)/(f_0/s_0) = f/f_0$. The values of k_f and α' are summarized in Table 4. The theoretical curves in Fig. 4 are calculated from (9).

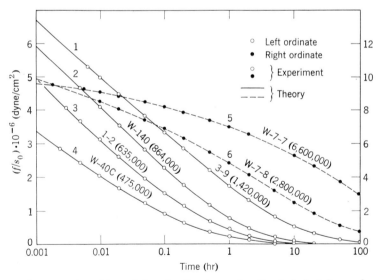

Fig. 4. Stress vs. logarithm of time for the stress relaxation in isobutylene polymers at 30°C. The codes and molecular weights of the samples are given for each curve. Experimental data are due to Tobolsky and his associates; theoretical curves 1, 2, 3, and 4 are calculated from equation (9), curves 5 and 6 are calculated from (9) by assuming that two kinds of relaxation sites act in the stress decay.

Table 4

PARAMETERS OF POLYISOBUTYLENE AT $30°C$

Code	Molecular Weight $\times 10^{-6}$	k_f (hr^{-1})	α'	$(f_0/s_0) \times 10^{-6}$ [a] (dyne/cm^2)	Reference
W-40c	0.475	1.29	4.92	3.34	[b]
1-2	0.635	0.759	5.18	4.94	[b]
1-2	0.635	0.813	5.21	3.86	[c]
1-1	0.665	0.708	4.93	3.52	[c]
W-140-1	0.864	0.363	5.72	5.90	[b]
2-6	0.880	0.240	6.06	4.89	[c]
2-5	0.880	0.224	5.98	4.64	[c]
3-10	1.34	0.0668	7.40	5.40	[c]
3-9	1.42	0.0550	7.35	6.62	[b]
3-9	1.42	0.0596	7.08	5.02	[c]
W-7-8	2.80	6.31×10^{-3}	(8.50)	9.80	[b]
W-7-8	6.60	4.47×10^{-4}	(7.20)	9.60	[b]

[a] The value of f/s_0 at 0.001 hr has been taken as f_0/s_0 and used in the calculations. The same is applied to Tables 5 and 7.

[b] Andrews and Tobolsky (1951); Tobolsky, Dunell, and Andrews (1951); Mark and Tobolsky (1950).

[c] Andrews, Hofman-Bang, and Tobolsky (1948).

One sees that the agreement between theory and experiment is perfect.

At temperatures higher than 30°C, the hyperbolic sine equation (7) does not hold exactly. Instead, the following holds.

$$-\frac{d \ln (f/f_0)}{dt} = k_f \exp (\alpha'f/f_0) - \exp (-\alpha''f/f_0) \tag{18}$$

Here

$$\alpha' = \sigma c \mu \lambda \lambda_2 \lambda_3 / kT$$

$$\alpha'' = \sigma c (1 - \mu) \lambda \lambda_2 \lambda_3 / kT \tag{19}$$

One sees that, if $\mu = \frac{1}{2}$, equation (18) becomes the hyperbolic sine function (equation 7). Applying (18) to the experimental results, we found the parametric values summarized in Table 5. The values of μ in Table 5 are calculated from the equation

$$\alpha'/\alpha'' = \mu/(1 - \mu) \tag{20}$$

Table 5

PARAMETERS OF POLYISOBUTYLENES AT HIGHER TEMPERATURES

Code	Molecular Weight $\times 10^{-6}$	Temperature (°C)	k_f (hr^{-1})	α'	α''	μ	Reference
1-1	0.665	50	3.45	4.18	6.09	0.408	a
1-1	0.665	70	8.32	3.92	9.05	0.303	a
2-5	0.880	50	0.875	5.22	8.13	0.391	a
2-5	0.880	70	3.79	4.00	9.25	0.302	a
2-5	0.880	100	17.0	2.89	9.71	0.229	a
3-10	1.34	50	0.280	5.90	6.45	0.478	a
3-10	1.34	70	1.67	4.35	7.55	0.365	a
3-10	1.34	100	8.91	3.39	6.50	0.342	a
3-9	1.42	50	0.337	5.83	5.91	0.498	a
3-9	1.42	70	1.05	5.20	6.75	0.435	a
3-9	1.42	100	4.57	4.21	5.14	0.450	a
W-7-7	6.60	50	1.59×10^{-3}	7.31	—	—	b
W-7-7	6.60	70	6.31×10^{-3}	6.36	—	—	b
W-7-7	6.60	100	0.0288	6.14	—	—	b
W-7-7	6.60	130	0.132	5.62	—	—	b

[a] Andrews, Hofman-Bang, and Tobolsky (1948).
[b] Andrews and Tobolsky (1951); Mark and Tobolsky (1950).

which is derived from equation (19). From Table 5 one draws the following conclusions:

1. The factor α' is smaller than α''; this phenomenon is more pronounced in the isobutylene polymers of low molecular weights than in the higher polymers.

2. μ decreases with increasing temperature; that is, high temperature favors the backward reaction more than it does the forward reaction.

From the values of k_f listed in Tables 4 and 5 one can calculate $\Delta H^{\ddagger}$ and $\Delta S^{\ddagger}$. These values are tabulated in Table 6. One sees that the activation heats for all the polymers are about the same, while the activation entropies decrease with increasing molecular weight. The constancy of the activation heat irrespective of molecular weights has already been reported (Andrews, Hofman-Bang, and Tobolsky, 1948). The same fact has been noted in the viscous flow of polyisobutylene (Fox and Flory,

Table 6

ACTIVATION HEAT AND ACTIVATION ENTROPY FOR THE STRESS
RELAXATION IN POLYISOBUTYLENES

Molecular Weight $\times 10^{-6}$	$\Delta H^{\ddagger}$ (kcal/mole)	$\Delta S^{\ddagger}$ (cal/deg/mole)
0.665	13.3	-31.4
0.880	13.4	-33.3
1.34	13.6	-34.7
1.42	13.1	-36.7
6.60	13.2	-46.3

1948). All the activation heats obtained by these authors agree with ours within 2 kcal/mole. The $\Delta H^{\ddagger}$ value for viscous flow of polyisobutylene of a molecular weight of 6000 is 15.8 kcal/mole (Harper, Markovitz, and DeWitt, 1952). Thus the constancy of $\Delta H^{\ddagger}$ seems to hold over a wide range of molecular weights, from 6000 to 6,600,000. This fact is due to the segmental behavior of the high polymers (GLE, 1941).

In contrast to the case of glass, the activation entropies for the stress relaxation in polyisobutylenes have negative values (-31.4 to -46.3 eu/mole). It is common to have negative activation entropies in creep and flow phenomena (e.g., Ree, Chen, and Eyring, 1951; Chen, Ree, and Eyring, 1952; Ree and Eyring, 1955 *). The negative activation entropy for viscous flow in high polymeric systems is considered to be due to the cooperative nature of segmental motion.

Relaxation Showing the Presence of Two Kinds of Relaxation Sites

The relaxation curves 5 and 6 for molecular weights of 6.60×10^6 and 2.80×10^6 in Fig. 4 cannot be explained by a single kind of site. Thus we use the procedure mentioned previously, assuming that two kinds of relaxation sites contribute in these cases. The parameters are summarized in Table 7. By using these parameters and equation (9), the theoretical curves, 5 and 6, are calculated. The agreement between theory and experiment is satisfactory.

* In this paper the $\Delta S^{\ddagger}$ values are not explicitly given. However, using the β_r values (the relaxation time reduced for temperature) tabulated for a wide variety of materials, the $\Delta S^{\ddagger}$ values are calculated from the equation of β_r on p. 807. One easily finds that the $\Delta S^{\ddagger}$ values for all the materials are negative.

Table 7

PARAMETRIC VALUES OF POLYISOBUTYLENES OF
HIGHER MOLECULAR WEIGHTS [a]

Molecular Weight $\times 10^{-6}$	Site Number	$k_f \times 10^3$ (hr^{-1})	α'	$f_0/s_0 \times 10^{-6}$ $(dyne/cm^2)$
2.80	2	4.20	9.08	9.08
6.60	2	0.450	5.25	7.50
2.80	1	50.0	1.07	1.07
6.60	1	4.96	1.34	1.91

[a] Mark and Tobolsky (1950).

The procedure above can be extended, in principle, to cases where more than two kinds of relaxation sites are present. However, transient phenomena involving more than two kinds of relaxation sites have not as yet been found.

It is worth while to mention here that Tobolsky and his associates (Tobolsky, 1958; Mark and Tobolsky, 1950) explain their relaxation data differently. For the flow unit they assume a *generalized* Maxwell model, which consists of a parallel arrangement of simple Maxwell elements. In addition, they assume that the relaxation times of the simple elements follow the so-called "box" distribution function. Using this model, they successfully explain stress relaxation in high polymers and calculate shear moduli (static and dynamic) from the stress relaxation data. Since non-Newtonian behavior is a commonly observed phenomena, our explanation seems a natural one.

Discussion of Results

Phenomena Due to the Same Molecular Process

We mentioned previously that in Daragan's experiments the decay of birefringence and the increase of density are brought about by the same molecular process. If this statement is true, the plots of $-d \ln f/dt$ and $-d \ln (v - v_e)/dt$ at time t will give a straight line. As shown in Fig. 5, this expectation is fulfilled.

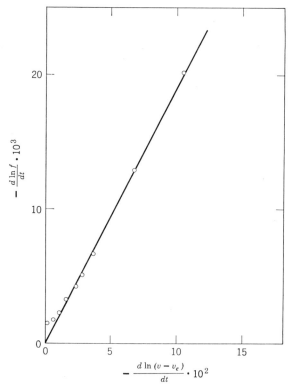

Fig. 5. Linear relationship between logarithmic rates of stress decay and of volume contraction in crown glass at 500°C. Experimental data from Daragan (1952).

Logarithmic Decay Rates of Stress versus Fluidity

Lillie (1936) measured the increase of viscosity with time in samples so prepared as to have as nearly as possible the same thermal history as the samples he had used earlier for the stress decay experiments. Plotting $-d \ln f/dt$ against $1/\eta$ (fluidity), he obtained a straight line the slope of which gave the shear modulus G of the glass.

To understand this, consider the equation

$$-\frac{d \ln f}{dt} = c k_f' \exp \alpha'' \frac{\eta_e - \eta}{\eta_e - \eta_0} \tag{21}$$

resulting from the two equations

$$-\frac{d \ln f}{dt} = k_f \exp \frac{\alpha' f}{f_0} \tag{22}$$

$$-\frac{d \ln (\eta_e - \eta)}{dt} = k_f' \exp \left(\alpha'' \frac{\eta_e - \eta}{\eta_e - \eta_0} \right) \tag{23}$$

These two equations are for stress decay and for increase of viscosity, respectively. (In fact, the two equations have already been used for treating the respective phenomenon in previous sections, although they were not explicitly written down.) The quantities k_f and α' for the viscosity increase have been primed to distinguish them from the corresponding quantities for stress decay. In equation (21) c is a proportionality constant. By assuming $\alpha''(\eta_e - \eta)/(\eta_e - \eta_0) \ll 1$, and expanding the exponential term of (21), we obtain

$$-\frac{d \ln f}{dt} \simeq \frac{ck_f'}{1 - \alpha''(\eta_e - \eta)/(\eta_e - \eta_0)} \tag{24}$$

If the condition

$$1 = \alpha'' \eta_e / (\eta_e - \eta_0) \tag{25}$$

is satisfied, (24) is transformed to

$$-\frac{d \ln f}{dt} = \frac{ck_f' \eta_e}{\alpha'' \eta} = \frac{G}{\eta} \tag{26}$$

Here the second equality of (26) is based on the Maxwell relation, $\eta = G\tau$ (τ = relaxation time). Thus equation (26) justifies Lillie's results (1936).

The justification of (26), however, hinges on relation (25). In order to test this relation, we analyzed Lillie's data (1936). The results are summarized in Table 8. One finds that (25) holds approximately, but not exactly. Since $G = ck_f' \eta_e / \alpha''$ (cf. equation 26), the shear modulus is calculated by assuming $c = 1$ and by using the data in Table 8. The calculated average value of G is 0.42×10^{11} dynes/cm^2, which agrees reasonably well with the observed value for ordinary glass.

Suppose that measurements for stress decay and viscosity change were made at a temperature lying in the transformation range, on a sample which had been chilled for a sufficient length of time at a lower temperature. In this case the viscosity decreases with time and the following equation holds instead of (23):

$$-\frac{d \ln (\eta - \eta_e)}{dt} = k_f' \exp \left(\alpha'' \frac{\eta - \eta_e}{\eta_0 - \eta_e} \right) \tag{27}$$

From equations (22) and (27) the following results:

$$-\frac{d \ln f}{dt} = ck_f' \exp \left(\alpha'' \frac{\eta - \eta_e}{\eta_0 - \eta_e} \right) \tag{28}$$

Table 8

PARAMETRIC VALUES FOR STRESS DECAY AND
FOR VISCOSITY INCREASE IN GLASS [a]

Temperature (°C)	$k_f \times 10^4$ (min^{-1})	α'	f_0 (mμ/cm)
Stress Relaxation			
471	8.23	3.50	120
453	2.34	4.00	200

Viscosity Increase

	$k_f^1 \times 10^4$ (min^{-1})	α''	$\eta_0 \times 10^{-16}$ (poise)	$\eta_e \times 10^{-16}$ (poise)
471	2.03	2.31	0.100	3.50
453	0.885	1.94	0.370	4.25

[a] Ordinary lime-bulb glass (cf. Lillie, 1936).

which corresponds to (21). By the procedure mentioned above, we obtain the following equation corresponding to (24):

$$-\frac{d \ln f}{dt} = \frac{ck_f'}{1 - \alpha''(\eta - \eta_e)/(\eta_0 - \eta_e)} \tag{29}$$

One sees readily that in this case an equation corresponding to (26) is not obtainable.

The stress relaxation for the Maxwell model is represented by $-d \ln f/dt = G/\eta$. That is, the equality between the first and third terms in (26) immediately follows. Thus Lillie (1936) proposed that the logarithmic decay rate of stress is proportional to the fluidity. The Maxwell relaxation formula is verified only for the case where the viscosity increases with time, but not for the case of viscosity decrease. In the latter case the term $-d \ln f/dt$, which is positive, decreases with time while G/η increases, G being nearly constant; that is, the relation $-d \ln f/dt = G/\eta$ does not hold. The inconsistency mentioned above shows that the Maxwell relaxation formula is not applicable to the case where η changes with time.

As we saw above, however, (29) holds for the case where viscosity decreases with time. There are no experiments which test (29).

Kinetic Derivation of Tool's Equation

We derive Tool's equation (Tool, 1945) from the general theory. Equation (8) may be transformed to

$$-\frac{d \ln \phi}{dt} = \frac{kT}{h} \exp \frac{\Delta S^{\ddagger}}{R} \exp \frac{-\Delta H^{\ddagger}}{RT} \exp (\alpha' \phi) \tag{30a}$$

Expanding the term $1/T$ in the neighborhood of θ (a fixed temperature) by Taylor's theorem, and neglecting terms higher than the second, one obtains

$$1/T = 1/\theta - (T - \theta)/\theta^2 \tag{30b}$$

Introducing equation (30b) into (30a) yields

$$-\frac{d \ln \phi}{dt} = k_0 \exp (\alpha' \phi) \exp \left(\frac{\Delta H^{\ddagger}}{R\theta^2} T\right) \tag{31}$$

where

$$k_0 = \frac{kT}{h} \exp \frac{\Delta S^{\ddagger}}{R} \exp \frac{-2\Delta H^{\ddagger}}{R\theta} \tag{32}$$

By substituting the relation $\phi = c_1(T' - T)$ into (31) one obtains

$$\frac{dT'}{dt} = k_0(T - T') \exp \frac{T}{g} \exp \frac{T'}{h'} \tag{33}$$

Here c_1 is a proportionality constant, and

$$1/g \equiv (\Delta H^{\ddagger}/R\theta^2) - \alpha' c_1$$

$$1/h' \equiv \alpha' c_1 \tag{34}$$

Equation (33) is called Tool's equation (Tool, 1945), where, T' is the so-called fictive temperature, T the annealing temperature, and k_0, g, and h' are constants which are independent of temperature.* One may see that the conception of the fictive temperature corresponds to our function ϕ, and that the Tool equation is a special case of the general theory developed here.

In order to explain the stress relaxation, Tool replaced the term $T' - T$ in his equation by $f/c_1 f_0$. Thus he obtained the following, which corresponds to our equation (22):

$$-\frac{d \ln f}{dt} = k_0 \exp \frac{T}{g'} \exp \frac{f}{c_1 h' f_0} \tag{35}$$

---

* k_0 contains T linearly as shown in equation (32); thus the temperature dependence of k_0 is very small compared to that of the term $\exp (T/g)$. As already mentioned, α' is a temperature-independent factor.

where $1/g' = (g + h')/gh'$. The change of index of refraction, n, during annealing was explained by Collyer, who replaced $T' - T$ by $c_2(n - n_e)$ (n_e = index of refraction at equilibrium), and he obtained the following equation (Collyer, 1947):

$$\frac{dn}{dt} = Q(n_e - n) \exp \frac{n}{p} \exp \frac{T}{g'} \tag{36}$$

where Q and p are constants introduced by the substitution just indicated. Equations (35) and (36) were claimed by the respective authors to fit the experimental data. We find, however, that both equations apply only in a limited range of temperature. This fact is natural, since the expansion (30b) holds only when $|T - \theta| \ll 1$.

Summary

1. When glass is quenched, internal stress develops in the glass. Annealing is a process which relieves the stress as the system passes to equilibrium. The internal stress F is determined by how far the system is from equilibrium, i.e., by $q - q_e$ or by $\phi \equiv (q - q_e)/(q_0 - q_e)$, where q is a property of the system at time t, q_0 and q_e being the corresponding quantities at time zero and at equilibrium, respectively. The property q may be the birefringence, the specific volume, the viscosity, the specific heat, etc. It is reasonable to assume that the number of strained sites (relaxation sites) per unit volume, n_f, is proportional to F, i.e., to ϕ (cf. equation 1). Here the relaxation site is an atom, a molecule, or a group of atoms or molecules displaced from the equilibrium position.

The internal stress and the relaxation sites can also be produced by external shear stress, hydrostatic pressure, temperature, field (magnetic, electric), etc., to a system in equilibrium. The quantities F and n_f in these cases are also proportional to ϕ.

2. Stress relaxation, which includes annealing, is brought about by the decay of the relaxation sites. Applying rate process theory to this decay, we obtain the two equations

$$-\frac{d \ln \phi}{dt} = k_f \exp (\alpha' \phi) \tag{a}$$

and

$$-\frac{d \ln \phi}{dt} = 2k_f \sinh \alpha' \phi \tag{b}$$

Equations (a) and (b) are applied to the annealing of glass and to stress relaxation in polyisobutylene polymers, respectively, with good results.

3. All phenomena accompanying glass annealing are brought about by the molecular process mentioned above. Thus the plot of the logarithmic rates of stress decay against the logarithmic rates of volume contraction, for the same sample, give a good straight line.

It is a well-established fact that the logarithmic rates of stress decay in glass are proportional to the fluidity of the glass. This is also explained by assuming that the stress decay and the increase of viscosity are brought out by the same molecular process.

4. By replacing the function ϕ in equation (a) by $T' - T$ (T' is the fictive temperature, T the annealing temperature), Tool's equation is derived as a special case.

5. The non-Newtonian relaxation theory developed here explains the stress relaxation in polyisobutylenes very well. Since non-Newtonian relaxation is a commonly observed phenomenon not only in high polymeric systems, but also in glass and metal, our stress relaxation theory for high polymeric systems seems a natural one.

ACKNOWLEDGMENTS

This research was supported in part by a grant from the Petroleum Research Fund administered by the American Chemical Society. Grateful acknowledgment is hereby made to the donors of said fund. We also wish to express our appreciation to the National Science Foundation for partial support of this work.

REFERENCES

Adams, L. H., and Williamson, E. D., *J. Franklin Inst.* **190**, 597, 835 (1920).
Andrews, R. D., Hofman-Bang, N., and Tobolsky, A. V., *J. Polymer Sci.* **3**, 669 (1948).
Andrews, R. D., and Tobolsky, A. V., *J. Polymer Sci.* **7**, 221 (1951).
Brown, G. M., and Tobolsky, A. V., *J. Polymer Sci.* **6**, 165 (1951).
Cagle, F. W., and Eyring, H., *J. Appl. Phys.* **22**, 771 (1951).
Chen, M. C., Ree, T., and Eyring, H., *Textile Research J.* **22**, 416 (1952).
Collyer, P. W., *J. Am. Ceram. Soc.* **30**, 338 (1947).
Condon, E. U., *Am. J. Phys.* **22**, 43, 132, 224, 310 (1954).
Daragan, B., *Glass Ind.* **33**, 69 (1952).
Davies, R. O., and Jones, G. O., *Proc. Roy. Soc. (London)* **A217**, 26 (1953).
Eyring, H., *J. Chem. Phys.* **3**, 107 (1935).
Eyring, H., *J. Chem. Phys.* **4**, 283 (1936).
Fava, A., and Eyring, H., *J. Phys. Chem.* **60**, 890 (1956).
Fox, T. G., and Flory, F. J., *J. Am. Chem. Soc.* **70**, 2384 (1948).

Glasstone, H., Laidler, K. J., and Eyring, H., *The Theory of Rate Processes*, McGraw-Hill, New York, 1941.

Harper, R. C., Markovitz, H., and DeWitt, T. W., *J. Polymer Sci.* **8**, 435 (1952).

Hirai, N., Ree, T., and Eyring, H., to be published.

Jahnke, E., and Emde, F., *Tables of Functions*, Dover, New York, 1945.

Lillie, H. R., *J. Am. Ceram. Soc.* **16**, 619 (1933).

Lillie, H. R., *J. Am. Ceram. Soc.* **19**, 45 (1936).

Lowan, A. N., *Tables of Sine, Cosine and Exponential Integrals*, Vols. I and II, National Bureau of Standards, Washington, D. C., 1940.

Mark, H., and Tobolsky, A. V., *Physical Chemistry of High Polymers*, Interscience, New York, 1950.

Morey, G. W., *The Properties of Glass*, Reinhold, New York, 1954

Powell, R. E., and Eyring, H., *Nature* **154**, 427 (1944).

Ree, T., Chen, M. C., and Eyring, H., *Textile Research J.* **21**, 799 (1951).

Ree, T., and Eyring, H., *J. Appl. Phys.* **26**, 793, 800 (1955).

Ree, T., and Eyring, H., in *Rheology*, Vol. II (ed. F. R. Eirich), 1958, Academic, Press, New York, pp. 83–144.

Ree, T., Fava, A., Higuchi, I., and Eyring, H., *NLGI Spokesman* **20**, No. 3, 10 (1956).

Ree, T., Hahn, S. J., and Eyring, H., *Proc. Intern. Wool Textile Research Conf., Australia* **D**, 234 (1955).

Robinson, H. A., and Peterson, C. A., *J. Am. Ceram. Soc.* **27**, 129 (1944).

Stanworth, J. E., *Physical Properties of Glass*, Clarendon Press, Oxford, 1950.

Tobolsky, A. V., *Rheology*, Vol. II (ed. F. R. Eirich), 1958, Academic Press, New York, p. 63.

Tobolsky, A. V., Dunell, B. A., and Andrews, R. D., *Textile Research J.* **21**, 404 (1951).

Tobolsky, A. V., and McLaughlin, J. R., *J. Polymer Sci.* **8**, 548 (1952).

Tool, A. Q., *J. Research Natl. Bur. Standards* **34**, 199 (1945).

Tool, A. Q., *J. Am. Ceram. Soc.* **29**, 240 (1946).

Weyl, W. A., in *Phase Transformation in Solids* (ed. by Smoluchowski, Mayer, and Weyl), Wiley, New York, 1951, p. 296.

DISCUSSION

H. R. LILLIE

In the experiments which Dr. Ree has cited, I was trying to show that viscosity was the controlling property in stress release. I was not attempting to show that changes in viscosity, stress, and density proceeded by the same mechanism. In the kind of samples we were dealing with at that time, I believe that viscosity was indeed the controlling property for stress release.

Perhaps I can illustrate my point by considering two idealized and imaginary glasses. Of course, it must be recognized that, in the real case, one cannot actually observe separately the two effects that I shall describe, because of their interdependence; however, we shall for the moment pretend that this can be done. The first imaginary glass has no thermal expansivity, but we shall assume that very small samples of the material can be made to show a variety of densities at room temperature by appropriate variation of the high temperature history prior to and during cooling. In a single large sample of this material we can have an exterior density which is different from the density of the center because the two regions will in ordinary cooling have different high temperature histories. The sample will accordingly show the presence of some internal stress created by these density differences.

Now let us consider a second idealized glass characterized by a very large thermal expansivity but lacking the structural states of differing density attributed to the first material. Very small samples of this second glass will all have the same density at room temperature whatever the preceding high temperature history. However, a massive sample of this second imaginary material will show internal stress and birefringence after cooling, because the outer and inner regions passed through the temperature region for flow at different times during the cooling process and therefore are stressed when the temperature lag is removed. The internal stresses in this sample would relax, I believe, via a flow process in which viscosity would be a controlling factor. The relaxation would resemble that seen in a sample of real glass relaxing under an *externally* applied stress.

However, the relaxation processes which would remove the density differences in the first imaginary sample have to do with structural changes. Just how shear viscosity is involved in these processes is unclear, but I think the relation between relaxation rates and viscosity might very well be different from that in the second type of material.

In the samples which Dr. Ree discussed, the two effects, which I have pretended can be isolated in the two hypothetical materials, are certainly both present. Perhaps this is why he seems to have more than one mechanism working in the relaxation process.

T. REE

Do you think, then, that there are many mechanisms in a relaxation, more than one?

H. R. LILLIE

I certainly believe that there is more than one variety of stress present in a rapidly cooled specimen, and I suppose that these different kinds of stress might have different mechanisms for their release. In the experiments of ours which you cite, the two effects are not distinguished because that wasn't what we were trying to do in those days. But I think experiments to do so could be devised today.

T. REE

I believe that in Daragan's experiments also the two effects, which you have just discussed, are present. If increase in density and decrease in birefringence (internal stesss) with time have different mechanisms, how do you explain the fact that the values of $\Delta H^{\ddagger}$, $\Delta S^{\ddagger}$, and α' for the two processes are approximately equal (cf. Tables 1 and 2)? And how do you account for the linearity of the relationship between the logarithmic rate of stress decay and that of volume contraction (cf. Fig. 5)? I recognize that the values of $\Delta H^{\ddagger}$, $\Delta S^{\ddagger}$, and α' in Tables 1 and 2 are *apparent* values. But I believe that the agreement of these values in the two experiments requires the conclusion that the changes of density and of birefringence are brought about by the same molecular mechanism.

R. O. DAVIES

Seeing that the "internal stress" defined and used by you (equation 2) is not a stress, how can the theory of Glasstone, Laidler, and Eyring (which *is* about stress) be applied?

T. REE

In a non-equilibrium system, such, for example, as glass over the temperature range of transformation, molecules (or molecular groups) are displaced from the equilibrium position, i.e., the potential minimum. Thus the molecules of the system experience stress, which is relieved during annealing. The stress is assumed to be given by equation (2). We believe that the assumption, which is expressed by equation (2), is very natural. This equation shows that stress becomes zero at equilibrium. One may readily see why Eyring's relaxation theory is applicable to annealing problems. Only a brief account has for this reason been given in the context. A more detailed explanation is to be found in our previous publications [Cagle and Eyring, *J. Appl. Phys.* **22**, 771 (1951); Eyring, *J. Chem. Phys.* **4**, 283 (1936); Fava and Eyring, *ibid.* **60**, 890 (1956); Ree, Hahn, and Eyring, *Proc. Intern. Wool Textile Research Conf., Australia* **D**, 234 (1955); Ree, Fava, Higuchi, and Eyring, *NLGI Spokesman* **20**, No. 3, 10 (1956).

R. O. DAVIES

It seems to be claimed that the annealing equation (7) is superior to that of Tool (35). Ritland, however, shows that his careful measurements can be well fitted to Tool's equation. Can you obtain a better fit?

T. REE

Yes, our equation (7) (or 8) is better than Tool's equation (33) (or 35). We referred to H. N. Ritland's work on the annealing of borosilicate crown glass [*J. Am. Ceram. Soc.* **37**, 370 (1954)]. Actually, he did not use Tool's equation, since it does not fit his data well. He used a modified Tool equation,

$$\frac{dT'}{dt} = k_0(T - T')[1 + B(T - T')] \exp \frac{T}{g} \exp \frac{T'}{h'}$$

His results are shown as the two dotted curves in Fig. 1. Using our equation (8), where $\phi = (v - v_e)/(v_o - v_e)$ (cf. equation 13), we obtained the full curves. The following parametric values were used: for the upper curve, $\alpha' = 0.5$, $k_f = 0.034$ hr^{-1}, $\rho_e = 2.521$, and $\rho_0 = 2.529$; for the lower curve, $\alpha' = 3.0$, $k_f = 0.0040$ hr^{-1}, $\rho_e = 2.521$, and $\rho_0 = 2.505$. One may see that our equation (8) is definitely better than Tool's equation and is even better than Ritland's modified equation. In view of the fact that our equation (8) contains only two adjustable parameters, k_f and α', while the modified Tool equation contains four adjust-

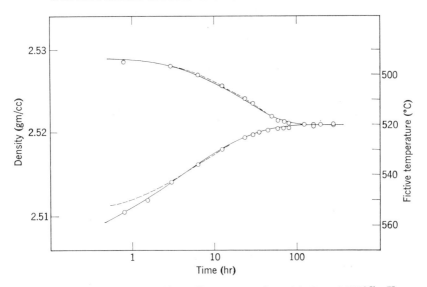

Fig. 1. Change of the density of borosilicate crown glass with time at 520°C. Upper curves, heated glass; lower curve, chilled glass. Circles, experimental values; broken curves, Ritland; solid curves, Hahn-Ree-Eyring.

able parameters, k_0, B, g, and h', our equation is certainly better than Tool's or Ritland's equation.

P. DEBYE

I believe that I understand the mathematics of your theory. I do not see at all the physical model to which your formulas apply. For instance, what are your "sites," of which you say that you have a certain number which will decrease during relaxation?

T. REE

As we mentioned in the context and as I said in the answer to Dr. Davies' question, the relaxing site is considered to be a molecule or a molecular group displaced from its equilibrium position. Such a model suffices for applying Eyring's relaxation theory to annealing. If you ask for the detailed structure of the site, I must say that we do not yet have a definite model, but we claim that our interpretation of the results is a useful step toward establishing such a model. For example, the values of the parameters, k_f and α', for various systems will be very useful in deciding between possible models.

13

by

J. A. Prins

Laboratorium voor Technische Fysica, Delft, Netherlands

Amorphous Sulfur and Selenium

When taking up, about 30 years ago, the question of structure and structural properties of liquids, I ran into the old puzzle: Why do some liquids vitrify on supercooling and others do not? The point is brought out by the remark (essentially due to Maxwell) that vitrification sets in when the viscosity gets higher than 10^{12} poise. This, of course, is no explanation; there still remains the question: Why can this high viscosity, indicating strong molecular interaction, be reached without crystallization? Another way to state the problem without solving it is to say that the vitrifying liquids already at their melting point are so viscous that a moderate supercooling is sufficient to freeze all configurational changes. The question still remains: Why is the melting point so low on the viscosity scale?

Before trying to answer the question, let us consider some examples, shown in Fig. 1. Here the horizontal scale is really a T^{-1} scale, but it is marked with the corresponding T values and $(T - 273)$ values. All ordinary liquids lie quite low in the figure. Turnbull (1950) has given the rule that these normal liquids can only be supercooled to $0.8T_m$, where T_m is the absolute melting point.

The exceptional liquids that are so viscous at their melting point that vitrification at supercooling is possible fill the upper part of the figure. They may be divided into three classes: (1) the oxide glasses like SiO_2 and B_2O_3, (2) the linear polymers like rubber and selenium, and (3) the smaller organic molecules, like glycerol, that are rich in OH groups.

For class 1 the current explanation of vitrification (Zachariasen, 1932) starts from the directional character and strength of the valency bond, leading to "wrong" connections which, once formed, are difficult to readjust (for instance 5- or 7-rings, when crystallization requires 6-rings).

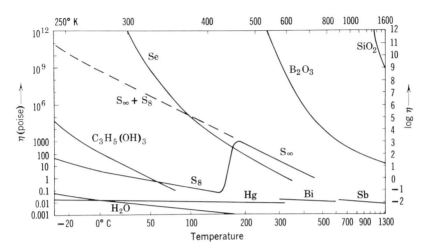

Fig. 1. Viscosity of ordinary liquids (below 1 poise) and vitrifying liquids (upper part) as a function of temperature.

We need not make a distinction here between SiO_2, where the network is supposed to extend in three dimensions, and B_2O_3, where the B-O-B-network is probably two-dimensional. In both cases we may call this class "network" or "coordination" glasses.

In class 2 of the linear polymers a somewhat different difficulty is met with in crystallizing: the worm-like long molecules are difficult to disentangle and to organize in the right way for crystallization. This "geometrical" difficulty is different from the ring binding in the previous class. On the other hand, both classes have in common that the entanglements not only slow down the process of crystallization, but also lower the melting point (because of their high entropy) and at the same time maintain the high viscosity.

Class 3 resembles class 1 with hydrogen bonds substituted for valency bonds. Glucose glass, once a popular candy, "barley sugar," belongs to this class and so do other supercooled syrups, which, in general, retain some water. Water itself does not vitrify easily, but alcohol does.

In all three classes the possibility of drawing fibers is connected with the high viscosity. This property together with the surface tension produces the cylindrical shape in the first stage of drawing. In the second stage it is important that the fiber should not break at its thinnest points. Here a more subtle mechanism which gives extra strength to the thinnest parts, comes into action. This "stabilizing" mechanism is of varying origin: with quartz fibers it is the quicker cooling and so quicker hardening of thin parts; with metal wires (where the shearing process is not very different from viscous flow) it is the stronger work hardening at the thinnest parts; and with solutions it may be a stiffening of the thinner parts by a quicker evaporation of the mobile solvent.

At any rate, the drawing process is not necessarily connected with the presence of long chain molecules, nor even with a strong orientation in the liquid. In common quartz and glass fibers there is hardly any orientational anisotropy at all; in plastics it may be completely absent from the amorphous phase, even when the crystalline part is strongly oriented. This means that the amorphous x-ray halo often retains perfect circular symmetry, even when the crystalline component of the same fiber may give a rotation diagram of points, proving its complete orientation.

In the hope of shedding more light on the nature of the glassy state, I have again and again studied selenium and sulfur. Both are readily obtained in the glassy state by quenching the viscous melt. Chemically they are the most simple glasses possible. This creates the possibility of, and so the obligation for, a sharper test of our picture than is possible with more complex substances.

It is evident that we shall try to fit selenium into class 2, because long spirals are certainly present in the stable hexagonal crystalline modification. All known data can be reconciled with the idea that long chain molecules also form the bulk of the liquid and the glassy state, though the future may have in store some minor corrections and additions to this picture.

Two questions are often put in this connection. One is: "Why do you not simply measure the diffraction pattern exactly and calculate from it the radial distribution function for the atoms, to see whether it corresponds to rings or to long chains?" My answer is that "exactly" is a tricky word. By measuring very carefully one can at most find the distances and roughly the number of first and perhaps of second neighbors. These are too much alike for different models to make a discrimination. The other question is: "Why try to prove there are long chains in viscous and glassy sulfur and selenium when everyone is convinced they are present?" My answer is that a little circumspection seems justified, as the curious results given below for sulfur prove.

The story for sulfur is too long to be told here completely. The reader is referred to the recent literature (Prins, 1957, in press; Schenk, 1956). One complication is that sulfur at room temperature in its stable rhombic crystal structure (Table 1) is made up of S_8 rings. These molecules presumably also make up the melt from 120° to 160°C, where the viscosity is low. It is only above 160° that a high viscosity sets in rather abruptly and the presence of long chains is postulated. The change in the diffraction pattern from 120° to 250° is, however, too gradual and too weak to give conclusive evidence for this molecular change, though later it may be looked upon as compatible with it.

Table 1

STATES OF SULFUR AND PROPOSED SYMBOLS (1958)

All states (except π and ε) are different stackings of S_8 rings or long spirals S_∞, or both. Selenium shows more or less similar states. The states shown in italics are characterized by their x-ray diagram, viscosity, or solubility in CS_2.

α. *Rhombic.* Below 98°. S_8 rings packed to "crankshafts" stacked in crossed layers. Structure given by Warren and Burwell. $\qquad \alpha$

α'. *Pseudomonoclinic* anamorphosis of α (Neumann, Wachters). Needles parallel to face diagonal [101].

β. *Monoclinic.* 98–122°. Probably not very different from α (Burwell): $a = 10.90$; $b = 10.96$; $c = 11.02$; $\beta = 83°$; $n = 6$ S_8 ring.

γ. *Monoclinic* (Muthmann). Obtained from special solvents as needles parallel to c-axis. Also from melt, when cooled judiciously so as to avoid nucleation by α (Hartshorne). Transforms quickly and completely to α when nucleated. Stabilized by addition of Se. Structure (de Haan): $a' = 8.57$; $b' = 13.05$; $c' = 8.23$; $\beta' = 112°.54'$; $n' = 4.S_8$. An equivalent description is: base-centered pseudorhombic lattice with: $a = 13.96$; $b = 13.05$; $c = 9.26$; $\beta = 92°.11'$; $n = 8.S_8$. $\qquad \gamma$

S_8 rings are stacked as in "sheared penny rolls," these rolls in turn forming a more or less close packed hexagonal arrangement in two dimensions.

ε. *Rhombohedral trigonal* (Engel). $a = 10.9$; $c = 4.24$; $n = 3.S_6$ (Whitfield and Frondel). Metastable, transforming, on scratching, into ω.

λ. *Liquid* below 160°. Probably S_8 rings. Yellow.

μ. Viscous sulfur's effective component (ca. 40%) above 160°. Presumably spiral long chains S_∞. Brown.

π. Preform of μ, with small molecules, soluble in CS_2 (Aten). Probably S_6. Also called S_ρ.

κ. *"Colloidal."* Shorthand for viscous sulfur solidified in small quantities (not to be confused with colloidal sulfur milk). Typical x-ray pattern, intermediate between liquid pattern and crystalline ($\gamma + \omega$), not changing in a month at room temperature, although the initial transparency slowly disappears.

ν. *Plastic* sulfur, from chilling larger quantities of viscous sulfur. Initially roughly identical with κ, but soon contaminated with α. May be stabilized by 1% P (probably network) or vitrified in liquid air without change of the liquid pattern. The usual product is possibly stabilized by atmospheric N; it gets brittle after a few hours. With P it may stay elastic for a month. In liquid air lifetime, of course, infinite.

φ. *Fibers,* drawn at room temperature from freshly chilled ν, originally >300°. X-ray fiber diagram (Trillat and Forestier) shows hardly any trace of amorphous ring. Structure (Prins, Schenk, Hospel, Wachters): $\varphi = \psi + \gamma = S_\infty + S_8$, the first component stretched micelles, the second included as small oriented crystals (with c-axis//fiber). Lifetime about 2 years. Yellow.

Table 1 (Continued)

ψ. The same *extracted* with CS_2 (Prins). Presumably S_∞ pure. In fiber diagram only a few φ spots remain, but these were enhanced. Structure: spirals S_∞, more or less as in hexagonal Se. Lifetime at least 2 years. Cream color.

ω. *Not oriented* crystalline residue of *extracted* ν (Das). Powder diagram, showing structure akin to ψ, but not quite identical with it.

ω'. The same *slightly oriented* by extension preceding extraction, smaller than φ extension.

κ'. The same as ω', *before* extraction with CS_2. Akin to κ.

Lifetime of last three states about a month.

More information may fortunately be obtained from the diffraction pattern of fibers drawn from fresh plastic sulfur (Trillat and Forestier, 1932; Meyer and Go, 1934). In these fibers the organization is much higher than in the undrawn mass, and the amorphous pattern has completely switched over to a rotation diagram of somewhat broadened spots. Part of this diagram disappears when the fiber is put in CS_2 for about 10 minutes. It is well known from earlier research that micromolecular sulfur is dissolved in this way and the macromolecular component remains. In this way we come rather conclusively to the picture of the fiber given in Fig. 2.

The micromolecular component has been proved to be Muthmann's γ-sulfur, of which de Haan (1958) has recently determined the structure: close-packed "coin rolls" of S_8 rings. The macromolecular component presumably consists of micelles of long spirals, called S_∞ for brevity, which differ little from the spirals in hexagonal selenium.

We assume that the same elements (S_8 and S_∞ in about equal portions) are present in the plastic sulfur before the drawing process, but that they are mixed and arranged there in the more irregular way characteristic for a liquid.

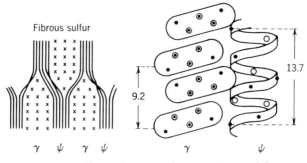

Fig. 2. "Amorphous" φ sulfur as found in fibers, a mixture of S_8 rings in small γ-crystals and S_∞ chains in ψ micelles.

It is important to note that the rings play their part in the amorphous state as well as the chains do. Not only do they act as plasticizers in the drawing process, but also at low temperatures it is their function to keep the chains apart and vice versa. This is proved by the fact that elution of the amorphous mass with CS_2 immediately makes the chains join up to micelles (these, of course, are now not oriented and show a powder pattern that has been described by Das (1938), who called this state ω-sulfur).

On the other hand, when in quenching the cooling is somewhat slower than usual, not only do we get more rings but also these join up more or less to embryonic γ-crystals. This state, which depends on the rate of cooling, I have called colloidal sulfur. At room temperature it is stable for at least a month when a small quantity is sealed in a Keesom tube. In larger lumps all plastic sulfur exposed to the atmosphere cracks and by chance seeding is soon reduced to the stable rhombic state, at least as regards the γ-component. The chains need more time to transform. Indeed, the fibers mentioned above and ω-sulfur have a lifetime of about 2 years at least.

I think not only that the "case of amorphous sulfur" has exercised an attraction like a detective story for the successive unravelers of the mystery, but also that it contains the lesson that oversimplification may obscure important features, even in the interpretation of an amorphous pattern.

REFERENCES

So much research has been done on the general problems of the glassy state (Tammann, Simon, Mme. Winter, Stevels, Smekal, Warren, to mention a few) that I refer to the periodicals on "Glass" and "Plastics" and the books of Randall and of Jones and the thesis (Paris, 1957) of Prod'homme for more information than I have found possible to read. For sulfur, literature is to be found in the references given below; for selenium, one should also consult the publications of the Purdue group (Lark-Horovitz) and other work on semiconductors. The list below is restricted to immediate connections with the text.

Das, S. R., *Indian J. Phys.* **12**, 163 (1938).
de Haan, Y. M., *Physica* **24**, 855 (1958).
Meyer, K. H., and Go, Y., *Helv. Chim. Acta* **17**, 1081 (1934).
Prins, J. A., *Solid State Physics*, Academic Press, New York, in press.
Prins, J. A., Schenk, J., and Wachters, L. H. J., *Physica* **23**, 746 (1957).
Schenk, J., Thesis, Delft, 1956, and *Physica*, **23**, 325 (1957).
Trillat, J. J., and Forestier, H., *Bull. soc. chim. France* **51**, 248 (1932).
Turnbull, D., *J. Appl. Phys.* **21**, 1022 (1950).
Zachariasen, W. H., *J. Am. Chem. Soc.* **54**, 3841 (1932).

14

by

D. A. Vermilyea

General Electric Company

Kinetics of Ion Motion in Anodic Oxide Films

When a tantalum specimen is made anodic in almost any dilute aqueous solution, an amorphous, dense, homogeneous film of Ta_2O_5 is formed between the tantalum and the solution (Vermilyea, 1953; Young, 1954). The thickness of the film is roughly proportional to the voltage applied to the cell and may be nearly as great as 1 μ. The formation voltage can be as large as about 450 volts.

The films exhibit very beautiful and striking interference colors which pass through several orders as the film thickens. The density, refractive index, and dielectric constant of the films are all known to within a few percent (Vermilyea, 1953, 1955; Polling and Charlesby, 1955). During film growth essentially all the current passing through the cell is ionic, the electronic leakage being negligible. The films are chemically very inert, being attacked rapidly only by concentrated hydrofluoric acid. Because of all the desirable characteristics of the films and because so many physical properties are known, these Ta_2O_5 films are very attractive subjects for experimentation. Some other metals, such as aluminum, zirconium, and niobium, can also be anodized although the films formed are not so stable and not so many film constants are available.

Many studies of the formation of anodic films on tantalum have already been made, and several conclusions may be drawn from these studies. First of all, the tantalum ions move out through the film so that new oxide is added at the outer surface (Vermilyea, 1954). Sec-

328

ondly, the controlling step in the process of oxidation is the migration of ions through the film and not the passage across an interface barrier (Young, 1956a; Vermilyea, 1956). Finally, the electric field in the oxide film is constant throughout the thickness to at least 1% (Vermilyea, 1957a), so that any electric space charge must be very small. The interpretation that a drift in the value of capacitance of a film with time (Young, 1956b) is the result of a space charge seems very questionable. The same effect could be produced by a redistribution of charge within the film locally, the sort of relaxation postulated in this chapter. Van Geel (1956) interprets the recovery of a potential difference across a momentarily shorted capacitor having an Al_2O_3 dielectric as a local charge relaxation.

Studies of the kinetics of ion migration in the films (Vermilyea, 1955) have yielded values of the activation energy for motion, Q, the preexponential factor A, and the parameter $q\lambda$ which characterizes the effect of the electric field on the motion according to the equation

$$j = A \exp\left(-\frac{Q - q\lambda E}{kT}\right) \tag{1}$$

where E is the electric field strength and j the current density. Since the films are amorphous, the various kinetic parameters must be considered as averages. The field strengths employed in these studies ranged from 4×10^6 to 8×10^6 v/cm. According to a simple theory, q should represent the charge on the mobile ion and λ one-half the distance of a unit ionic jump. The values of $q\lambda$ which have been obtained range from 11.7 to $23e \cdot$Å, depending on the value of the electric field employed. If $q = 5$ and $\lambda = 1.4$ Å, then $q\lambda$ should be only $7.0e \cdot$Å and the observed values are much too large. In an effort to explain these large values of $q\lambda$ and the change by a factor of 2 which occurs at a certain field strength, Bean, Fisher, and Vermilyea (1956) developed a theory of ion conduction at high field strengths. According to the theory there is a field-dependent concentration of interstitial tantalum ions and tantalum vacancies in the film. If that were true, then transients in the current should be observed after a change of field strength.

The work reported in this chapter was motivated by this prediction that transients would be observed. Transients were in fact observed (Vermilyea, 1957b), but observations of chemical behavior and x-ray diffraction (Vermilyea, 1957c) made it unlikely that the theory was correct. It now appears that the structure of the film changes with changes in formation field and temperature, and that the transients result from structural changes which occur after a change of formation conditions or during annealing.

Experimental Technique

Measurement of Film Thickness

There are two convenient methods of estimating the film thickness, and both have been used. The first method is to measure the capacitance of a cell consisting of a platinized platinum electrode of large area, a suitable electrolytic solution (5% HNO_3, for example), and the specimen. A small error is introduced by the presence of a double layer in the solution near the specimen, but, since double-layer capacitances are of the order of 10–100 $\mu f/cm^2$, the error is very small for a film having a capacitance of 0.1 $\mu f/cm^2$. The dielectric constant used was 25.

The second method consisted of a color comparison with specimens of known thickness (Vermilyea, 1953). The optical step gauge was prepared by anodizing many specimens under the same conditions at a series of voltages. The specimens were calibrated by measurements of weight changes, of intensity of reflected light as a function of wavelength, and by direct observation of stripped sections of the film using the electron microscope (Vermilyea, 1955). All measurements agreed within about 5%, and it is felt that the absolute film thickness is not in error by more than this amount. Unknown film thickness was estimated by visual comparison with the calibrated specimens, and in selected ranges of film thickness where the color changed rapidly with thickness the precision was about 1%.

Specimen Preparation and Anodizing

Specimens were made of tantalum obtained from Fansteel Metallurgical Company and stated to be 99.9% pure. The specimens were $\frac{1}{4}$ x 2 inches cut from 0.005-inch annealed rolled sheet. They were chemically polished by dipping for a few seconds in a mixture consisting of 5 parts 96% H_2SO_4, 2 parts 70% HNO_3, and $1\frac{1}{2}$ parts 48% HF. The polishing solution leaves a thin (about 20 Å) film of unknown composition on the specimen; studies have shown that this film does not influence the kinetics in any detectable way. This polishing film was usually removed by a dip in hydrofluoric acid. However, when it was desired to remove a film after formation, the polishing film was left in place because it does not adhere well to the tantalum and films formed on top of it could easily be removed mechanically (Hillig, 1957).

The anodizing solution was usually 2% Na_2SO_4 in water. Identical results are obtained by using any dilute ($\leq 1\%$) aqueous solution, and only when the solution is largely non-aqueous are films of different composition and properties formed (Vermilyea, 1954).

X-ray Diffraction and Film Dissolution Studies

X-ray diffraction patterns were obtained from specimens consisting of six layers of oxide films each about 3000 Å thick. The films were stripped from the substrate, mounted over a hole $\frac{1}{8}$ inch in diameter in a small piece of platinum, annealed at various temperatures, and diffraction patterns were taken using Cr Kα radiation.

When anodic Ta_2O_5 films are dipped in 48% HF they dissolve uniformly at about 5–20 Å/sec. The rate of dissolution was determined by measuring the thickness as a function of time with the optical step gauge.

Conductivity Measurements

The ionic conductivity was measured both directly by measuring the current flowing through the film at a given field strength and indirectly by measuring the thickness change in a given time and computing the current density. The latter method was particularly useful at very low current densities where the electronic leakage current at defects became comparable with the ionic current.

Many of the results reported deal with transient currents after sudden changes of voltage or after an annealing treatment. The apparatus for making sudden voltage changes consisted simply of a resistor in series with the cell. A small voltage (1–2 volts) across the resistor was controlled with a switch to add to or subtract from the main voltage.

Results

Transients at Constant Voltage

Figure 1 shows an oscillogram of current versus time for specimens about 400 Å thick growing at elevated temperatures. After a sudden drop in voltage from about 25 to about 23 volts there was a sudden drop in current and then a more gradual decrease over a period of about a second. After a sudden voltage increase there was a sudden increase in current followed by a more gradual increase. It is possible to obtain a value for $q\lambda$ from such measurements. Writing equation (1) for two values of field and current density, dividing, and rearranging gives

$$q\lambda = \frac{kT}{E_1 - E_2} \ln \frac{j_1}{j_2} \qquad (2)$$

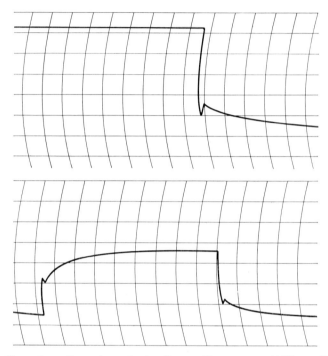

Fig. 1. Current vs. time at constant voltage. Upper trace, 91°C, small vertical division = 0.05 ma, field changed from 0.056 to 0.0515 v/Å. Lower trace, 81°C, small vertical division = 0.4 ma, field changed from 0.062 to 0.0575 v/Å. Both curves, one horizontal division = 0.04 sec. (Vermilyea, 1957b.)

Values of $q\lambda$ obtained in this manner are shown in Fig. 2. The two interesting points about these results are that the values ($q\lambda = 4.5$–6 $e \cdot$ Å) are now more in line with the expected value of 7 $e \cdot$ Å, and secondly that the value depends on the temperature at which the experiment was conducted. At any one temperature, $q\lambda$ was independent of film thickness and field within the rather large experimental uncertainty. The value of $q\lambda$ is also a function of the history of the film. Specimens formed at 29°C then annealed at 100°C for 5 minutes gave values of $q\lambda$ of 6.3 $e \cdot$ Å in the transient experiment. After a few seconds of current flow, however, the $q\lambda$ values decreased to the 4.7 $e \cdot$ Å expected from Fig. 2.

The activation energy for ion flow was obtained from such measurements by forming several specimens under the same conditions, annealing them 5 minutes at 100°C to bring them all to the same initial condition and eliminate any rapid alteration in conductivity at the test temperature; and the initial current density was measured at different

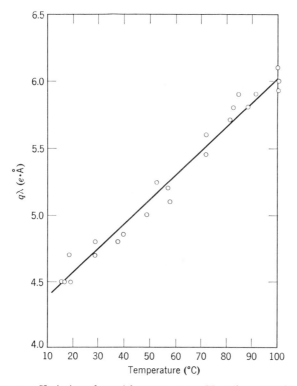

Fig. 2. Variation of $q\lambda$ with temperature (Vermilyea, 1957b).

temperatures, a field strength of 0.058 v/$\overset{\circ}{A}$ being used. Since $q\lambda$ for this condition was found earlier to be 6.3 $e\cdot\overset{\circ}{A}$, the activation energy can be calculated from the slope of an Arrhenius plot (Fig. 3) and equation (1); it was 1.06 ev. This value is considerably lower than the values 2.2 ev and 1.5 ev reported in the earlier investigations.

It is interesting to note that, when the value of field strength after the transient has died away is used in equation (2), the value of $q\lambda$ obtained is 12.1 $e\cdot\overset{\circ}{A}$, in good agreement with the earlier value of 11.7 $e\cdot\overset{\circ}{A}$ from steady state tests. The difference in the two types of measurement of $q\lambda$ arises solely from the fact that one is a steady state measurement after whatever relaxation occurs, while the other is a measurement made in such a short time that no relaxation can occur.

Transients at Constant Current

In order to investigate the transients further and also to see the effects of heat treatment on the conductivity for comparison with effects

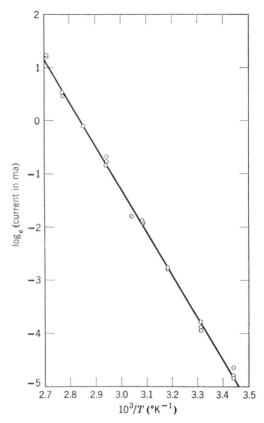

Fig. 3. Logarithm of the current produced by a field of 0.058 v/Å on specimens annealed 5 minutes, at 100°C vs. $1/T$ (Vermilyea, 1957b).

of heat treatment on other properties, some experiments were performed using constant current. Figure 4 shows oscillograms of the voltage versus time at a constant current density of 1.56 ma/cm^2 after a film 1760 Å thick was annealed for various periods of time at 100°C. The voltage rises slowly because of the large capacitance of the oxide film, reaches a maximum at about 120 volts (for a specimen annealed for 1.5×10^5 sec), and falls in 15 sec to about 100 volts. During the transient the film increases in thickness by only 5 Å, so no appreciable error is made in calculating the field strength from the data.

Figure 5 shows the maximum field reached during the transient as a function of time and temperature of annealing. It may be seen that the initial field increases with increasing time and temperature to a value about 20% higher than the value after no annealing; the con-

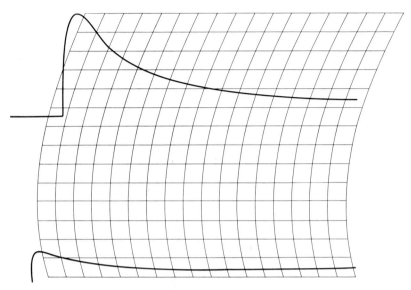

Fig. 4. Voltage vs. time at constant current. Upper curve, specimen annealed 1.5×10^5 sec at $100\,°C$; lower curve, specimen annealed 4 sec at $100\,°C$. Each small division in the vertical direction is 1.0 volt, and each division in the horizontal direction is 0.2 sec. (Vermilyea, 1957b.)

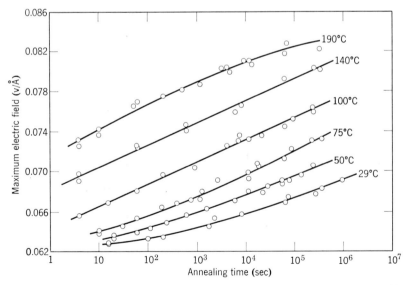

Fig. 5. Maximum field reached during formation of films at constant current after annealing for various times at different temperatures (Vermilyea, 1957b).

ductivity is accordingly decreased by about a factor of 200 upon annealing at 190°C for a few minutes.

The activation energy for the process responsible for annealing was obtained from the data of Fig. 5 by plotting the logarithm of the time required to reach a given maximum field against the reciprocal of the absolute temperature and using the Arrhenius equation. The values of activation energy (Fig. 6) increase with the extent of annealing from about 0.8 ev to about 1.4 ev.

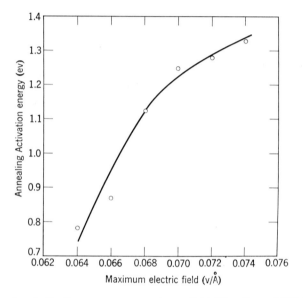

Fig. 6. Activation energy vs. maximum field (Vermilyea, 1957b).

As might be expected from the constant voltage transient experiments, the results of experiments using constant current are also a function of specimen history. Figure 7 shows results of annealing at 140°C for three specimens having different histories. The behavior upon annealing at 140°C is quite different when a film with a maximum field of 0.074 v/Å is produced by annealing at 140°C for 200 sec or by forming a film at 0.5 ma/cm², 80°C.

Transient Experiments Using Other Metals

Constant voltage transient experiments similar to those performed with anodic Ta_2O_5 films were also performed with aluminum, zirconium, and niobium oxide films (Vermilyea, 1957b). Niobium and aluminum

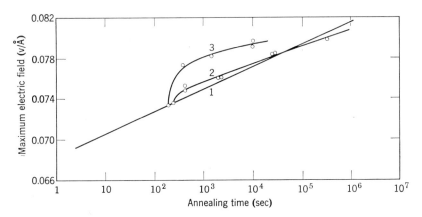

Fig. 7. History effects. Curve 1, annealing at 140°C alone; 2, after annealing 10 sec at 190°C; 3, on forming at 0.5 ma, 80°C. (Vermilyea, 1957b.)

behaved like tantalum, yielding small values of $q\lambda$ when measurements were made quickly and large values on static tests. Zirconium showed only large $q\lambda$ values and no transients, indicating a different mechanism.

X-ray Diffraction Studies

Plots of diffracted intensity versus angle were obtained from x-ray patterns taken by transmission through anodic films annealed at different temperatures. The data in Table 1 show that, as the annealing

Table 1

Annealing Temperature	Line Breadth at Half-Height Arbitrary Units
25 (as formed)	1.03
210	0.93
375	0.90
555	0.83

temperature is increased, the breadth of the diffuse ring decreases by about 20%. Apparently there is a definite change of film structure during annealing, the glass-like structure becoming more ordered as annealing progresses.

Studies of Dissolution of the Films in Hydrofluoric Acid

Films formed at 1.56 ma/cm^2, 29°C to 120 volts in 1% Na$_2$SO$_4$ solution were annealed at various temperatures, dipped into 48% HF solution, and the rate of dissolution determined. Figure 8 shows that the

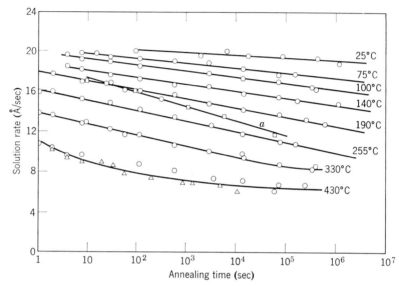

Fig. 8. Change of relative solution rate with time of annealing at various temperatures. For the 430°C anneal the circles denote that the films were heated in air, while the triangles denote films heated in molten KCl-LiCl mixture. The squares are used for the data obtained when films were held at 140°C with an applied electric field of 0.029 v/Å (curve *a*). (Vermilyea, 1957c.)

rate of dissolution decreases nearly linearly with the logarithm of the annealing time, except for the highest annealing temperatures, and that the results are not dependent on the heating medium. The behavior at 330°C and 430°C is probably influenced by solution in the tantalum of some of the oxygen from the film (Vermilyea, 1957d).

The activation energy for the process responsible for the decreased dissolution rate, obtained from Arrhenius plots of the time to reach a certain corrosion rate, increases from 1.0 to 2.0 ev as the annealing temperature increases (Fig. 9). When compared after a given annealing treatment, these activation energies are very similar in magnitude to those obtained from conductivity changes caused by annealing. Presumably, therefore, the same process controls both the change in dissolution behavior and the change in conductivity.

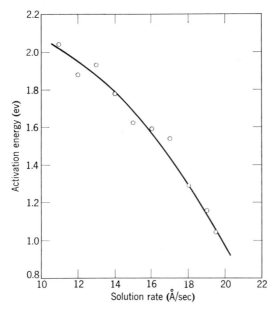

Fig. 9. Activation energy vs. extent of annealing as measured by solution rate (Vermilyea, 1957c).

The dissolution behavior is also affected by the history of the film; if the films with the same solution rate are produced in different ways, they will behave differently on subsequent annealing. Figure 10 shows

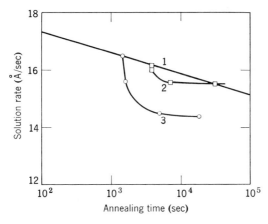

Fig. 10. Effect of history in annealing. Curve 1 is the same as that for 140°C in Fig. 8. Curves 2 and 3 are for films heated at 140°C after holding for 100 sec at 190°C, and at 80°C with applied field of 0.055 v/Å, respectively. (Vermilyea, 1957c.)

the very different curves of solution rate versus time at 140°C for three specimens with different histories. It should be noted that formation at 80°C, 0.055 v/Å results in the same dissolution rate as annealing at 140°C for 1400 sec. Presumably the presence of an electric field during annealing assists whatever ionic motion within the film is responsible for the effects. In Fig. 8, curve a shows that annealing at 140°C with an applied field of 0.028 v/Å (too small to cause any measurable current) is about equivalent to annealing at 200°C in the absence of a field.

Changes in the dissolution rate also occur when the formation rate is changed at one temperature. At room temperature, for example, dissolution rates of 19.3 Å/sec and 20.3 Å/sec were measured for films formed at 0.4 Å/sec and 40 Å/sec, respectively. Hence it appears that even films formed at the same temperature are not quite identical.

Discussion of Results

The experimental results have demonstrated that when anodic Ta_2O_5 films are annealed their ionic conductivity and dissolution rate in hydrofluoric acid decrease and the diffraction of x-rays by the films becomes less diffuse. Changes in dissolution rates also occur when a film is formed at different rates at the same temperature. The activation energies for the processes responsible for changes in conductivity and dissolution rate are the same, an indication that the same process is responsible for both effects. The values of $q\lambda$ are reasonable when computed from transient data but too large when computed from data after the film reaches a steady state.

These facts suggest the following picture of the conduction process and of the nature of the oxide film. The film consists of an amorphous, glass-like oxide. In this structure some tantalum ions are in positions of higher energy than the average, for example, as a result of being closer to other tantalum ions and farther from oxygen ions than the average. These favorably located ions would very probably be in positions where the activation energy for jumping into a neighboring position would be abnormally low, and would therefore be the most mobile ions in the film. Now if the film is annealed there is a rearrangement of ions within the film, the result of which is a reduction in both the number of these ions in high energy positions and probably also an increase in the activation energy for their motion. In other words, the film becomes more ordered. As a result, there is a decrease in the diffuseness of diffraction of x-rays, a decrease in the dissolution rate (crystalline Ta_2O_5 dissolves extremely slowly in hydrofluoric acid), and a decrease in the conductivity. The number of ions in high energy positions is a function of the rate and temperature of formation of the film, and consequently changes in conductivity and dissolution behavior accompany changes in formation condition. Transients occur because of these changes in local arrangement upon annealing or upon changing formation conditions. Such changes are reasonable, since differences of local configuration in ordinary glasses heat-treated in different ways are believed to be responsible for differences in density, conductivity, refractive index, and heat content.

According to this picture the explanation of the transient experiments is as follows. Upon a sudden change in applied field the current suddenly falls to a value determined by the atomic arrangement just before the change. After the sudden change of current there is a more gradual change as the film structure relaxes to the new steady state configuration. The net result is that the change of field has produced a larger change in current than that due solely to the smaller force on ions about to make a jump; the change of field has also changed the number of ions in position to jump the barrier opposing their motion.

The values of $q\lambda$ from the transient measurement, according to this picture, represent the true values characteristic of the film. The values obtained after relaxation to the steady state are not representative of any simple physical process, since a change of structure has occurred. Similar statements can be made about the activation energy; the only meaningful values are those obtained from measurements made so rapidly that the structure does not have time to change.

The pre-exponential factor obtained from Fig. 3 is 1.6×10^6 amp cm^{-2}. This factor should be given by $2\lambda\nu Ne$, where ν is the vibrational frequency, N the number of ions in position to jump, and e is the ionic charge. If $\nu = 5 \times 10^{12}$ sec^{-1}, $\lambda = 1$ Å, $e = 8 \times 10^{-19}$ coulombs, then $N = 2 \times 10^{19}$ ions cm^{-3}, so that for a film treated in that manner about one tantalum ion in one thousand is in a position to jump.

In a recent article Winkel, Pistorius, and Van Geel (1958), using an a-c method have obtained values for the parameters of equation (1) which are similar to those reported here. They considered correctly that, since the film is a glass, there is really no one value of activation energy or $q\lambda$. Their values, in my terminology, are $q\lambda = 4.5$ $e \cdot$Å, $Q = 0.9$ ev, $N = 6 \times 10^{20}$ ions cm^{-3}. Except for their larger value for N, these values are very similar to those which I obtained for films formed at room temperature. The conclusions of Winkel and coworkers were similar to those of this investigation, namely, that the kinetic parameters only refer to a simple physical process when they are measured under suitable conditions in which the film does not change in any way during the measurement.

A different interpretation of the transients, based upon the theory of Bean, Fisher, and Vermilyea, has been given by Dewald (1957). For the following reasons I do not believe that it is likely that this explanation is correct. In the first place the theory of Bean et al. as applied by Dewald does not predict a variation of $q\lambda$ with different formation conditions. Secondly, a real change of structure accompanies the change of conductivity produced by annealing, as shown by the changes in x-ray diffraction. Since the transients produced by annealing are clearly similar to those produced by simply changing formation conditions, it is reasonable to suppose that similar structural changes occur in the latter case and that the variation of $q\lambda$ with changing conditions is real. Finally, the changes in dissolution behavior also indicate that changes in the nature of the film occur. In support of Dewald's theory it may be argued that all these effects (change in $q\lambda$, x-ray diffraction, and dissolution rate) occur because the interstitial ions are close enough together to interact strongly. In this event, however, the simple theory of Bean, Fisher, and Vermilyea would no longer be valid.

Summary

Studies have been made of the ionic conductivity, structure, and resistance to dissolution in hydrofluoric acid of anodic tantalum oxide films. These studies have shown that the film structure, which is glassy, changes with changes in formation conditions and when the films are heated after formation. As a result of these structural changes the conductivity and dissolution rate decrease as the film is annealed at elevated temperatures or as it is formed at higher temperatures and slower rates. When a sudden change of field is made, there is a transient change in the current as a new structural configuration is produced. Similar transients observed with other films make it likely that the phenomena observed are quite general for amorphous oxide films.

REFERENCES

Bean, C. P., Fisher, J. C., and Vermilyea, D. A., *Phys. Rev.* **101**, 551 (1956).
Dewald, J. F., *J. Phys. Chem. Solids* **2**, 55 (1957).
Hillig, W. B., private communication, 1957.
Polling, J. J., and Charlesby, A., *Proc. Roy. Soc. (London)* **A227**, 434 (1955).
Van Geel, W. Ch., private communication, 1956.

Vermilyea, D. A., *Acta Met.* **1**, 283 (1953).
Vermilyea, D. A., *Acta Met.* **2**, 482 (1954).
Vermilyea, D. A., *J. Electrochem. Soc.* **102**, 655 (1955).
Vermilyea, D. A., *J. Electrochem. Soc.* **103**, 690 (1956).
Vermilyea, D. A., *J. Electrochem. Soc.* **104**, 140 (1957) (a).
Vermilyea, D. A., *J. Electrochem. Soc.* **104**, 427 (1957) (b).
Vermilyea, D. A., *J. Electrochem. Soc.* **104**, 485 (1957) (c).
Vermilyea, D. A., *Acta Met.* **5**, 113 (1957) (d).
Winkel, P., Pistorius, C. A., and Van Geel, W. Ch., *Philips Research Repts.* **13**, 277 (1958).
Young, L., *Trans. Faraday Soc.* **50**, 153 (1954).
Young, L., *Trans. Faraday Soc.* **53**, 841 (1956) (a).
Young, L., *Acta Met.* **4**, 101 (1956) (b).

DISCUSSION

I. SIMON

I would like to ask you to comment on the melting point when annealing. Do these films melt? And is it known what happens to the structure? Do they become crystalline?

D. A. VERMILYEA

Well, they become crystalline long before they melt. They crystallize approximately at about 650°C.

I don't know whether tantalum oxide melts; I think it decomposes at around 1400°, although these films have not been heated to this temperature.

I. SIMON

I was wondering if the films you described can be indeed called a glass? Tantalum oxide does not normally form a glass, does it?

D. A. VERMILYEA

No, it is normally crystalline.

I. SIMON

If we could establish that they are a glass, this would be a unique way of obtaining a glass. It might be possible to obtain other oxide glasses.

D. A. VERMILYEA

Yes, aluminum also forms similar films, zirconium does, niobium does, and there are probably some other materials. I don't know what a good definition of a glass is, so that I can't tell whether it is a glass or not.

I. SIMON

I think that the criteria which Dr. Vermilyea applied are the conditions necessary for an amorphous solid to be a glass, but, in addition, we would have to know, for instance, the flow properties of this material as a function of temperature.

If there is a transformation range, where the flow changes character, through viscous flow, through the rubber-like transition, I think we have a glass, but this wouldn't be easy here.

D. A. VERMILYEA

The films crystallize at such a low temperature that flow measurements would probably not be possible.

I. SIMON

Are the layers of aluminum oxide amorphous to the same extent as determined by x-ray diffraction?

D. A. VERMILYEA

Yes, just the same. This seems to be so for all the materials on which you can form these films.

G. J. DIENES

Is the aluminum oxide in an anhydrous condition when you form it this way?

D. A. VERMILYEA

When you form it this way it is, yes. There are several kinds of anodic films which can be formed on aluminum. One is the thick, porous one in which you can dissolve dyes, color to look pretty, and seal to make abrasive-resistant; that type is hydrated.

But you can form films on aluminum which are anhydrous like this one if you use a boric acid solution.

J. A. PRINS

By anhydrous do you mean there is no water in it, or that there are no OH groups present, or that there is no hydrogen at all in it?

D. A. VERMILYEA

There is very little hydrogen in it.

J. A. PRINS

Thank you.

D. A. VERMILYEA

People have looked for the infrared OH absorption, and found it absent.

J. A. KRUMHANSL

I would like to ask, is the spread in $q\lambda$ values rather characteristic of all these films, or are there any in which there is a well-defined $q\lambda$?

D. A. VERMILYEA

I have made measurements on some of the other films. The aluminum and niobium films behave about the same way; that is, you can find two values of

$q\lambda$, depending on whether you make the measurements in a short time or a long time. Whether they change with formation conditions has not been determined.

Zirconium, however, was interesting because it didn't show any small value of $q\lambda$. It was always too big. I don't know the reason for this.

R. A. VAN NORDSTRAND

Are all your annealings done in contact with the metal film?

D. A. VERMILYEA

Yes, otherwise I couldn't put it back and anodize it further. Of course, those that I did the x-ray diffraction patterns on were stripped first.

R. A. VAN NORDSTRAND

Do you have any reason to believe there is a change of valence or change in the metal content of your films during this annealing?

D. A. VERMILYEA

I have no evidence to lead me to think that there is any such change.

R. A. VAN NORDSTRAND

You attribute a higher activation energy, as I understand it, to the fact that you had a distribution of activation energies, and state that, if the distribution changes, the average will change. But, with the exponential role of activation energies, is this reasonable? Only those which have the lowest activation energy show up anyway on a temperature plot.

D. A. VERMILYEA

Yes, they would be the most prevalent and in this sense they do change.

M. L. HUGGINS

In theoretical discussions of this type of problem and many others, it is customary to speak of "interstitial" atoms or ions. I believe, however, that in many such cases there is a rearrangement of the atoms or ions in the immediate vicinity of the extra one, in such a way as to give a lower energy than would be possible by mere insertion of the extra atom or ion interstitially, with slight displacements of the surrounding units.

For example, I have shown [*J. Chem. Phys.* **11**, 412, 419 (1943)] that an extra silver ion or atom in a crystal of silver chloride or silver bromide can be accommodated more readily, energetically speaking, if the structure in the immediate vicinity changes to one of the tetrahedral types. In these tetrahedral structures each ion has a coordination number of four. (This is also the coordination number of the interstitial ion.)

If such a rearrangement occurs around an extra ion, the activation energy involved obviously depends on the nature of the structural change.

D. A. VERMILYEA

Yes, in the original theory which we considered for explaining this change of slope, we thought of going from a normal position into an interstitial. I no longer think that is what happens, but believe that there are some ions present which are in configurations which make them likely to move.

A. B. LIDIARD

In connection with Dr. Huggins' remark on AgCl, I would like to say that, while in general one should guard against being too specific about defect models, recent ionic conductivity and isotope diffusion results do enable one to obtain detailed information about interstitital movements. I refer to the fact that tracer diffusion coefficients include a factor expressing the existence of correlations in the directions of successive tracer jumps which exists for certain mechanisms (vacancy, interstitialcy). One can summarize by saying that the results for AgCl and AgBr are not only consistent with the b.c.c. model of the interstitial but are such as to argue against any large increase in the number of Ag neighbors of the interstitial over the value four as given by this b.c.c. model [Miller and Maurer, *J. Phys. Chem. Solids* **4**, 196 (1958); Compton and Maurer, *ibid.* **1**, 191 (1956); Compaan and Haven, *Trans. Faraday Soc.* **54**, 1498 (1958)]. However, the detailed predictions of each reasonable model have to be investigated separately and compared with experimental results.

M. L. HUGGINS

Has it been shown that it is inconsistent with the picture I have given?

A. B. LIDIARD

I think it would be inconsistent with a picture in which the number of neighbors changes very considerably. It is based on the assumption that the interstitials at the center of the cube have four neighbors, and the predictions of this model are very sensitive to the number of neighbors and the geometry of the surrounding atoms.

W. A. WEYL

In the last few years my associate, Professor E. C. Marboe, and I have worked on structures which are closely related to the amorphous tantalum oxide film. The conditions of formation are conducive to defect structures which contain protons. Such a substance may be described by the formula

$$\mathrm{Ta}_{2-x}^{5+}(\mathrm{C.V.})_x\mathrm{H}_{5x}^{+}\mathrm{O}_5^{2-} \quad \text{or} \quad \mathrm{Ta}_{2-x}^{5+}(\mathrm{C.V.})_x\mathrm{O}_{5-5x}^{2-}(\mathrm{OH}^{-})_{5x}$$

The protons participate in the structure in the form of OH^- ions replacing the regular O^{2-} ions. Such a system has vacant cation sites (C.V) which are very important for the ionic conductivity. It is very unlikely that a film of stoichiometric $\mathrm{Ta_2O_5}$ at ordinary temperature would be conducive to ionic diffusion. The values of x may be very small considering the atomic weight Ta vs. H— small concentrations of OH^- ions are extremely effective. The absolute value of x is a function of the rate of formation of the film, and the temperature. The cation vacancies aid both diffusion and chemical reactions; e.g., they increase the solution rate in hydrofluoric acid.

D. A. VERMILYEA

Well, of course, there may be some OH present in some small amount. I think it would be a very minor amount, however.

W. A. WEYL

A minor amount is extremely effective.

D. A. VERMILYEA

Of course, this is not a crystalline material, and I am not sure that you are required to have vacancies or interstitials especially, or that you can really think in these terms with materials such as these. However, I agree that the effect of water should be looked into.

J. M. STEVELS

In the case of SiO_2, we feel nowadays that even when there are small concentrations of OH groups, there are very great effects; therefore I think Dr. Weyl is right in drawing attention to the effect of these.

15

R. Hilsch

Amorphous Layers and Their Physical Properties

In the course of investigations of the properties of thin layers which have been in progress in the Institute at Göttingen for some years it has been shown that layers prepared by condensation from the vapor state can be disordered to a high degree, i.e., the atoms or molecules of the layer assume positions which deviate more or less strongly from those of the corresponding crystalline form. Defects such as vacancies, interstitial atoms, dislocations, and grain boundaries can on occasion be present in numbers so great that one cannot speak of a crystalline state at all. Such materials must be designated "amorphous." The special properties which have been disclosed during the course of investigations of them will be reviewed. From scattering and diffraction of x-rays and electrons it is known, for example, that even in liquids there exists a certain short range ordering of atoms, while larger coherent regions are absent. These methods are useful for distinguishing whether a substance is crystalline or amorphous. Optical methods can also be used under some circumstances to disclose the structural state. Materials such as salts and other non-metals which in certain spectral ranges are transparent often show characteristic optical absorption bands in other regions of the spectrum. Their positions and shapes may be very sensitive to structure. Many other properties influence them strongly also. It is not always easy to learn how the properties influenced by

Translation from the German by V. D. Fréchette.

disorder would appear in the completely ordered state. Nevertheless, it seems important to discuss the general phenomena. In this chapter will be considered to what extent this is possible at the present time. One must determine whether the disorder of a material is in thermal equilibrium or whether it is the consequence of freezing in. Such an investigation involves the use of very low temperatures. However, it can also be carried out by other means, e.g., through introduction of foreign atoms at not too low concentrations.

Preparation of Condensed Layers

The preparation of condensed layers will be described briefly. The apparatus was designed so that atoms or molecules streaming in a high vacuum from an appropriate vapor source condensed on a plate whose temperature could be controlled in the range from liquid helium to 300°C. A metal cryostat (Fig. 1) was used for this purpose. Several copper containers were located within the vacuum chamber. One of these could be filled with liquid helium. A copper plate was fastened to its lower end in thermal contact with the layer support, a crystalline quartz or alumina plate. Two additional vessels surrounded the helium vessel to decrease vapor loss. They contained liquid hydrogen or liquid nitrogen and shielded the innermost space completely with the help of coupled copper beakers against thermal radiation from without, and especially against foreign gases which in certain cases could pass from the outer parts of the vacuum chamber at room temperature to condense on the layer support. All the vessels were supported by thin German silver tubes let through the lid of the cryostat. The evaporating device consisted principally of a strip of tungsten, molybdenum, or tantalum foil. It was placed within the evacuated cryostat and constructed, as far as possible, to be free from foreign gases from the vacuum pumps, etc. The vapor coating process was conducted through small slits in the shield beakers. These slits could be closed afterwards. The cooling of the individual vessels proceeded, one after another, from the outside in so that contamination of the support and the condensed layer could be avoided as much as possible. It can be assumed that a very good vacuum existed in the central helium space.

In many cases the vapor source was arranged so that several substances could be evaporated simultaneously to yield a desired composition. For this purpose it was necessary to allow only small portions of the mixture to drop onto the glowing foil with the aid of a remotely operated feeder. Fractionation due to the various vapor pressures of

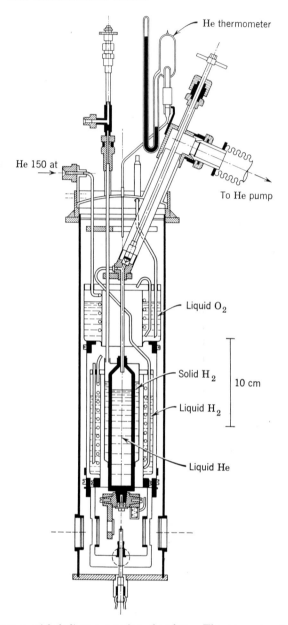

Fig. 1. Cryostat with helium-expansion chamber. The apparatus is fitted with quartz windows for optical purposes and can be easily modified for x-ray and electron diffraction.

the components was thus rendered negligible because each small portion produced only a monatomic layer and so a homogeneous layer was formed.

Such an apparatus built wholly of metal can be used for a very wide variety of purposes. With the help of suitable windows it can be used for optical measurements in all regions of the spectrum. For electron diffraction experiments (the layer support for this purpose is a collodion film 25 μ thick) an electron source and plate camera were built on. For x-ray diffraction a 10-μ aluminum foil in strip form was used. For measurements of electrical resistance, leads were fastened to evaporated-metal contacts on the quartz plate. The layer itself was prepared for this purpose in a strip 10 mm long and 1 mm wide, using a stencil. The resistance was obtained from current-voltage measurements.

Salt Layers

Debye-Scherrer x-ray diagrams have been taken on many alkali halides in layers about 5000 Å thick supported on aluminum foil (Rühl, 1956a). The photographic darkening curve for the 200 reflection of potassium iodide shown in Fig. 2 can serve as an example of many such diagrams. At a condensation temperature of 20°K, a large half-width of 0.65° is observed. By tempering, this reduced gradually to the "apparatus width" of 0.15°. From such measurements it can be concluded that in the case of these salts prepared at the lowest condensation temperatures there are still small coherent regions. If the large line width is interpreted as a particle size effect, one obtains about 100–200 Å as the linear dimension. Since the broadening of interferences of different orders is not the same, it follows that not only is there a particle size effect but also other defects play a role. A possible correct picture of the layer structure can be drawn from a two-dimensional crystal model in which small magnets serve as model ions (Hilsch, 1954). One detects a considerable disordering if the frozen-in state is reproduced using this model. A good demarcation of the separate crystalline regions is scarcely possible. Vacancies can be recognized as well as short dislocations, false location of single ions, etc. With shaking the magnets of the surface model simulate annealing. As a result much larger and very well-ordered regions arise. According to Fig. 2 crystals in the KI layer at room temperature finally reach the size of the layer thickness itself (ca. 5000 Å).

Such relations in "quenched condensation" layers are to be found in all the alkali halides. They can still be designated crystalline, although

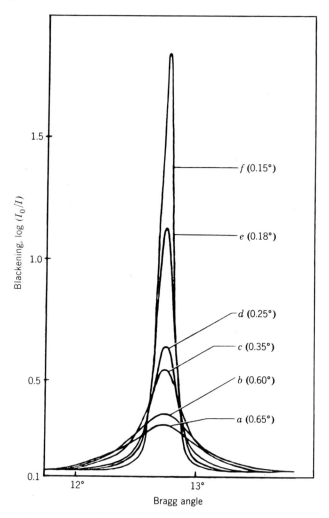

Fig. 2. Blackening curves for the 200 interference of KI in a layer condensed at 20°K with half-widths expressed in angular degrees. Diagrams obtained at: a and b, 20°K; c to f, 90°K. Previous annealing temperature: b, 90°K; c, 170°K; d, 290°K; e, 370°K; f, 15 hr at 290°K.

a considerable fraction of ions is disordered. The ultraviolet absorption spectrum has been studied in a detailed investigation (Fischer, 1954). In the upper series of Fig. 3 are the spectra for pure KI prepared at various condensation temperatures. The measurements in some cases were made after cooling to 20°K. The layer prepared at room temperature showed, a long time after condensation, the dotted curve with

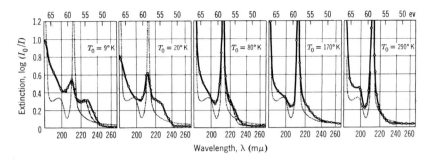

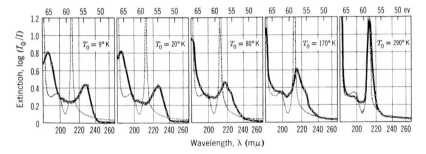

Fig. 3. *Above.* Absorption curves for KI layers condensed at T_0 and measured at 20°K (9°K). Dotted curves indicate values after annealing. *Below.* KI + 10 mole % KF condensed simultaneously (strongly disordered and stabilized to higher temperature than those above).

quite a sharp exciton band. The layer condensed at 9°K showed quite another character. As a result of disordering of the ions a long wave maximum at 228 mμ appears at the expense of the sharp 213 mμ peak. From this it can be estimated that perhaps half of the ion pairs contribute to the varied absorption at 9°K. After annealing at 300°K, the sharp band at 213 mμ is in every case restored. Behavior with respect to light absorption in the exciton band according to our present-day understanding is determined by the properties of ions and their nearest neighbors. It is obvious therefore that the absorption spectrum is very sensitive to disorder.

To prepare x-ray amorphous layers of KI a second substance was evaporated simultaneously with it. This must be incapable of forming a solid solution with KI in order to prevent crystallization. Many materials can be used for this purpose. In the present work KF was used because it is itself transparent in the absorption region of KI. A content of 10 mole % causes such a disordering of the layer that the x-ray interferences are too broad to be measurable. The interfering

F^- ions stabilize an amorphous KI phase. In the second series in Fig. 3 the absorption bands corresponding to the lowest condensation temperatures (9°K and 20°K) are shifted completely. The influence of the statistical distribution in the arrangement of the KI molecule is clearly evident in the width of the bands. In each of the figures the sharp band reappearing after annealing at room temperature and belonging to the crystalline state is shown by dotted lines. Thus the interfering KF is separated from the KI through annealing. This process has also been followed separately by x-rays (Queisser, 1958).

Another interesting fact can be brought with the aid of light absorption. The absorption spectrum for KI + 10 mole % KF at 9°K in the amorphous state shows broad bands at 190 mμ and 228 mμ. The bands for pure KI at room temperature in the crystalline state appear at shorter wavelengths and are sharper. However, if pure KI is warmed above room temperature and bands measured at 480°K, they broaden and shift toward longer wavelengths so that the absorption spectrum corresponds exactly with that of amorphous KI at low temperature! At high temperatures the KI is in quite another state. There are no frozen-in defects but only thermal disorder in dynamic equilibrium. It can be concluded from this, in any case for optical absorption, that the static disorder at low temperature is fully equivalent to the dynamic disorder at high temperature (Martienssen, 1957).

Various solid solution systems of alkali halides have been thoroughly investigated by optical and x-ray methods (Queisser, 1958). In one case the appearance of a new structure has been observed (Rühl, 1956a). LiI appears in hexagonal form if it is condensed at low temperature. It changes slowly at room temperature into the ordinary cubic modification. Doubtless this is a case of a quenched state stabilized through disordering to form a high temperature modification not hitherto observed. The disordering corresponds to higher temperature.

To summarize: At low temperatures alkali halides form in disordered layers which are still crystalline in small domains (100–200 Å). Through simultaneous condensation with foreign ions they can be forced into an amorphous state.

Heavy Metal Halides

The behavior of the alkali metal halides corresponds to that of the heavy metal halides CuCl, AgCl, and AgBr. A new observation was encountered with CuI, AgI, and especially with TlCl, TlBr, and TlI (Rühl, 1956b). With these the x-ray diagrams showed very broad interference maxima (2–4° Bragg angle) similar to those found in liquids. No connection exists between this and the crystal interferences in the thallium halides. In Fig. 4, TlCl is taken as an example of this. The photographic blackening curves of the interferences after condensation at 20°K remain broad up to 110°K annealing. In a very narrow temperature range appear (in Fig. 4b) the interferences of the CsCl structure. The crystallization temperatures observed for TlBr and TlI are

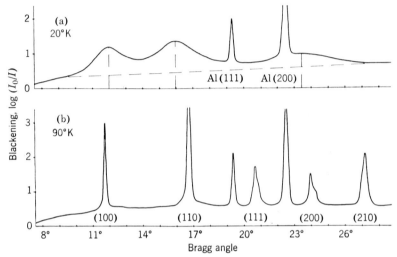

Fig. 4. Blackening curves for Debye-Scherrer diagrams of a TlCl layer condensed at 20°K; (a) after formation, (b) after annealing to 115°K, diagram obtained at 90°K. Exposure time 1.5 hr.

110°K and 140°K respectively. It was also observed that the transition from amorphous to crystalline shifted to higher temperatures if a second interfering substance was condensed simultaneously (e.g., TlCl + 10 mole % NaCl).

The relationships described apply also to variations in optical absorption. Zinngrebe (unpublished dissertation) thoroughly investigated TlCl. In Fig. 5a, the curve for the amorphous state does not show selective maxima as does the curve in Fig. 5b for the crystalline state. The exciton band at 360 mμ is missing. In the amorphous state it was apparently shifted toward shorter wavelengths and broadened. It is established that this exciton band, in contrast to those of other salts, also shows a shift toward shorter wavelengths with increasing temperature. As shown in Fig. 6 the change in the TlCl spectrum occurs suddenly in a narrow temperature interval. A suitable wavelength in the region of the exciton band was used for this determination.

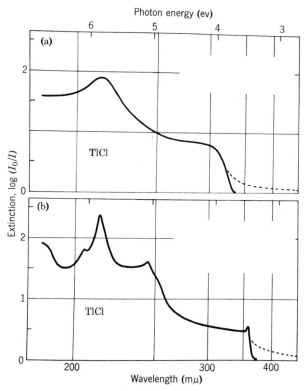

Fig. 5. Optical absorption spectra for a TlCl layer condensed at 20°K. (a) Amorphous state, measured at 20°K; (b) after crystallization (CsCl structure), by annealing at 270°K, measured at 20°K.

This is an example of materials which at low temperatures form spontaneously in the amorphous state. A condition for this relationship seems to be the distinction between the interatomic distances in the crystal and in the vapor molecule. In alkali halides this difference amounts to about 10%, while in thallium halides it is about 30%! Thus the vapor TlCl molecule impinging on the cooled underlayers must greatly increase its interatomic distances if a crystal is to be formed. Often this does not occur because the mobility is too low and the intermolecular forces are too much weakened by polarization.

Thus it is observed that predominantly heteropolar salts can still form crystalline layers; those with a considerable degree of polarization can also form in the amorphous state.*

* Materials with short range bonding forces like Si and Ge are known to form amorphous layers even at room temperature and to crystallize only at a quite high temperature (about 300°C).

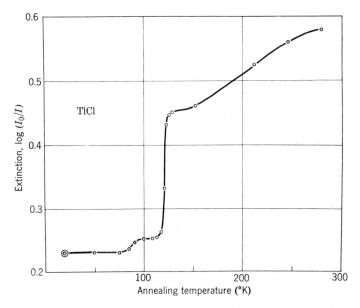

Fig. 6. Variation in light absorption at $\lambda = 358$ mμ of a TlCl layer as a function of annealing temperature; measured at $20\,^{\circ}$K. The discontinuity shows the sudden change in the absorption curves of Fig. 5.

Pure Metal Layers

X-ray and electron diffraction are quite as suitable for the study of metal layers as for salt layers. Very much less clear are the optical transmission and reflection measurements which are still in progress. The influence of conduction electrons is not easy to explain in broad regions of the spectrum. Conductivity measurements can be used with advantage in the study of metal layers.

A series of pure metals, especially those showing superconductivity was first investigated, including Hg, Pb, Tl, In, Sn, Zn, Al, Ga, and Bi. All these metals are relatively easy to evaporate and are not too sensitive to the presence of impurities. The high melting metals such as Nb and Ta, which exhibit strong getter action, present great difficulties. By electron bombardment they may be easily melted and evaporated, but up to now in spite of all precautions they have not been produced in layers free from gases. The relationship between electrical resistance and condensation temperature T_0 is typified for almost all metals by the example of Sn shown in Fig. 7. At the lowest T_0 a very large but

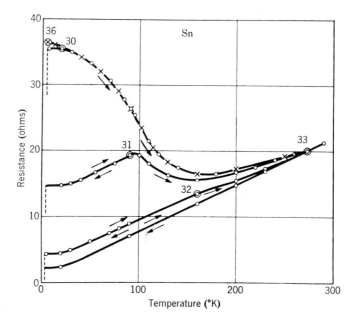

Fig. 7. Electrical resistance of Sn layers with various condensation temperatures T_0 (designated by the numbers at the double circles). Layer thickness 500 Å, length 10 mm, breadth 1 mm, layer support crystalline quartz.

reproducible specific resistance is observed, some thousands of times larger than for compact metals. Here disorder exerts a very strong influence. This becomes less with higher T_0 or after higher temperature annealing of the condensed layer. Variations in temperature below each T_0 cause reversible changes in the resistance. These parallel curve segments demonstrate the validity of Mathiessen's rule. It can be shown in detail that the temperature-dependent part of the resistance which is independent of the degree of disorder indicates the specific resistance of the compact material if layer thicknesses of more than 500 Å are used. The residual resistance measured at low temperature depends uniquely on the previous history of the layer. It may be said approximately that the highest temperature to which the layer has been exposed determines the residual resistance. If the temperature of the support is raised to the vicinity of the melting point, a residual resistance almost as low as for the compact material is observed.

With superconductors the influence of the condensation temperature T_0 on the superconductivity transition temperature T_s can be measured. This is illustrated for Sn in Fig. 8. It should be noted that in every case the layer is crystalline. The T_s transitions are dependent on the

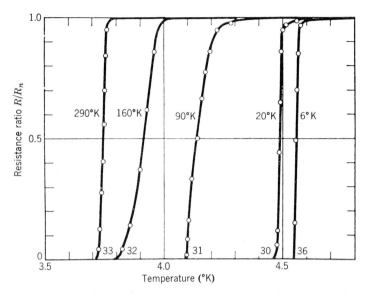

Fig. 8. Transition to superconductivity for the Sn layers of various condensation temperatures T_0 corresponding to Fig. 7.

degree of disorder, as is the case for the residual resistance. For Sn the value of T_s is shifted by quenching condensation from 3.7° to 4.6°K.* When condensed at He temperature, most of the other superconductors mentioned also show increases in their transition temperatures T_s (Buckel and Hilsch, 1952, 1954). In general, it is evident that the annealing-out of disorder follows a course similar to that of the characteristic Debye temperature. The relative shift of T_s also agrees with this. Aluminum shows the largest relative effect so far observed, T_s being shifted from 1.1° to 2.7°K. Structural studies by x-ray and electron diffraction were conducted parallel to the electrical measurements (Rühl, 1954; Buckel, 1954). From these studies the same result was obtained as for pure KI in the case of salt layers. With the metals a crystalline structure was observed with a domain width of 100–200 Å. Electron diffraction results for pure Sn are given in Fig. 9 as an example.

An exception was found in the case of Bi and Ga. Both of these metals when condensed at He temperature exhibit an *amorphous* structure. Both are known to have greater densities in the liquid than in

---

* By superconductivity investigation it may also be established whether a layer was hotter than the support during deposition, as might be the case because of radiation and heat of condensation. In the temperature range of liquid helium the layer will form in the superconducting state if the support is cooled only 0.1°K below T_s!

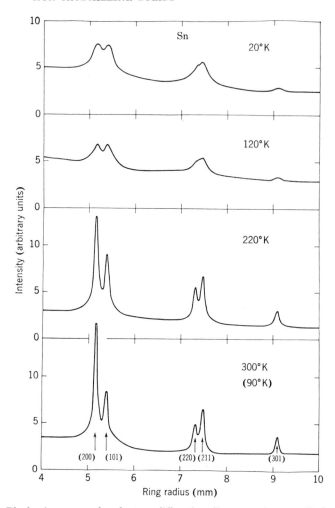

Fig. 9. Blackening curves for electron diffraction diagrams of a pure Sn layer condensed at $20°K$ and annealed at the temperatures indicated. The bottom diagram was taken at $90°K$.

the solid state. At $T > 15°K$ both crystallize spontaneously. Bismuth appears with normal lattice structure, while Ga appears in a new hitherto unknown modification (analogous to LiI cited above) which must correspond to a high temperature modification. At $70°K$ it inverts to the normal Ga structure. Evidence for these conclusions appears in Figs. 10 and 11. The diagrams for Bi in the amorphous state as shown in Fig. 10 have recently been analyzed more exactly by H. Richter. The Bi atoms were found to be in cubic coordination. Because of this dense

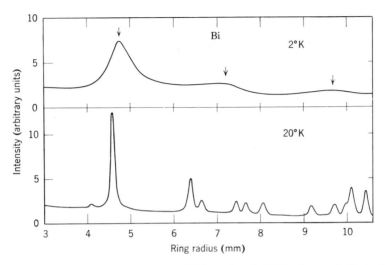

Fig. 10. Electron diffraction patterns of Bi at 2° and 20°K. Arrows indicate the positions of maxima in the diagram of molten Bi.

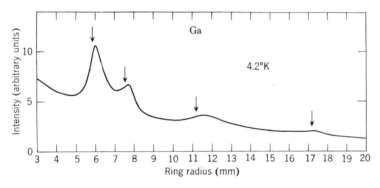

Fig. 11. Electron diffraction diagram of a Ga layer condensed at 4.2°K. The arrows indicate interferences in Ga supercooled from the melt.

packing it is understandable that in the amorphous state Bi has a lower resistance than after crystallization. In the meantime Buckel has been able to show directly by Hall effect measurements that its electron concentration in the amorphous state is about 5000 times as great. Moreover, it had been shown earlier that Bi, which is otherwise not a superconductor, becomes superconducting at 6°K in the amorphous state.

In Fig. 11 is shown the diffraction pattern of amorphous Ga. The good agreement of the maxima with those of supercooled Ga melts (arrows) is remarkable. Since the amorphous pattern was obtained at low temperature, the small displacements of the maxima are understandable.

The transition temperature T_s for Ga was considerably higher than in the normally crystallized state ($1.1°$K). The new modification stable between $15°$ and $70°$K had $T_s = 6°$K.

Formation and Stabilization of Amorphous Layers by Admixtures

The method of obtaining normally crystalline materials in amorphous form by simultaneous condensation of interfering additions can also be applied to metals. Sn is a typical example. With an addition of $>8\%$ Cu it condenses in the amorphous state. Figure 12 shows the effect for a content of 10 atom $\%$ Cu at $12°$K. In a narrow range close to $20°$K, crystallization begins spontaneously. Only by warming to nearly room temperature do the separated Cu atoms become fixed in the form of an intermetallic compound. The character of the electrical resistance shown in Fig. 13 indicates crystallization by a drop at $20°$K and separation of Cu as a compound (Cu_3Sn) at $250°$K in the course of annealing. The temperature T_s is shifted for amorphous Sn to $7°$K, but after warming to room temperature it is restored to $3.7°$K, the T_s for compact Sn. With a greater content of Cu the crystallization temperature is shifted to higher values, while the T_s value slowly sinks. If the data are extrapolated to amorphous Sn with 0% Cu, a value of more than $8°$K is obtained.

For these experiments to produce metals in amorphous form the kind of admixture is not critical. It should not form solid solutions with the metal in question. For Sn and other metals, admixtures of Ag, Au, Ni, Cu, Zn, and As behave basically alike. Non-metals such as LiF and SiO can also be used successfully. As an additional example, Al with 10% Cu might be mentioned; T_s is shifted from $1.2°$K to $5.5°$K by this means!

These methods of preparation open a wide field for the investigation of the properties of metals in amorphous form. Also, they make possible a whole new class of alloys if various components are simultaneously condensed at quenching temperatures. The influence of small admixtures of transition metals such as Mn on superconductivity has already been investigated. T_s decreases in proportion to concentration. For Sn, for example, the superconductivity is just annulled by the presence of 7.10^{-4} Mn. Upon warming, the statistically distributed Mn atoms separate and have no more effect on the superconductivity.

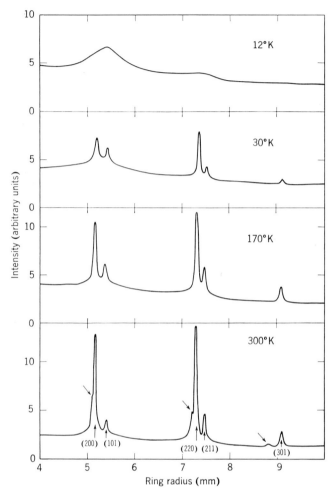

Fig. 12. Electron diffraction patterns of Sn + 10 atom % Cu condensed at 12°K and annealed. The arrows designate alloy lines appearing at 250°K.

The analogous influence of Mn on amorphous Sn (with admixtures of SiO) will be investigated soon.

The admixture method can also be used on metals which form in the amorphous state (Barth, 1955). With Bi, admixtures of Cu, LiF, and Sb raise the crystallization temperature (to about 200°K). With Ga the new modification, normally stable only to 70°K, can be stabilized to room temperature (Buckel, Hilsch, and von Minnigerode, 1957). It is not yet foreseeable what possibilities may appear if the stabilizing can be extended to room temperature in many cases.

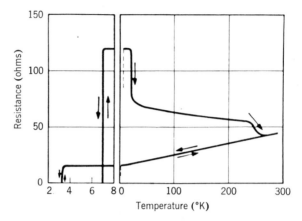

Fig. 13. Electrical resistance and superconductivity of an Sn + 10 atom % Cu layer (length 10 mm, breadth 1 mm, thickness 500 Å). Double arrows indicate reversible changes; single arrows, irreversible changes with annealing.

Up to now, the good metals with high electron concentration have not been thoroughly investigated. Work in progress by E. Feldtkeller gives a preliminary indication. Copper was condensed to a layer thickness suitable for electron diffraction (ca. 200 Å). Figure 14 shows the resulting diagrams. In the upper curve pure Cu condensed at 300°K already shows relatively broad interferences. At 4°K with 10 mole % SiO the interferences appear to wash out to such an extent that apparently the material is amorphous as in the previous cases. Upon annealing, the interferences become sharper without, however, attaining the narrow form observed with pure copper. This experiment must be verified. In Fig. 15, the behavior of the resistance with temperature and its high value of 50,000 ohms immediately after condensation at 4°K are remarkable. Pure Cu in this layer thickness would have only a few ohms resistance. In this case of a metal with especially good conductivity, the electrical properties are fundamentally altered.

Energy of Disorder of Condensed Layers

It can be expected that a heat effect will be observed during the annealing of disordered layers which will correspond to the amount of stored energy of disorder. While this will amount to only small absolute quantities of heat because of the small thickness of the layers, it can be measured quite well, especially in the low temperature range (Sander, 1957). Here the small heat capacity of the layer and support

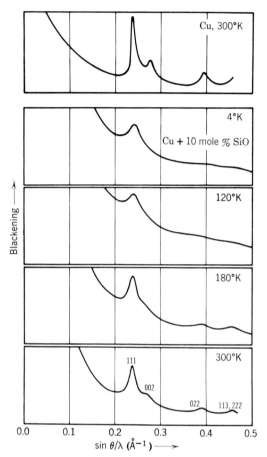

Fig. 14. Electron diffraction diagram of pure Cu and Cu + 10 mole % SiO condensed at 4°K and annealed at the temperatures indicated.

are of great advantage. The measurement was made as follows: As layer support a 2 cm² aluminum foil 10 μ thick was suspended from nylon threads for thermal isolation. The foil could be pressed by means of a mechanical arrangement against a cooled metal frame when desired; in this position it was coated with a layer condensed at, for example, 10°K. It was then isolated again and warmed by a constant flow of heat (from a small incandescent lamp) on its blackened back surface. The resulting temperature rise was measured as a function of time with a sensitive thermoelement. The energy of disorder irreversibly released during the heating affected this heating curve. It was absent, on the other hand, on a second curve obtained after the

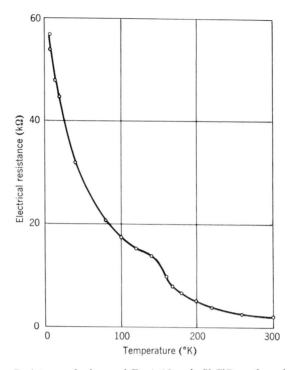

Fig. 15. Resistance of a layer of Cu + 10 mole % SiO condensed at 4°K.

original temperature was restored. The heat energy measured as the difference between the first and second heating curves could then be calculated per mole of layer substance. For amorphous Bi the heat evolved at 15°K amounted to 1.45 kcal/mole. This is considerable and comparable to the heat of fusion of Bi at 271°C, i.e., 2.65 kcal/mole. This is good evidence for the amorphous character of the Bi layer.

Corresponding experiments on the transformation of amorphous Ga took place in two steps. First, 0.29 kcal/mole was released in the inversion to the new crystal structure and then, at 70°K, the transformation to the normal lattice released an additional 0.58 kcal/mole. The total heat of transformation, amounting to 0.87 kcal/mole, is again more than half the heat of fusion of Ga, i.e., 1.34 kcal/mole. Sander has also determined an activation energy for the transformation velocity; this is 0.04 ev. Such values for activation energy and the energy stored in amorphous layers are relatively large. They are decidedly lower in cases of disordered crystalline layers. W. Mönch has obtained preliminary results for pure Cu condensed at 18°K after refining the procedure to make it still more sensitive. Here the interest lies in comparison of the energy released with the decrease in excess resistance as a result of annealing the layer. He obtained ca. 2 $(cal/g)/\mu$ ohm cm, in fair agreement with measurements which have been made on disordered copper by other methods (Blewitt, Coltman, Noggle, and Holmes, 1956; Overhauser, 1954). This investigation is still in progress and promises to disclose the mean energy of disorder of the copper atom.

Summary

For more of the details which form the basis of this chapter the original publications should be consulted. It has been shown that, with quenching condensation at low temperatures, all the materials so far investigated can be obtained in amorphous form. As a consequence many properties are profoundly altered. With suitable admixtures the amorphous form can be achieved or stabilized to higher temperatures. The disorder reaches extremely high values, such as no other methods, e.g., cold working or high energy irradiation, have so far been able to achieve.

REFERENCES

Barth, N., Z. *Physik* **142**, 58 (1955).
Blewitt, T. H., Coltman, R. R., Noggle, T. S., and Holmes, D. K., *Bull. Am. Phys. Soc.* [II] **1**, 130 (1956).
Buckel, W., Z. *Physik* **138**, 136 (1954).
Buckel, W., and Hilsch, R., Z. *Physik* **132**, 420 (1952).
Buckel, W., and Hilsch, R., Z. *Physik* **138**, 109 (1954).
Buckel, W., Hilsch, R., and von Minnigerode, G., *Acta Phys. Acad. Sci. Hung.* **8**, 5 (1957).
Fischer, F., Z. *Physik* **139**, 328 (1954).
Hilsch, R., Z. *Physik* **138**, 432 (1954).
Martienssen, W., *J. Phys. Chem. Solids* **2**, 257 (1957).
Overhauser, A. W., *Phys. Rev.* **94**, 1551 (1954).
Queisser, H.-J., Z. *Physik* **152**, 507 (1958).
Rühl, W., Z. *Physik* **138**, 121 (1954).
Rühl, W., Z. *Physik* **143**, 591 (1956) (a).
Rühl, W., Z. *Physik* **143**, 605 (1956) (b).
Sander, W., Z. *Physik* **147**, 361 (1957).

DISCUSSION

W. A. WEYL

It is important to point out the striking similarity in the behavior of the condensed halides with that of glasses. According to definition, these halides are not glasses, just as tantalum oxide precipitated through anodic oxidation is not a glass. But some of the characteristic features of glass can be found in these alkali halides.

One is the memory effect. We know that the properties of a glass depend on its thermal history. The properties of a glass also depend on its previous pressure [Tammann and Jellinghaus, *Ann. Physik* **2**, 264 (1929)]. And, then, Guyer [*J. Am. Ceram. Soc.* **16**, 607 (1933)] points out that the electrical response of a glass depends on its electrical history.

But the striking similarity goes even farther. I think some of you no doubt will have seen the pictures of glass formation modeled by magnets floating on the surface of water at the Max Planck Institute in Würzberg [Dietzel and Deeg, *Veröffentl. Max-Planck-Institut für Silikatforsch.* **17**, 1 (1957); *Glastech. Ber.* **30**, 282 (1957)]. The ionic forces were imitated by magnetic forces corresponding to Si^{4+} and O^{2-}. But, no matter what was done, the magnets always assumed a high degree of order. But, when the model ions were "polarized" or, in other words, when a dipole moment was superimposed on the ionic field by bringing the magnet slightly out of center, "glass formation" was obtained immediately. In the case of the halides, too, those ions which show very little polarizability, such as potassium, are not so likely to favor the amorphous state as the strongly deformable ions such as thorium.

It is remarkable how far this similarity goes in these simple systems.

Also, the "complexity principle" which is so important in glass technology can be applied to rapidly condensed vapors of salt molecules. The stability of glasses is greatly improved if the number of constituents is increased. The so-called soda-lime-silica glasses contain Al_2O_3, MgO, and often K_2O as minor constituents. Under conditions where a single salt crystallizes, a mixture of salts remains amorphous. This principle has also been used by St. von Bogdandy and associates [*Z. Physik* **40**, 211 (1926–27)].

R. SMOLUCHOWSKI

Bismuth has an unusually low number of free electrons caused by the small overlap of the Fermi surface. For this reason one would expect a large influence of lattice imperfections on its Hall coefficient. Did you observe similarly large effects in other metals?

R. HILSCH

We only measured gallium, where conditions are somewhat more complicated. Of course, there is a change in all these metals.

R. SMOLUCHOWSKI

But surely not so radical as for bismuth.

R. HILSCH

Certainly not.

R. SMOLUCHOWSKI

Is there an indication of a critical size of crystallites for the appearance of a sharp exciton band?

R. HILSCH

There is no critical size. The optical absorption depends only on the ion and its nearest neighbors. But, if you have many defects, then, of course, you have a broadening and a shift. One could say that very small crystals have almost the same effect as a higher temperature.

J. ZARZYCKI

Hilsch has demonstrated very clearly one important point, namely, that we have to do with charged particles each of which dictates its immediate surrounding. In your picture, each ion was shown to be surrounded by four, or (*correcting at R. Hilsch's intercession*) less in a two-dimensional model. Your domains of 100 Å contain a large amount of ions. Now, if you would impose thermal motion ("shake" your model), could you not obtain smaller domains, arriving at a picture similar to the "clusters" I have presented? (See p. 135.)

Of course, the particles are not separated. In my computations I have used an idealized case, but I have shown, and stressed, the fact that there is considerable bridge formation and that fissures are only apparent, so that the "clusters" are not completely isolated.

R. HILSCH

From the narrowing of the diffraction lines on annealing it can be derived that the crystal is of the dimension of the layer thickness and grows. This is just what you want.

J. ZARZYCKI

Could this model demonstrate the liquid state?

R. HILSCH

No, not this model. But amorphous potassium iodide is just like the liquid you have shown.

J. ZARZYCKI

It seems important to me that one should not speak of a mere superimposition of different coordination schemes. For instance, in the case of the neutral particles in liquid argon, one can, of course, have different coordination schemes, since this liquid can be treated as a collection of rigid spheres with various amounts of cluster formation.

P. DEBYE

It depends upon the temperature.

J. ZARZYCKI

The amount, of course, depends upon the temperature.

R. HILSCH

Yes. That is just what Professor Debye says. If one takes out some molecules, the lattice will collapse in some way, but the collapse is not perfect.

J. ZARZYCKI

I do not say that the collapse is perfect: the model I have given presents only an average picture useful for calculation.

P. G. KLEMENS

I would like to refer to the electrical resistance of the stabilized amorphous metal layers. In principle there would be two possible sources of resistance, say the copper atom in tin, which is now distributed uniformly, and normally would not be, or the amorphous structure of the tin itself. Have you got any information as to which is the important source of resistance, or can you sort it out in any way?

R. HILSCH

Not too well. Considering tin with bismuth, and rubidium iodide, we can see which of the two substances would be first in the crystalline state. The tin remains for a longer time in the amorphous state, while the rubidium iodide which separates out at first becomes crystalline, and from the measurement of the electrical resistance you could see which is more important. But this has not been solved; we are making additional experiments.

J. A. PRINS

It is so difficult to make a remark, because your experiments and your conclusions agree with mine! But I think you have not done one thing that I would have done: you have not measured the scattering at small angles. And now I predict—and you could verify it—that in most cases the scattering at small angles will be of the same order of magnitude as the broadening of the lines, for instance, in the case of the alkali halides; but that, in the cases of bismuth, antimony, and gallium, you will have much less scattering at small angles than corresponds to the broad maxima. I hope you will sometime try that.

S. H. BAUER

In general, I agree with your model for the formation of amorphous films, but I wish to state that there are data which support a more complicated mechanism for the formation of these films. Reference is made to my remarks following the chapter by Dr. J. Zarzycki (p. 140). Instead of simply considering the effect of condensing streams of diatoms upon the cold substrate, one should also keep in mind that in most cases the major fraction of the incident molecules is tetratomic, these molecules being dimers of the alkali metal halides. For example, in lithium chloride at about 1100°, there are approximately four times as many dimers as there are monomers. When such a variety of molecules condenses on a cold substrate, clearly extensive rearrangement must take place. This occurs very slowly at the low temperatures. It is our presumption that, whereas in the monomers the interatomic distances are perhaps 10% less than those present in the crystal, the interatomic distances in the dimers are probably midway between the larger values observed in the bulk crystal and the values determined in the gaseous state for the monomers. In the case of the evaporation of mixtures, it has been demonstrated by mass spectroscopic analysis that the mixed dimer ($M^{(1)}M^{(2)}X_2$) is more prevalent than either of the pure dimers, because it is favored entropywise. Hence a further disparity exists between distances as they are present in the quenched film and the well-crystallized material. It is not surprising that a small amount of an admixed metal halide will provide more stable amorphous films than would be obtained from the pure material.

Bauer, Diner, and Porter [*J. Chem. Phys.* **29,** 991 (1958)] deduced wherein a linear relation between the expected interionic distances in the dimer and the dissociation energy into monomers is deduced. In that paper, values for the entropies of dimerization were also computed, so that for any system, given the vapor pressure at some temperature [Eisenstadt, Rothberg, and Kush, *J. Chem. Phys.* **29,** 797 (1958)], one can readily compute the equilibrium composition of the vapor phase. Of course, such computations will be valid only when the area of the exit hole in the furnace is small compared to the total area, so that attainment of equilibrium between the vapor phase and the melt is permitted.

G. J. DIENES

Does the substrate play any role in these low temperature formations?

R. HILSCH

No. We tried many kinds of substrates. The substrate usually can also be a copper plate which has been oxidized to cuprous oxide and polished.

G. J. DIENES

How about sodium chloride evaporated on sodium chloride?

R. HILSCH

We obtain the same qualities, but we are somewhat afraid that there might be a layer of a solid gas at low temperature. But, at this low temperature, the nucleus formation is not important. They always stick. It is important at high temperatures, when you would form single crystals.

J. A. KRUMHANSL

If one looks at the simple expression for the exciton energy, this involves the difference between the ionization potential of the halogen ion, and the ionization potential of the metal ions surrounding it, and a term of Coulomb interaction between the electron and the hole.

Now, is it not true that this expression doesn't show much sensitivity to coordination, since its principal sensitivity is to the mean spacing between the metal ions on which the excited electron finds itself and the halogen ion from which it came, and it really doesn't tell you whether there are three metal ions which are sharing the excitation or six metal ions?

R. HILSCH

No, it is very sensitive.

There are new calculations which show exactly that this term which belongs to the lattice energy is changed when the surrounding is different.

J. A. KRUMHANSL

Is the change due to change in mean spacing, though?

R. HILSCH

No, it is not the spacing, it is the different surroundings.

Fischer [Z. *Physik* **139**, 328 (1954); cf. p. 340] in our laboratory [Göttingen], has calculated all the different possibilities. The Madelung numbers will become different, and that is the important point.

Therefore you have a shift of the sharp exciton band to longer wavelengths. You can really relate it to the lowering of the coordination number.

J. A. KRUMHANSL

Then, if this is so, wouldn't one expect to see, in an amorphous material with considerable disorder, not only an agreement between the position and the shape of the exciton band in this amorphous material, and the same band in a high temperature material, but also other lines which are due to 4-coordination, 6-coordination, etc.?

R. HILSCH

That's very difficult. We have shown that this sharp absorption band changes to the very broad absorption band indicated. We must conclude that there are superimposed very small maxima originating from different coordinations.

But there are so many different kinds that you cannot separate them, for we haven't the random distribution of all kinds of coordination numbers.

J. A. KRUMHANSL

This picture is basically different from the high temperature broadening, where the coordination stays the same.

R. HILSCH

Yes, it is basically different. What you have in time at a high temperature you have in space at a low temperature, frozen in. This has been brought out by Martienssen [*J. Phys. Chem. Solids* **2**, 257 (1957)] with two different lattices, where the cesium chloride ion mixes with the sodium chloride ion.

T. J. GRAY

A question and an observation. The observation goes back to 1946. From bitter experience it was found, exactly in agreement with your findings, that, if metal films, particularly of copper, zinc, and transition metals, were evaporated onto a substrate at liquid nitrogen temperature and subsequently warmed to room temperature, providing you started with very pure metal, they would not oxidize beyond a few surface monolayers.

If, however, oxygen was admitted at liquid nitrogen temperature, then the whole of the metal surface was apparently sealed against annealing, and oxidation proceeded at room temperature and above in a perfectly rational manner.

Now, this is exactly in keeping with your findings. And it also, perhaps, explains why sometimes you get good oxide diffraction patterns for the surface oxide layer and sometimes you don't.

However, I have one question about your copper films. I noticed silicon monoxide present. One of the things that was found in the case of copper is that deposition on a substrate which has been subjected to chromic acid treatment, which, of course, induces some monoxide in the surface, always gave some cuprous oxide in that surface.

I am wondering whether, under the molecular beam conditions that you are using, you are not actually putting down some cuprous oxide in your film, so that it is not actually a film of copper, but a composite mixture of copper, copper oxide, and perhaps a little copper silicate, so that the pronounced negative temperature coefficient that you get may in fact be due to this to some extent.

R. HILSCH

Yes, it may be that some cuprous oxide is formed. It is somewhat difficult to see what happens when you heat copper and silicon monoxide at a high temperature. But there is not a negative temperature coefficient, only an irreversible drop by annealing. Since this is work just in progress, I cannot say more. We were very surprised that this happened.

But in other cases, e.g., if you add lithium fluoride to tin and condense, nothing happens. And, if there were cuprous oxide, it would be an insulator just as lithium fluoride, at low temperature.

T. J. GRAY

Well, actually, cuprous oxide, in the presence of excess copper, is still a very good conductor, indeed, and it is n-type material. And that, of course, is what you have.

R. HILSCH

No, there must be excess oxygen.

T. J. GRAY

Not necessarily; we have also been able to demonstrate this in the presence of excess copper during the formation of the initial oxide film on copper. This is confirmed by the work of Schilling [Z. *Naturforsch.* **7a,** 211 (1952)] and is in accord with the observations of Parratt [A.F.O.S.R. (AF18(600)-300), and private communication].

Even for thicker layers of p-type oxide on a metal, it is probable that at the metal interface the oxide remains n-type, thereby forming an internal n-p junction from the metal outwards.

R. HILSCH

Then you would be right.

by

R. W. Douglas

The University, Sheffield

The Chemical
Approach to Problems
of the Glassy State

The Physics of Glasses

Glasses are liquids which have cooled below the freezing point without crystallizing. When the coefficient of viscosity rises to about 10^{13} poise, the physical properties change with time, after a sudden change of temperature, or pressure, to attain equilibrium values in the new conditions. The atomic configuration in a liquid is a function of the temperature and pressure, and at these high viscosities the time for the configuration to reach equilibrium has become long compared with the time required to measure a physical property. At still lower temperatures the configuration changes are so slow as to be immeasurably small, and thereafter, on cooling, the configuration may be considered constant. The temperatures at which the properties of a glass may be observed to vary with time are called the transformation range. Below the transformation range the atoms are arranged in space as in a liquid but are executing thermal vibrations about fixed positions; in this condition the materials may formally be described as glasses.

This summary of the nature of the glassy state is illustrated in Fig. 1. At the freezing point, if the substance freezes, there is a discontinuous change in volume. The coefficient of expansion of the liquid is normally greater than that of the crystal by virtue of the contribution from the change of configuration with temperature and, if the liquid supercools, the coefficient of expansion of the liquid state is retained until the trans-

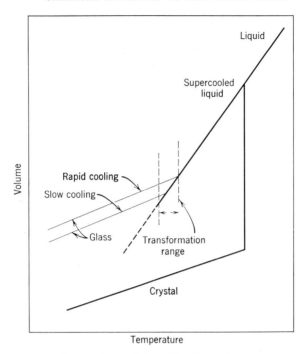

Fig. 1. The origin of the glassy state.

formation range is reached. Below the transformation range the contribution from configuration change is absent and the contraction is approximately equal to that of the crystal. The exact path followed is, however, dependent upon the rate of cooling; if the cooling is fast the contribution of configuration becomes ineffective at a higher temperature than if the cooling is slow.

In the transformation range the properties may be caused to vary reversibly with time and temperature, as illustrated in Fig. 2. For example, a rapid change of temperature from T_1 to T_2 will cause the volume to change along the line AB. If the temperature is then held constant, the volume will relax along the line BC. By another rapid change of temperature the volume will increase along CD, and finally at constant temperature T_1 the volume will relax to its original value at A.

Suppose a piece of glass has been brought to equilibrium at the point F and the temperature is suddenly changed to T_2; the equilibrium at C will be approached along GC. Similarly the same equilibrium may be approached along BC. Typical of experiments of this type is the well-known study of viscosity by Lillie (1933) summarized in Fig. 3. In these experiments the viscosity was measured of a glass which had been

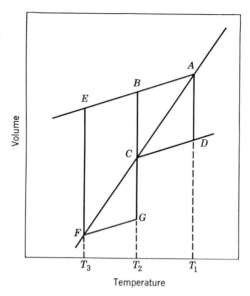

Fig. 2. Change of properties with time in the transformation range.

brought to equilibrium at temperatures above and below the temperature at which the measurement was made. The approach to equilibrium from both sides is illustrated and also the fact that the approach is more rapid as the temperature is increased.

This equilibrium configuration will correspond to a minimum in the free energy of the system; this has been confirmed by Borelius and Paulson (1946) in experiments on selenium glass. The results are given in Fig. 4.

$$\Delta F = F_g - F_c = \Delta U - T \Delta S$$

where F_g is the free energy of the glass, F_c is the free energy of the crystal, and U, T, and S have the usual connotations.

It was established that ΔU and ΔS depended on the configuration and were substantially independent of temperature; F_c is also nearly independent of temperature; therefore a minimum in ΔF corresponds to a minimum in F_g. The arrows indicate the values of ΔV determined experimentally. It will be seen that there is excellent correspondence between these values of ΔV and the minimum values of ΔF at successive temperatures.

These arguments and the typical experimental results which have been quoted show that the structure or atomic configuration in a glass must be liquid-like. So far an "ideal" glass has been discussed; it should be recognized that in practical or "real" glasses it may well be that there

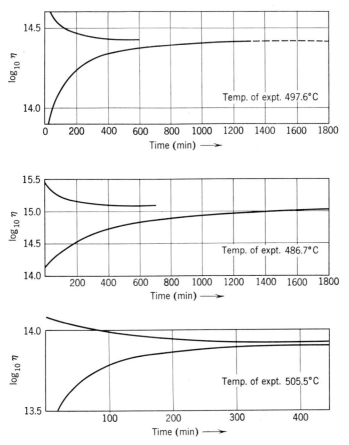

Fig. 3. Approach to equilibrium viscosity (Lillie, 1933).

are local inhomogeneities which might depart a little from the liquid-like arrangements. This appears to have been the situation in the experiments of Florinskaya and Pechenkina (1953) on fused silica. In these experiments absorption bands in the infrared were given by some specimens which corresponded closely with bands shown by quartz alone of the crystalline forms of silica. However, the specimens which showed these bands had been prepared by heating only about 50°C above the melting point. Specimens prepared at higher temperatures do not show these bands.

Even in an ideal glass, thermal fluctuations of volume and composition will be expected, and at room temperature these will correspond to the high temperature configuration which was "frozen in" by the rate of cooling; this is conveniently but not accurately described by a constant,

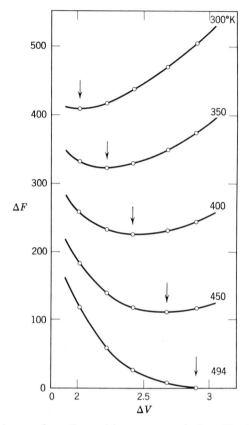

Fig. 4. Equilibrium configuration and free energy—selenium (Borelius and Paulson, 1946).

T_f, the fictive temperature, i.e., the temperature at which the configuration would be in equilibrium. Maurer's (1956) observations of light scattering by glasses appear to confirm the presence of these frozen-in high temperature fluctuations at room temperature.

The Formation of Glasses

The transformation range phenomena are typical of the change from a supercooled liquid to a glass, a glass being thus defined as a liquid with a relaxation time so long as to be unobservable. The possibility of the formation of a glass, however, rests entirely with the kinetics of crystallization (in the present context it is better to avoid the use of the technologist's word "devitrification"). The precipitation of crystals involves nucleation and growth. When the nucleation is homogeneous, the rate of nucleation will increase as the temperature falls below the freezing point; the rate of growth, however, will be controlled by the rate of sorting out and alignment of the atoms of the liquid to form the growing crystal. The forces restricting this growth process are thus akin to the forces of viscosity, and the liquids which have high viscosity at the melting point might be expected to form a glass.

When complex glasses are being considered, the freezing point must be replaced by the liquidus temperature, and at the liquidus temperature the crystal and liquid in equilibrium will not, in general, be of the same composition. Thus, in addition, glass formation will be likely in liquids in which nucleation is difficult owing to the complexity of the crystal to be formed. Unfortunately, there are very few data to quote in support of these arguments. In Fig. 5 the liquidus curves for lithium, sodium,

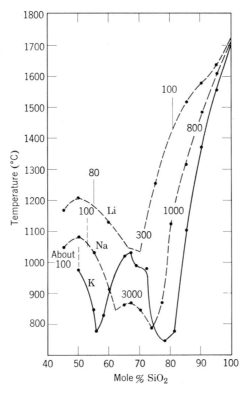

Fig. 5. Liquidus curves for lithium, sodium, and potassium silicates. Figures denote viscosity at the liquidus.

and potassium silicates are given; these are based on the data of Kracek (1930) quoted by Rey (1948). On these curves the limits of easy glass formation are given. These limits are, of course, arbitrary; those quoted are taken from Moore and Carey (1951) and Moore and McMillan (1956), who chose to define glass formation by reference to a 0.5 gram sample; the range of glass formation includes all those compositions which did not show any devitrification when cooled by pouring from the melt. A larger sample with its consequent lower cooling rate would reduce the range of glass formation. The viscosity at the liquidus has also been indicated on these curves; these figures were taken from Shartsis, Spinner, and Capps (1952). The reason for the reduced glass-forming range of lithium oxide-silica glasses compared with that of potassium and sodium oxide glasses is clear, for, owing to the rapid decrease in viscosity with increasing temperature, the viscosity at the liquidus temperature decreases very markedly outside the regions of glass formation marked. The viscosity will also decrease with increasing silica content and decrease with increasing alkali content, but except for the region around 100% SiO_2 the effect of temperature will be greater than the effect of composition. It is very interesting to note, also, that Morey (1954) records the extreme difficulty of devitrifying melts with compositions around 25% sodium oxide where the viscosity at the liquidus is particularly high.

In Fig. 6 similar information on the glass-forming system $CaNO_3$–KNO_3 is given (Dietzel and Poegel, 1953). Unfortunately, the viscosity is recorded only of the "best" glass; by this Dietzel meant the glass most difficult to crystallize. A little extrapolation gives 80 poise as the viscosity of this glass at the liquidus temperature. Figure 7 gives the scanty

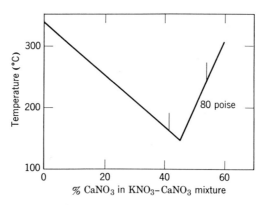

Fig. 6. Liquidus curves for the glass-forming system $CaNO_3$–KNO_3 (Dietzel and Peogel, 1953).

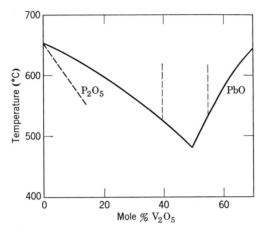

Fig. 7. Liquidus curves for PbO, V_2O_5, and P_2O_5–V_2O_5 mixtures (Dietzel and Peogel, 1953).

information available on V_2O_5 glasses. The larger range of glass-forming compositions when P_2O_5 is added compared with PbO additions is seen to fit in with the general view of the low liquidus temperature-high viscosity criterion of glass formation. Many examples of the relation of glass formation to the regions of low temperature on the liquidus curve have been given by Rawson (1956), and the kinetic basis of glass formation has been stressed by Weyl (1957).

The Structure of Glasses

Although these kinetic conditions for glass formation were recognized many years ago (Tammann, 1925), the great concentration on silicate glasses which arises from their industrial importance led to very considerable emphasis being given to the well-known Zachariasen (1932)–Warren (1937) description of the structure of a glass in terms of network formers and network modifiers. In pure silica glass, for example, there is a network of silicon atoms surrounded by four oxygen atoms, each oxygen being shared between two silicon atoms exactly as in the crystalline forms of silica, but the long-distance order is lacking; this is described as a random network. (The word atom is used deliberately to avoid having repeatedly to refer to the partially covalent nature of the bonding in glasses.)

In Na_2O–SiO_2 glasses some of the oxygens in the network are no longer shared, and the sodium ions are said to be in "holes" in the network;

thus silica is described as a network former and Na_2O as a network modifier. Although this model is roughly correct in recognizing the different roles which might be played by the various oxides, it is obviously not sufficiently sophisticated, the atoms of one network-modifying element necessarily having a different quantitative effect from another. To lower the liquidus temperature of silica from 1723° to 1500°C requires 16 mole % of Li_2O, 10 mole % of Na_2O, 7 mole % of K_2O, 5 mole % of Rb_2O and Cs_2O. The lowering of the freezing point by Rb_2O, Cs_2O has been shown (Forland, 1955) to be ideal; the remaining silica and alkali and alkaline earth oxide systems show increasing positive departure from ideality until the divalent oxides SrO, CaO, MgO show large zones of immiscibility. This clearly indicates that the ionization of the network-modifying oxides is incomplete and that this incompleteness ought to be reflected in other physical properties. However, the addition of quite small amounts of a third oxide usually removes the immiscibility, but there naturally still remains a marked variability in properties as one network-modifying oxide is substituted for another. This will be discussed later.

The network-former-modifier description is a useful one, but it has influenced unduly the discussion of glass formation. Undoubtedly the strong, directed bonds in fused silica and silicate glass contribute to the restriction of crystallization, but, as has been indicated earlier in this chapter, there are other structural ways of doing this. For example, TeO_2 will not form a glass by itself but will with 10% Li_2O, 7% ZnO, or 10% PbO. TeO_2 has the brookite structure in which there are octahedral TeO_6 groups, and each octahedron shares edges with three neighboring ones. Brady (1957) has suggested that when Li_2O is used with TeO_2 to form a glass the joined edges of the octahedra are, as it were, prized apart to enable a random network of groups of octahedra, joined to other groups by corners, to be formed.

Brady confirmed by x-ray diffraction that tellurium atoms remain 6-coordinated with oxygen in the glass as in the crystal. This is also confirmed by infrared transmission measurements on the crystal, using the KBr disk technique, and on thin films of a glass containing TeO_2 and ZnF_2. The main peak occurs at about 13.2 μ in the glass and 12.87 μ in the crystal (unpublished work in progress in the Department of Glass Technology, Sheffield). If the coordination in the glass were reduced from 6 to 4, a greater reduction in wavelength of the absorption peak would be expected than was found.

The silicate glasses may be considered to form a particular class of glass-forming substances, and the relations between the structure and physical properties of the silicate glasses form an interesting study with its own intrinsic value. Although the silicate type of structure is not necessary for glass formation, it is of interest to consider how far it provides a guide to substances which are likely to form glasses. There are two types of analog; the first type may be considered to be related in a similar way to the silica structure, as are certain intermetallic compounds related in structure and properties to the elements silicon and germanium. For example, aluminum phosphide is a semiconductor similar to silicon; gallium arsenide, zinc selenide, copper bromide are all semiconductors not only having the diamond structure but also having very nearly the same lattice constant as has germanium, which may be considered the prototype of the series. Thus $AlPO_4$ may be considered to be derived from SiO_2 by the substitution of the pair aluminum and phosphorus for silicon. Beryllium fluoride may be considered to be derived from SiO_2 by the substitution of beryllium for silicon simultaneously with the substitution of 2F for 2O, thus keeping the mean number of valence electrons per atom constant. As these substitutions are made, however, the bonds become more and more ionic and the radii of the ions introduced cause the structure of the crystalline substances to cease to be silica-like; very few glass-forming substances can be so derived, but the silica structure is in this restricted sense confirmed as a glass-forming structure.

The other type of substitution is typified by the substitution of the pair sodium aluminum for silicon. As is well known, in silicate structures aluminum is often found 4-coordinated in the network where the extra oxygen has been donated by Na_2O as in the crystal carnegieite, $NaAlSiO_4$; the network modifier, Na_2O, may be said to enable the aluminum to become a network former. The compound ZnS has either the wurzite or zinc blende structure, in both of which each zinc is surrounded tetrahedrally by four sulfur atoms and each sulfur atom is surrounded tetrahedrally by four zinc atoms. It was thought probable that, if another sulfide were added in which the bond strength was considerably less than that in zinc sulfide, it might possibly donate two sulfurs to the zinc sulfide network, so that instead of the 4-4 coordination the zinc sulfide would remain 4-coordinated with sulfur but each sulfur would be shared only between two zinc atoms. It was found that glasses could be made with compositions consisting of equimolecular proportions of barium sulfide and zinc sulfide. The range of glass formation was very small, and departures from equimolecular proportions could not be greater than 1% or 2%. Replacement of barium sulfide by calcium sulfide or sodium sulfide prevented any glass being obtained. The melts appeared homogeneous, and a possible explanation might be that the liquidus temperature is not lowered sufficiently by CaS, whereas with Na_2S, although the liquidus temperature is lowered below that of the BaS glass, the viscosity is reduced much more. Although quantitative information on these systems is lacking, the qualitative observations appear to confirm once again that the general criterion for glass formation is that of high viscosity at the liquidus temperature, and that only in certain restricted fields can structural relations and analogies guide the search for glass-forming materials.

It should be mentioned that there is a family of glasses, quite distinct from the silicate, or three-dimensional network, glasses, which could be said to have a structural origin. These are the long chain glasses in which the high viscosity may be taken roughly to arise from the entanglement of the long chain molecules. Inorganic examples are sulfur and selenium and certain phosphate glasses (Brady, 1958).

Silicate Glasses

Although the classification of the components of silicate glasses into network formers and network modifiers could be regarded as an elementary classification which gives little more than a crude description of the structure of glass in the crystallographer's sense, it still provides a very useful background for the discussion of the contribution of various oxides to the properties of glasses. The network formers are the glass-forming oxides, SiO_2, B_2O_3, P_2O_5; the modifiers are the alkaline earths and the alkalis, CaO, BaO, Na_2O, K_2O, etc., and there are intermediates such as Al_2O_3 which may sometimes play the role of network former and sometimes of modifier. If the oxides are set out in order of electrostatic binding energy [Sun's (1947) single bond energies] or the field strength of the cation, they are then arrayed in a table leading progressively from network former to modifier; see, for example, Stanworth (1950).

X-ray diffraction, unfortunately, does not give very precise data on the structure of glasses, and relatively little work has been done. From information deduced mainly from observations on the trend of the physical properties of a family of glasses in which the composition has been varied systematically, coupled with other data, particularly from the known behavior of the particular cation in oxide crystals, the coordination of various network modifiers is becoming better established. A typical example of the method may be based on Fig. 8, which is due to Schairer and Bowen (1956). It will be apparent that change of slope of the lines of equal refractive index occurs on the join SiO_2 to Na_2O–Al_2O_3. It is inferred that on the Na_2O side of this join the aluminum is 4-coordinated, the extra oxygen being provided by the Na_2O. To the

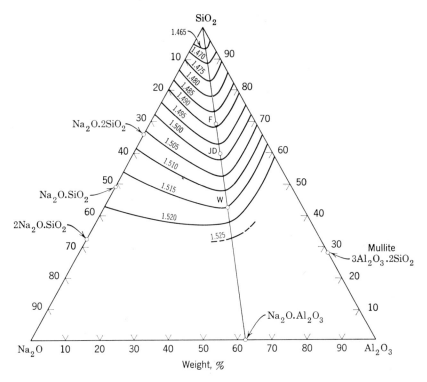

Fig. 8. Refractive indices of glasses in the Na₂O–Al₂O₃–SiO₂ system. F = albite (Na₂O·Al₂O₃·6SiO₂); JD = jadeite composition (Na₂O·Al₂O₃·4SiO₂); W = nepheline, carnegieite (Na₂O·Al₂O₃·2SiO₂). (Schairer and Bowen, 1956.)

right of the line there is insufficient oxygen to allow all the aluminum to be 4-coordinated, and the excess aluminum becomes 6-coordinated or, in other words, acts as a network modifier, whereas to the left of the line the aluminum is regarded as a network former. It may be noted that the molar refractivity of aluminum when 4-coordinated with oxygen is 12.3, and 10.5 when 6-coordinated (Safford and Silverman, 1947). The increase in refractive index when aluminum goes into 6-coordination is undoubtedly due to the increase in density, which increases the refractive index much more than the decrease due to the lower molar refractivity of the aluminum in 6-coordination. This increase of density can easily be pictured on the network-former-modifier hypothesis. When aluminum goes into the network the structure becomes more open, whereas when it adopts the network-modifier position of 6-coordination the number of atoms per unit volume is increased.

The electrical properties of this system of glasses are of particular interest. The compositions of four series of glasses are shown in Fig. 9. Series I lies along the join SiO_2–Na_2O–Al_2O_3; along this line there is exactly the required amount of Na_2O to cause all the aluminum to be 4-coordinated with oxygen. Series II and III, on the other hand, cross this join so that on the Na_2O-rich side all the aluminum will be 4-

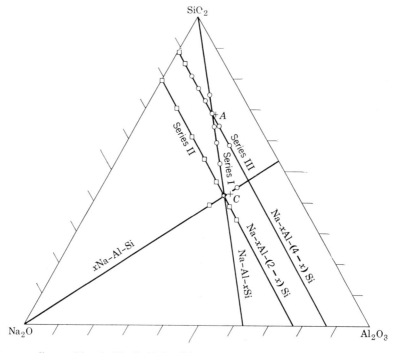

Fig. 9. Composition in Na_2O–Al_2O_3–SiO_2 system of which the electrical properties have been studied. Pot melts: circles = batch composition + chemical analysis; platinum melts: squares = batch composition; A = $NaAlSi_3O_3$ (albite); C = $NaAlSiO_4$ (carnegieite).

coordinated and there will be a number of non-bridging oxygens. On the Al_2O_3 side of the join there will be an increasing number of 6-coordinated aluminums. As can be seen from Figs. 10 and 11 both Series II and III show a minimum of activation energy where the join is crossed. Thus the activation energy for conduction is a minimum when there are no non-bridging oxygens and no 6-coordinated aluminums. The values of ρ_0 are the values of the pre-exponential constant in the Rasch and Henrichson formula for the resistivity:

$$\rho = \rho_0 \exp (E/kT)$$

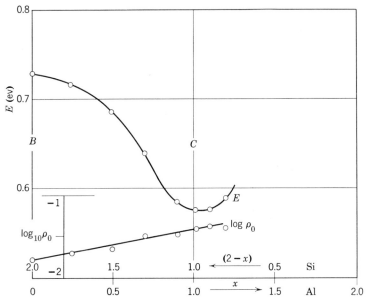

Fig. 10. Activation energies for electrical conduction in the Na_2O–Al_2O_3–SiO_2 system, Series II. Na–xAl–$(2 - x)$Si. E = activation energy; ρ_0 = constant term of electrical resistivity (platinum melts).

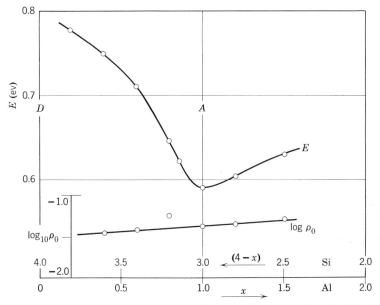

Fig. 11. Activation energies for electrical conduction in the Na_2O–Al_2O_3–SiO_2 system, Series III. Na–xAl–$(4 - x)$Si. E = activation energy; ρ_0 constant term of electrical resistivity.

Throughout the three series ρ_0 varies only slightly and shows no maximum or minimum at the line of equal content of sodium and aluminum atoms.

Figure 12 shows the activation energy for electrical conduction for the glasses in Series I along the join SiO_2–Al_2O_3–Na_2O; this activation energy is nearly constant and shows no minimum, as would be predicted.

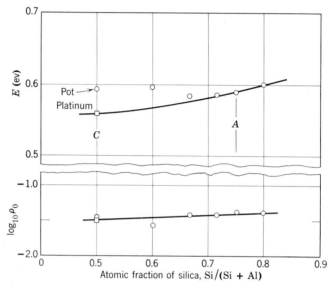

Fig. 12. Activation energies for electrical conduction in the Na_2O–Al_2O_3–SiO_2 system, Series I. Na–Al–xSi. E = activation energy; ρ_0 = constant term of electrical resistivity.

Figure 13 compares the electrical resistivity of some sodium-aluminum silicate glasses with a soda-lime-silica and binary silicate glasses. When the Na_2O is donating its oxygen to form AlO_4 groups, the Na^+ ion seems particularly mobile and the conductivity is very high, much greater than in the corresponding glass with CaO substituted for Al_2O_3. At the same time the viscosity is very considerably increased by the strengthening of the network by the AlO_4 groups. The increased mobility of the sodium ion when it donates its oxygen to the aluminum is of particular interest and underlines the usefulness of the network hypothesis as a first approximation. As has been noted earlier, the phase diagrams of the binary silicates immediately show that the network hypothesis lacks detail. This does not invalidate the hypothesis but calls for more detail to be added as the various properties of the glasses come under close examination.

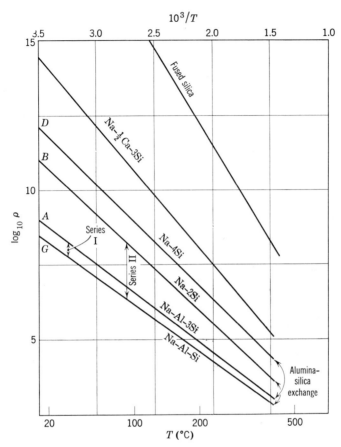

Fig. 13. Electrical resistivity of some $Na_2O–Al_2O_3–SiO_2$ glasses compared with certain $Na_2O–SiO_2$ and $Na_2O–CaO–SiO_2$ glasses.

There has been much discussion in the literature of the so-called "boric oxide anomaly," by which is meant that the trend of properties of a family of glasses as the boric oxide content is increased may alter considerably at a particular composition. For a general account see Stanworth (1950). To mention only one example, when Na_2O is added to B_2O_3, the thermal expansion of the glasses first decreases until the molar composition is about 14% Na_2O, 86% B_2O_3; addition of more Na_2O then causes the expansion to increase. The network theory explanation is as follows. In B_2O_3 glass each boron is surrounded by three oxygens, each oxygen is attached to two borons. On adding Na_2O, for each sodium ion added one boron becomes 4-coordinated with oxygen; this process, however, is limited. Experimentally it is found (as indicated by the trend of a physical property such as thermal expansion) that this process stops when about one in five borons becomes 4-coordinated, i.e., at about 16 mole % Na_2O; Warren (1942) suggested that this limit is dictated by the fact that each boron-oxygen tetrahedron must touch two sodium ions in order to satisfy the unsaturated oxygens, because it is impossible for one sodium to touch all four oxygens. This hypothesis imposes a geometrical restriction which leads to a maximum number of 4-coordinated borons at 13.4 mole % Na_2O. An alternative hypothesis proposed by Abe (1952) is that each boron tetrahedral group must be screened from others by surrounding itself by four 3-coordinated boron groups. This leads simply to the critical ratio 1Na:5B or 16.6% Na_2O:83.4% B_2O_3.

Warren's (1942) hypothesis involves the size of the sodium ion and would thus lead to different limiting compositions for lithium and potassium borates (16.2% Li, 13.4% Na_2O, 9.0% K_2O), whereas Abe's hypothesis in its simple form leads to a limiting composition independent of the univalent ion added. The experimental results do not confirm either hypothesis satisfactorily. The critical composition from thermal expansion data are 14% Li, 13% Na, 9% K, while infrared absorption and reflection curves can be interpreted as showing a maximum number of BO_4 groups at the composition $18 \pm 2\%$ for all three ions, lithium, sodium, and potassium (Jellyman and Proctor, 1955). It would appear that a sufficiently detailed theory is not yet available. Reference should, however, be made to recent papers on this subject by Huggins, e.g., Huggins and Abe (1957).

These examples of aluminum and boron are two in which the available coordination numbers appear reasonably well established. Information about the coordination of other ions in silicate glasses is more difficult to establish precisely. There is, for example, a lack of agreement about the coordination of Fe^{2+}, Fe^{3+} ions and the absorption of radiation associated with these ions. It is well established that ferrous iron produces blue-green glasses and ferric iron brown glasses, these being the colors produced in glasses containing iron when melted in reducing and oxidizing conditions respectively; moreover, ferric iron probably exists in two states of coordination. Moore and Prasad (1949, 1950) have shown by attempting to relate quantitatively the absorption curves to the condition of the iron in the glass that it is possible that when ferric iron is a network former, i.e., is in tetrahedral coordination, it causes no absorption in the visible spectrum. It is now possible to investigate such suggestions by ligand-field theory, an example of which will be given later; if this theory is applicable, precise information can be obtained.

Another aspect of the situation of network-modifier ions is the implied assumption of a random distribution of these ions in holes in the network;

evidence is accumulating which suggests that this assumption may not be justified. Forland (1955) has discussed the lowering of the liquidus temperature in binary silicates, has pointed out that the low entropy of fusion of silica shows that the liquid must have a highly ordered structure, and has also stressed that the positive deviations from ideality imply some groupings in the liquid which are departures from complete randomness.

Levin and Block (1957) have extended Warren's (1942) discussion of immiscibility in alkali silicates. They were able to predict the zones of immiscibility in binary silicates with some accuracy. The argument is a geometrical one based on Warren's discussion of the boric oxide anomaly and immiscibility on the calcium oxide-silica system. Warren proposed that each unshared oxygen should touch two divalent ions in order that the calcium ions might surround themselves with the maximum number of unshared oxygens. For example, two calcium atoms so bonded to the same unshared oxygen could not be more than 4.7 Å apart. Brosset (1958) reported x-ray diffraction evidence from which he draws the conclusion that barium ions introduced into a soda-lime-silica glass are to be found in pairs only 4 Å apart. This is clearly a subject which will repay further development.

The Viscosity of Glasses

Perhaps the most characteristic physical property of a glass is its viscosity and the variation of the viscosity with temperature. The composite viscosity-temperature curve from room temperature to the founding temperature is shown as AD in Fig. 14. This curve includes the results of several observers all of whom worked on commercial glasses of slightly different composition, as shown in Table 1. For the accuracy

Table 1

Author	Analysis of Glass Used (%)							Range of Viscosity Measured (poise)
	SiO_2	CaO	Na_2O	K_2O	MgO	R_2O_3	TiO_2	
Pearson (1952)	68.78	5.67	17.95	—	3.17	2.82	0.08	10^{21}–10^{19}
Jones (1944)	72.29	8.77	12.96	0.87	2.99	1.66	—	$10^{17.5}$–10^{12}
Lillie (1933)	69.72	9.05	20.96	Tr.	—	0.18	—	10^{14}–10^{2}

of the present discussion, however, it is safe to assume that this curve represents the general trend of viscosity with temperature.

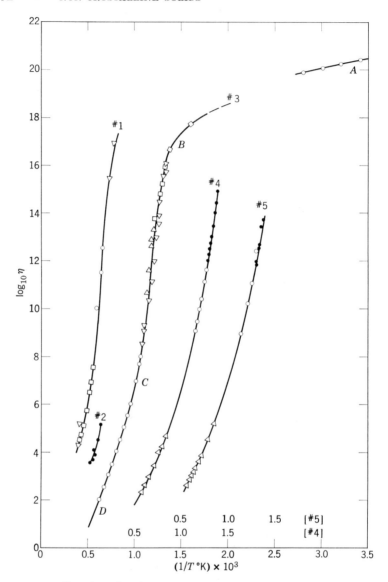

Fig. 14. Complete viscosity-temperature curves for some typical glasses.

The behavior below the transformation range is not well understood. Although Pearson (1952) and Jones (1944) appear to have measured Newtonian viscosities in the range 10^{20} to 10^{17} poise, as judged by the usual tests of proportionality of shear force to shear strain rate and constancy of rate of strain, it can be remarked that the *total* strain measured varied between about $\frac{1}{500}$ and $\frac{1}{10}$ of the instantaneous elastic strain; the possibility that the rate of strain might not be truly constant cannot be ruled out. The sources of information on which the other curves of Fig. 14 are based are given in Table 2.

Table 2

Glass	Author	Symbol	$\log \eta$ (range)	$E\eta$ (kcal)	Curve No.
19.84% Na_2O, 79% SiO_2	Taylor and Dear (1937)	●	11–15	153	4
20.13% Na_2O, 79.87% SiO_2	Poole (1949)	⊙	9–11.8	150	4
20% Na_2O, 80% SiO_2	Shartsis et al. (1952)	▽	2.2–4.7	43	4
24.4% K_2O, 74.8% SiO_2	Taylor and Doran (1941)	●	10–14	106	5
24.5% K_2O, 75.5 SiO_2	Poole (1949)	O	9–11.8	100	5
24.2% K_2O, 75.8% SiO_2	Bockris et al. (1955)	△	3.5–6.74	45	5
23.9% K_2O, 76.1% SiO_2	Shartsis et al. (1952)	▽	2.6–4.5	45	5
SiO_2	Douglas and Isard (1951)	▽	15–17	ca. 170	1
SiO_2	Volarovich and Leontieva (1936)	O	10–13	170	1
SiO_2	Solomin (1940)	□	4.5–7.5	170	1
SiO_2	Bockris et al. (1955)	△	4.2–5.0	170	1
GeO_2	Mackenzie (1958)	●	3.5–5.0	50–100	2

Above the transformation range the most important feature is that the logarithm of the viscosity does not vary linearly with the reciprocal of the absolute temperature. The complete viscosity curve in this range can be represented almost but not exactly (H. R. Lillie, private communication) to within experimental accuracy by the Fulcher equation,

$$\eta = A \exp \frac{B}{T - T_0}$$

but there appears to be no theoretical basis for this convenient empirical relation. In the transformation range the viscosity of a glass varies with time at the same speed as the volume relaxes with time; the viscosity is thus directly related to the configuration.

Very approximately, the log viscosity vs. $1/T$ curve can be divided into two straight lines, one of which applies from the transformation range, i.e., $\eta = 10^{13}$, down to $\eta = 10^4$; the observations at viscosities lower than this can be represented by another straight line. The slopes of these lines may be considered as giving the activation energies for flow, and these two activation energies will be referred to as the "high" and "low" temperature activation energies.

Attempts have been made to develop theories which suggest that the low temperature activation energy is the sum of a configuration term and a flow term (Douglas, 1949); at high temperatures the configuration term has become small compared with the flow term. However, results which have become available in the last few years show conclusively that the activation energy for the viscosity in the low temperature range is, at least within present experimental accuracy, equal to the activation energy for volume relaxation. These results are summarized in Table 3.

Table 3

Glass	$E\eta_v$	$E\eta$	Authors
Fused SiO_2	156 ± 25	170	Douglas and Isard (1951)
Soda-lime	140	160	Lillie (1933)
Soda-lime	150	150	Van Zee and Noritake (1958)
Glucose	132 ± 10	125 ± 10	Davies and Jones (1953)
		106	Parks et al. (1934)
Glycerol	25 ± 2	23	Davies and Jones (1953) [ex-
		28	trapolations of Tammann and Hesse (1926) using two methods of extrapolation]

If the viscosity is defined as $\eta = G\bar{\tau}$, where G is a rigidity modulus and $\bar{\tau}$ a mean relaxation time, the rate of change of viscosity with temperature will be determined by the rate of change of $\bar{\tau}$ with temperature. The relaxing processes governing the shear and volume strains must be of the same origin, and it is perhaps not surprising that both configuration change and shear viscosity show the same activation energy.

The main features of curve 3 in Fig. 14 are the small gradient at low temperatures, AB, the steep gradient at intermediate temperatures, BC, and the subsequent decrease in the gradient at very high temperatures, CD. In the past these changes of slope have been taken to indicate changes of the energy of activation of some unitary flow processes. It seems very likely that the decrease in slope at low temperatures is associated with the freezing-in of a configuration appropriate to some higher temperature—the fictive temperature—and also that the observations include contributions from delayed elasticity. When the relaxation function spreads over a very long time, it may be difficult to distinguish between delayed elasticity and an apparent viscous flow; see Chapter 11.

An explanation of the change of slope at high temperatures is still awaited. In the context of this chapter it is useful to look at a few results in which the effect of composition has been studied in both the high temperature and the low temperature regions. To illustrate the general theme of this chapter, the results of Moore and Dingwall (1953) will be quoted. In these experiments a soda-lime-silica glass of composition 74% SiO_2, 10% CaO, and 16% Na_2O was taken as the starting point and was modified by substitution on a molecular basis, or on a cation-for-cation basis, up to 8% of the silica in the glass by other oxides. These authors summarize their results by giving the effect of these substitutions on the viscosity at 1400°C and on the temperature at which the viscosity is 10^{12} poise. It is quite clear, as shown in Figs. 15 and 16, that the effect of the various oxides is quite different at high temperatures and at low temperatures. At high temperatures the effect is proportional to the effective field strength of an ion (a correction to the field strength of the non-noble gaseous ions calculated from the partial refractivities brings all the points on Fig. 15 on to one straight line). At low temperatures it will be seen that each straight line joins those ions for which the ratio of the radius of the ion to that of oxygen corresponds to one type of coordination as indicated in the figure. This may perhaps be taken to show that in the high viscosity range the viscosity is determined through the volume by a fairly close packing of the ions, whereas at high temperatures this structure becomes much more open by virtue of the enhanced thermal vibrations. This situation would appear to invite much further experimentation along these lines, coupled with the measurement of other physical properties; some additional evidence is now becoming available from the study of the devitrification of glasses.

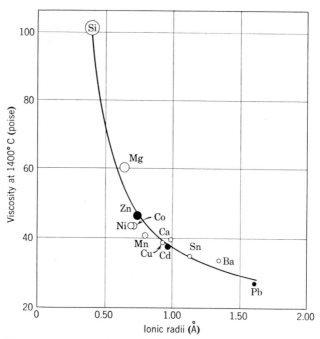

Fig. 15. Effect on viscosity of substitution of silica by other oxides in an Na_2O–CaO–SiO_2 glass.

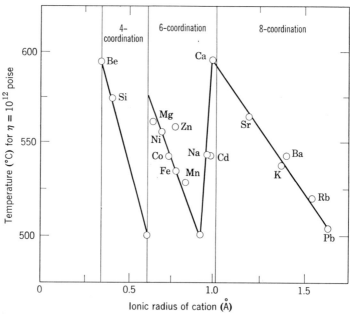

Fig. 16. Temperature at which viscosity is 10^{12} poise plotted as a function of cationic radius.

Effect of Minor Additives on the Liquidus Temperature of Soda-Lime-Silica Glasses

In the course of a study of the effect of substituting other divalent oxides for calcium oxide in Na_2O–CaO–SiO_2 glasses an interesting point has arisen which has a bearing on the problem of coordination numbers in silicate glasses. In Fig. 17 the results are summarized for the changes

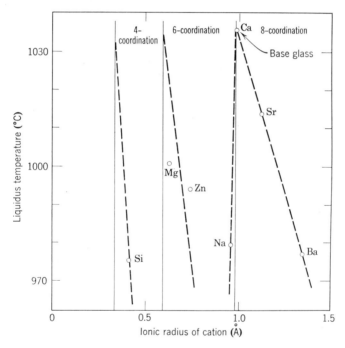

Fig. 17. Changes in liquidus temperature of a Na_2O–CaO–SiO_2 glass with various substitutions.

in liquidus temperature for various substitutions of MgO, ZnO, BaO, SrO, and CaO. It will be clear that CaO, SrO, BaO fall into one group and ZnO, MgO fall into another. The correlation of these results with the low temperature viscosity observations of Moore and Dingwall (1953) is striking. In Fig. 18 the oxygen densities, i.e., the number of oxygens per unit volume, in these glasses have been calculated from measurements of the density. It will be seen that the oxygen density is a smooth function of the ionic radius, although magnesium and zinc cause a contraction of the network, whereas strontium and barium cause it to

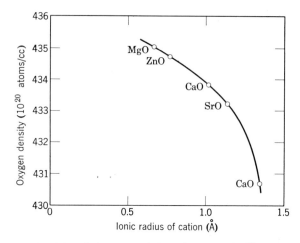

Fig. 18. Oxygen densities of glasses consisting of 70.86 mole % SiO_2, 17.39% Na_2O, 11.75% CaO plus 3.0% of oxide shown.

expand. The specific effect of each ion on the oxygen density shows quite clearly, as would be expected, that each ion dictates its own surroundings as the glass cools from the melt. This appears to be confirmed by the early results of some further studies on the effect of adding mixtures of these divalent oxides to the soda-lime-silica glass. In Fig. 19 it can be seen that the lowering of the liquidus caused by a mixture of ZnO and MgO is intermediate between the effect of the zinc and magnesia separately. Although this work is in an early stage, it seems from the calculations we have made that there can be very little, if any, contribution to the entropy by mixing magnesium and zinc on similar sites, thus confirming strongly that the ions in this region are dictating their own surroundings.

Consideration of Coloring Ions

The evidence of the coordination of various ions in glasses, apart perhaps from sodium and potassium ions which have been studied by x-ray diffraction, is inferential; that is to say, it has been deduced from the trend of physical 'properties with composition coupled with crystallographic ionic radii. It is interesting, therefore, that it is possible to obtain direct evidence of the coordination of ions with incomplete d shells from ligand-field theory (Orgel, 1955). In complexes of this type of ion the ligands are arranged with octahedral or distorted octahedral and, in

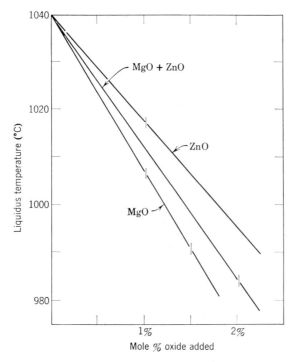

Fig. 19. Effect on liquidus of mixtures of ZnO and MgO. Base glass: 74.78 mole % SiO₂, 15.09% Na₂O, 10.13% CaO.

a few cases, tetrahedral symmetry. The electrostatic field of the ligands causes splitting of the free ion levels, and quantum numbers describing the new set of levels can be calculated from group theory (Bethe, 1929).

The free ion states are split by an octahedral ligand field as follows:

Free Ion State	Ligand-Field States
S	Γ_1
P	Γ_4
D	Γ_3, Γ_5
F	$\Gamma_2, \Gamma_4, \Gamma_5$
G	$\Gamma_1, \Gamma_3, \Gamma_4, \Gamma_5$

The energy of these levels can be expressed as a function of the strength of the octahedral field in terms of a parameter Δ and of B and C, the

Racah parameters of electrostatic intersection:

$$E = a\Delta + bB + cC$$

In the free ion the ratio C/B varies only between 4 and 5; it is assumed in the Orgel (1955) diagram that C/B is constant and equal to 4 in the present example. It then turns out that the relation between the energy E of the ligand-field levels and the strength of the field Δ can be expressed in terms of E/B and Δ/B; see Fig. 20. The levels in any particular complex will then correspond to one value of Δ/B.

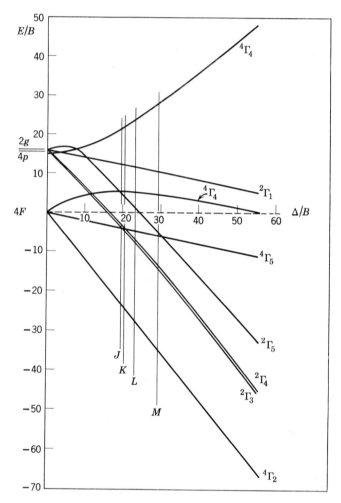

Fig. 20. Orgel diagram.

In Table 4 the spin-allowed transitions are

$$^4\Gamma_2 \to {}^4\Gamma_5$$
$$\to {}^4\Gamma_4 \quad (F)$$
$$\to {}^4\Gamma_4 \quad (P)$$

Table 4

	Ligands	Transition		Experimental	Theoretical
				Position of Peak	
L	$6H_2O$	$^4\Gamma_2 \to {}^4\Gamma_5$	Bands	17,400 cm^{-1}	17,400 cm^{-1}
		$\to {}^4\Gamma_4$		24,700	24,700
		$\to {}^4\Gamma_4$		37,000	38,700
		$\to {}^2\Gamma_3$	Lines	14,900	14,900
		$\to {}^2\Gamma_4$		15,100	15,300
		$\to {}^2\Gamma_5$		21,000	21,200
M	$6NH_3$	$^4\Gamma_2 \to {}^4\Gamma_5$	Bands	21,500	21,500
		$\to {}^4\Gamma_4$		28,500	29,400
		$\to {}^4\Gamma_4$		—	44,400
		$\to {}^2\Gamma_3$	Lines	15,200	15,000
		$\to {}^2\Gamma_4$		15,400	15,400
		$\to {}^2\Gamma_5$		—	29,800
K	Soda-lime-silica glass	$^4\Gamma_2 \to {}^4\Gamma_5$	Bands	15,300	15,300
		$\to {}^4\Gamma_4$		22,200	22,200
		$\to {}^4\Gamma_4$		—	34,800
		$\to {}^2\Gamma_3$	Lines	14,600	14,900
		$\to {}^2\Gamma_4$		15,750	15,300
		$\to {}^2\Gamma_5$		—	21,200

and these are in order of increasing energy. The observed energies for these bands are noted, and it will be found that there is only one vertical line which can be drawn on the diagram to give corresponding values of E/B in this ratio. Thus B may be determined; in fact, when the lig nds are oxygen atoms and the central ion is Cr^{3+}, B is constant.

In addition to the main absorption bands there may occur spin-forbidden transitions which arise because there is a small amount of mixing of the S quantum numbers. In the complex these transitions will lead to "line" absorption because they arise from transitions between levels which are represented by parallel lines on the Orgel diagram. It should be noted that the breadth of the bands arises from coupling between the thermal vibration of the atoms and the electronic transitions and does not indicate a spatial randomness of the arrangement of the ligands.

The data entered under L in Table 4 correspond to a crystalline hydrate, but it will be seen that curve L in Fig. 21, which is Cr^{3+} in aqueous solution, corresponds closely to the absorptions in the table. Addition of sulfuric acid shifts the bands to longer wavelengths; presumably the complexes in the dilute sulfuric acid contain mixed ligands, but it appears to be satisfactory to use a mean value of Δ. Attention is drawn to the small absorption peaks between 6000 and 7000 Å. As shown in the table, these correspond to the transitions $^4\Gamma_2 \rightarrow {}^2\Gamma_{3,4}$. It will be observed that the peaks shift little, compared with the absorption bands,

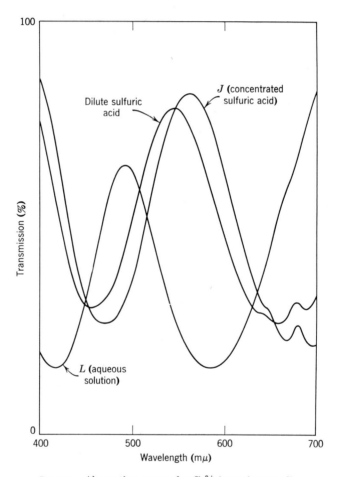

Fig. 21. Absorption curves for Cr^{3+} in various media.

as the complex changes. That this should be so can be inferred from the fact that $^4\Gamma_2$, $^2\Gamma_3$, $^2\Gamma_4$ lines are parallel on the Orgel diagram. In the curve for dilute aqueous solutions the line absorptions fall on the steep shoulder of the absorption curve and are not well resolved. Their presence is, however, clearly indicated. In the glass represented in Fig. 22 however, and in the dilute sulfuric acid solution which gives a very nearly identical absorption curve, the $^4\Gamma_2 \rightarrow {}^2\Gamma_3$, $^4\Gamma_2 \rightarrow {}^2\Gamma_4$ are more widely spaced than the diagram suggests (compare the observed lines 14,600, 15,750 with the theoretical 14,900, 15,300). However, the vertical line K, which is marked at the appropriate value of Δ/B for the glass, shows that it passes through the region where the lines $^2\Gamma_3$, $^2\Gamma_4$, and $^4\Gamma_5$

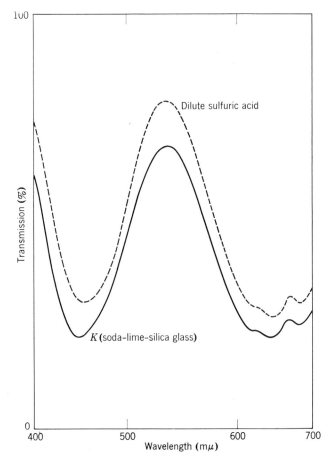

Fig. 22. Absorption curves for Cr^{3+} in a soda-lime-silica glass and in dilute sulfuric acid.

would intersect; when this happens, mixing will occur and instead of the lines crossing they will develop as shown in Fig. 23. This results in the observed increase in the spacing of the lines.

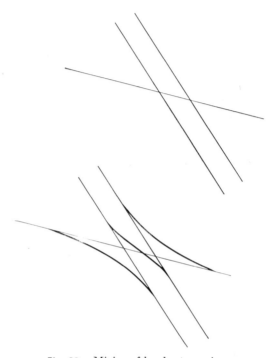

Fig. 23. Mixing of levels at crossing.

It is also possible to discuss in similar terms, in addition to the requirements of ionic radius, the relative stability of the octahedral and tetrahedral complexes of the same ion. It turns out that for Fe^{3+} the octahedral and tetrahedral complexes have nearly equal stability. The conclusion so far drawn from the absorption curves of Fe in various glasses, that Fe^{3+} can be either a network former (4-coordinated) or a modifier (6-coordinated), is thus confirmed by the ligand-field theory.

SUMMARY AND CONCLUSIONS

In this brief review a general systematic approach to an understanding of the physical properties of glass and the relation of these properties to the chemical composition of glasses has been attempted. The theme is as follows.

1. Glasses are formed when a liquid cools below the liquidus temperature without precipitating crystals.

2. The formation of a glass is a kinetic process, a sufficient condition being that the viscosity must be high at the liquidus temperature.

3. Silicate glasses form one particular family of glass-forming substances. It is not necessary for a glass-forming substance to have a structure at all related to the silicate structures.

4. The network-former-modifier hypothesis can be regarded as a convenient first approximation to be used in relating the physical properties of silicate-type glasses to their chemical compositions. This approximation is sufficiently good to throw considerable light on the behavior of certain atoms such as aluminum and boron in glasses.

5. As a second approximation the nature of the chemical binding of a given atom in a glass must be considered. In some cases this may be conveniently described in terms of coordination number and ionic field strength.

6. The qualitative application of such ideas has been illustrated with reference to the electrical conductivity and the viscosity of glass and the alteration of the liquidus temperature of a ternary glass by additives of a fourth component.

7. Finally, the colors of chromium in glass have been discussed as an example of a case where direct evidence of the type and energy of binding can be derived directly by the application of quantum mechanics to the observation of the absorption of light due to the chromium in the glass.

ACKNOWLEDGMENTS

It is a pleasure to thank my colleagues and students for their help and their ready cooperation in preparing this paper which contains so many references to their unpublished work. J. O. Isard is concerned with electrical properties, R. V. Adams and A. J. Worrall with glass formation, C. R. Kurkjian with viscosity, S. P. Jones with devitrification, and T. E. Bates with the absorption due to ions with incomplete d shells.

REFERENCES

Abe, T., *J. Am. Ceram. Soc.* **35**, 284 (1952).
Bethe, H., *Ann. Physik* (5) **3**, 133 (1929).
Bockris, J. O'M., et al., *Trans. Faraday Soc.* **51**, 1734 (1955).
Borelius, G., and Paulson, K. A., *Arkiv Mat. Astron. Fysik utgivet av Kgl. Svenska Vetenskapsakad.* **33A**, No. 7 (1946).

Brady, G. W., *J. Chem. Phys.* **28**, 48 (1958).

Brady, G. W., *J. Chem. Phys.* **27**, 300 (1957).

Brosset, C., *J. Soc. Glass Technol.* **42**, 125 (1958).

Davies, R. O., and Jones, G. O., *Proc. Roy. Soc. (London)* **A217**, 26 (1953).

Dietzel, A., and Peogel, H. J., *Atti III congr. intern. vetro, Venezia*, 1953, p. 219.

Douglas, R. W., *J. Soc. Glass Technol.* **33**, 138 (1949).

Douglas, R. W., and Isard, J. O., *J. Soc. Glass Technol.* **35**, 206 (1951).

Florinskaya, W. A., and Pechenkina, R. S., *Trans. Conf. on Structure of Glass*, Leningrad, 1953, p. 70.

Forland, T., Office of Naval Research (U. S.) Tech. Rept. No. 63 (1955).

Huggins, M. L., and Abe, T., *J. Am. Ceram. Soc.* **40**, 287 (1957).

Jellyman, P. E., and Proctor, J. B., *J. Soc. Glass Technol.* **39**, 173 (1955).

Jones, G. O., *J. Soc. Glass Technol.* **28**, 432 (1944).

Kracek, F. C., *J. Am. Chem. Soc.* **52**, 1436 (1930).

Levin, E. M., and Block, S., *J. Am. Ceram. Soc.* **40**, No. 3, 95 (1957).

Lillie, H. R., *J. Am. Ceram. Soc.* **16**, 619 (1933).

Mackenzie, J. D., G. E. Research Lab. Rept. 58-RL-1994, 1958.

Maurer, R. D., *J. Chem. Phys.* **25**, No. 6, 1206 (1956).

Moore, H., and Carey, M., *J. Soc. Glass Technol.* **35**, 43 (1951).

Moore, H., and Dingwall, A. G. F., *J. Soc. Glass Technol.* **37**, 316 (1953).

Moore, H., and McMillan, P. W., *J. Soc. Glass Technol.* **40**, 66 (1956).

Moore, H., and Prasad, S. N., *J. Soc. Glass Technol.* **33**, 336 (1949).

Moore, H., and Prasad, S. N., *J. Soc. Glass Technol.* **34**, 173 (1950).

Morey, G. W., *Properties of Glass*, Reinhold, New York, 1954, p. 39.

Orgel, L. E., *J. Chem. Phys.* **23**, 1004 (1955).

Parks, G. S., Barton, L. E., Spaght, M. E., and Richardson, J. W., *Physics* **5**, 193 (1934).

Pearson, S., *J. Soc. Glass Technol.* **36**, 105 (1952).

Poole, J. P., *J. Am. Ceram. Soc.* **32**, 220 (1949).

Rawson, H., *Trav. IV congr. Intern. du verre*, 1956, p. 62.

Rey, M., *Disc. Faraday Soc.* No. 4, 257 (1948).

Safford, H. W., and Silverman, A., *J. Am. Ceram. Soc.* **30**, 203 (1947).

Schairer, J. F., and Bowen, N. L., *Am. J. Sci.* **254**, 129 (1956).

Shartsis, L., Spinner, S., and Capps, W., *J. Am. Ceram. Soc.* **35**, 155 (1952).

Solomin, N. V., *J. Phys. Chem. (U.S.S.R.)* **14**, 235 (1940).

Stanworth, J. E., *Physical Properties of Glass*, Clarendon Press, Oxford, 1950.

Sun, K. H., *J. Am. Ceram. Soc.* **30**, 277 (1947).

Tammann, G., *J. Soc. Glass Technol.* **9**, 166 (1925).

Tammann, G., and Hesse, W., *Z. anorg. allgem. Chem.* **156**, 245 (1926).

Tanabe, Y., and Sugano, S., *J. Phys. Soc. Japan* **9**, 753, 766 (1954).

Taylor, N. W., and Dear, P. S., *J. Am. Ceram. Soc.* **20**, 296 (1937).

Taylor, N. W., and Doran, R. M., *J. Am. Ceram. Soc.* **24**, 103 (1941).

Van Zee, A. F., and Noritake, H. M., *J. Am. Chem. Soc.* **41**, 164 (1958).

Volarovich, M. P., and A. A. Leontieva, *J. Soc. Glass Technol.* **20**, 139 (1936).

Warren, B. E., *J. Appl. Phys.* **13**, 602 (1942).

Warren, B. E., *J. Appl. Phys.* **8**, 645 (1937).

Weyl, W. A., *Central Glass & Ceram. Research Inst. Bull. (India)* **4**, 121 (1957).

Zachariasen, W. H., *J. Am. Ceram. Soc.* **54**, 3841 (1932).

DISCUSSION

Editor's Note. In response to queries, Dr. Douglas discussed the structural problems in glasses containing boric oxide. Reference was made to the change in the coordination of the boron from triangular to tetrahedral with change in the alkali oxide content of the sample.* The sudden changes in the infrared reflection curves * and in the densities when alkali oxide content exceeds 16 mole % are connected to these boron coordination changes. Careful experiments with the different alkalis should be run to learn where the point of rapid changeover lies in each case. Such data could suggest which of several conflicting views concerning the arrangement of boron oxide structural elements is preferable.*

M. L. HUGGINS

In further discussion of the so-called "B_2O_3 anomaly," I should like to point out [cf. Huggins and Abe, *J. Am. Ceram. Soc.* **40**, 287 (1957)] that a plot of the expansion coefficient against N_{Na}, the number of sodium atoms per oxygen atom, shows two *straight* lines, meeting at a composition of $N_{Na} \approx 0.11$, and that from this one can conclude that at this break there is a sudden change in the composition of the glass, expressed in terms of the types of "structons" present. Moreover, it can be shown that this change, as N_{Na} increases, consists of the disappearance of O(2B) structons and the appearance of O(B, yNa) structons.

I suggest that, in studying the variations of properties resulting from the substitution of small amounts of other components for a corresponding amount of a given component in a "base glass," it should help to use a base glass of known structon composition, such as a simple sodium silicate or sodium borate glass.

O. L. ANDERSON

Since we are having such a broad discussion of the structure of glass, I think it appropriate to emphasize some experiments of Forland, to which reference is made in the chapter. From the change in liquidus temperature with glass composition, he has computed the free energy of solution of certain ions and is able to decide whether the ions enter the liquid phase as singlets, doublets, or triplets. I believe he found that aluminum ions enter soda-silica glasses as doublets. This seems a very powerful method for getting at details of glass structure.

H. COLE

You have suggested that the reason for glass formation is the high viscosity at the liquidus. But, of course, the high viscosity must be due to structure. I am not carping, but only suggesting that it does not advance matters very much

* See, e.g., Stanworth, *Physical Properties of Glass*, Clarendon Press, Oxford, 1950.

to attribute glass formation to high viscosity or even to attribute the high viscosity to structure.

R. W. DOUGLAS

However, I have listed the various structural ways by which you can get high viscosity.

H. COLE

Another point of perhaps more fundamental importance, particularly when we are talking about structure and the position of ions or atoms, is this term "coordination number." I have tried to find for a long time another term which would emphasize the fact that the term "coordination number" as used by crystallographers normally means the number of nearest neighbors, and in general has no significance with regard to the type and magnitude of the chemical bonding. The chemist's "coordination number," on the other hand, does refer to the number of coordinate or covalent links. Usually any information we have, taken at its first approximation, refers only to the number of nearest neighbors. We have to deduce later whether those nearest neighbors are bonded or not.

In forming a coordination complex, as you have remarked, there are two factors which come into play. One is the influence of the surrounding medium, as it were, and the other is the influence of the ion itself.

And you have shown that in many cases the ion dictates what coordination number it is going to have.

It is possible, however, that in certain cases, where the proportion of introduced ions is very small, the surrounding structure dictates the number of oxygens around the ion. Thus, if you have a silica network or any other network which is fairly rigid and then introduce a very small amount of sodium, that sodium can have very little influence on the network. It will inevitably be surrounded by a predetermined number of oxygens, perhaps eight or six. With more sodium entering the system, the sodium begins to dictate the structure.

Taking another aspect, if cobalt is introduced into a series of $Na_2O-B_2O_3$ glasses, with a very high B_2O_3 content, the number of oxygens surrounding that cobalt is dictated by the network and will probably turn out to be six oxygens. With more soda present, the network is broken up, and the cobalt can then dictate its surroundings, giving probably a true CoO_4 coordination.

What I wish to emphasize is that the 6-coordination in the first case is not a chemical coordination. Rather we have here an ordinary cobalt ion which happens to be within the range of about six oxygens.

R. W. DOUGLAS

A helpful interjection from Professor Prins reminded me to say that by *coordination* I have meant just the number of oxygen atoms surrounding the cobalt atom. The only place where I discuss the type of bonds is in dealing with ions with incomplete d shells. And here the discussion is only implicit and only because I used the ligand-field theory. I believe we shall be able to give precise experimental answers to Dr. Cole's comments on cobalt coordination in various sodium borate glasses. He may turn out to be right, but I hope that within twelve months we shall be able to say whether he is right or wrong.

With regard to the behavior of sodium ions in silica glass of very low soda content, again he may be right, but I believe the data on systems of this composition are not sufficiently good to permit precise discussion.

A. E. R. WESTMAN

In his general discussion of the glassy state, Dr. Douglas referred to "long chain glasses in which the high viscosity may be taken roughly to arise from the entanglement of the long chain molecules" and to recent x-ray studies of a glass of the sodium metaphosphate composition by Brady [*J. Chem. Phys.* **28**, 48 (1958)]. An expansion of these references may be of interest.

Recent studies of amorphous phosphates have formed part of a very rapid expansion in our knowledge of the chemistry of phosphates brought about largely by the application of polymer techniques and theory to compounds of high molecular weight [Van Wazer, *J. Am. Chem. Soc.* **72**, No. 2, 644 (1950); Strauss, Smith, and Wineman, *ibid.* **75**, No. 16, 3935 (1953)] and of filter paper chromatography and analogous techniques to compounds of lower molecular weight [Westman and Gartaganis, *J. Am. Ceram. Soc.* **40**, No. 9, 293 (1957); Ebel, *Bull. soc. chim. France* **20**, 991 (1953); Grunze and Thilo, *Die Papierchromatographie der kondensierten Phosphate*, 2 Aufl., Akademische-Verlag, Berlin, 1955]. The results may be summed up best by reference to the $Na_2O–P_2O_5–H_2O$ composition diagram shown in Fig. 1.

In Fig. 1 the compositions of most of the crystalline phases studied are shown by circles. Paper chromatographic and other methods of examination agree in

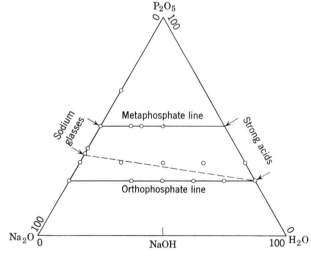

Fig. 1.

showing them to consist of molecule ions having skeletons formed of PO_4 tetrahedra which can arrange themselves in chains or rings by sharing oxygens. In some cases the chains may be branched or cross-linked. Finite chains can be assigned the general formula $M_{n+2}P_nO_{3n+1}$, which for $P = 1$ describes an orthophosphate. Rings or infinite chains have the formula $(MPO_3)_n$, which describes a metaphosphate.

Amorphous phases can be made readily from compositions lying between the metaphosphate line and the broken line in Fig. 1 by heating to form a homogeneous melt and then quenching. They vary from brittle solids at the left side of this area to thin liquids at the lower right. At least some compositions above the metaphosphate line can be quenched to amorphous phases and are now under investigation.

When dissolved and chromatographed, these amorphous phases are found to yield the same kinds of molecule ions as do the crystalline phases. They usually consist of a large number of such ions which have apparently reached a dynamic equilibrium in the melt. Linear chains up to about $n = 10$ have been separated by paper chromatography and rings up to about $n = 6$ [Van Wazer and Karl-Kroupa, *J. Am. Chem. Soc.* **78**, No. 8, 1772 (1956)].

By analyzing a series of glasses with compositions lying along lines joining the P_2O_5 corner of the diagram with the base, distribution diagrams such as that shown in Fig. 2 can be prepared. In addition, potassium and lithium glasses have been investigated (Westman, *loc. cit.*).

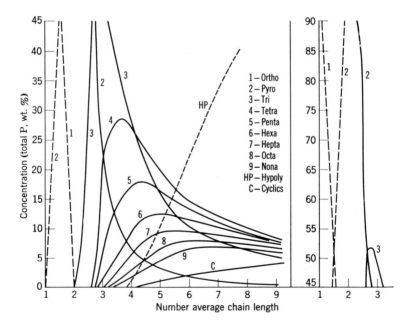

Fig. 2.

The general conclusions regarding amorphous phases may be summed up as follows.

1. Orthophosphate molecule ions have been found as yet only in phases containing hydrogen.

2. Apart from this, a change in the cation used causes a detectable but not striking change in the distribution diagram.

3. As the M/P atomic ratio is reduced, short chain molecule ions are replaced progressively and smoothly by long chains and finally partially by rings. Consequently, abrupt changes in physical properties with composition would not be expected.

It would be interesting to relate these findings on phosphate glasses to Dr. Douglas' discussion of the silicate glasses. One way to do this would be to consider P^{5+} as equivalent to Na^+Si^{4+} as far as chain or network formation is concerned. This would place the phosphate glasses studied entirely to the left of the lower limit of silicate glass formation in Dr. Douglas' Fig. 5.

Scientific interest in amorphous phosphates stems partly from the fact that they provide a field of investigation in which ceramics, polymer chemistry, and inorganic chemistry meet. Most needed at present are investigations of the physical properties of these phases.

17

by

J. M. Stevels

Philips Research Laboratories, Eindhoven, Netherlands

Network Defects
in Non-crystalline Solids

INTRODUCTION

In the last few years considerable progress has been made in the knowledge of lattice and network defects in crystalline and non-crystalline solids by using such tools as optical absorption spectra, dielectric loss measurements, and paramagnetic resonance measurements. In this chapter a few results of these methods will be discussed. By studying the network defects present in glasses in general and quartz glass and fused silica in particular before and after irradiation by x-rays or fast neutrons, it is possible to draw up "operational equations" which describe the processes induced by these irradiations. Remarkable differences between quartz crystal and quartz glass will be pointed out.

Since about 1940 the interaction of electromagnetic waves and glass has been investigated in the Philips Research Laboratories, special attention being paid to the dielectric losses and the dielectric constant, at room temperatures and higher and at frequencies ranging from 1 to 10^{10} cps.

In recent years the field of investigation has been extended to cover extremely low temperatures, high frequencies, and crystalline solids. As a result, our knowledge of lattice and network defects has increased considerably and your attention is drawn to some of the aspects of this subject.

Glass will be discussed first, and after that the differences in behavior of quartz glass and of quartz crystal will be treated.

The electromagnetic waves, referred to in the title of this chapter, must, for the sake of convenience, be split up into "long" waves—which, in contrast to the concepts used in telecommunication, have frequencies between 1 and 10^{10} cps—and "short" waves, with frequencies between 10^{14} and 10^{18} cps, and hence pertaining to infrared, visible, ultraviolet, x-ray, and γ-radiation. On the other hand, we shall find that results obtained with one of these categories are often valuable for the interpretation of phenomena encountered with the other category.

The Structure of Glass

The vitreous state of a substance is characterized by the absence of both symmetry and periodicity from its structure. Quartz *crystal* (and the other crystalline forms of SiO_2) is built up of SiO_4 tetrahedra arranged in a *regular* lattice, whereas quartz *glass* is built up as an *irregular* network of tetrahedra. Figure 1 gives a two-dimensional representation of both arrangements. In either case every oxygen ion is bound to two silicon ions, hence the name "bridging oxygen ion." The glasses used for technical purposes all have a more complicated structure. Nevertheless the silicate glasses—to which we shall confine ourselves—obtainable by fusing SiO_2 with metal oxides, such as Na_2O, K_2O, PbO, CaO, BaO,† have an Si-O network showing great resemblance to that mentioned above: SiO_4 tetrahedra with large interstices. The excess oxygen ions are taken up by the network in such a way that each time a bridging oxygen ion is replaced by two non-bridging oxygen ions (bound to one silicon ion only). The metal ions find a place in the interstices nearby, so that the electroneutrality is maintained. These interstitial cations are called network modifiers, in contrast to the silicon ions which nearly always act as network formers. Figure 2 gives a schematic two-dimensional representation of the structure of such a glass, a concept which is associated with the names of Zachariasen and Warren.

This simple concept is at present no longer fully accepted. What is doubted most is whether it is possible for the network of any glass to be fully irregular. The representation by a three-dimensional network, however, still is a good approximation of the actual conditions.

It follows from the network theory that quartz glass, and silicate glasses in general, may be considered to contain a practically infinite number of lattice imperfections when the structure of an ideal quartz crystal is taken as a standard. The real quartz crystal may, however,

† As a rule the added substance is a carbonate or a nitrate which gives the oxide upon decomposition.

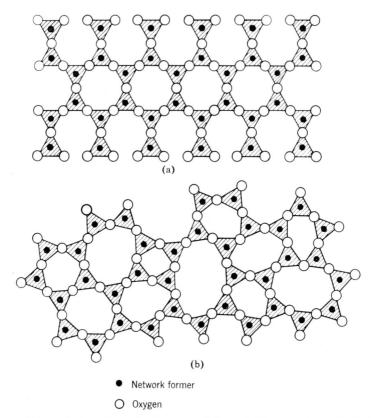

(a)

(b)

● Network former

○ Oxygen

Fig. 1. Schematic two-dimensional representation of (a) a quartz crystal lattice and (b) a quartz glass network.

Table 1

CRITERIA FOR THE SIX GROUPS OF NETWORK DEFECTS WHICH MAY OCCUR IN Si-O NETWORKS

Symbol	Oxygen Vacancy	Non-bridging Oxygen Ion Present	Network Modifier (Interstitial Ion) Present
A			
B	*		
D		*	*
P			*
Q		*	
T	*		*

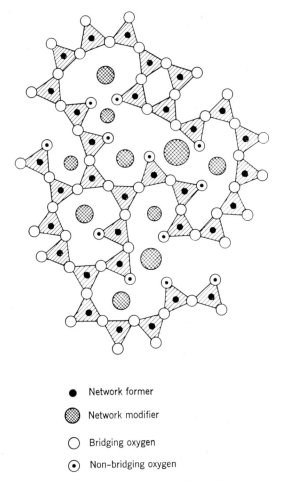

● Network former

⊠ Network modifier

○ Bridging oxygen

⊙ Non-bridging oxygen

Fig. 2. Schematic two-dimensional representation of the structure of glass.

already show all kinds of network defects (in this case lattice defects): oxygen ions may be missing; silicon ions may have been replaced by aluminum or other network-forming ions; interstitial alkali ions may be present.

It has been found convenient to arrange network and lattice defects in six groups denoted by the symbols A, B, D, P, Q, and T, each group being defined by a number of criteria which are listed in Table 1. Detailed information on the imperfections is rendered through a number of indices, so that all possible types of centers can be designated (Stevels and Kats, 1956). Figures 3 to 8 show schematic examples of these groups of centers.

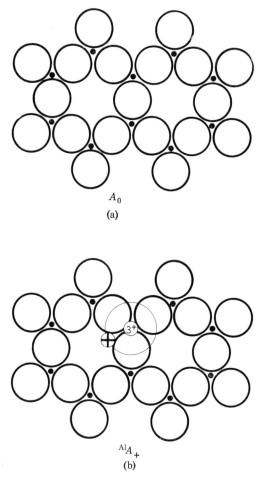

A_0

(a)

$^{Al}A_+$

(b)

Fig. 3. Schematic representation of (a) a virgin Si–O network, A_0, and (b) an $^{Al}A_+$ center.

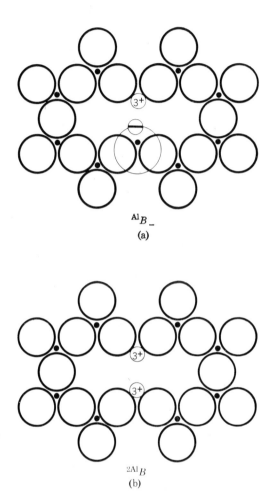

$^{Al}B_-$

(a)

^{2Al}B

(b)

Fig. 4. Schematic representation of (a) an $^{Al}B_-$ center and (b) an ^{2Al}B center.

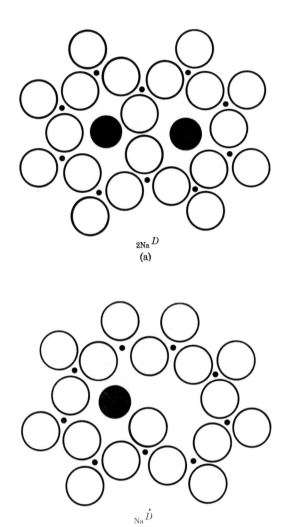

$_{2\mathrm{Na}}D$

(a)

$_{\mathrm{Na}}\overset{\cdot}{D}$

(b)

Fig. 5. Schematic representation of (a) a $_{2\mathrm{Na}}D$ center and (b) an $_{\mathrm{Na}}\overset{\cdot}{D}$ center.

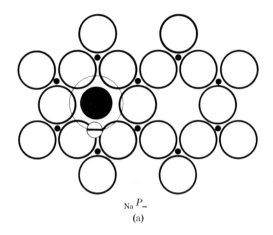

$_{\mathrm{Na}}P_-$

(a)

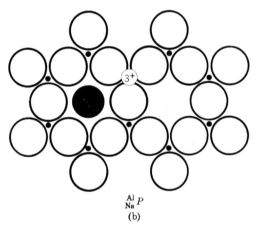

$_{\mathrm{Na}}^{\mathrm{Al}}P$

(b)

Fig. 6. Schematic representation of (a) an $_{\mathrm{Na}}P_-$ center and (b) an $_{\mathrm{Na}}^{\mathrm{Al}}P$ center.

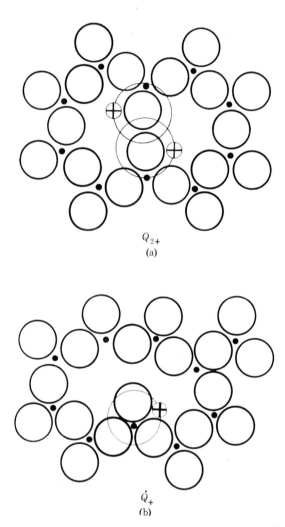

Q_{2+}

(a)

$\dot{Q}_{+}$

(b)

Fig. 7. Schematic representation of (a) a Q_{2+} center and (b) a $\dot{Q}_{+}$ center.

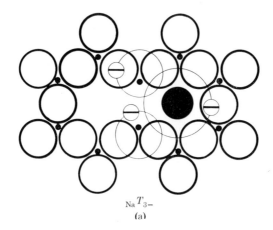

$_{Na}T_{3-}$
(a)

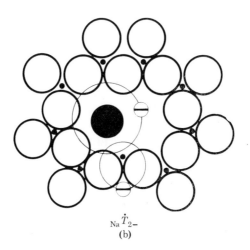

$_{Na}\dot{T}_{2-}$
(b)

Fig. 8. Schematic representation of (a) an $_{Na}T_{3-}$ center and (b) an $_{Na}\dot{T}_{2}$ center.

Silicate glasses are usually characterized by a network with a large number of non-bridging oxygen ions the excess charge of which is neutralized by cations. These glasses may therefore be said to contain D centers. A distinction must, however, be made between glasses with a relatively low network-modifier concentration (in which the non-bridging oxygen ions may be assumed to occur *associated* in pairs) and those in which, owing to the high concentration of network modifiers, the network has been broken up and "blown" up so that *individual* non-bridging oxygen ions occur.† The resulting centers are denoted D and D centers, respectively (see Fig. 5, a and b).

Quartz glass and crystals nearly always contain impurities such as Al, H, Li, and Na ions. The concentration of Al ions is always the highest one, so that $_{Na}^{Al}P$ and $_{Li}^{Al}P$ centers may be expected (Fig. 6a); the excess Al may, for instance, be present in the form of $_{H}^{Al}P$ or ^{2Al}B (Fig. 4b) centers.

Interaction between Long Wave Electromagnetic Radiations and Glass

The phenomenologist may characterize this interaction by means of the dielectric constant, ε', and the dielectric loss angle, δ. The knowledge of ε' as a function of temperature, frequency, and composition of the glass does not in first approximation provide much interesting information. Tan δ plotted as a function of temperature and frequency is shown as a surface in a tan δ, f, T model; see Fig. 9.

Four kinds of dielectric losses can occur in glasses (Stevels, 1957); their character will now be discussed briefly. This discussion may be facilitated by examining a number of cross sections of the model in Fig. 9.

Figure 10 shows tan δ of a borate glass as a function of temperature, measured at two different frequencies. The rising part to the right represents the *migration* losses, caused by network-modifying ions moving from interstice to interstice under the influence of the alternating electric field. The maximum to the left is caused by *deformation* losses aris-

---

† A nomenclature characterizing the network imperfections can be constructed from the symbols given in Table 1 by setting, at the four corners of the appropriate symbol, information concerning the nature of the imperfections:

Substitution for Si   Substitution for O

Nature of network   Number of trapped
modifier   electrons or holes

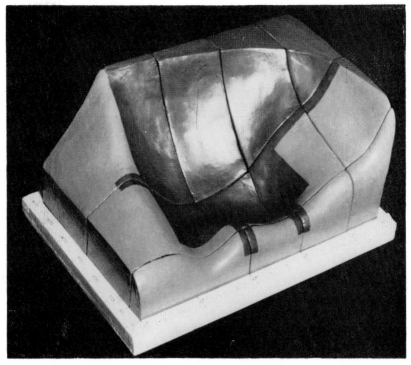

Fig. 9. Three-dimensional model of the relation between tan δ, frequency f of the alternating field, and temperature T in the case of glasses.

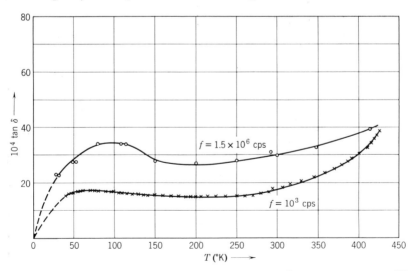

Fig. 10. Dielectric losses of a borate glass as a function of temperature at two different frequencies.

ing from movements of parts of the network, actually from small atom movements as we shall see later.

Figure 11 represents two cross sections through the tan δ, f, T model of Fig. 9 for two different temperatures and as functions of the frequency. Curves 1 and 2 represent migration losses caused by conduction (1) and short range ion migration (2), respectively. Except at very low fre-

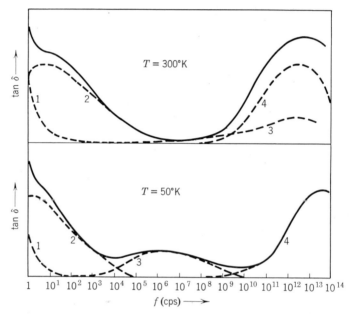

Fig. 11. Over-all picture of the dielectric losses of glass as a function of frequency at 50° and 300°K.

quencies of the order of 10^{-1} to 10^{-2} cps the conduction losses are obliterated by the migration losses. Curve 3 gives the deformation losses.

Losses of the fourth kind must be mentioned for the sake of completeness, but they are not relevant to the subject under discussion. These losses are caused by the damped oscillations of the network-modifying ions in their respective interstices. These *vibration losses* are a typical resonance phenomenon and, owing in part to their nature, they tend to occur at higher frequencies as the temperature decreases.

It should be noticed that the maxima of Figs. 9, 10, and 11 do not coincide. Figure 10 shows the results for a special glass; Figs. 9 and 11 are rough illustrations of the behavior of glass in general.

The migration and deformation losses have a typical relaxation character (Volger, Stevels, and van Amerongen, 1955; Volger, 1957), or, in other words, they may be represented by the classical formulas for the relaxation of dipoles embedded in a matrix with dielectric constant ε_∞, their concentration being N and their moment p. By approximation,

$$\varepsilon = \varepsilon_\infty + \frac{\varepsilon_s - \varepsilon_\infty}{1 + \omega^2 \tau^2} \tag{1}$$

$$\tan \delta = \frac{\varepsilon_s - \varepsilon_\infty}{\delta_\infty} \frac{\omega \tau}{1 + \omega^2 \tau^2} \tag{2}$$

provided $\varepsilon_s - \varepsilon_\infty \ll \varepsilon_\infty$, and where

ε_s = the dielectric constant of the matrix
ε_∞ = the static value of the dielectric constant
$\omega = 2\pi f$ = the circular frequency of the alternating field
τ = the relaxation time.

The relaxation time is given as a function of temperature by

$$\tau = \tau_0 \exp (Q/kT) \tag{3}$$

where Q is the activation energy. In addition, the following equation is applicable when N is small:

$$\varepsilon_s - \varepsilon_\infty = \Delta\varepsilon = \frac{4(\varepsilon_\infty + 2)^2 \pi N p^2}{27kT} \tag{4}$$

Experiments with a large amount of material have provided some information on the order of magnitude of τ_0, Q, N, and p. For both categories of dielectric losses τ_0 is of the order of 10^{-13} sec.

The activation energy Q, found in the case of the *migration losses*, is of the order of 0.5–1.0 ev, an acceptable value which can also be found from the relation between temperature and conductivity and between temperature and the diffusion constant for self-diffusion. Q is simply the height of the potential peak which an interstitial ion must overcome in order to move from one interstice to the other.

The activation energy found in the case of the *deformation* losses is much smaller and is of the order of 0.1 ev. It is evident that no transport of ions can take place in this instance. These are more likely to be slight local deformations or a regrouping of ions of and in the network.

It may be noted that the mechanical analog of the deformation losses has been found for silicate glasses (Marx and Sivertsen, 1953) and for quartz glass (Anderson and Bömmel, 1955).

Interaction between Long Wave Electromagnetic Radiations and Quartz Crystal

Whereas the various types of glass, including quartz glass, exhibit a wide variety of losses because there are many types of centers, this is not the case with quartz crystal. Figure 12 shows tan δ (plotted against

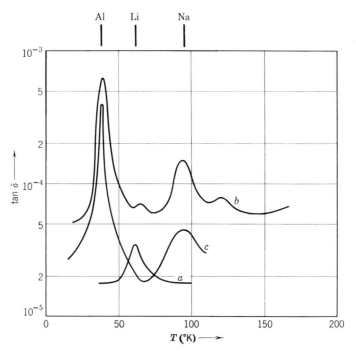

Fig. 12. Dielectric losses as a function of T for a number of monocrystals of clear quartz; measuring frequency 32 kc/sec. Curve a, sample of natural Brazilian quartz; b, sample of synthetic quartz (Bell Telephone Laboratories); c, sample of synthetic quartz (G. E. C. Laboratories, Wembley).

temperature) of three quartz crystals from various sources. A number of distinct maxima can be seen which are tied to lattice imperfections caused by the elements listed in Fig. 12. This becomes clear when a large number of crystals is analyzed, the relation between the degree of contamination caused by certain elements and the height of the maxima then being found.

The maximum at 38°K † is present only in the case of synthetic quartz

† Unless stated otherwise, the frequency for the loss measurements is 32 kc/sec.

crystals; in addition, only this kind of crystal shows an absorption peak at 2.79 μ in the infrared region. For a large number of crystals the height of the maximum varies in the same way as the Al concentration (which is known as a result of chemical analyses and which usually is of the order of 10^{18} cm^{-3}). These facts suggest that these phenomena may be due to $_\mathrm{H}^\mathrm{Al}P$ centers. The fact, proved by means of paramagnetic resonance measurements (O'Brien, 1955), that x-rays or fast neutrons give rise to a lattice in which an electron hole trapped on an oxygen ion near an Al ion also supports this theory: the H ion has moved, leaving an $^\mathrm{Al}A_+$ center behind. The height of the peak at 38°K and also the absorption peak in the infrared region at 2.79 μ decrease considerably, but they will never become zero (see Fig. 15). The original condition can usually be restored by heating. †

An analysis of the peak at 38°K gives $\tau = 10^{-13}$ sec and $Q = 0.055$ ev. The mechanical analog is also known as a result of measurements on the internal damping in a quartz crystal; see Fig. 13 (King, 1959). The measuring frequency was 5 Mc/sec, and the peak was found at 50°K. The analysis also gives: $\tau = 10^{-13}$ and $Q = 0.056$ ev.

The peaks at 60°K ‡ and 96°K ‡ (see Fig. 12) are attributed to $_\mathrm{Li}^\mathrm{Al}P$ and $_\mathrm{Na}^\mathrm{Al}P$ centers, respectively. There is a strong correlation between the peak at 96°K and the sodium content of the crystal. It should be noted that natural crystals contain a larger content of lithium impurities (maximum at 60°K) than the synthetic ones, which in their turn contain more sodium. This is not surprising when the methods of manufacturing these crystals are taken into account. Table 2 lists the results of the analysis of a number of quartz crystals. It can be seen that the number

Table 2

Nature of Defect	Temp. (°K) at which Peak Arises at $f = 32$ kc/sec	Q(ev)	τ_0 (sec)	Np^2 (C^2 cm^{-1}) Calculated with Eq. (4)	Estimated Value of N (cm^{-3}) for $p = 1$ D	N Calculated from Chemical Analyses (cm^{-3})
$_\mathrm{H}^\mathrm{Al}P$	38.5	0.055	2×10^{-13}	1.6×10^{-37}	1.5×10^{18}	3.10^{18}
$_\mathrm{Li}^\mathrm{Al}P$	60	0.089	2×10^{-13}	6.3×10^{-39}	5.7×10^{16}	3 to 10×10^{16}
$_\mathrm{Na}^\mathrm{Al}P$	96	0.143	2×10^{-13}	5.4×10^{-38}	4.8×10^{17}	3×10^{17}

† It should be mentioned that there is no relation between the height of the absorption peak at 2.79 μ and the loss peak at 38°K if one compares crystals grown under different conditions such as pressure or temperature.

‡ Unless stated otherwise, the frequency for the loss measurements is 32 kc/sec.

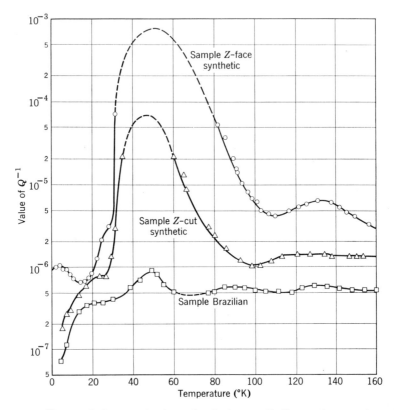

Fig. 13. Characteristic acoustic absorption in two synthetic quartz resonators vibrating in thickness shear at 5 mc. Orientation of seed crystals used in the hydrothermal synthesis of samples were: upper curve, parallel with a z-minor rhombohedron; center curve, parallel with the basal plane. Absorption in a natural Brazilian quartz specimen is included for comparison purposes. (King, 1959.)

of lattice defects, N, derived from the dielectric losses shows a remarkable conformity with the results of chemical analyses, if the dipole moment is taken to be 1 Debye unit ($= 10^{-18}$ esu $= 3.33 \times 10^{-28}$ C cm).

Extensive experiments have been carried out in the Philips Research Laboratories to determine the effect of ultraviolet and x-ray radiations on glass and quartz crystal (see the next two sections). Usually coloration occurs. When the dielectric losses of the colored substance are measured, it is found that neither the deformation losses nor the migration losses of glasses, including quartz glass, have changed. However, the tan δ versus T curve of quartz crystal changes considerably, as is indicated by Figs. 14 and 15 for a natural and a synthetic crystal, respectively. There is a strong dependency of the position of the maximum on

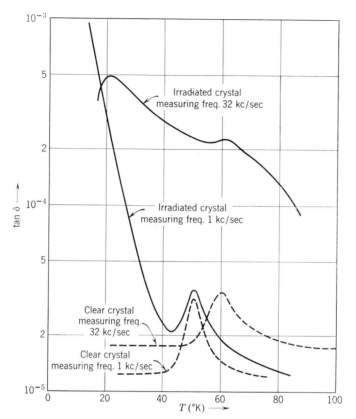

Fig. 14. Effect of irradiation with electrons on the low temperature dielectric losses of a monocrystal of Brazilian quartz.

the measuring frequency. This means that the process is characterized by a low activation energy. At present nothing is known about the static polarizability of the centers nor about the way in which the relaxation time τ varies with the temperature. If one tries to characterize τ by means of an exponential Boltzmann function (as in equation 3), then Q is found to be of the order of 0.01 ev; the pre-exponential factor τ_0 is much larger than 10^{-13} sec (Volger, Stevels, van Amerongen, 1955; Volger and Stevels, 1956b). Estimation of the concentrations indicate that the dipole moment is many times stronger than in the case of the deformation losses, viz., something of the order of 10 Debye units.

The losses described above, which may be termed color center dipole losses, occur in quartz crystals irradiated in the laboratory as well as in natural smoky quartz. In both cases clear crystals can be obtained, with $\tan \delta$ versus T curves as shown in Fig. 12, by heating to 300° and 400°C,

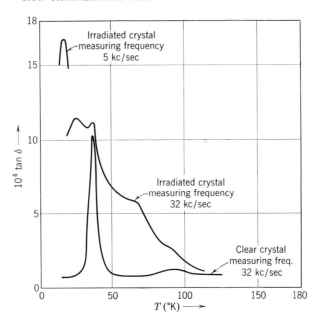

Fig. 15. Effect of irradiation with x-rays on the low temperature dielectric losses of a synthetic monocrystal. A secondary effect is visible, viz., the decrease of the peak at 38°K from about 10^{-3} to about 10^{-4}.

respectively. The conclusion, which is affirmed by optical measurements (see "Interaction between Short Electromagnetic Waves and Quartz Crystal or Quartz Glass" below) is that smoky quartz is merely quartz irradiated in nature.

It follows from the above that color center dipole losses are different from deformation losses, and the theory has been put forward (Volger and Stevels, 1956a; Volger, 1957) that the former are caused by trapped electrons or electron holes. As is the case with F centers in KCl crystals, the trapped electron may be considered to belong alternatively to one of a number of ions, arranged symmetrically around the vacancy. An analogous arrangement has been assumed for the electron holes in the V center of the KCl crystal (Känzig, 1955), a theory which has since been refined and modified (Woodruff and Känzig, 1958). This assumption gives rise to the model in which, *at very low temperatures*, the electron or the hole can find equivalent positions *around the actual center* and in which these positions can be consolidated by small deformations of the lattice. Electrically active transitions between these equivalent positions may give rise to color center dipole losses, which can be described with the help of very small activation energies and large dipole moments.

Although in glasses color centers may be caused by irradiation and will appear in high concentrations, they will *not* result in color center dipole losses, owing to the fact that the essential characteristic of the model, viz., perfect symmetry, is absent in glass.

A flux of 10^{18} fast neutrons also causes color center dipole losses (Fig. 16) in a quartz crystal. However, after bleaching at 350°C the original

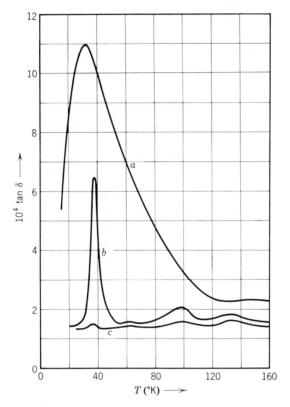

Fig. 16. Dielectric losses of a quartz crystal. Curve *a* after, and curve *b* before, irradiation by a flux of 10^{18} fast neutrons per square centimeter, and curve *c*, after subsequent thermal bleaching at 350°K, measured at 32 kc/sec.

maxima in the tan δ versus T curve have practically disappeared, though low maxima of the order of 10^{-5} are still visible. This may be explained by a local vitrification of the crystal.

It is well known that the final product of extensive irradiation of quartz crystal is an amorphous solid very similar to thermally fused silica (Simon, 1957, 1958).

Interaction between Short Electromagnetic Waves (Light) and Glass

It has been known for a long time that glass changes its color when subjected to light. This solarization of glass has been studied during some decades of years.

The reason why the problem of solarization could not be solved earlier is that no distinction was made between the two contributing effects which became known not so long ago.

Most kinds of glass to be used for technical purposes are made from sand containing traces of iron which mainly contribute ferrous ions to the glass. Upon irradiation these are converted into ferric ions which cause a yellow-brown color due to absorption in the nearby ultraviolet region with an extension into the violet visible part of the spectrum.

In the past, some manganese oxide was added to the glass for special reasons. The Mn^{2+} ions, thus present, are converted partly into Mn^{3+} ions when subjected to light, so that the glass is colored violet (old window panes). Investigations have shown that traces of elements with multivalent ions strongly promote coloration of glass by irradiation. Even light rays with a wavelength *above* about 3000 Å (4.1 ev) will cause coloration of such types of glass.

The fact that very small amounts of such ions are sufficient to produce coloration is also proved when glass (even though it may be free of multivalent ions) is polished with the classical polishing agents, such as English red (Fe_2O_3) or CeO_2; during the process enough material is rubbed into the outer glass layer to cause solarization after irradiation by long wave light rays (Kats and Stevels, 1956).

Glass *without* multivalent ions can be colored only by light with a wavelength below about 3000 Å (4.1 ev). It makes no difference whether one uses ultraviolet, x- or γ-rays; qualitatively the same result is obtained, viz., 3 absorption bands are formed in the 2000–10,000 Å range; see Fig. 17.

We have carried out a systematic investigation into the nature of the centers formed in simple silicate glasses, such as alkali silicate glasses with 30%, 5%, and 1% alkali oxides, alkaline earth silicate glasses, and glasses of various compositions (Kats and Stevels, 1956).

This investigation proved that radiation energy above about 4.1 ev is sufficient for removing an electron from an oxygen ion of a D or $\dot{D}$ center. The remaining oxygen with (one) electron hole(s) (Q_{2+} or $\dot{Q}_+$ centers) is responsible for the absorption band in the neighborhood of 3000 Å. This band is independent of the nature of the network modifiers which are present, but its position is governed to a certain degree by the fact

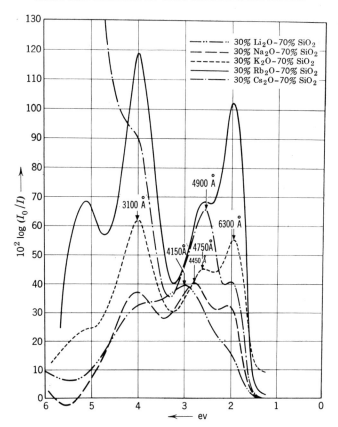

Fig. 17. Absorption spectra of glasses containing 30 mole % of alkali oxide and 70 mole % of SiO—after irradiation with x-rays (200 kv, 20 ma, 10^6 r).

that the concentration of the non-bridging oxygen ions is either high or low, in other words: that the centers are of the Q_{2+} or $\dot{Q}_+$ type.†

Once an electron has been removed from an oxygen ion, the network modifier(s) in the vicinity will tend to recede. Eventually they will lodge themselves in an interstice, together with a trapped electron, thus creating a P center.

The position of the absorption band belonging to the P center depends on the nature of the network modifier involved but not on the *concentration*. In this way one finds an absorption band at 4150 Å for an $_{Li}P_-$ center, at 4500 Å for the $_{Na}P_-$ center, at 4750 Å for the $_{K}P_-$ center, at 4850 Å for the $_{Rb}P_-$ center, and at 4900 Å for the $_{Cs}P_-$ center (see Fig. 17).

† Actually the situation is complicated by the presence of Q_+ centers (Kats and Stevels, 1956).

The behavior of the P_- and Q_+ centers in glass is analogous to that of F and V centers in alkali halides. These centers can be made to disappear simultaneously by thermal bleaching and by irradiation with rays having the wavelength of one of the two absorption bands.

After irradiation two kinds of centers can be found by means of paramagnetic resonance tests, one with a trapped electron hole, the other with a trapped electron. It was found that the type of center mentioned first corresponds to the optical band at 3000 Å, the other to the optical band at 4500 Å (van Wieringen and Kats, 1957).

The "operational equation" for the effects of irradiation could be written

$$_{2\,Na}D \rightarrow {}_{2\,Na}P_- + Q_{2+}$$

in the case of silicate glasses with small amounts of alkali oxides, or

$$_{Na}\dot{D} \rightarrow {}_{Na}P_- + \dot{Q}_+$$

in the case of silicate glasses with large amounts of alkali oxides.

The third band at about 6200 Å is attributed to T centers, i.e., centers created by P centers trapped in the vicinity of an oxygen vacancy (B centers). This is quite acceptable since it is plausible that the irradiation is also capable of *making non-bridging oxygen ions move*. When such ions find their places somewhere in the network, again as non-bridging ions, then we may assume that the over-all operational equation is the same as that given above. Sometimes, however, the moving ions become interstitial ions (cf. the next section).

When considering simple silicate glasses with low alkali oxide concentrations, it is expected that, after the removal of one out of a pair of non-bridging oxygen ions, the remaining ion closes the gap. Under these circumstances no T centers can be formed (see, for instance, Fig. 18). In the case of glasses with *high* alkali oxide glasses, however, in which the non-bridging oxygen ions have created $\dot{D}$ centers, the gap cannot be closed and the formation of $\dot{T}$ centers will be easy. These groups of glasses have a well-developed absorption band at 6200 Å. T centers can be bleached in the same way as P centers.

Interaction between Short Electromagnetic Waves and Quartz Crystal or Quartz Glass

As far as coloring is concerned, *quartz crystals* show much similarity to silicate glasses with low alkali oxide concentration. Natural smoky quartz shows the same absorption spectrum as natural and synthetic

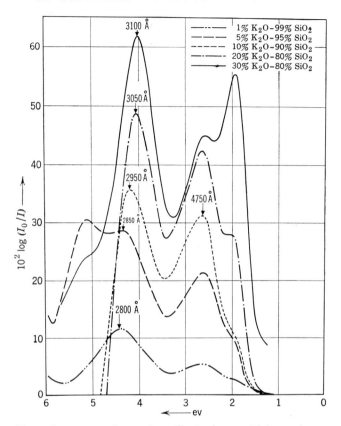

Fig. 18. Absorption spectra of potassium silicate glasses with increasing percentages of K_2O after irradiation by x-rays (200 kv, 20 ma, 10^6 r). When comparing the bands at 6200 Å (2 ev) at decreasing concentrations of K_2O, the changes will be found to be larger than those in the bands at 4750 Å and 3000 Å.

quartz crystals which were irradiated in the laboratory. Figure 19 shows some typical examples.

What happens when clear quartz crystal is irradiated? The $_{Na}^{Al}P$ centers present will give rise to the following process:

$$_{Na}^{Al}P \rightarrow {}^{Al}A_+ + {}_{Na}P_-$$

and the $_{H}^{Al}P$ centers and $_{Li}^{Al}P$ centers will undergo analogous processes. As has been stated previously (see "Interaction between Long Wave Electromagnetic Radiations and Quartz Crystal" above), measurements in the infrared region have established the presence of many $_{H}^{Al}P$ centers in synthetic quartz crystals. Figure 19 shows, for the natural and the synthetic quartz crystals,

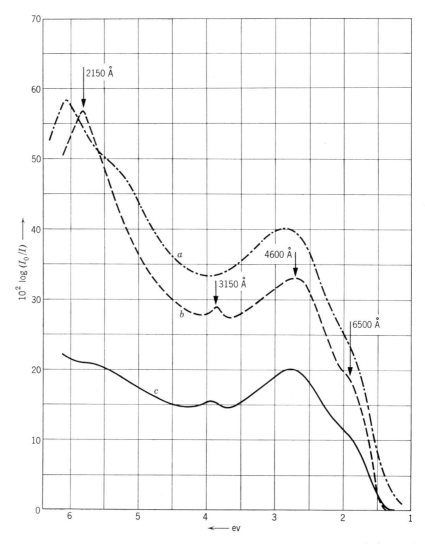

Fig. 19. Absorption spectra of (*a*) Ukrainian smoky quartz, measured before and after bleaching; (*b*) irradiated synthetic quartz crystal from Bell Telephone Laboratories (200 kv, 20 ma, 3×10^6 r); (*c*) irradiated natural crystal from Madagascar (500 kv, 20 ma $\pm 3 \times 10^6$ r).

a band at 3150 Å, which is attributed to the $^{Al}A_+$ center †,

a band at 4600 Å, caused by $_{Na}P_-$ centers and already known from the previously mentioned glass research ‡),

a very high maximum at 2150 Å which is probably due to $_HP_-$ centers (Stevels and Kats, 1958).

It may be repeated here that the presence of $^{Al}A_+$ centers in irradiated quartz crystal and natural smoky quartz crystal has been established by means of paramagnetic resonance measurements (O'Brien, 1955).

In this way centers with electron holes can be found but unfortunately, at present, those with trapped electrons cannot. It should be stressed, however, that paramagnetic resonance measurements do not always yield the desired results, even if centers are known to be present.

However, if quartz crystals are subjected to bombardment by fast *neutrons*, which leads to incomplete vitrification (see page 427), centers with trapped electrons are found with the aid of paramagnetic resonance measurements. Such centers also occur in quartz glass (see below), and there they are firmly tied to the phenomenon of absorption at about 2150 Å.

Another effect of irradiation of quartz crystal by fast neutrons which cannot be brought about by x-rays is the migration of oxygen according to the operational equation

$$^{Al}_{H}P \rightarrow {}^{Al}B_- + O + {}_HP_-$$

In this case there is an absorption peak at 5500 Å which may, with some reservation, be attributed to the $^{Al}B_-$ centers (Kats and Stevels, 1956). An acceptable theory has been put forward stating that an absorption occurring at 1640 Å in that case is caused by interstitial oxygen ions which have lost an electron (Mitchell and Paige, 1956). The band caused by the $_HP_-$ centers can also be found at about 2150 Å in this case.

The behavior of *quartz glass* is different from that of quartz crystal. Non-irradiated quartz glass shows an absorption band at 2420 Å (Fig. 20 ¶). Irradiation by light having this wavelength produces blue fluorescence. This band must be attributed to the presence of a Ge^{4+} ion in the vicinity of one or more oxygen vacancies (Kats, 1958). It has been proved by Garino-Canina (1956) that, even at concentrations as low as

---

† The fact that some types of crystals (e.g., the Ukrainian crystal shown) do not exhibit this band may be due to it being obliterated by the adjacent bands.

‡ In crystals this band is always found at a higher wavelength than in glass, the shift being due to the greater density of crystals.

¶ *Note added in proof:* The band at 1975 Å may probably be due to stray light, as is the case for the band at 2050 Å in pure fused GeO_2 [cf. Garino-Canina, *Compt. rend.* **248**, 1488 (1959)].

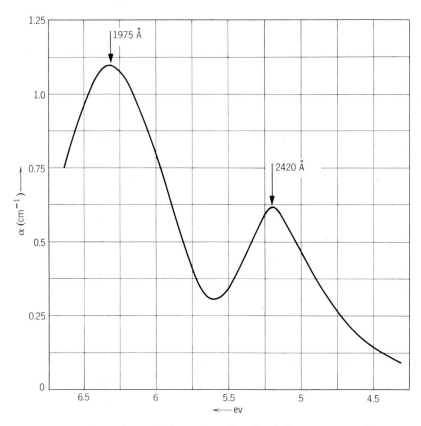

Fig. 20. Absorption coefficients of non-irradiated Hereaus quartz glass.

$10^{-6}g$ Ge/g (which he obtained by "thinning" the quartz glass), the peak height is proportional to the Ge content. Quartz crystals contaminated by Ge do not show the peak; with vitreous GeO_2 the peak appears at the same wavelength, 2420 Å. Apparently the Ge^{4+} ion must be in vitreous surroundings.

When quartz glass is heated to 1100°C, the absorption and the associated fluorescence will decrease strongly and will reappear at 1400°C. This looks as if in the 1100–1400°C range some local ordering takes place around the Ge ion or, in other words, the glass crystallizes locally which order is counteracted by heating above 1400°C (Kats, 1958).

Most of the quartz glasses contain many $_H^{Al}P$ centers. When these are irradiated, $_HP_-$, $^{Al}A_+$, and $^{Al}B_-$ centers are again produced which show absorption at 2150 Å, 2950 Å, and 5500 Å (Fig. 21). Remarkably enough, in this case x-rays produce the band mentioned last. Using

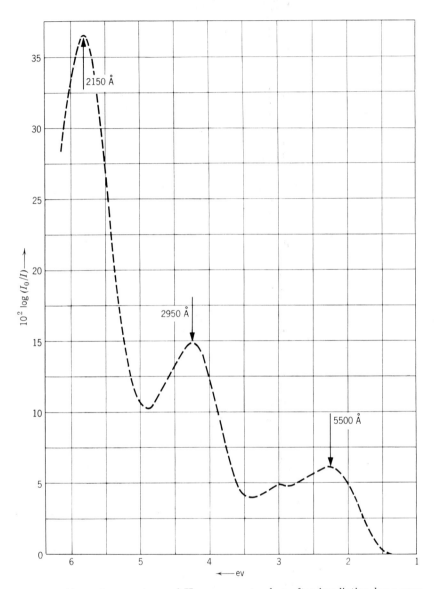

Fig. 21. Absorption spectrum of Hereaus quartz glass after irradiation by x-rays (22 kv, 20 ma, 10^6 r).

paramagnetic resonance measurements, van Wieringen and Kats (1957) established the fact that the center causing the band at 2150 Å contained a trapped electron. As has been stated, this absoprtion may be attributed to $_HP_-$ centers, while the band produced at 2950 Å is due to the $^{A1}A_+$ center. Finally, the center producing the 5500 Å band in quartz glass may be supposed to be of the $^{A1}B_-$ type. It has been found (Mitchell and Paige, 1956) that irradiation of quartz glass, again with x-rays, gave rise to formation of interstitial oxygen ions, indicated by the 1640 Å band. Absorption at 5500 Å can be increased by reducing the quartz glass with C or Si before irradiation. The intensity varies widely with the sample and is clearly governed by the degree of contamination by Al and Fe.

We have already discussed the fact that a bombardment by fast neutrons can vitrify quartz crystal locally to such an extent that the irradiation results in the band at 5500 Å being present.

Finally, attention must be directed to a minor problem. Some samples of anhydrous quartz glass still produce an absorption band at 2150 Å. The solution may be found in the fact that this glass is manufactured in a graphite container, so that hydrocarbons may be the source of the hydrogen.

SUMMARY AND CONCLUSIONS

Summarizing, the following conclusions can be made.

1. Dielectric loss measurements enable us to distinguish quantitatively among five different ways in which ions and electrons may move in glass and quartz crystal.

2. The combination of dielectric loss measurements at low temperatures and optical absorption measurements and paramagnetic resonance measurements enables us to recognize and identify a number of network defects in glasses and quartz crystal.

3. The measuring methods mentioned above provide not only valuable information on network structures but, in some cases, also on local "conditions of aggregation," such as local crystallization in a glass or local vitrification in a crystal.

4. In a number of cases the "operational equations" can be given, representing the effects of irradiation with short ultraviolet, x-rays, and fast neutrons.

REFERENCES

Anderson, O. L., and Bömmel, H. J., *J. Am. Ceram. Soc.* **38**, 125 (1955).

Fine, M. E., Van Duyne, H., and Kenney, N. T., *J. Appl. Phys.* **25**, 402 (1954).

Garino-Canina, V., *Verres et réfractaires* **10**, 151 (1956).

Känzig, W., *Phys. Rev.* **99**, 1890 (1955).

Kats, A., *Verres et réfractaires* **12**, 191 (1958).

Kats, A., and Stevels, J. M., *Philips Research Repts.* **11**, 115 (1956).

King, J. C., *Bell System Tech. J.* **38**, 573 (1959).

Marx, J. W., and Sivertsen, J. M., *J. Appl. Phys.* **24**, 81 (1953).

Mitchell, E. J. W., and Paige, E. G. S., *Phil. Mag.* **12**, 1103 (1956).

O'Brien, M. C. M., *Proc. Roy. Soc. (London)* **A231**, 404 (1955).

Simon, J., *J. Am. Ceram. Soc.* **40**, 150 (1957).

Simon, J., *J. Am. Ceram. Soc.* **41**, 116 (1958).

Stevels, J. M., "The Electrical Properties of Glass," in *Handbuch der Physik*, Vol. XX, 1957, Berlin, Göttingen, Heidelberg, pp. 350–391.

Stevels, J. M., and Kats, A., *Philips Research Repts.* **11**, 103 (1956).

Stevels, J. M., and Kats, A., *Compt. rend. 31e congr. Intern. chim. ind.*, 1958.

van Wieringen, J. S., and Kats, A., *Philips Research Repts.* **12**, 432 (1957).

Volger, J., *Discussions Faraday Soc.* **23**, 63 (1957).

Volger, J., and Stevels, J. M., *Philips Research Repts.* **11**, 452 (1956) (a).

Volger, J., and Stevels, J. M., *Philips Research Repts.* **11**, 79 (1956) (b).

Volger, J., Stevels, J. M., and van Amerongen, C., *Philips Research Repts.* **10**, 260 (1955).

Woodruff, T. O., and Känzig, W., *J. Phys. Chem. Solids* **5**, 268 (1958).

DISCUSSION

A. J. COHEN

The words of that illustrious Roman † who is downstream from our Grecian Temple, who said the other night—I think I have quoted him properly—"We are studying the perfections in nearly imperfect solids here," illustrated half of the approach to glass structure we took five years ago. We wanted to study the imperfections in nearly perfect solids so that we could understand the perfections in nearly imperfect solids, because it is the imperfections in quartz (which is thought to be nearly perfect) which are almost identical to the perfections in the silica, which is almost imperfect. And I would like to quote from the first paragraph of Stevels' chapter: "Remarkable differences between quartz crystal and fused silica are pointed out."

Well, to me the thing that is really remarkable is that our experimental data are virtually the same wherever we have done the same work. We are almost always in agreement experimentally.

† Roman Smoluchowski–Banquet remarks.

Yet the interpretations are such that I might say that we find remarkable similarities between quartz crystal and fused silica. And at this point the remarkable thing is shrinking, and we are saying now we are finding logical similarities and logical dissimilarities between quartz crystal and quartz glass.

J. M. STEVELS

Well, of course, there are many similarities between the two, but there are dissimilarities, as I pointed out. Roughly, one could say that quartz crystal resembles the glasses, and fused silica does bear resemblance less to glasses than to quartz crystals.

A. J. COHEN

Well, perhaps. I will give an instance of earlier work where dissimilarities were proposed for color centers in crystalline quartz and fused silica [Cohen, *J. Chem. Phys.* **22**, 570 (1954)]. Niira [*Busseiron Kenkyu* **50**, 17 (1952)], a Japanese theoretician, taking Yokota's [*J. Phys. Soc. Japan* **7**, 222, 316 (1952)] experimental work, where Yokota picked two centers, one from fused silica and one from crystalline quartz, and said these were both F centers, was lulled into taking what we now know to be the aluminum band, the 4600 Å band, the O'Brien [*Proc. Roy. Soc. (London)* **A231**, 404 (1955)] center, and comparing this with the 5500 Å band in fused silica, and he developed a beautiful molecular orbital treatment and from this derived very nicely the Si-O distances in crystalline quartz and fused silica, and showed their differences, which seemed quite logical.

But one thing that wasn't quite logical was a comparison of the bands of differing energies. Since there is a 5500 Å band in crystalline quartz (the material known as amethyst) also, it has about the same width at half-maximum and is apparently the same band, and, if you are going to conclude about Si-O distances from this, you must say that they are identical. But, really, it may not have anything to do with Si-O distances; it merely shows that in the crystalline materials and in the glassy material the nearest neighbors are the really important things, and the crystalline or amorphous state has very little to do with it except possibly to cause some perturbations by the next nearest neighbors.

For example, I can take the 1975 Å band in fused silica which you have just presented and take a paper which was published in March [Cohen and Smith, *J. Chem. Phys.* **28**, 401 (1958)] which shows two narrower bands in germanium-doped quartz at 1900 Å and 2050 Å, which on continued x-irradiation lose resolution and form a peak at 1950 Å, which is about as broad as yours. However, these are color center bands; whereas yours is in the material as produced. Perhaps further study may bring out some close relationships among these bands.

So, again, this shows the similarity between crystalline quartz and fused silica. Where there are dissimilarities, they may be due to the fact that certain color centers in the crystal are pinned by interstitials, as in the O'Brien model, where presumably lithium interstitial pins it. In that case, when you go over to the amorphous state, you no longer have that interstitial, the lithium can no longer take its tetrahedral position, and, therefore, in the glass you get a center of different energy.

Now, this appears to be true also of a center we are studying in germanium-doped quartz, where evidence from electron spin resonance hyperfine structure indicates that lithium is related to our structure, which results in a color center band at 2750 Å. This band does not appear in germanium-doped fused silica.

So, I say, if a color center appears in a crystalline quartz and fails to appear in the amorphous silica, this is a logical dissimilarity rather than a remarkable one.

J. M. STEVELS

Whether logical or illogical, it is a dissimilarity.

J. C. KING (submitted in writing)

As Stevels has pointed out, it is generally agreed that the defect responsible for the dielectric absorption at 38°K also gives rise to a mechanical absorption occurring at 50°K for a frequency of vibration of 5 megacycles. Measurements of the low temperature anelasticity of quartz [King, *Phys. Rev.* **109**, 1552 (1958)] have shown differences of several decades in the amplitude of the 50°K absorption in various samples, including synthetic specimens grown on two different seed plate orientations. Nevertheless, spectrochemical analysis of these samples reveals the Al content to vary no more than 20–100 ppm by weight. This information alone leads one to suspect that the 50°K defect is not directly associated with Al.

Recently [King, *Bell System Tech. J.* **38**, 573 (1959)] a mechanical relaxation absorption has been observed to occur at 100°K for a frequency of 5 megacycles in natural and artificially induced smoky quartz. This absorption is not found in x-irradiated quartz, which does not darken. It is clear that the 100°K defect derives from the progenitor of the optical A band absorption, namely, $_{Na}^{Al}P$ or $_{Li}^{Al}P$. Through measurements of the acoustic absorption in electrolytically purified quartz (King, *loc. cit.*) we are able to identify $^{Al}A_{+}$ as the defect underlying the 100°K absorption. Let us assume that, as Stevels suggests, the $_{H}^{Al}P$ defect gives rise to the 50°K mechanical absorption. The most likely modification of $_{H}^{Al}P$ through x-irradiation would involve the production of $^{Al}A_{+}$ defects. This being the case, one would expect that a specimen of quartz, which exhibits a large mechanical absorption at 50°K, such as, for example, synthetic grown on a basal cut seed plate, will show a large absorption at 100°K after x-irradiation. No 100°K absorption is observed in basal cut seed grown quartz [significantly Brown and Thomas, *Nature* **169**, 39 (1952), report that no smoky color can be induced in synthetic quartz grown on a basal cut seed plate] notwithstanding the initial presence of a relatively large absorption at 50°K. This evidence gives one cause to question the proposed association of $_{H}^{Al}P$ defect with the 38°K dielectric absorption.

J. M. STEVELS

In his first remark King states that the mechanical absorption at 50°K for a frequency of vibration of 5 Mc/sec is different in samples grown on two different seed plate orientations. We have found the same for the dielectric absorption at 38°K. King, in his first-mentioned paper, compared natural with synthetic specimens. Though the Al content varies relatively little, the absorption at 50°K varies considerably. We have reasons to believe that one ought to be careful when comparing natural and synthetic quartzes, because certain defects in which Al is involved are built in different manners. In any case, the phenomenon is no argument *against* the idea that the "50°K defect" is associated with aluminum.

As to his second remark, I agree with King that the acoustic absorption at 100°K may be coupled with the $^{Al}A_+$ center. It is true that there are x-irradiated quartz specimens which do not darken (cf. my reply to Hensler below); a number of reasons may be responsible for this. There is a case in which the corresponding virgin crystals *do* show the dielectric absorption at 38°K (for 32 kc/sec) and the infrared absorption at $2.79/\mu$.

One cannot conclude in *these* cases that the precursor $^{Al}_H P$ is absent, one can only say—and we have reasons to believe so—that *here* the reaction $^{Al}_H P \rightarrow$ $^{Al}A_+ + {}_H P_-$ is suppressed considerably. It may be that the synthetic quartz mentioned by King is a similar crystal, which shows little or no discoloration after irradiation, though the normal quantities of Al are present.

J. R. HENSLER (submitted in writing)

I have two comments based on some experiments I should like to describe.

We have been successful in synthesizing the aluminum impurity center analyzed by O'Brien (*loc. cit.*) in smoky quartz. This was done by doping very high purity silica powder, which in itself could not be colored by radiation, by sintering the powder at 1500°C after wetting it with a solution containing the desired contaminants.

Samples doped with Al + Li were colored purple by exposure to γ-radiation of 10^6 r. The color center could not be produced by doping with Al alone. Cohen [*J. Chem. Phys.* **25,** 904 (1956)] has shown by his measurements of the anistropy of the absorption that the Al must be substitutional. Substitution of Al^{3+} for Si^{4+} requires charge compensation by a second ion such as Li^+.

In several experiments Li was replaced by other ions selected to supply the excess positive charge to allow the substitution of Al for silicon without necessarily supplying traps for the electron released from the Al-O bond under radiation. Ag, Mg, P when added in combination with Al produced coloration under radiation. Ag may be considered to have an action similar to Li in being present interstitially and in providing an electron trap. P, on the other hand, should be considered substitutional because of its high charge and its normal four-fold coordination with oxygen. The P would not necessarily provide an electron trap. Mg must be considered intermediate. These experiments allow us to generalize the O'Brien impurity center.

The undoped silica which showed no coloration after exposure had a very intense thermoluminescence with a maximum at about 280°C. The exposed SiO_2 (Al, Li) samples showed luminescence maxima in the same region but with lower intensities. The luminescence for SiO_2 (0.01 Al, 0.01 Li) was measured for several dose levels. Although the coloration in these samples increased with dose, the thermoluminescence at first increased and then decreased. The luminescence of the pure SiO_2 sample was considered to be due to a process in which interstitial oxygens plus trapped holes annihilate with oxygen vacancies plus trapped electrons; Mitchell and Paige [*Phil. Mag.* **1**, Ser. 8, 1085 (1956)] had proposed these centers corresponding to two absorption bands in the ultraviolet region. The quenching of this luminescence in the presence of the Al center is evidence for an interaction of the Al centers and the ultraviolet absorbing centers. The probability of the interaction would be expected to increase as the concentration increased, and therefore the luminescence shows a maximum at an intermediate dose.

Li can play a predominant role in the interaction of these centers while bleaching. The Li in an interstitial position would be quite mobile, expecially after being discharged by electron capture. With the Al-P combination, on the other hand, the P would be expected to be in substitution for Si because of its charge and its normal 4-coordination with oxygen. Both Li^+ and P^{5+}, however, will stabilize Al^{3+} in the substitutional position which is required in the precursor. We expect that the low mobility of substitutional P compared to the high mobility of the interstitial discharged Li should have a strong effect on the degree of interaction of the centers upon bleaching. We plan to study the bleaching of the Al center in SiO_2 (Al, P) as well as SiO_2 and SiO_2 (Al, Li) in fused silica samples where the absorption as well as the luminescence can be followed during the bleaching process. The comments derived from these experiments are:

1. SiO_2 doped with Al only did not color under radiation in spite of the fact that water was present in the powder because of its derivation from hydrolyzed $SiCl_4$. This indicates that the reaction $^{Al}_H P \rightarrow {}_H P_- + {}^{Al} A_+$ does not in fact take place either because $^{Al}_H P$ cannot form or $_H P_-$ cannot form, and therefore the 2150 Å band cannot be attributed to $_H P_-$ centers.

2. Since SiO_2 (Al, P) became colored under radiation the same as SiO_2 (Al, Li), the visible absorption band corresponding to the 4600 Å band in smoky quartz cannot be due to alkali but must be due to the Al as O'Brien proposed.

J. M. STEVELS

1. It should be kept in mind that the method used by Hensler, in which he dopes powders of fused silica with solutions containing contaminants, followed by sintering, may give quite different results, as compared to cases where samples of fused silica are prepared in the usual way at very high temperatures. The concentrations of the impurities discussed in my chapter are of the order of 10 to 1000 ppm. In Hensler's case there may be far more impurities present, but on the other hand it is not certain if a sintering process at 1500°C is sufficient to get an equally good distribution of the network defects as in the above case.

It may be true that high purity fused silica cannot be colored itself by ionizing radiation, but it *does* become colored at low temperatures in the ultraviolet, so that one cannot conclude an absence of impurities in this fused silica.

In any case the high purity fused silica contains very little Al, whereas a large amount of water is present, possibly as "molecular" water but very likely in the form of OH groups bonded to Si ions. It is still an open question whether configurations like

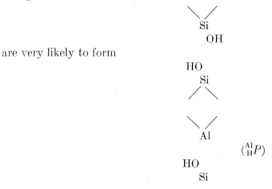

are very likely to form

with the techniques used by Hensler, as long as he dopes with Al alone. Suppose, however, that Al *is* taken up by Hensler's technique in the form of $^{Al}_H P$ (it should be noted that there is also the possibility of the formation of ^{2Al}B centers which do not give rise to reactions on ionizing radiation), then on irradiation a reaction

$$^{Al}_H P \rightarrow {}_H P_- + {}^{Al}A_+$$

may occur. However, the result is not a (visible) coloration, since we pointed out that the absorption bands of $_H P_-$ and $^{Al}A_+$ are found in the ultraviolet part of the spectrum.

It is interesting to note that we have certain natural quartz crystals available which contain $^{Al}_H P$ centers (concluded from dielectric loss and infrared measurements) which do not show absorptions after ionizing irradiation. This indicates that $^{Al}_H P$ centers on irradiation do not necessarily have to give rise to the centers under consideration. From a lack of absorption fater irradiation one cannot conclude that a given impurity is not present.

2. Apparently SiO$_2$, in the form of fused silica, contaminated with Al and P, shows the same purple color after irradiation as this substance contaminated with Al and Li. This absorption at 5500 Å is assigned in my chapter to a defect, which contains an electron in the neighborhood of an aluminum. This band, however, has no relation with the 4600 Å band, which causes the smoky color of irradiated quartz *crystal*. The chapter gives the evidence that this band is due to an $_{Na}P_-$ center. We believe that O'Brien erroneously assigned the 4600 Å band to the $^{Al}A_+$ center, but that this center causes the absorption band at 3000 Å. From the study of glasses it is known that the Q_+ center causes an absorption band at 3100 Å. The O'Brien center $^{Al}A_+$) should have an absorption band at about the same wavelength. A difference of nearly 1.5 ev between the two is not very probable.

J. H. CRAWFORD (submitted in writing)

I have two comments to make on the 2150 Å band in fused silica discussed by Stevels.

1. Nelson [*Bull. Am. Phys. Soc.* **3**, 136 (1958)] and Weeks of ORNL [*Bull. Am. Phys. Soc.* **3**, 136 (1958)] have been able to demonstrate that this band is associated with a trapped electron. This assignment was made possible by a combination of optical absorption and electron spin resonance measurements during preferential thermal bleaching of neutron-irradiated specimens of high purity Corning fused silica. On heating below 550°C, the 2150 Å band is removed much more rapidly than the absorption at shorter wavelengths. ESR studies after the same heat treatment indicate that the narrow resonance with $\bar{g} < 2.003$ (characteristic of electrons) is weakened to nearly the same extent as the 2150 Å band, whereas the broad resonance system ($\bar{g} > 2.0023$, characteristic of holes) like the absorption below 2000 Å was little affected. It is therefore inferred that the trapped electrons give rise to the 2150 Å absorption band, and trapped holes to the short wavelength band (or bands), presumably the band at 1650 Å observed by Mitchell and Paige (*loc. cit.*).

2. The second point concerns Stevels' interpretation of the 2150 Å band. From extensive studies by Nelson (oral communication) of a wide variety of fused silica specimens exposed to Co^{60} γ-rays or to fast neutrons in a reactor, it would appear that this band is associated with a fundamental network defect and not with an $_HP_-$ center as Stevels suggests. The saturation intensity of this band on prolonged neutron bombardment is essentially independent of the source of fused silica specimens. Moreover, the hydrogen content appears to have little, if any, influence on the amplitude or rate of development of this band produced by Co^{60} γ-ray exposure. Finally, the presence of hydrogen in the center would be expected to produce the characteristic hyperfine splitting of the ESR line into two components. Weeks has not observed any hyperfine lines in the resonance of this center which could be reasonably attributed to the presence of hydrogen.

J. M. STEVELS

1. The fact that trapped electrons give rise to the 2150 Å absorption band, as demonstrated by Nelson (*loc. cit.*) and Weeks (*loc. cit.*), had been discovered earlier by van Wieringen and Kats [*Philips Research Repts.* **12**, 432 (1957)] and reported for the first time by Kats and Stevels [*Philips Research Repts.* **11**, 115 (1956)]. As stated in the text of my chapter, I also believe that the absorption band at 1640 Å observed by Mitchell and Paige (*loc. cit.*) is due to centers with trapped holes, viz., oxygen ions which have lost one or two electrons.

2. As to Crawford's second remark, I am still inclined to believe that the 2150 Å band is coupled with the $_HP_-$ center, but I admit that there is no direct proof for it. This is the reason why in the text it has been stated that the 2150 Å band is *probably* due to $_HP_-$ centers.

Much positive evidence is given in the chapter in the case of quartz crystal: the series of the precursors $_H^{Al}P$, $_{Li}^{Al}P$, $_{Na}^{Al}P$ fits in very well with the data on dielectric loss measurements, analytical data confirm the coupling of the two latter peaks with the Li and Na contents, whereas Kats and Haven have shown by hydrogen-deuterium exchange experiments (studied with I.R. absorption techniques, to be published before long) that normally in quartz crystals hydrogen is present in the neighborhood of 10^{17} to 10^9 cm^{-3}. Weeks [*Bull. Am. Phys. Soc.* **1**, 12 (1956)] suggested that the absorption band at 2150 Å did not arise from impurities, since he used highly purified Corning silica. But it should be kept in mind that at that time this fused silica did contain many OH groups, as was shown by infrared measurements.

Dealing now with Crawford's remarks in detail, the following can be said:

The absorption band at 2150 Å is even produced in purified Corning fused silica by rather weak ionizing radiation (x-rays) at 78°K, as has been shown by Kats [*Verres et réfractaires* **12**, 196 (1958)]. This suggests that the absorption band is not coupled to a *created* fundamental *network defect* (vacancies or interstitials) but might be caused by a defect which may be very easily obtained, that is, in the case under consideration by a displacement of a hydrogen ion which traps an electron.

In the case of x-ray treatment at room temperature the rate of development *is* strongly dependent on the source of the fused silica specimen.

Finally, the random structure of the fused silica may be the reason why the hyperfine splitting of the ESR line cannot be found. It is not permissible to draw conclusions from negative results in hyperfine splitting.

Note added in proof: It should be kept in mind that Weeks, in his paper, "Defects of the quartz system produced by neutron irradiation" (Symposium on "The Defect Structure of Quartz and Glassy Silica," Mellon Institute), reported hyperfine splitting at room temperature in γ-rayed fused silica, probably due to hydrogen.

Van Wieringen and Kats [*Arch. Sciences (Geneva)* **12**, 203 (1959)] have shown that specimens of high purity Corning fused silica, after irradiation at 80°K with x-rays, gives an electron spin resonance with a hyperfine splitting into two lines and, after exchange of H by D, a hyperfine splitting into three lines of width 1 gauss. These lines are attributed to proton hyperfine splitting. From the position of the lines the following parameters were determined: $g = 2.003 \pm 0.001$ and hyperfine parameter $A = 1.428$ MHz. These values, together with the isotropy of the lines, are explained by the presence of protons. This was checked by replacing part of the protons by deuterons. Then a hyperfine splitting into three lines is observed.

It seems not unlikely, therefore, that the absorption band at about 2150 Å consists of two bands, which coincide to a great extent, one due to $_H P$ centers, and the other due to a fundamental network defect of the B_- type.

18

by

O. L. Anderson

Bell Telephone Laboratories, Inc.

G. J. Dienes

Brookhaven National Laboratories

The Anomalous Properties
of Vitreous Silica

The purpose of this chapter is to examine the particular physical properties of vitreous silica which are anomalous, and to find to what extent these properties can be reconciled with the general characteristics of solids which have been deduced from lattice dynamics and statistical mechanics.

These discussions will not be based upon any particular assumption of the structure of vitreous silica. The authors recognize that there are several competing theories which purport to characterize the structure of vitreous silica, and that the data from some x-ray diffraction studies and neutron diffraction studies are not wholly in agreement at the present time.†

The general approach will be to adopt the methods and equations which have been successful in understanding crystalline solids of the non-molecular, non-metallic type. Our starting point is to assume that the vibrational properties of vitreous silica, in the long wave region, are the same as for a non-metallic crystal in the long wave region. Thus the low temperature properties are not affected by the

† The results of x-ray diffraction studies led Zarzycki (1957) to conclude that the Si-O-Si angle of vitreous silica is no larger than 160°. This conflicts with the neutron diffraction studies of Breen et al. (1957) and earlier x-ray work, in which the angle is reported to be 180°, the same as for cristobalite.

lack of long range order. However, our assumption requires that there be close range order, which is to say there must be a well-defined inter-atomic distance and a fixed coordination about each type of ion.

The equations which are used are strictly applicable to a class of crystalline solids which Grüneisen (1924) has labeled "polyatomic lattices without group formation." A group formation in a lattice is a chemical molecule or radical, or any cluster of atoms which exhibit stronger bonds within the group than between groups. The second general assumption which we use is that the vibrational properties of vitreous silica are not affected by group formation, if indeed any such groups exist. Evidence against group formation is presented in the next section.

Under these assumptions, and for the purposes of this chapter, the vibrational properties of vitreous silica in the long wave region fall some-where between those of an ionic solid (such as KCl) and those of a covalent solid (such as diamond).

Evidence for Treating Vitreous Silica as a Polyatomic Lattice without Groups

We shall show that the acoustic and optical vibrational properties of vitreous silica and quartz are in line with those of ionic solids. Comparison will be made with KCl, ZnS, CaF_2, and MgO: KCl represents the most ideal ionic solid; MgO is an oxide; ZnS has tetrahedral coordination and has about the same degree of ionic bonding as silica; and CaF_2 is triatomic.

It turns out that for all these solids the mean sound velocity v_m (which is calculated from the elastic constants and density) is ordered in the same way as the melting points (Anderson, 1959). This is shown in Table 1, which shows that it is reasonable to classify silica with ionic solids in so far as acoustic vibrations are concerned.

The degree of ionic bonding in polyatomic lattices can be calculated by Szigeti's (1949) formula relating polarizability to infrared dispersion. In Table 2 a comparison is made of the various polarizing properties of vitreous silica and the four ionic solids (Szigeti's equation does not apply to trigonal symmetry, so quartz is not included in the table).

The quantity called long range interaction arises because of the motion of the electron clouds relative to the nuclei: it is, therefore, a measure of the deformability of the ions. The quantity e^*/e, the ratio of the effective electronic charge to the electronic charge, is the quantity computed by the Szigeti formula; it is considered to be a measure of the

Table 1

COMPARISON OF MEAN SOUND VELOCITY AND MELTING POINT [a]

(v_m in units of 10^5 cm/sec)

Solid	KCl	ZnS	CaF$_2$	Vitreous SiO$_2$	Quartz SiO$_2$	MgO
v_m	2.52	2.92	4.08	4.11	4.37	6.71
T_s (°K)	776	1020	1360	~1350 [b]	1470	2500

[a] All values from calculations and references listed in Anderson (1959).

[b] Estimated by finding center of interval where C_p changes from the Dulong and Petit limit to the value of liquid silica.

Table 2

COMPARISON OF POLARIZING PROPERTIES [a]

Property	Symbol	KCl	ZnS	MgO	CaF$_2$	Vitreous SiO$_2$
Total polarization	ϵ_0	4.68	8.3	9.8	8.43	3.78
Ultraviolet polarization	ϵ_∞	2.13	5.07	2.95	1.99	1.98
Infrared polarization	$\epsilon_0 - \epsilon_\infty$	2.55	3.23	6.85	6.44	1.80
Dispersion wavelength (μs)	λ_0	70.7	33	15.3	51.5	21.5
Long range interaction	$(\epsilon_\infty + 2)/3$	1.39	2.69	1.65	1.33	1.33
Degree of ionic bonding	e^*/e	0.78	0.48	0.99	0.75	0.44

[a] All values from calculations and references listed in Anderson (1959).

ionic overlap and a measure of the ionic bonding. As can be seen in Table 2, the properties of vitreous silica are of the same order as the corresponding properties of the other solids.

The computation of e^*/e agrees well with other methods of finding the degree of ionic bonding, as shown in Table 3. The reasonable agree-

Table 3

COMPARISON OF DEGREE OF IONIC BONDING BY SEVERAL METHODS [a]

Method	NaCl	ZnS	MgO	CaF$_2$	Vitreous Silica
Electronegativity of ions	95%	51%	91%	98%	50%
Electron density, x-rays	100	—	<100	—	~50
Infrared dispersion, e^*/e (Szigeti equation)	74	48	99	75	44

[a] All values from calculations and references, listed in Anderson (1959).

ment confirms the applicability of the Szigeti equation for e^*/e to vitreous silica. Table 3 confirms the computation of e^*/e shown in Table 2. It should be recalled that the Szigeti equation is based upon the assumption that the *Reststrahlen* are standing waves of vibrations of two oppositely charged ions in a polyatomic lattice. It follows that the optical vibrational properties of vitreous silica should be classed with ionic solids (with mixed covalent bonding).

This conclusion is at variance with some authors who have suggested (Babcock et al., 1954; Dank and Barber, 1955) that vitreous silica is a solid which is composed of groups (for example, Si_3O_6) which vibrate as units. If this were the case, the vibrational properties of vitreous silica would be classed with those of molecular solids. In view of the strong similarities between silica and ionic solids, as far as vibrational properties are concerned, it appears that there are no groups. The conclusion that the vibrational properties of vitreous silica can be classed with those of ionic solids is consistent with Zachariasen's (1932) view that vitreous silica is a completely cross-linked network with fixed coordination about every ion. Therefore the equations that we shall use for vitreous silica in the subsequent sections are those which are valid for ionic solids.

Low Temperature Specific Heat

θ (elastic) and θ_0

The low temperature vibrational behavior of vitreous silica is anomalous in the sense that there is serious disagreement between the two

Debye temperatures calculated from thermal measurements and from acoustic measurements. The same discrepancy does not exist in quartz. A more detailed discussion of this effect has been presented elsewhere (Anderson, 1959). This section briefly describes the situation.

The definition used for the Debye temperature of polyatomic ionic lattices (using thermal data) is (Grüneisen, 1924)

$$\theta \text{ (thermal)} = T(464.5p/C_V)^{1/3} \tag{1}$$

where C_V is in calories per gram molecule and p is the number of atoms per molecule. θ (thermal) is often a function of T, but at sufficiently low temperature it becomes constant. In particular,

$$\theta_0 = \theta \text{ (thermal) as } T \to 0$$

Applying Westrum's and Morrison's data it is found (Anderson, 1959) that

$$\theta_0 = 375°\text{K} \quad \text{for vitreous silica}$$

and

$$\theta_0 = 620°\text{K} \quad \text{for quartz}$$

Using elastic data, the Debye temperature is

$$\theta \text{ (elastic)} = \frac{\hbar}{k}\left(\frac{3N}{4\pi V}\right)^{1/3} v_m \tag{2}$$

where v_m is the mean sound velocity obtained from averaging the elastic constants in all directions; $\hbar/k$ is the ratio of Planck's constant to the Boltzmann constant, N is Avogadro's number, and V is the volume of a *mean* gram atom (molecular weight divided by density and p). Using the low temperature elastic constant data of McSkimin (1953) and Fine (1954), we find (see Fig. 1)

$$\theta \text{ (elastic)} = 495°\text{K} \quad \text{for vitreous silica}$$

Using the room temperature elastic constant data of Koga (1958), we find θ (elastic) = 570°K for quartz, but, estimating the correction to 0°K, the better value is (Anderson, 1959)

$$\theta \text{ (elastic)} = 600°\text{K} \quad \text{for quartz}$$

The agreement between the two ϑ's for quartz is satisfactory. For vitreous silica, the discrepancy indicates that there is excess specific heat at very low temperatures.

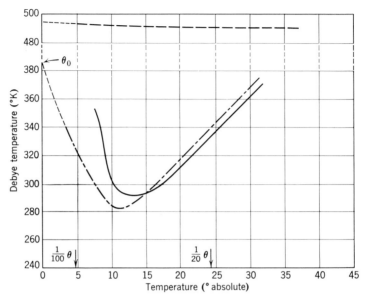

Fig. 1. A plot of θ (elastic) and θ (thermal) for vitreous silica. The extrapolated value of θ_0 is estimated to be $375\,°K$, in marked contrast to the value of θ (elastic), which is found to be $495\,°K$. This shows that the elastic constants do not account for all the heat even at temperatures as low as $2\,°K$. The plot of θ (thermal) for cristobalite is presented to show the similarity in the low temperature vibrational properties of vitreous silica and cristobalite (data of Westrum). Vitreous silica: broken curve, θ (elastic); dot-dash curve, θ (thermal) $= T(1393/C_V)^{1/3}$. Cristobalite: solid curve, θ (thermal) $= T(1393/C_V)^{1/3}$.

Discussion

The discrepancy between θ_0 and θ (elastic) requires further verification down to at least $2\,°K$. The present evidence indicates that there is considerable excess heat at values of $T/\theta < 0.01$. This is of considerable importance to the theory of the glassy state. (It is notable that all the low temperature lattice heat of quartz is accountable to acoustic vibrations.) If the non-acoustic specific heat is estimated by subtracting a Debye function from Westrum's measurements, it is found for vitreous silica that over half the specific heat up to $35\,°K$ arises from non-acoustic vibrations. This excess heat requires the presence of a low frequency optical branch, or an acoustic branch which has curvature at low wave numbers.

The source of this excess heat is, at this time, a matter for speculation. But some positive statements can be made. First, this excess heat, if optical, will be represented by a sum of monochromatic vibrations.

Whatever the source of the extra heat may be, the specific heat must vanish at absolute zero if the vibrations are optical, because Einstein functions vanish rapidly near absolute zero. Second, the frequencies of the vibrations are small. Low frequencies can arise from small force constants or large masses. The conclusions of the preceding section preclude the vibrations of large masses. Consequently this distribution of frequencies must arise from very small force constants. Therefore, in order to correlate this extra heat with the structure of vitreous silica, one must account for a spectrum of modes that is activated at low temperatures without affecting the acoustical vibrational energy. A possibility is some type of hindered rotation in which the molecules "are free to change their orientation through a small angle, being held to a particular orientation by linear restoring forces" (Slater, 1939, p. 253).

For example, all the experimental facts appear to be consistent with Smyth's conjecture (1953) that the vibration which accounts mostly for the low temperature specific heat is the transverse mode of the oxygen ion.[†] The oxygen ion finds itself in a very unsymmetrical field (unlike the silicon ion) because vibrations along the Si-O bond encounter the strong field of the silicon, while vibrations transverse to the Si-O bond encounter little, if any, repulsive forces. Consequently the restoring force of this mode of vibration is low, leading to small frequencies. This mode of vibration is very important in other phenomena which occur at low temperatures. When the center of the oxygen ion is off the line joining two silicon ions, this transverse oxygen mode attenuates high frequency sound waves at about 50°K (Anderson and Bömmel, 1955).

However, the speculation above about vitreous silica can only be considered tentative because Smyth's conjecture presupposes that the close range structure of vitreous silica is that of cristobalite, and it is not known whether the specific heat anomaly exists in cristobalite. Therefore it is not possible to suggest, at this time, that the specific heat anomaly is found only in the vitreous state. The data which exist for cristobalite are not sufficient to establish the anomaly for this solid (see Fig. 1). However, the data on low temperature specific heat do show that the close range structure of vitreous silica is closer to cristobalite than to quartz, in agreement with Warren's x-ray studies (Warren and Biscoe, 1938).

[†] Smyth's work (1953) is based upon an empirical analysis of specific heat using three Einstein functions for a model.

Temperature Dependence of the Elastic Moduli

Experimental Situation

The temperature dependence of the elastic moduli of vitreous silica is anomalous in the sense that the moduli of this substance increase with increasing temperature above 60°K. A theoretical investigation of this anomalous behavior has been carried out recently (Dienes, 1958). According to this investigation the anomalous temperature dependence of the moduli is phenomenologically related to the very low coefficient of thermal expansion of vitreous silica. A brief description of the experimental background and of the theoretical development is given.

The anomalous positive temperature coefficients of the elastic moduli of vitreous silica have been studied experimentally in considerable detail in the last few years. The measurements of Marx and Sivertson (1953) showed that Young's modulus E for fused silica increases continuously with temperature T from $-170°$ to $1000°C$. The E versus T curve is essentially linear from $25°$ to $1000°C$. This behavior was also found by Spinner (1956). These unusual results were fully confirmed by McSkimin (1953) over the temperature range $-200°$ to $40°C$. He also showed that the shear modulus as a function of temperature behaves in the same way as Young's modulus. Fine (1954) extended the measurements to $4°K$ and showed that there is an internal friction peak in the neighborhood of $35°K$ at $50-100$ kc,† and a minimum in the moduli near $60°K$. Above $60°K$ the moduli (Young's modulus, shear modulus) and also Poisson's ratio increase continuously with increasing temperature. Newer data are presented under "Variation of Compressibility with Pressure" below, and in Figs. 2 and 3 and Table 6.

It has been suggested (Babcock et al., 1954; Spinner, 1956) that this dependence of the elastic moduli of vitreous silica on temperature cannot be reconciled with the current view of its structure, namely, the network hypothesis of Zachariasen (1932) and Warren and Biscoe (1938). Vitreous silica, however, is anomalous in another important respect since it has a very low (and at low temperature negative) coefficient of thermal expansion. Thus one can ask the following question: Should a solid of very low coefficient of thermal expansion possess a positive modulus-temperature coefficient over some temperature range? An attempt is made in this section to answer this question theoretically.

---

† See explanation in section titled "The Acoustic and Dielectric Loss Due to Lattice Distortion" below.

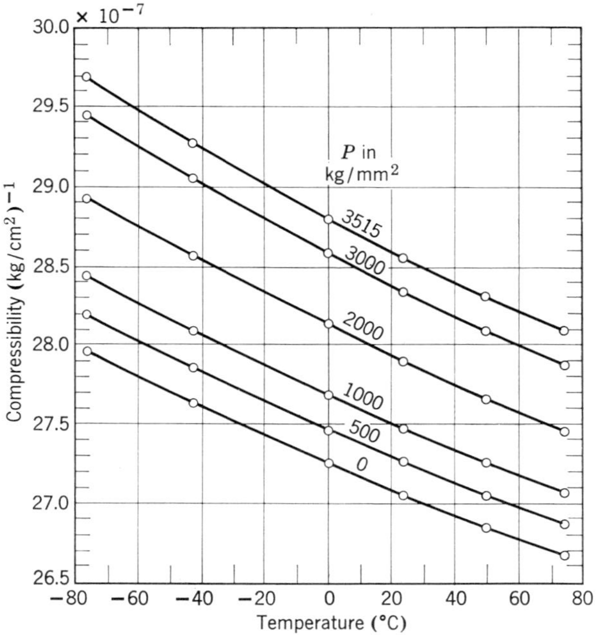

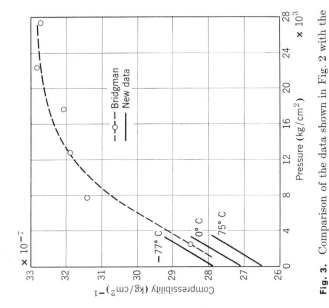

Fig. 3. Comparison of the data shown in Fig. 2 with the data of Bridgman (1948). The variation of χ with P is anomalous up to about 20,000 kg/cm², after which it becomes normal.

Fig. 2. A plot of the compressibility of vitreous silica against temperature for pressures up to 3515 kg/cm². Data of McSkimin (1953).

We might anticipate the answer by stating that a very low coefficient of expansion implies a positive modulus-temperature coefficient for a Born-von Kármán type of solid at elevated temperatures.

Theoretical Formulation

The Born-von Kármán solid. Any modulus M may be considered a function of volume and temperature (Lazarus, 1949) †

$$M = M(V, T) \tag{3}$$

The temperature dependence is then given by

$$\frac{dM}{dT} = \left(\frac{\partial M}{\partial V}\right)_T \left(\frac{\partial V}{\partial T}\right)_P + \left(\frac{\partial M}{\partial T}\right)_V \tag{4}$$

With the use of the coefficient of thermal expansion,

$$\beta = \frac{1}{V}\left(\frac{\partial V}{\partial T}\right)_P$$

equation (4) may be written in the form

$$\frac{dM}{dT} = \beta V \left(\frac{\partial M}{\partial V}\right)_T + \left(\frac{\partial M}{\partial T}\right)_V \tag{5}$$

Equation (5) may also be put in the alternative form

$$\frac{dM}{dT} = -K\beta \left(\frac{\partial M}{\partial P}\right)_T + \left(\frac{\partial M}{\partial T}\right)_V \tag{6}$$

where K is the bulk modulus, given by

$$K = -V(\partial P/\partial V)_T$$

If β is negligibly small, it is clear from equation (5) that the sign of dM/dT will be governed by the sign of $(\partial M/\partial T)_V$. The two partial derivatives in equation (5) will be evaluated theoretically with particular emphasis on the $(\partial M/\partial T)_V$ term.

In the following an isotropic solid will be treated for which all elastic properties are defined by two moduli, the bulk modulus K, and the shear modulus μ. Pure dilation ϵ_1 and pure shear ϵ_2 will be used as the two corresponding strains. If A is the Helmholtz free energy of the

---

† Equation (3) deviates from the usual expression for the moduli used for alkali halides, where $M = M(V)$ is satisfactory. Consequently the treatment of Born (1923), in which central forces between ions suffice to establish the equation for M, could not produce the required result which is established in this section.

system, then the bulk and shear moduli are given by

$$K = \frac{1}{V_0} \frac{\partial^2 A}{\partial \epsilon_1{}^2}$$

$$\mu = \frac{1}{V_0} \frac{\partial^2 A}{\partial \epsilon_2{}^2} \tag{7}$$

where V_0 is the molar or atomic volume at $T = 0$. The Helmholtz free energy is expressed as a function of strain and temperature, in the usual way (Born and Huang, 1954), by the equation

$$A(\epsilon_1, \epsilon_2, T) = f(\epsilon_1, \epsilon_2) + kT \sum_i \ln\left[1 - \exp\left(-\hbar\nu_i/kT\right)\right] \tag{8}$$

where f is a function of the strains only and the ν_i are functions of the strains but not of the temperature, and where the zero point vibrations have been neglected. At any finite temperature and zero pressure, $\epsilon_1 = \epsilon_1{}^0$, where $\epsilon_1{}^0$ represents the dilation due to thermal expansion. Let the function f be expanded around $\epsilon_1{}^0$ in a power series (Slater, 1939, p. 253). This yields

$$f(\epsilon_1, \epsilon_2) = f(\epsilon_1{}^0, 0) + f_1(\epsilon_1{}^0, 0)(\epsilon_1 - \epsilon_1{}^0) + f_2(\epsilon_1{}^0, 0)\epsilon_2$$

$$+ \tfrac{1}{2}[f_{11}(\epsilon_1{}^0, 0)(\epsilon_1 - \epsilon_1{}^0)^2 + 2f_{12}(\epsilon_1{}^0, 0)(\epsilon_1 - \epsilon_1{}^0)\epsilon_2$$

$$+ f_{22}(\epsilon_1{}^0, 0)\epsilon_2{}^2] + \cdots \tag{9}$$

where $f_1 = \partial f/\partial \epsilon_1$, etc. Then

$$\frac{\partial A}{\partial \epsilon_1} = f_1 + f_{11}(\epsilon_1 - \epsilon_1{}^0) + f_{12}\epsilon_2 + \sum_i Z \frac{\partial \ln \nu_i}{\partial \epsilon_1} \tag{10}$$

where

$$Z = \hbar\nu_i[\exp\left(\hbar\nu_i/kT\right) - 1]^{-1} \tag{11}$$

and f_1, f_{11}, etc., are functions of $\epsilon_1{}^0$ only. The derivative of f_1 with respect to ϵ_1 is zero, and therefore, after considerable reduction, the moduli are finally given by the relations

$$KV_0 = K' = f_{11}(\epsilon_1{}^0, 0)$$

$$+ \sum_i \left[\left(\frac{\partial \ln \nu_i}{\partial \epsilon_1}\right)^2 Z \left(1 - \frac{Z}{kT} \exp \frac{\hbar\nu_i}{kT}\right) + Z \frac{\partial^2 \ln \nu_i}{\partial \epsilon_1{}^2}\right] \tag{12}$$

$$\mu V_0 = \mu' = f_{22}(\epsilon_1{}^0, 0)$$

$$+ \sum_i \left[\left(\frac{\partial \ln \nu_i}{\partial \epsilon_2}\right)^2 Z \left(1 - \frac{Z}{kT} \exp \frac{\hbar\nu_i}{kT}\right) + Z \frac{\partial^2 \ln \nu_i}{\partial \epsilon_2{}^2}\right] \tag{13}$$

At high temperature, $\hbar\nu_i/kT \to 0$ and $Z \to kT$, and, therefore, the first term in the brackets of equations (12) and (13) approaches zero. At low temperature the first term dominates and the second term may be neglected. The derivatives of equation (5) can then be evaluated in these two approximations. The details of the calculations are given by Dienes (1958). It is sufficient here to give the final results, which are summarized in Table 4.

Table 4

THE SIGN OF THE VARIOUS TERMS IN THE EXPRESSION FOR THE TEMPERATURE COEFFICIENT OF THE MODULUS (EQUATION 5)

Term	$T = 0°\text{K}$	Low Temperature	High Temperature Large β	High Temperature Small β
$(\partial M/\partial T)_V$	0	−	−	+
$(\partial M/\partial V)_T$	− or +	− or +	−	−
dM/dT	0	−	−	+

β = coefficient of thermal expansion

$$dM/dT = \beta V(\partial M/\partial V)_T + (\partial M/\partial T)_V$$

The most important result in this table is the positive value for $(\partial M/\partial T)_V$ for a small coefficient of the thermal expansion, β, as given in the last column. The values for $(\partial M/\partial V)_T$ are also given, although the contribution of this term to dM/dT is negligibly small since it is multiplied by β. Thus the phenomenological theory presented here indicates strongly that the anomalous temperature dependence of the moduli and the anomalously low thermal expansion are intimately connected.

The Debye and Grüneisen solid. The general conclusions derived for the Born-von Kármán solid also hold for the Debye solid and the Grüneisen solid, although with slightly more restriction.

Consider the equation relating sound velocities and the Debye temperature.

$$\vartheta^3 V(v_l^{-3} + 2v_t^{-3}) = \text{constant} \tag{14}$$

The differential of this equation with respect to temperature is

$$3\frac{d\ln\theta}{dT} + \beta = \frac{3}{(1+2/\Delta^3)}\frac{d\ln v_l}{dT} + \frac{6}{(2+\Delta^3)}\frac{d\ln v_t}{dT}$$

where Δ is the ratio of transverse to longitudinal velocity.

The differentials in velocity can be changed to differentials in moduli, and the relations between moduli can be manipulated so that any differential of modulus is expressed as follows:

$$\frac{d \ln M}{dT} = \frac{2d \ln \theta}{dT} - \frac{1}{3}\beta + f(\sigma)\frac{d\sigma}{dT} \tag{15}$$

where σ is Poisson's ratio. For example, when M is the Young's modulus, $f(\sigma) = [2^{5/2}(1 + \sigma)^{1/2}]/[1 + 2^{5/2}(1 + \sigma)^{3/2}]$. In the normal situation $d\sigma/dT$ is positive, but β dominates the right side of equation (15), so that ordinarily E decreases with increasing T. However, if β is sufficiently small, then $d\sigma/dT$ controls the sign of dM/dT and anomalies may occur.

The above argument holds for a Grüneisen solid in which

$$\gamma = \text{constant} = \frac{\beta V}{\chi C_v} \tag{16}$$

where χ is the compressibility.

The differential of the above is

$$\frac{d \ln \chi}{dT} = \beta + \frac{d \ln \beta}{dT} - \frac{d \ln C_v}{dT}$$

Ordinarily β and C_v increase with T, so the compressibility temperature coefficient depends on the detailed balance of positive and negative terms. However, for small β and $d\beta/dT$, χ decreases with T, i.e., the lower the temperature, the "softer" the solid.

The main point of this section is that all the elastic moduli are functions of the vibrational frequencies and the volume, so that the differentials of all variables balance. Consequently a number of reasonable situations can be constructed whereby the temperature dependence of the moduli are positive or negative, depending upon the smallness of the expansivity.

Discussion

The following points can be made on the basis of the theoretical work described under "Temperature Dependence of the Elastic Moduli" above.

1. Most solids are characterized by appreciable thermal expansion and, consequently, by a negative temperature coefficient of the moduli. In those cases where the pure volume and pure temperature terms have been investigated † (Born, 1923) (by means of variation of moduli with

† This approach was suggested by some work of Huntington (1958).

pressure) both terms have been found to be negative (β is large in all these cases).

2. For an isotropic substance of low thermal expansion the thermal expansion coefficient plays two important roles in reversing the sign of the temperature coefficient: (a) the smallness of β eliminates the negative volume term, and (b) at small β the pure temperature term becomes positive at elevated temperatures.

3. It is of interest to estimate the pure volume component, since it has been assumed all along that for silica it is very small compared to dM/dT. One can do this on the basis of equation (4), using the pressure variation of the modulus. From the data of McSkimin (1953) one obtains, for the $-60°$ to $40°C$ region, for the temperature coefficient of the bulk modulus

$$dK/dT = 12.3 \times 10^7 \text{ dynes cm}^{-2}/°C$$

From the data shown under "Variation of Compressibility with Pressure" below, one can estimate the variation of the bulk modulus with pressure. This dimensionless coefficient is about -4.3 at $25°C$ and decreases with increasing temperature. With $\beta = 2 \times 10^{-6}$ and $K = 3.65 \times 10^{11}$ one obtains

$$\beta V(\partial K/\partial V)_T = -K\beta(\partial K/\partial P)_T = 0.3 \times 10^7 \text{ dynes cm}^{-2}/°C$$

which is very small compared to the total dK/dT of 12.3×10^7 dynes cm$^{-2}/°C$, in agreement with the assumptions made in this chapter.

4. The density of vitreous silica can be appreciably increased by reactor irradiation. In some recent work Mayer and Gigon (1957) found that there is a corresponding increase in the modulus. Furthermore, preliminary measurements by Mayer (private communication to G. J. Dienes) and by Simon (1958) indicate that the coefficient of thermal expansion decreases upon irradiation and that there is a corresponding increase in the positive temperature coefficient of Young's modulus. These experimental results are in qualitative agreement with the theory proposed here.

In some ways the results given here are disappointing. The theory indicates that the anomalous modulus-temperature behavior is phenomenologically related to the small coefficient of thermal expansion of silica. Consequently one can conclude nothing about the structure of silica from this anomalous behavior. What is required is an explanation of the thermal expansion behavior of this substance based on first principles, a problem which has not been solved for silica. This will be discussed in detail under "Variation of Thermal Expansion with Temperature" below.

Variation of Refractive Index with Temperature

The Polarizability Relation

In this section we intend to show why the temperature coefficient of the refractive index is positive, in contrast to the negative coefficients found in other ionic solids. The approach used will be similar to that of Santen and Jonker (1948); it consists in taking derivatives with respect to temperature of the fundamental relation between the index of refraction n and the effective molecular polarizability.

Consider the relation for ionic crystals,

$$f(n) = \frac{4\pi}{3} \frac{N}{V} \alpha \qquad (17)$$

where $f(n)$ is some function of the index of refraction, N is Avogadro's number, V is the molecular volume, and α is the mean molecular polarizability.

The derivative of (17) with respect to T is

$$g(n) \, (dn/dT) = (\alpha' - \beta) \qquad (18)$$

where β is the coefficient of volume expansion $(1/V) \, (dV/dT)$; α' is the relative change in polarizability $(1/\alpha) \, (d\alpha/dT)$, and $g(n)$ is $f(n)/f'(n)$. Three of the more common approximations of $f(n)$ are shown in the accompanying tabulation, with the corresponding values of $g(n)$.

Approximation	$f(n)$	$g(n)$
Clausius-Mossotti	$(n^2 - 1)/(n^2 + 2)$	$6n/[(n^2 - 1)(n^2 + 2)]$
Drude	$(n^2 - 1)/3$	$2n/(n^2 - 1)$
Empirical (Gladstone-Dale)	$(n - 1)/3$	$1/(n - 1)$

The Clausius-Mossotti equation is considered the most representative for the alkali halides. Ritland (1955) has shown that the Drude equation is accurate for multicomponent glasses, and the empirical equation is of some historical interest (Sosman, 1927, p. 589).

Since $g(n)$ is always positive, the sign of dn/dT depends upon the difference $(\alpha' - \beta)$. In the idealized model of point charges and dipoles, α is independent of temperature. In real ionic solids, α will depend slightly on T, but the sign of dn/dT depends upon the relative magnitudes of α' and β. For those solids with a sufficiently small β, $\beta < \alpha'$ and consequently the sign of dn/dT is the sign of α'.

In Table 5 it is shown that for vitreous silica dn/dT is positive because

Table 5

COMPUTATION OF $(1/\alpha)$ $(d\alpha/dT) \times 10^5$ FOR SEVERAL SOLIDS BY EQUATION (18)

| | | | | | α' | |
Solid	n	dn/dT $\times 10^5$	β $\times 10^5$	Drude	Empirical	C-M
NaCl	1.53	-3.8	12.04	2.76	0.1	6.04
CaF$_2$	1.43	-1.1	5.7	2.8	2.7	3.5
Quartz ($\perp$)	2.11	-0.66	4.26	3.5	3.0	3.66
Quartz ($\parallel$)	2.15	-0.76	2.51	1.6	0.8	2.1
Vitreous silica	1.40	1.00	0.111	2.8	3.5	2.3

β is very small. The experimentally measured quantities are n, dn/dT, and β. They are taken from Table 168 of Landolt-Börnstein, except for the values for silica which are taken from Sosman (1927, p. 589). The value of n is the value reported at 1 μ.

The main point to be made from Table 5 is that there is nothing anomalous about the value of α' for vitreous silica: it is comparable to the value for the other solids. Therefore we conclude that the positive dn/dT appears to come from the exceedingly small coefficient of thermal expansion and not from any unusual relation between electronic displacement and temperature.

As for the case discussed in the preceding section, this anomaly is largely a reflection of the low expansivity of vitreous silica. Otherwise the relation between n and α is typical of the better-known ionic solids. Consequently the results of this section can be used as further evidence to support the conclusion of the section above titled "Evidence for Treating Viscous Silica as a Polyatomic Lattice without Groups."

It should be mentioned that the variation of the polarizability with pressure has been measured by Reitzel (1956). He found (at 2500 cps) that $d\epsilon_0/dp$ is 60×10^{-7} at 20°C and 50×10^{-7} at 138°C. Using equation (17), we find

$$\frac{1}{\alpha}\frac{d\alpha}{dp} = \frac{f'(\epsilon)}{f(\epsilon)}\frac{d\epsilon_0}{dp} + \frac{1}{V}\frac{dV}{dp}$$

For the Clausius-Mossotti approximation,

$$f'(\epsilon_0)/f(\epsilon_0) = 3/(\epsilon_0 + 2)(\epsilon_0 - 1) = 0.28$$

and, using 2.8×10^{-6} cm^2/kg for the compressibility, we find $(1/\alpha)\,(d\alpha/dp) \approx -1.3 \times 10^{-6}$ per kg/cm^2 at 20°C. This value is lower than that for most non-polar liquids, but it is not unreasonable for ionic solids.

Variation of Compressibility with Pressure

The Experimental Situation

It is a well-known fact that for vitreous silica the compressibility increases as the pressure increases, at least in the lower pressure range. This unusual behavior, which is not found in quartz (Bridgman, 1925) or other polyatomic lattices, indicates that vitreous silica becomes "softer" as the volume decreases. The experimental data have been reviewed by Reitzel, Simon, and Walker (1957), who also reported new data (determined from static measurements) accurate to about 1%. Their new data confirmed previous reports that the compressibility is proportional to the first power of P. Their data, taken in the 22–259°C temperature range and the 0–3000 kg/cm^2 pressure range, was reported by the equation

$$\chi = a(T) + b(T)P \qquad (19)$$

where

$$a(T) = (26.43 - 0.0025T) \times 10^{-7} \text{ (kg/cm}^2)^{-1}$$
$$b(T) = (43.6 - 0.080T) \times 10^{-12} \text{ (kg/cm}^2)^{-2}$$

$(T$ in °C$)$

More accurate results can be made by using ultrasonic measurements. Very good sensitivity is possible because of new experimental techniques, such as the phase balance method of McSkimin (1958) and because the equations have been derived (Cook, 1957) which permit second-order corrections to be made.

At the authors' request Mr. H. J. McSkimin kindly measured new data on a piece of optical quality vitreous silica from Amersil Company. Measurements were made by determining the change in frequency necessary to produce phase balance as a function of P at constant T. Measurements were made at 6 temperatures (-77°C, -42°C, 0°C, 24°C, 50°C, 75°C) for each of six pressures between 1 atm and 50,000 psi. The basic data were converted by one of us (O.L.A.) into units of compressibility (kg/cm$^2)^{-1}$, using methods already described

(McSkimin, 1958). With the kind permission of Mr. McSkimin, these data are reported here for the first time. According to the new data, the compressibility in the temperature and pressure range indicated is given by

$$\chi = a_0 + a_1(T - T_0) + a_2(T - T_0)^2 + [b_0 + b_1(T - T_0)]P \quad (20)$$

where

$$a_0 = (27.259) \times 10^{-7} \text{ (kg/cm}^2)^{-1}$$

$$a_1 = (8.29 \pm 0.08) \times 10^{-10}$$

$$a_2 = (8 \pm 2) \times 10^{-13}$$

$$b_0 = (4.37 \pm 1) \times 10^{-11} \text{ (kg/cm}^2)^{-2} \qquad (21)$$

$$b_1 = (7.8 \pm 1) \times 10^{-14}$$

$$T_0 = 0°C$$

$$P \text{ in units of kg/cm}^2$$

The values reported in (21) are accurate relative to the value of a_0. This value was found by careful determination of the absolute value of the sound velocities at 25°C. For the specimen used, it was found that $v_t = (3.7555 \pm 0.003) \times 10^5$ cm/sec and $v = (5.9655 \pm 0.006) \times 10^5$ cm/sec. (The fifth significant figure is reproducible. The uncertainty is maximum probable error.) Slightly different values of a_0 and b_0 are to be expected from two different samples because of method of preparation and purity; consequently no significance can be attached to the fact that the disagreement for the constants a_0 and b_0 between different specimens is outside experimental error. What is more significant is that these more accurate measurements confirm previous reports that the compressibility increases linearly with pressure. A plot of these data is shown in Fig. 2.

The equation of state over the measured temperature and pressure range is therefore (Slater, 1939, p. 207) [let $(V - V_0)/V$ be equal to $(V - V_0)/V_0$]

$$- (V - V_0)/V = c(T) + a(T)P + b(T)P^2 \qquad (22)$$

where

$$a(T) = a_0 + a_1(T - T_0) + a_2(T - T_0)^2 \quad \text{(see equation 21)}$$

and

$$2b(T) = b_0 + b_1(T - T_0) \qquad \text{(see equation 21)}$$

$$c(T) = 0 \quad \text{for } T = T_0$$

$$V_0 = \text{volume at } P = 1, T = T_0$$

and where $c(T)$ is related to the coefficient of expansion by

$$\beta = \frac{dc(T)}{dT}$$

Because the coefficient of the P term in equation (20) is small and there are no P^2 or higher terms, the equation of state can also be written

$$P = P_0(T) + P_1(T) \cdot \left(\frac{V_0 - V}{V_0}\right) + P_2(T) \cdot \left(\frac{V_0 - V}{V_0}\right)^2$$

where the values of the P's are computed from the a's and b's, using equations presented by Slater (1939, p. 203).

One of the advantages of the ultrasonic technique is that longitudinal and shear velocities are measured separately. Consequently the variation of the shear modulus and the Young's modulus with P and T is also found.

Using the general expression for the moduli as

$$M = c_0 + c_1(T - T_0) + c_2(T - T_0)^2 + [d_0 + d_1(T - T_0)]P$$

the constants for three elastic moduli are listed in Table 6.

Table 6

CONSTANTS FOR ELASTIC MODULI USING MC SKIMIN'S DATA [a]

	Young's Modulus, Y	Shear Modulus, μ	Longitudinal Modulus, c_{11}
$c_0 \times 10^{-5}$	7.3911	3.1577	7.7979
c_1	1.29 ± 0.01	0.419 ± 0.04	1.668 ± 0.01
c_2	Negative	Negative	-0.001 ± 0.0005
d_0	-8.06 ± 0.2	-3.07 ± 0.1	-9.63 ± 0.1
$d_1 \times 10^4$	26.0 ± 1	6.7 ± 1	50.0 ± 2

[a] Units of M and P in kilograms per square centimeter.

Discussion

It has already been shown above under "Temperature Dependence of the Elastic Moduli" that the temperature coefficients of the elastic moduli are anomalous because of the small coefficient of thermal expansion. Thus one is led to ask, Should a solid with an anomalous coefficient of thermal expansion possess a negative modulus-pressure coefficient over some temperature range? An attempt is made to answer this question in this section. In anticipation, we may state that a *negative* low temperature coefficient of thermal expansion implies negative values for at least some of the modulus-pressure coefficients over some temperature range.

In order to show this it is necessary to relate pressure coefficients and thermal expansion to the frequency spectrum. This is done by defining the Grüneisen constant,

$$\gamma_j = -\frac{d \ln \nu_j}{d \ln V} \tag{23}$$

which means that for each frequency there is a corresponding value of the Grüneisen constant. The parameter γ_j is fundamentally related to the coefficient of thermal expansion by an expression derived in statistical mechanics which shows that thermal expansion of a mole of quantized oscillators is (Slater, 1939, p. 219)

$$\beta = \frac{\chi}{V} \sum_{j=1}^{N} \gamma_j \frac{dE_j}{dT} \tag{24}$$

The parameter E_j is the thermal energy of the jth oscillator and is related to the specific heat by the relation

$$C_v = \sum_{j=1}^{N} \frac{dE_j}{dT} \tag{25}$$

It is easy to see, from equation (24), that β is negative whenever a sufficient number of the γ_j's are negative. Equation (24) is quite general for non-metallic solids. The usual expression for β is given in another form and involves two drastic assumptions: (1) all the γ_j's are equal to a single value (γ_{Gr}); and (2) the frequency spectrum is given by the Debye approximation. In this case we have the famous Grüneisen relation, in place of equation (24),

$$\gamma_{\text{Gr}} = -\frac{d \ln (\nu_{\text{max}})}{d \ln V} = \frac{\beta V}{\chi C_v} \tag{26}$$

where V is the volume per gram molecule. All the variables on the far right side of (26) are experimentally measured functions of temperature. When β is negative, γ_{Gr} is also negative. In the general case γ_{Gr} as a function of T is regarded as an integrated value of γ which often departs from constancy just as the empirical value of the Debye temperature departs from constancy.

The Grüneisen constant can be related to the pressure coefficient of the elastic modulus M by means of the simplified relations between frequency, sound velocity, and wave number which exist in the low wave number region of the frequency spectrum.†

At low values of the wave number k we have

$$\nu_i = v_i k \qquad (i = 1, 2, 3) \tag{27}$$

for the three acoustic branches, which can be written in differential form as

$$\frac{d \ln \nu_i}{d \ln V} = \frac{d \ln v_i}{d \ln V} + \frac{d \ln k}{d \ln V} \tag{28}$$

Using the relation $v_i = \rho M_i^2$ (M_i is the appropriate elastic constant), we see that

$$\frac{d \ln v_i}{d \ln V} = \frac{1}{2} \frac{d \ln M_i}{d \ln V} + \frac{1}{2} \tag{29}$$

In a sample where sound is propagated by keeping the number of wavelengths fixed, the wavelength is proportional to the length, and we have

$$\frac{d \ln k}{d \ln V} = -\frac{1}{3} \tag{30}$$

Using equations (28), (29), and (30) in (23), we have

$$\gamma_j = -\frac{1}{2} \frac{d \ln M_j}{d \ln V} - \frac{1}{6} \tag{31}$$

The volume derivative can be expressed as a pressure derivative,

$$\frac{d \ln M_j}{d \ln V} = -\frac{1}{\chi} \frac{d \ln M_j}{dP} \tag{32}$$

where χ is the isothermal compressibility and the derivatives are for zero pressure.

Finally, let us suppose that the moduli are found by experiment to be related to the pressure (at low values of P) by

$$M_j = a_j + b_j P \tag{33}$$

† We are very much indebted to Professor C. Smith of the Case Institute of Technology, who revealed the simplified derivation shown in equations (27) through (32) to one of us (O.L.A.) before his own publication. This derivation is published here through his kind permission.

Then, using equations (32) and (33), we find that (31) can be expressed as

$$\gamma_j = \frac{1}{2\chi}\left(\frac{b_j}{a_j}\right) - \frac{1}{6} \tag{34}$$

Equation (34) demonstrates that a negative b_j (modulus-pressure coefficient) leads to a corresponding negative γ_j at low temperatures. In order to compare the γ_j found from pressure measurements to γ_{Gr} found from thermal measurements, it is necessary to integrate equation (34) over all directions and the three values of j. Barron (1957) has shown that the average low temperature γ is

$$\gamma_0 = \frac{\displaystyle\sum_{j=1}^{3} \int \frac{\gamma_j\, d\Omega}{v_j^3 4\pi}}{\displaystyle\sum_{j=1}^{3} \int \frac{d\Omega}{v_j^3 4\pi}} \tag{35}$$

where j numbers the three solutions, the integrals are taken over the solid angle, and v_j is the required sound velocity. For an isotropic solid where the sound velocity is independent of direction, equation (35) reduces to

$$\gamma_0 = \frac{1}{(2 + \Delta^3)}\,(\Delta^3 \gamma_l + 2\gamma_s) \tag{36}$$

where $\Delta = v_t/v_l$ and the subscripts refer to the values found from equation (34) from longitudinal and shear measurements.

We are now in a position to compare pressure and thermal measurements. What is required for γ_0 is the value of the ratio b_j/a_j at temperatures sufficiently low that equation (27) is valid. Using the values found at the lowest measured temperature, we find, from (21) and (22),

$$\gamma_0 = -1.55$$

This value compares very well with the low temperature values of γ_{Gr} obtained from thermal measurements according to equation (26), which are shown in Table 8 in the next section.

The agreement is better than should be expected, considering that the pressure experiments were not taken near absolute zero. However, the computations illustrate the main point of this section, namely, that a low temperature negative coefficient of thermal expansion implies that some (if not all) of the modulus-pressure coefficients are negative. Thus the main problem again shifts to that of the elucidation of the anomalous thermal expansion coefficient which is found in vitreous silica.

An important consequence of the measurements reported in this section is that the derivative

$$\left(\frac{d \ln M}{dT}\right)_V$$

can be evaluated. Lazarus (1949) pointed out that, if this derivative is significantly different from zero, it is erroneous to employ assumptions that the moduli are unique functions of volume. This derivative is especially important for vitreous silica, since it was shown above under "Temperature Dependence of the Elastic Moduli," that it dominates the change of modulus with temperature.

Assume that the moduli are functions of temperature as well as volume (interatomic separation); then

$$M = M(V, T) \tag{3}$$

The ratio

$$R_M = \frac{\left(\dfrac{d \ln M}{dT}\right)_V}{\left(\dfrac{d \ln M}{dT}\right)_P} = 1 + \frac{\beta}{\chi} \frac{\left(\dfrac{d \ln M}{\partial P}\right)_T}{\left(\dfrac{d \ln M}{dT}\right)_P} \tag{37}$$

can be derived from equation (3) and gives a measure of the explicit dependence of the modulus on temperature at constant volume.

Equation (37) can be expressed in terms of the compressibility and the shear modulus through equation (24) and Table 6. Taking the values for β and χ to be 0.11×10^{-5} and 0.26×10^{-5}, we find

$$R_\chi = \frac{\left(\dfrac{\partial \ln \chi}{\partial T}\right)_V}{\left(\dfrac{\partial \ln \chi}{\partial T}\right)_P} = 1 + \frac{\beta_0 \, b_0}{\chi_0 \, a_1} = 0.78$$

and

$$R_\mu = \frac{\left(\dfrac{\partial \ln \mu}{\partial T}\right)_V}{\left(\dfrac{\partial \ln \mu}{\partial T}\right)_P} = 1 + \frac{\beta_0 \, d_0}{\chi_0 \, c_1} = 0.96$$

These values are compared in Table 7 with similar ratios found by Lazarus (1949) for several other solids. It is evident that for vitreous

Table 7

RATIO OF $[(d \ln M)/dT]_V$ AND $[(d \ln M)/dT]_p$ FOR SEVERAL SOLIDS

Solid	Vitreous Silica	NaCl	CuZn	Cu	Al	KCl
R_χ	0.78	0.14	0.47	1.51	0.42	—
R_μ	0.96	0.76	—	—	—	1.49

silica, just as for the solids discussed by Lazarus, it is doubtful whether it is justifiable to assume that the moduli are unique functions of inter-atomic separation.

An attempt to explain the negative pressure coefficient of compressi-bility, based upon the network hypothesis, has been made by Smyth et al. (1953). Their mechanism is simply that pressure has the effect of making a bent Si-O-Si bond more bent. Smyth was able to account for a positive value of $d\chi/dP$ in a qualitative, but not entirely satisfactory, way. Among other things, Smyth assumed that the potential energy of the atoms was a Born type involving a repulsion and coulombic attraction. In doing this, he assumed that the moduli were unique func-tions of interatomic separation. In view of the computations made by equation (37), the results of Smyth's calculation are suspect, although his general idea may be reasonable.

The variation of χ with pressure is anomalous up to about 20,000 kg/cm^2 according to the measurements of Bridgman (1948). Beyond that point, the compressibility becomes normal. This is shown in Fig. 3. Using the values of the constants in equation (24) in (25), we find that at 0°C the change of volume due to a pressure P is

$$-\Delta V/V = 26.522 \times 10^{-7}P + 41.62 \times 10^{-12}P^2$$

so that for, $P = 2 \times 10^4$ kg/cm^2, we have by extrapolation $-\Delta V/V = 0.07$. This extrapolation leads to a value which is slightly too high. It is, however, significantly close to the relative difference between the volumes of cristobalite and vitreous silica which can be computed from their densities, $\Delta\rho/\rho = (2.32 - 2.20)/2.20 = 0.055$. Thus it can be stated that, when the volume of the non-crystalline phase is reduced to the point where the packing is as efficient as in a crystalline phase (cristobalite), the compressibility varies with pressure in the normal manner.

Variation of Thermal Expansion with Temperature

The Experimental Situation

Vitreous silica has been noted as a solid which has negative expansivity below 200°K; i.e., in the region below 200°K a decrease of temperature results in an increase of volume. The expansivity of quartz, in contrast to vitreous silica, is normal. Because of the different behavior of these two phases of silica, some speculations on the structure of vitreous silica have been made on the premise that, as far as expansivity is concerned, vitreous silica is unique among homogeneous solid substances (Babcock et al., 1954).

Contrary to the above supposition, negative expansivities had previously been reported in a variety of substances including crystalline silicon (Erfling, 1942), crystalline zinc blende (Adenstadt, 1936), and polycrystalline α-uranium (Schuck and Laquer, 1952). A very recent addition to this list is crystalline indium antimonide (Gibbons, 1958). It is not apparent that any significance can be attached to the fact that quartz has a normal expansivity while vitreous silica has not. Silicon and germanium have structures and vibrational spectra which resemble each other more than the structures and vibrational spectra of quartz and vitreous silica resemble each other. Yet germanium has a normal expansivity, while the expansivity of silicon is negative below 120°K (Gibbons, 1958). The low temperature expansivity of cristobalite is not clearly established; this crystalline phase of silica may have a negative expansivity. Sosman (1927, p. 398) reviewed that situation and came to the conclusion that the evidence is in favor of a negative expansivity in this phase of silica.

It appears that the negative expansivity in vitreous silica has little, if any, connection with the departure from crystallinity. The characteristics of structure that the above-mentioned solids, crystalline and non-crystalline, have in common (Gibbons, 1958) are tetrahedral coordination and loose packing of their structures. It is likely that the negative expansivity of vitreous silica arises from peculiarities of the vibrational spectra caused by the above characteristics.

The General Theoretical Situation

Until very recently, it has been commonly supposed that any idealized crystal which is composed of harmonic oscillators held together by reasonable force laws would always exhibit a positive expansion coefficient at all temperatures. This classical viewpoint is due to Grüneisen, who derived the equation for β (equation 26), using the assumptions that the vibrational spectra could be represented by the maximum frequency ν_{max}, and this frequency was inversely proportional to the volume raised to some constant power called γ.

The importance of equation (26) lies in the fact that β can be computed as a function of temperature with only one arbitrary parameter since χ, C_v, and V are measured quantities. The difficulty in equation (26), which was not apparent for many years after Grüneisen's derivation, is that γ is not a constant at lower temperatures (Bijl and Pullman, 1955)—the very region where the Debye approximation basic to equation (26) is most valid.

Barron has shown (1955, 1957) that qualitative agreement with low temperature experiments can be obtained, if the general definition of γ is retained, namely, equation (23), in which for every different frequency ν_j, a different value of γ_j is possible. The specific assumptions made by Barron are: at low temperatures the frequencies are given by equation (27), i.e., for any direction of wave propagation there are three frequencies; and the equation between the velocity and the volume can be established by the relation between elastic constants and interatomic separation, a relation which requires knowledge of the Madelung constants and the interatomic force laws. (This tacitly amounts to taking $[(d \ln M)/dT]_V = 0$.)

Using these assumptions, three γ_j's are computed for every direction, and the value of γ at very low temperatures is computed by equation (35).

Barron predicted that γ_0 would be considerably lower than the γ for the high temperature, and that at temperatures about at $T/\theta = 0.3$, the change from the high temperature γ toward γ_0 would occur. Gibbons (1958) later experimentally verified Barron's predictions. While Barron showed that some of the values of γ_j would be negative, it was Blackman (1958) who actually was able to compute a negative γ_0 using a reasonable model.

Blackman, using equation (35), found $\gamma_0 = -2.5$ for the zinc blende structure. He derived the Madelung constants for this structure according to the method of Born and Bollman (1920). He used two terms for the potential interaction: the coulombic electrostatic term and the Born repulsive term ($n = 6$ for the exponent). Blackman was also able to account for a positive γ_{Gr} at high temperatures. The triumph of the work of Barron and Blackman is that they have shown that a negative expansivity can be accounted for within the framework of ionic crystal physics merely by retaining general concepts derived from statistical mechanics.

Some of the details of their work are probably applicable to the analysis of the expansivity of vitreous silica. It turns out that the values of γ_j which are most negative are associated with transverse vibrations. Consequently the magnitude and sign of the expansivity depend upon the balance between the negative γ_j's arising from some transverse modes and the positive γ_j's arising from the longitudinal modes and some transverse modes. At low temperatures, vibrations associated with the weakest elastic constants tend to dominate, and the converse is true at high temperatures. This is how it happens that at low temperatures the value of γ is weighted toward negative γ_j's but weighted toward positive γ's at high temperatures.

The set of γ_j's associated with c_{44} is much more negative for the zinc blende structure than for the rock salt structure. This difference arises from the different Madelung constants involved; apparently an open structure is much more likely to have a negative expansivity than a closely packed one. The physical meaning of this observation is obvious: in an open structure, transverse vibrations do not encounter the high repulsive forces found in a closely packed structure, and consequently they tend to contract the lattice points. [See the mechanical analogy in Barron's paper (1957).]

The Expansivity of Vitreous Silica

The plot of volume expansion versus temperature $(3\Delta l/l_{273})$ below $273°$K for vitreous silica is shown in Fig. 4. The open circles are from the data of Beattie et al. (1941), and the crosses represent new data kindly measured by Dr. D. F. Gibbons at our request. From a theoretical point of view, the most significant way of plotting low temperature expansivity data is to plot the experimental γ_{Gr} from equation (26) against the dimensionless temperature T/θ_∞, where θ_∞ is the high temperature Debye temperature (Barron, 1957). Such plots are presented in Fig. 5 (Gibbons, 1958) for ZnS, Si, InSb, Ge, and vitreous silica. The data on Ge are presented in contrast to Si to illustrate the point that large differences are possible between two structures which in many other ways resemble each other. The value of θ_∞ for vitreous silica was taken to be equal to θ (elastic) $= 495°$, which, although not strictly correct, is sufficiently accurate for purposes of comparison. The datum for ZnS is not so accurate as that for the other solids, because the room temperature value of χ was used for all temperatures. This error could change the lower end of the curve, but it would not affect significantly the place where it crosses the x-axis. The values of the Grüneisen constant, using equation (26), are shown in Table 8.

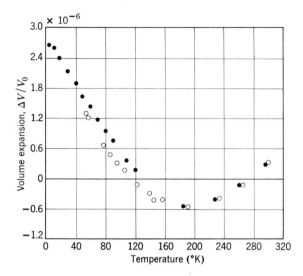

Fig. 4. A plot of the volume expansion of vitreous silica from room temperature downward. The open circles (G.E. SiO$_2$) are data from Beattie et al. (1941); closed circles (Amersil SiO$_2$) are new data privately measured by Dr. D. F. Gibbons (1958) of Bell Telephone Laboratories for this chapter.

Table 8

GRÜNEISEN CONSTANT FOR VITREOUS SILICA [a]

Absolute Temperature

	T	10	30	50	70	90	110	130
	T/θ	0.0202	0.0606	0.101	0.141	0.182	0.222	0.262
Specific heat (erg/g mole $\times 10^{-6}$)	C_p	7.93	91.7	61.2	306.2	416.0	522.0	623.0
Volume (cc/g mole)	V	27.48	27.48	27.48	27.48	27.48	27.48	27.48
Expansivity $\times 10^{-6}$	β	1.302	2.481	2.439	2.319	2.118	1.845	1.509
Grüneisen constant	γ_{Gr}	−4.511	−0.743	−0.392	−0.208	−0.140	+0.097	+0.0665

[a] $\theta = 495° = \theta$ (elastic). Data on β from Gibbons (1958). Data on C_p from Westrum and Morrison (Anderson, 1959).

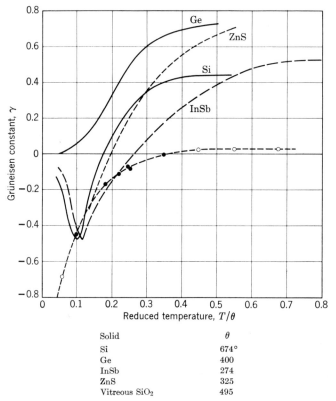

Solid	θ
Si	674°
Ge	400
InSb	274
ZnS	325
Vitreous SiO_2	495

Fig. 5. A plot of γ vs. T/θ for four solids with negative expansivities (Si, ZnS, InSb, and vitreous silica) and one solid (Ge) without a negative expansivity. The plot was prepared, except for the data on ZnS (Adenstadt, 1936), by Dr. D. F. Gibbons (1958). The value of γ_{Gr} for all four solids departs from the high value γ_{Gr} at about $0.3T/\theta$ as predicted by Barron (1957) and becomes zero between 0.1 and $0.3T/\theta$.

From Fig. 5 it is seen that there is more similarity between the expansivity of vitreous silica, ZnS, and Si than between Si and Ge. The negative expansivity of ZnS is now understood. It is, therefore, tempting to speculate if the same approach which was used for ZnS would also explain the results for vitreous silica. On the positive side, there is the fact that both these solids have roughly 50% covalent bonds (see Table 3), so that there is hope that the solution of Blackman for ZnS based upon the ionic force approximation might also work for SiO_2. The chief theoretical difficulty is that the Madelung constants for cristobalite are not known. This is a somewhat formidable problem, because the silicon and oxygen ions have different coordination. On the negative side, there is the fact that the expansivity of cristobalite itself is not known: it is only *suspected* to be negative because of circumstantial evidence (Sosman, 1927, p. 398). Clearly, while theoretical progress might be possible on the cristobalite structure, it would have little significance so far as vitreous silica is concerned until the plot of γ_{Gr} versus T/θ for cristobalite is experimentally proved to be similar to that of vitreous silica. Furthermore, there is reason to believe that the moduli cannot be functions of the volume alone, as shown in the last section.

The following positive statements which are related to the conclusions of Barron and Blackman, can be made, however. First, it is not surprising that vitreous silica has a negative expansivity, because (a) there is tetrahedral coordination around the silicon, and (b) there is very loose packing in this structure. Second, the position of the oxygen in the cristobalite structure indicates that bending vibrations of the Si-O-Si bond would occur with small interaction of neighboring charges; this bending vibration is a transverse wave with a small force constant, and, therefore, it would tend to predominate at low temperatures.

With regard to the point about the bending vibration of the Si-O-Si bond, Smyth (1955) speculated that this vibration was the probable cause of the negative expansivity in vitreous silica; his argument was based upon more drastic assumptions than those of Barron and Blackman. It is not clear whether this bending vibration is acoustic or not; the results of the section above titled "Low Temperature Specific Heat" indicate that it may not be. The distinction between the mechanism of Barron and Blackman and that of Smyth is that the former authors were exclusively concerned with negative expansivities arising from acoustic transverse vibrations, while the latter's mechanism is a special type of transverse vibration which may be non-acoustic.

It should be pointed out that inefficient packing of the structure, although important, is not in itself enough to explain some negative expansivities. This explanation has been used to account for the difference between the expansivities of quartz and vitreous silica (Smyth, 1955). It does not suffice, however, for the difference between silicon and germanium, because these two structures presumably have the same excluded volume. For these two solids the net balance between the negative and positive values of γ_j depend upon the fine details of the force constants. It is conceivable that γ_{Gr} would remain positive at all temperatures for germanium, while with slightly different force constants (silicon) the low temperature value of γ_{Gr} would be negative (Gibbons, 1958). Correspondingly, for the silicas, the fine details of the force constants may have an important effect on the expansivities, quite apart from the gross features of the geometric structures.

The Acoustic and Dielectric Loss Due to Lattice Distortion

The Experimental Situation

In vitreous silica, acoustic (Anderson and Bömmel, 1955) and dielectric (Volger and Stevels, 1956; see also Chapter 17 of this book) measurements at low temperatures and high frequency reveal a large internal friction effect. This loss is caused by a structural relaxation which is characterized by low activation energy and virtually no entropy of activation. The corresponding losses exist in quartz, both in the acoustic (Bömmel et al., 1956) and the dielectric (Volger et al., 1955) aspects. The acoustic loss peak in vitreous silica is about three orders of magnitude higher than in natural quartz. The difference is less between the peaks for vitreous silica and synthetic quartz.

The losses in quartz are relatively sharp, and they approximate a single relaxation mechanism. On the other hand, the loss curves in vitreous silica are broad, requiring a distribution of relaxation times. The height and width of the internal friction peaks show that a great deal more heat is generated from the lattice waves in the non-crystalline phase than in the crystalline phase.

The acoustic loss results from the propagation of both longitudinal waves and transverse waves. A longitudinal wave involves a dilatation and a distortion. The distortion loss component in the longitudinal measurement is almost identical with the transverse loss. Hence the loss is most probably associated with a transverse vibration.

Accompanying the acoustic loss is a 2% relaxation of the shear modulus. This small relaxation means that only a small amount of the total volume is relaxing at any given moment.

The acoustic loss in vitreous silica is directly proportional to the log frequency, which can only be accounted for by a distribution function of relaxation times.

The loss versus temperature is shown in Fig. 6, the loss versus frequency in Fig. 7, the shear modulus relaxation in Fig. 8, and the relation between the temperature at which the loss is maximum against frequency is shown in Fig. 9.

Mechanism of Loss

Figure 9 shows that the data can be plotted by the equation

$$\omega = \nu_{max} \exp\left(-q/kT_m\right) \tag{38}$$

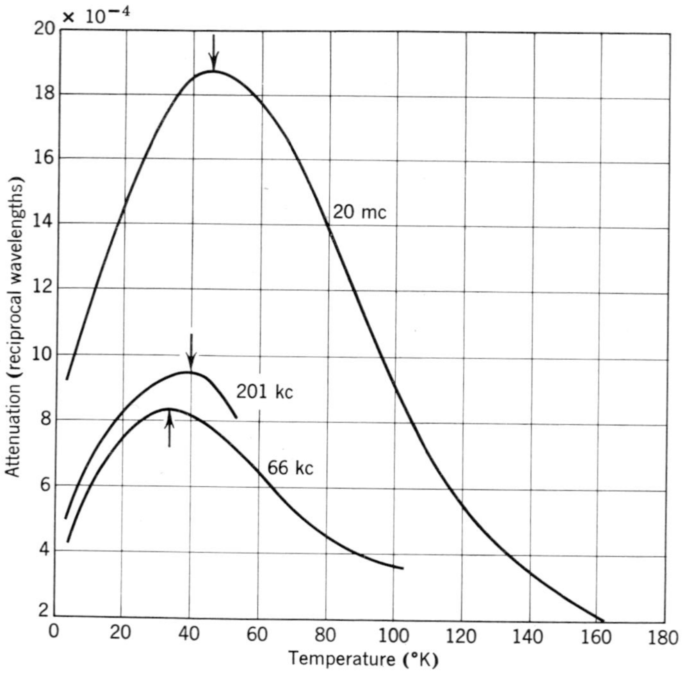

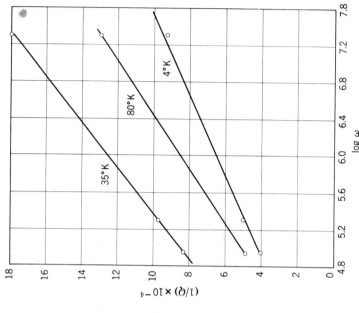

Fig. 7. Acoustic loss vs. frequency (log ω) for three different temperatures. The linear dependence indicates a wide distribution function of relaxation times. (Anderson and Bömmel, 1955.)

Fig. 6. Acoustic loss vs. T for three different frequencies. The shift of the peak with frequency is typical of a relaxation. The increase of peak height with frequency results from the nature of the distribution function. Curve for 20 mc from Anderson and Bömmel (1955); curves for 201 kc and 66 kc from Fine et al. (1954).

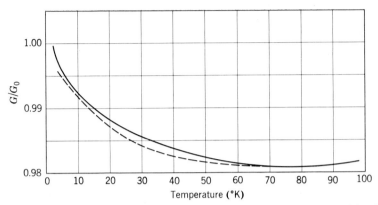

Fig. 8. The shear modulus vs. temperature at two different frequencies. The shift to the right at higher frequencies and the relaxation of the modulus in the neighborhood of the absorption peak temperature are typical of a structural relaxation. Broken curve, 66 kc/sec; solid curve, 20 mc/sec. (Anderson and Bömmel, 1955.)

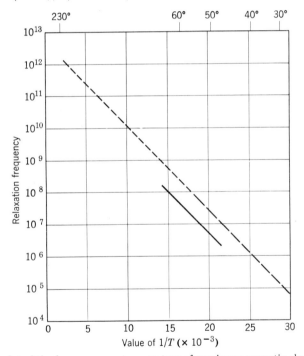

Fig. 9. A plot of the frequency vs. temperature of maximum acoustic absorption for vitreous silica. Broken curve, $\omega = \nu_{max} \exp(-1340/RT)$ (Anderson and Bömmel, 1955); quartz solid curve, $\omega = \nu_{max} \exp(-1600/RT)$ (Bömmel et al., 1956). Both curves show that the equation $\omega = \nu_{max} \exp(-q/RT)$ holds, where q is found from the slope of the line, and ν_{max} is the Debye frequency calculated from elastic constants. The experimental data for vitreous silica are extrapolated to room temperature to show the probable existence of a relaxation at 10^{12} cps.

where ν_{max} refers to the Debye frequencies calculated from the elastic constants in the section "Low Temperature Specific Heat," and T_m refers to the temperature at which the loss is a maximum for a given frequency ω. The fact that the pre-exponential factor is equal to the Debye frequency indicates that there is essentially no entropy of activation. Consequently the relaxation proceeds with no reorganization of the structure surrounding the relaxing species.

The activation energy is very small in comparison with relaxation processes connected with, for example, diffusion of ions in silica. The total loss is much greater for non-crystalline silica than for quartz, as Table 9 shows (internal friction is identified as $1/Q$).

Table 9

MEASURED QUANTITIES IN ACOUSTIC AND DIELECTRIC LOSS

Material	q (cal/mole)	Max $1/Q$
Vitreous silica (acoustic)	1340	2×10^{-3}
Quartz (acoustic)	1600	2×10^{-6}
Vitreous silica (dielectric)	1900	10^{-4}
Quartz (dielectric)	1900	2×10^{-5}

The values shown in Table 9 are intended only to show order of magnitude. The maximum value $1/Q$ depends to some extent on the sample and the frequency (see Fig. 6).

A remarkable result is the low magnitude of q. This energy is very much smaller than the energy required for diffusion, or the energy required for a molecular rotation (such as, for example, the tetrahedron). The energy is about right for a bending of the Si-O-Si bond joining tetrahedrons, as the following computation shows (Mason, 1958, p. 307). Assume that the energy required to push two silicon atoms apart as the bond flexes from an angle of $(\pi - \phi)$ to π is that associated with the transverse vibration of the oxygen atom. There are about 2.2×10^{22} SiO_2 molecules per cubic centimeter, and twice as many Si-O bonds. The expansion caused by a bond angle changing by ϕ (in radians) is

$$\delta l/l = (1 - \cos \phi) \approx \phi^2/2$$

The energy is approximately the expansion multiplied by the Young's modulus, or

$$q = \frac{EN \, (\delta l/l)}{J(4.4 \times 10^{22})} = 2.05 \times 10^5 \, \phi^2 \text{ cal/mole}$$

where E is Young's modulus (7.80×10^{11}), N is Avogadro's number (6.03×10^{23}), and J is the conversion factor between ergs and calories (4.18×10^7). Table 10 shows the activation energy for various angles found by the crude calculation shown above.

Table 10[a]

ENERGY TO FLEX AN Si-O-Si BOND IN A CRISTOBALITE-LIKE STRUCTURE

q (cal/mole)	36.5	145	330	580	910	1310	1800
ϕ (in deg)	1	2	3	4	5	6	7

[a] Mason (1958), p. 307.

The energy for $6°$ is equal to the measured value. The vitreous silica network could easily account for these bond flexures, since the variation in bond angle is about $\pm 5°$ according to x-ray analysis (Warren, 1937). Similarly, distortions of the bonds in the crystalline lattice would be sources of bond flexures in the region of impurities such as substitutional aluminum.

A wide distribution of relaxation times is required in order to account for the broad absorption peaks in vitreous silica. The distribution is much narrower in quartz. The distribution function can be derived (approximately) from the curves shown in Fig. 7.

Schwarzl (1953, p. 199) has shown that the relaxation time spectrum $\mathcal{L}(\ln \tau)$ can be approximated by knowledge of the $\delta(\ln \omega)$ curve (loss versus log frequency) by

$$\mathcal{L}(\ln \tau) = (2/\pi)(\delta - d^2\delta/d \ln \omega^2) \qquad (39)$$

This is a second-order approximation and therefore is fairly accurate, at least in the neighborhood of the measured frequencies.

From Fig. 7 it is evident that, in the measured range,

$$\delta(\ln \omega) = a + b \ln \omega$$

Since the curvature is zero, we have

$$\mathcal{L}(\ln \tau) = (2/\pi)(a - b \ln \tau) \qquad (40)$$

This distribution is very wide, and we see that there are fewer relaxation mechanisms for longer relaxation times.

Since the activation energy is related to τ by the formula $q/RT = (\ln \tau + \ln \nu_{max})$, the preponderance of relaxation mechanisms have small activation energies. A more detailed analysis of $\mathcal{L}(t)$, based upon numerical approximation methods, has been made by Mason (1958); he showed that the curves in Figs. 6 and 8 could be computed in detail by using the relaxation spectrum computed from Fig. 7. The fact that all these curves are interconnected by one relaxation spectrum is reassuring evidence that the loss is a relaxation.

Another interesting point is the low value of the relaxation strength. The small change in modulus (no more than 3%) shows that only a fraction of the relaxation species are relaxing at any one time. If all the species relaxed together, the relaxation strength would be about 50%.

The relaxation is of such a nature that there is very little change in volume, since the loss is dominated by shear waves. Consequently relaxation mechanisms which involve states of packing such as proposed by Hall (1948) for water are not important in this case. The values shown in Table 7 indicate that the same relaxation is involved in the dielectric and acoustic experiments, indicating that the relaxation species must be quite polarizable.

A considerable amount of information has been deduced from the dielectric and acoustic losses, which limit the possible mechanisms to explain this loss. A proposed mechanism based upon the random network hypothesis of glass was made by Anderson and Bömmel (1955) which accounts for all the facts and deductions of this section. According to the random network hypothesis † of the structure of silica glass, "Each silicon is tetrahedrally surrounded by 4 oxygens at a distance of about 1.62 Å, and each oxygen is shared by two silicons. The two bonds to an oxygen are nearly diametrically opposite one another but the angle may vary a little" (Warren and Biscoe, 1938). The gradual change from the close range ordered structure to distant disordered structure is a result of the small variation in bond angles. A kinked Si-O-Si bond angle corresponds to the oxygen atom in a higher than average energy state. For every kinked bond there is, however, another almost equivalent state which is the mirror image of the kinked bond. If the oxygen is to pass from one state to the mirror image, the two adjacent silicons must be pushed apart. Thermal energy can make the oxygen atom take up these equivalent positions alternately. A shear ultrasonic wave can bias one of the energy states with respect to the other, thus altering the time in each state. The time lag for equilibrium to be reached is the source of the relaxation.

Such vibrations of the oxygen atom would exert a strong dipole moment since the motion Si-O-Si is a transverse optical vibration. This

† It is recognized by the authors that the x-ray interpretations of vitreous silica are now a controversial matter; see footnote on p. 449.

vibration would require virtually no reorganization of the structure, thus satisfying the condition of zero entropy of activation. The number of bent bonds would determine the magnitude of the loss and the value of the relaxation strength. The spread of relaxation times would depend upon the variability of the bond angle. The data on quartz indicate that there is very little variability in the relaxation mechanism, no doubt because a particular kind of defect always produces the same distortion in a periodic structure. Three different defects have been proposed to account for the acoustic loss in quartz. Mason (1958) has proposed that the loss is due to a transverse oxygen vibration of a bent Si-O bond lying in the X-Z plane because of a B center (two substitutional aluminum atoms in place of silicon). Stevels (see Chapter 17) has proposed that the loss arises from distortions due to a P center (one substitutional aluminum for silicon plus a hydrogen ion to satisfy electroneutrality). King (see p. 443) proposes that the distortion arises from excess oxygen (two adjacent oxygens having no silicon to bridge them). In all these mechanisms for quartz the energy and the entropy would be about the same as in the mechanism proposed for vitreous silica.

The network hypothesis is a convenient framework to relate a specific motion to the loss for vitreous silica. It must be admitted that other structural hypotheses might also account for such a loss with perhaps a different vibration. However, it appears that some type of lattice vibration which becomes a relaxation when the silica lattice is distorted is almost certainly the cause of this loss.

In passing, it should be mentioned that a strong optical relaxation has been found in borate glasses by Ioffe (1956). This relaxation is similar in many ways to the optical relaxation observed in vitreous silica.

Conclusion

The work of this chapter has shown that all the anomalies are interrelated. From a phenomenological point of view, four of the anomalies—temperature dependence of the elastic moduli, variation of refractive index with temperature, of compressibility with pressure, and of thermal expansion with temperature—are equivalent. In these cases thermodynamic self-consistency is satisfied. However, these anomalies yield no direct evidence on the structure of vitreous silica.

All the anomalies can be easily explained in terms of the network hypothesis of glass structure of Warren and Zachariasen. This cannot be regarded as proof of the hypothesis, but at least there is no conflict. Other, more complicated hypotheses may also account for the anomalies. However, it appears that the controversy on the structure of vitreous silica must be settled on the basis of direct measurements of the structure itself: the physical properties of vitreous silica are not particularly helpful in deciding the issue. Until there is general agreement concerning the direct evidence for the structure of vitreous silica, the most useful picture, because of its simplicity, of this solid is the network hypothesis.

Further progress requires better understanding of the low temperature specific heat, and any one of the four anomalies mentioned above. The most needed experimental measurements are the elastic constants and low temperature expansivity of cristobalite. These data cannot be taken until a single crystal of cristobalite is successfully grown. Until these measurements are reported, the question whether the anomalies are unique to the non-crystalline state of silica must be regarded as open. An important theoretical problem is to account for the value of the $(dM/dT)_V$ derivative which is important in the properties of vitreous silica.

The application of equations valid for crystalline solids to vitreous silica has been successful in dealing with elastic moduli, specific heat, polarizability, and expansivity. This suggests that it is a valid approximation to regard vitreous silica as a crystalline solid when one is concerned with the properties connected with close range interaction of atoms.

Note added in proof: The excess specific heat described in the second section has been verified by J. Morrison and co-workers at the National Research Laboratories, Ottawa, Canada. B. Stoicheff and co-workers there found that the elastic constants at very high frequencies (10^{12} cps) were the same as reported here, evidence against acoustic dispersion. They also found a very low frequency spectrum of optical vibrations which appeared as a Raman shift in the 10-cm^{-1} to 50-cm^{-1} region. This is sufficient to explain the excess heat and supports the Si-O-Si vibration as the mechanism of loss [P. Flubacher, A. Leadbetter, J. Morrison, B. Stoicheff, *J. Phys. Chem. Solids*, **12**, 53 (1959)].

ACKNOWLEDGMENTS

We wish to thank Professor Westrum who provided his unpublished measurements on specific heat, Mr. H. J. McSkimin who made the measurements on sound velocity under pressure, and Dr. D. F. Gibbons who made new measurements on expansivity. Several manuscripts, kindly made available to us before publication, were a great help in the preparation of this chapter: Dr. D. F. Gibbons' paper on negative expansivity, Professor M. Blackman's paper on negative expansivity, Professor C. Smith's paper on Grüneisen constants, and Dr. W. P. Mason's book on acoustics.

REFERENCES

Adenstadt, H., *Ann. Physik* **26**, 69 (1936).

Anderson, O. L., *J. Phys. Chem. Solids* **12**, 41 (1959).

Anderson, O. L., and Bömmel, H. E., *J. Am. Ceram. Soc.* **38**, 125 (1955).

Babcock, C., et al., *Ind. Eng. Chem.* **46**, 161 (1954).

Barron, T. H. K., *Phil. Mag.* **46**, 720 (1955).

Barron, T. H. K., *Ann. Phys.* **1**, 77 (1957).

Beattie, J. A., et al., *Am. Acad. Arts Sci.* **74**, 327 (1941).

Bijl, D., and Pullman, H., *Physica* **21**, 285 (1955).

Blackman, M., *Phil. Mag.* **3**, 831 (1958).

Bömmel, H., Mason, W. P., and Warner, A. W., *Phys. Rev.* **102**, 64 (1956).

Born, M., *Atomtheorie des festen Zustandes,* Tuebner, Leipzig, 1923.

Born, M., and Bollman, E., *Ann. Physik.* **62**, 218 (1920).

Born, M., and Huang, K., *Dynamical Theory of Crystal Lattices*, Clarendon Press, Oxford, 1954, Chapter II, for example.

Breen, R. J., et al., *Phys. Rev.* **105**, 520 (1957).

Bridgman, P. W., *Am. J. Sci.*, **X**, 483 (1925).

Bridgman, P. W., *Am. Acad. Arts Sci.* **76**, 55 (1948).

Cook, R. K., *J. Acoust. Soc. Am.* **29**, 445 (1957).

Dank, M., and Barber, S. W., *J. Chem. Phys.* **23**, 597 (1955).

Dienes, G. J., *J. Phys. Chem. Solids* **7**, 290 (1958).

Erfling, H. D., *Ann. Physik* **41**, 467 (1942).

Fine, M. E., et al., *J. Appl. Phys.* **25**, 402 (1954).

Flubacher, P., et al., *J. Phys. Chem. Solids* **12**, 53 (1959).

Gibbons, D. F., *Phys. Rev.* **112**, 136 (1958).

Grüneisen, E., *Handbuch der Physik*, Vol. X, 1924, p. 5.

Hall, L., *Phys. Rev.* **73**, 775 (1948).

Huntington, H. B., in *Solid State Physics*, Academic Press, New York, 1958.

Ioffe, V. A., *J. Tech. Phys.* (U.S.S.R.) **XXVI** [3], 516 (1956).

Koga, I., et al., *Phys. Rev.* **109**, 1467 (1958).

Lazarus, D., *Phys. Rev.* **76**, 545 (1949).

McSkimin, H. J., *J. Appl. Phys.* **24**, 988 (1953).

McSkimin, H. J., *J. Acoust. Soc. Am.* **30**, 314 (1958).

Marx, J. W., and Sivertsen, J. M., *J. Appl. Phys.* **24**, 81 (1953).

Mason, W. P., *Physical Acoustics and Properties of Solids*, Van Nostrand, Princeton, N. J., 1958.

Mayer, G., and Gigon, J., *J. phys. radium* **18**, 109 (1957).

Reitzel, J., *Nature* **178**, 940 (1956).

Reitzel, J., Simon, I., and Walker, J. A., *Rev. Sci Instr.* **28**, 828 (1957).

Ritland, H. N., *J. Am. Ceram. Soc.* **38**, 86 (1955).

Schuck, A. F., and Laquer, H. L., *Phys. Rev.* **86**, 803 (1952).

Schwarzl, F., *Proc. 2nd Intern. Congr. Rheol., 1953*, p. 199.

Simon, I., *J. Am. Ceram. Soc.* **41**, 116 (1958).

Slater, J. C., *Introduction to Chemical Physics*, McGraw-Hill, New York, 1939.

Smyth, H. T., *J. Am. Ceram. Soc.* **38**, 140 (1955).

Smyth, H. T., et al., *J. Am. Ceram. Soc.* **36**, 238 (1953).

Smyth, H. T., et al., *J. Am. Ceram. Soc.* **36**, 327 (1953).

Sosman, R. B., *The Properties of Silica*, Chemical Catalog Co., New York, 1927.

Spinner, S., *J. Am. Ceram. Soc.* **39**, 113 (1956).

Szigeti, B., *Trans. Faraday Soc.* **45**, 155 (1949).

van Santen, J. H., and Jonker, G. H., *Philips Research Repts.* **3**, 371 (1948).

Volger, J., and Stevels, J. M., *Philips Research Repts.* **11**, 452 (1956).

Volger, J., Stevels, J. M., and Van Amerongen, C., *Philips Research Repts.* **10**, 260 (1955).

Warren, B. E., *J. Appl. Phys.* **8**, 645 (1937).

Warren, B. E., and Biscoe, J., *J. Am. Ceram. Soc.* **21**, 49 (1938).

Zachariasen, W. H., *J. Am. Chem. Soc.* **54**, 3841 (1932).

Zarzycki, J., *Verres et réfractaires* **11**, 3 (1957).

DISCUSSION

M. L. HUGGINS

I find this chapter very interesting, not only the relationships between the various properties, but also the final conclusions.

I would like to ask, however, if the arguments necessarily depend upon the assumption of ionic character in the solids. From your own figures, vitreous silica and zinc sulfide, for example, are about 50% covalent. I will agree that there is a great deal of ionic character in these solids, but on the other hand many of the properties of some of them, especially quartz, can be understood assuming complete covalency. In fact, long ago I deduced the structure of quartz completely neglecting ionicity [Huggins, *Phys. Rev.* **19**, 363 (1922)].

G. J. DIENES

The main arguments of the chapter do not depend on assuming ionic solids. Of course, when Blackman's arguments on zinc sulfide are repeated, the details tacitly rest upon the assumption of ionic bonding. Zinc sulfide is only partially ionic, but the only calculation that can be made from first principles requires the ionic assumption. What Blackman showed is that it is theoretically feasible to have a negative γ for an ionic zinc blende structure. We have no way of knowing how it is theoretically feasible for the diamond structure to have a negative γ starting from first principles. We did, however, show that one anomaly will lead to another, and this line of argument is independent of the degree of ionicity.

R. O. DAVIES

Blackman's calculation has a disposable constant (n) in the repulsive term. This constant is adjusted to experimental data. Therefore Blackman's method takes care to some extent—not entirely, no doubt, but to some extent—of the coordination, so the distinction between ionic and covalent bonds is not clear.

E. F. PONCELET

Would the arguments hold for solids with molecular structure or bonding?

O. L. ANDERSON

The arguments hold for any solid in which the vibrational properties can be approximated by a mole of harmonic coupled oscillators. Consequently the arguments very probably would not hold for a molecular solid like benzene. They should be true for the class of solids Grüneisen called "polyatomic solids without group formation" which would include diamond and KCl; and solids in between.

A. B. LIDIARD

I wonder if there is an inconsistency in the argument on the connection between the temperature coefficient of the moduli and the expansivity. A harmonic vibration formula for free energy is only formally applicable to a solid which is anharmonic, that is, a solid which has an a_3 term in your notation. Yet, when you compute dM/dT you end up only with terms in a_2 and a_4. It seems to me that under these conditions you cannot retain the relation between free energy and the frequencies ν_i.

G. J. DIENES

We really don't require that a_3 be zero or negative. We merely assume that a_4 dominates a_3 and look at the consequences. That is not the same as denying that the solid is anharmonic. Our argument, however, is critically dependent upon a positive value of a_4 in the three-dimensional case.

R. O. DAVIES

The thermal average $(\partial^2 \ln \gamma)/d\epsilon^2$ (corresponding to your a_4) for argon is positive in the three-dimensional case. However, the extension of the positive value from one dimension to three dimensions for vitreous silica should be made with caution, particularly in view of the negative γ.

J. A. KRUMHANSL

One cannot be exact in general, but the general idea that transverse vibrations in open structures are responsible for anomalous properties has been noted for the graphite and boron nitride layer structures. To some extent, there is an analogy between these covalent solids and Blackman's ionic zinc blende structure.

It is known that in these the interactions between layers is very small, and the "in-layer" thermal expansion is negative at low temperatures.

T. A. LITOVITZ

There is a purely covalent lattice in which all these anomalies occur—water. Furthermore, water exhibits a considerable amount of tetrahedral structure, leading me to believe that the tetrahedral structure has more to do with the anomalies in both water and quartz than the type of bonding.

O. L. ANDERSON

Dr. Litovitz has made a salient point. All the solids with negative expansivity are four-fold coordinated.

J. A. PRINS

I concur with Dr. Litovitz. It is the tetrahedral coordination, or more generally the open structure, which allows the possibility of contraction.

O. L. ANDERSON

In Blackman's calculation, the negative γ arises from the peculiar Madelung constant, which is a reflection of the open structure (or tetrahedral coordination). Consequently the assumption of ionicity in Blackman's calculations may be of secondary importance, just as Dr. Litovitz and Professor Prins suggest.

H. L. FRISCH

The effect of vibrational anharmonicity on lattice thermal properties has been studied analytically by Dugdale and MacDonald [*Phys. Rev.* **96**, 57 (1954)]. They studied a linear chain interacting through a Morse potential. A characteristic frequency is found which depends through the anharmonic terms on the atomic displacement. The Grüneisen relationship is stated to be valid in first approximation. What the results and methods are for three-dimensional lattice I do not know.

H. LILLIE

I would like to point out that in so far as the dn/dT anomaly is concerned, most glasses are anomalous in this respect, with or without the small expansivity.

O. L. ANDERSON

First, many of the reported anomalies that you speak of occur in the frequency range where dispersion is important, and that in itself may cause the positive dn/dT. Second, there are import chemical bonding considerations in complicated glasses which make the subject quite difficult to analyze.

W. A. WEYL

It is possible to find a positive value of dn/dT even in solids which have a high coefficient of expansion, for example, magnesium oxide. Expansion decreases the number of electrons per unit volume, but it also increases the polarizability of the anions because of the greater anion-cation distance. If the value of the last component exceeds that of the former, the refractive index increases with increasing temperature.

by

R. J. Charles

J. C. Fisher

General Electric Research Laboratory

Strength of Amorphous Solids

The strength of materials is limited by the magnitude of the forces that bind atoms together. Theoretically, a solid material should rupture when subjected to an elastic tensile strain of several percent, the required stress being several percent of the elastic modulus. Experiments on very carefully prepared specimens confirm the theory. Griffith (1921) and others have shown that glass fibers can extend as much as 10% without breaking, and Brenner (1956) has shown that fiber-like metal crystals can extend elastically as much as 5%.

Most samples of solid materials flow or rupture at elastic strains a factor of 100 to 1000 smaller than the theoretical limit. In many instances the reduced strength of these samples is known to be caused by imperfections or flaws. Some of the important imperfections in crystals are dislocations (wrinkles in the atom layers that make up the crystal: their motion produces plastic deformation), internal cavities, grain boundaries, surface notches, and included foreign particles. In glasses and other amorphous solids, the important imperfections are surface cracks or other flaws that grow under the influence of stress and chemical attack.

Statistical Theories of Fracture

Most theories of the strength of amorphous solids are essentially statistical in nature. They are based on the idea that the strength of ordinary objects is limited by flaws of one sort or another, and on the assumption that there exists an *a priori* probability of finding a flaw of given severity in each element of material. If the probability of finding each kind of flaw in each part of an object were known, the probable strength of the object could be deduced.

Statistical theories of fracture tend to fall into a pattern that has been summarized concisely by Epstein (1948):

1. Let the underlying probability distribution of flaw strengths s be $f(s)$, so that the probability that the strength of a given flaw lies between s_1 and s_2 is $\int_{s_1}^{s_2} f(s) \, ds$.

2. The associated cumulative distribution, giving the probability that the strength of a given flaw is less than s, then is $F(s) = \int_{-\infty}^{s} f(s) \, ds$.

3. The probability distribution of the strength of a sample containing n flaws then is $g_n(s) = nf(s)[1 - F(s)]^{n-1}$, for which

4. The associated cumulative distribution function is $G_n(s) = \int_{-\infty}^{s} g_n(s) \, ds = 1 - [1 - F(s)]^n$.

5. [When n is sufficiently large, the probability distribution of the strength of a sample containing n flaws simplifies to $g_n(s) \approx nf \exp(-nF)$, and the cumulative distribution to $G_n(s) \approx 1 - \exp(-nF)$, where f and F stand for $f(s)$ and $F(s)$.]

6. The most probable strength of a sample containing n flaws corresponds to the maximum of $g_n(s)$. It is S_n^* in the relationship

$$(n - 1)[f(S_n^*)]^2 = f'(S_n^*)[1 - F(S_n^*)]$$

7. Most statistical theories of fracture differ from one another only in the form of the distribution function $f(s)$ that is assumed.

On the basis of Epstein's treatment, it is convenient to classify statistical theories of fracture according to the various sorts of distribution laws $f(s)$ that are assumed to relate the probability of failure of a flaw to the stress.

1. Weibull (1939) and more recently Greene (1956) assume $f(s) = ks^m$. When their data cannot be fit with so simple a law, Weibull uses $f(s) = k(s - s_0)^m$, and Greene uses $f(s) = \Sigma_i k_i s^{m_i}$. Weibull fits the experimental fracture strengths of glazed porcelain, portland cement, Indian cotton fibers, cotton yarn, cotton fabric strips, green spruce, a mixture of stearic acid and plaster of Paris, aluminum die castings, malleable iron castings, and valve spring wire. Greene fits the strengths of glass samples of various sizes.

2. Kontorova (1940) does not assume a form of $f(s)$ directly but instead says that the important flaws are cracks that fail according to Griffith's formula $s = Ac^{-\frac{1}{2}}$ (s is the fracture stress, A a constant, c the crack diameter). The crack sizes are assumed to be distributed according to the probability law $p(c) \sim \exp[-\beta(c - c_0)^2]$.

3. Frenkel and Kontorova (1943) assume $f(s) \sim \exp[-\alpha(s - s_0)^2]$.

4. Fisher and Hollomon (1947) assume that the important flaws are cracks that respond to stress according to Griffith's formula, and that the crack diameters are distributed according to the probability law $\rho(c) = \lambda \exp(-\lambda c)$, with λ a constant. For hydrostatic tension, the corresponding $f(s)$ is $f(s) = (2s_0{}^2/s^3) \exp(-s_0{}^2/s^2)$, with s_0 a constant; and for other stress combinations $f(s)$ is a more complicated function. These workers fit the strengths of glass samples of various sizes.

5. Kase (1953, 1954) assumes that the important flaws are cracks, but that the tensile stress is reduced by a flaw of area A according to the equation $s = s_0(1 - \alpha A)$, where s_0 and α are constants. Assuming the flaw areas to be distributed according to the law $f(A) = \lambda \exp(-\lambda A)$, he obtains $F(s) = \exp\{-\exp[\beta(s - s^*)]\}$, with β and s^* constants, as the cumulative distribution law for the strength of samples containing many flaws, and fits the experimental data for samples of rubber.

Different as these several forms of $f(s)$ may be, they all can be made to fit at least a portion of the experimental data. They all predict that larger samples will be weaker, and that the distributions of fracture stresses will be skewed toward smaller stresses, as is observed. These observations do not enable the selection of any one of the proposed forms of $f(s)$ as most nearly correct, but they do suggest that the idea of randomly distributed flaws has merit.

It is instructive at this point to examine what is known of the mechanism of failure of glass and of other amorphous solids under stress, to see whether or not the fundamental assumptions of the statistical theory are indeed applicable. The first subject to be reviewed is the stress corrosion of glass, rubber, and plastics, which causes the flaws initially present to grow at a rate that depends upon stress. The second subject to be reviewed is the creep and relaxation of glass and plastics, which cause the bulk properties of the material to change at a rate that depends upon stress.

Role of Stress Corrosion in the Fracture of Amorphous Solids

When subjected to appropriate environments, many amorphous materials exhibit a type of failure in which the strength is markedly influenced by the time during which the load is applied. Many experiments have illustrated the fact that humid atmospheres reduce the breaking strength of silicate glasses; and similar reductions in strength have been found for natural rubbers in atmospheres containing ozone, and for some plastics when immersed in detergent solutions and solvents. Considerable evidence supports the idea that a chemical interaction occurs between components of the stressed material and components of the environment, and that this reaction may be influenced by applied stress:

1. In inert environments or at low temperatures, where the reaction rate should be negligibly slow, the breaking strengths of these materials become independent of the duration of load and always reach a relatively high value.

2. Similarly, high strengths are observed if the loading rate is rapid with respect to the reaction rate.

3. Subjecting these materials to reactive environments before, but not during, test generally has little effect on the most probable breaking loads, suggesting that the corrosion rate is accelerated by stress.

4. There is a continuous influence of temperature on the relationship between the time of loading and the failure stress.

Since breaking stresses are generally small in comparison with the theoretical limits, an explanation of the failure phenomena must include reference to defects or flaws, and, since failure is time-dependent, it is natural to conclude that the defects are subject to change during the test. The questions naturally arise: What are these changes, and how are they influenced by applied stress and environment? An alkali silica glass will be considered as an example of a material in which the delayed effects are pronounced.

Since the strength of silicate glasses is notably sensitive to abrasion, it is generally accepted that surface flaws are controlling influences. It seems logical to assume that delayed failure under constant load is caused by the growth of these flaws, under the influence of a reactive environment, to a critical size at which the stress concentration at the most critical flaw is sufficient for spontaneous failure. The growth process must be corrosive by nature, and a corrosion mechanism involving water vapor is indicated.

From silica chemistry it is reasonable to expect that silanol structures

$$(-\overset{|}{\underset{|}{Si}}-OH)$$

will be among the final products of the attack on a silica

glass by water. There are two structures in silicate glass where such attack might occur. One of them is an unending network in which silicon atoms are joined by oxygen atoms into chains [—Si—O—Si—] held together by bonds that are largely covalent. The other is a terminal structure in which alkali atoms are ionically associated with oxygen atoms within the glass [—Si—O[M]]. A reaction between water and the alkali ion is easily visualized, for it is essentially the hydrolysis reaction of the salt of a weak acid:

$$[—Si—O \, [M]] + H_2O \rightarrow [—SiOH] + M^+ + OH^- \qquad (1)$$

The reaction between water and the covalent chain,

$$[—Si—O—Si—] + H_2O \rightarrow 2[—SiOH] \qquad (2)$$

seems less important, as fused and crystalline quartz are notably insoluble in water at moderate temperature and neutral pH.

Although it does not seem possible that the network structure can undergo severe breakdown by the direct reaction of water, the following reactions, which are triggered by the initial terminal structure reaction, may be able to do so.

$$[—Si—O—Si—] + OH^- \rightarrow [—SiOH] + [—Si—O^-] \qquad (3)$$

$$[—Si—O^-] + H_2O \rightarrow [—Si—OH] + OH^- \qquad (4)$$

Reaction (4) gives rise to the same OH^- ion as does the initial hydrolysis reaction (1), and consequently the whole dissolution reaction of a simple alkali silicate glass in water vapor should be autocatalytic.

In the scheme above, the triggering reaction for dissolution (reaction 1) depends on the momentary vacating of an active site by an alkali metal ion, so that contact with a water molecule is possible. Thus the rate of the initial dissolution or corrosion of the glass in question should be roughly the same as that for alkali ion diffusion. Recent experimental results (Charles, 1958) show that the temperature dependence of the initial corrosion rate is indeed the same as that for alkali ion diffusion, lending support to the corrosion mechanism just described.

This mechanism provides a satisfactory explanation for the corrosion of glass by water under zero stress, but in order to explain time-dependent fracture it is necessary to extend the analysis to include preferential corrosion at the tip of a crack, accelerated by stress. The acceleration of corrosion by stress is a real possibility in silicate glasses, for it is known that expansion of the glass structure by suitable heat treatment (rapid cooling) leads to enhanced alkali ion diffusion and an associated increase in electrical losses, and to greater chemical reactivity. Such increases are held to be a consequence of the increased number of alkali ions situated in the loose interstices created when the glass structure is expanded, or to a decrease in the activation energy for diffusion occasioned by the more open structure. It seems likely that a high state of triaxial tension, such as found at the tip of a crack-like flaw, would expand the glass structure and speed the corrosion rate at the flaw tip relative to that at the flaw sides where the stress conditions are much less severe. Under conditions of high local stress where the corrosion rate at the tip of the flaw is sufficiently accelerated, the flaw will sharpen and deepen until the stress concentration builds up to that required for rupture. Smaller applied stresses, on the other hand, could lead to a rounding off of the tip of the flaw, owing to insufficient enhancement of the corrosion rate by stress, so that the sample, in a reactive environment, might actually end up stronger than when it was in its initial state. Strengthening of this sort is found in practice when samples are etched under small stresses.

If cracks deepen under stress, as they must if the stress corrosion mechanism under discussion is correct, then a specimen stressed for either an insufficient time or intensity to cause failure should, when subsequently loaded rapidly to failure, prove weaker than it would have been without the prestressing treatment. In practice, such weakening often is not observed, a fact that has caused a great deal of confusion in the reporting and analysis of experimental work in the past; but it can be resolved if one considers that the acceleration of the growth rate of flaws is very small until the flaw size approaches the necessary size for spontaneous failure. Unless the prestressing treatment is of nearly sufficient severity and duration to cause fracture itself, there should be little observable change in the fracture stress upon subsequent rapid loading.

It is interesting to compare the failure of natural rubbers in atmospheres containing small amounts of ozone with the failure of silicate glasses in water-containing atmospheres, for many similarities may be observed even though the physical characteristics of the two materials are vastly different. As illustrated in Fig. 1, taken from the results of

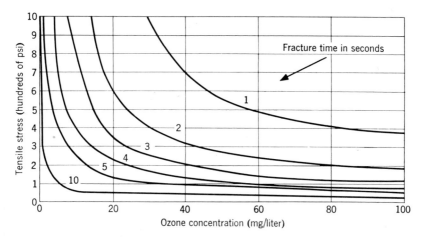

Fig. 1. Influence of ozone and tensile stress on the fracture time of semicured rubber (Norton, 1940).

an investigation by Norton (1940), failure of rubber specimens under static load is very much dependent on the concentration of ozone and the duration of the stress. Norton also states that exposure of unstressed rubber specimens in atmospheres containing ozone only slightly affects the failure results. It is natural to conclude that applied stress again markedly influences the reaction between the atmosphere and components of the test material.

The shapes of the curves in Fig. 1 show many of the characteristics that have been observed for static failure of glasses. However, one phenomenon that occurs during rubber failure is much more difficult to observe in glass. The Young's modulus of rubber is so low and the strain to fracture is so high that one would predict that the flaws responsible for fracture must be large enough to be clearly visible. Experiment does in fact reveal large cracks; and, as shown in Fig. 2, the cracks that develop from surface flaws arrange themselves with their long dimensions perpendicular to the tensile stress directions.

It is evident that failure of natural rubber in ozone is a direct result of oxidation of the rubber, and that this oxidation is accelerated if the rubber is under tensile stress. The specific mechanisms of oxidation are as yet not clear, but one might guess that the uncoiling of molecular chains during stretching could in some way increase the number of active points (carbon-carbon bonding?) that become accessible to the diffusing ozone molecules, causing preferential oxidation at local regions under high stress. Thus the mechanisms of stress corrosion are virtually

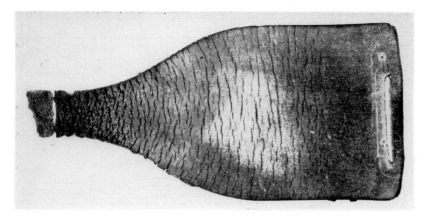

Fig. 2. Large cracks developed in semicured rubber subjected to tensile stress in the presence of ozone (Norton, 1940).

the same for alkali silicate glasses and for rubber, except that the chemical reactions are quite different.

Organic chemists have long been familiar with the problem of "stress cracking" in plastics subjected to tension and a weak solvent. Details of the stress cracking mechanisms are not clear, but it appears that the solvent preferentially attacks local areas of high tensile stress arising from stress concentrators, allowing the solvent to loosen and remove polymer chains at a faster rate near the tip of a flaw than elsewhere on the surface of the plastic. Such conditions would lead to accelerated flaw growth and to the development of cracks oriented perpendicular to the direction of maximum tensile stress.

It might be expected that strong solvents would be less effective in bringing about stress cracking in plastics, for the action of these solvents may be sufficiently fast that the accelerating influence of stress becomes relatively unimportant in determining the dissolution rate. Flaw tips would then round out and stress concentrators disappear, in spite of the presence of a stress. The contrasting influences of weak and strong solvents are illustrated in Fig. 3, which shows stress cracking on the surface of a beam of Plexiglas that was loaded to a uniform extreme fiber tension of about 4000 psi. Part (a) of this figure shows the severe stress cracks arising from the action of a drop of the weak solvent acetone. Part (b) shows the effect of a drop of the stronger solvent, ethylene dichloride, applied for the same length of time but causing only slight stress cracking and an appreciable amount of dissolution.

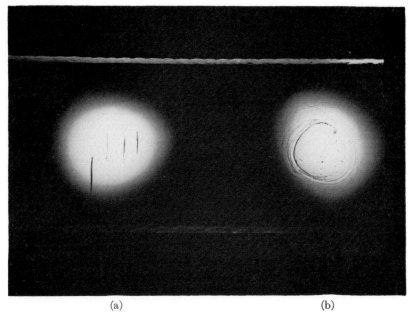

(a)   (b)

Fig. 3. Stress cracking in Plexiglas: (a) in the presence of the weak solvent acetone; (b) in the presence of the strong solvent ethylene dichloride.

Role of Creep and Relaxation in the Fracture of Amorphous Solids

It is of interest to consider the change in geometry of a crack or flaw that is subjected to strain. The maximum stress σ_{max} at the root of an ellipsoidal crack is related to the average stress σ_{avg} by a relationship of the form $\sigma_{max}/\sigma_{avg} \approx 1 + 2w/t$, where w is the width of the crack and t its thickness. When the sample containing the crack is stretched to a strain ϵ, the crack width is approximately unchanged, $d \approx d_0$, and the crack thickness is increased approximately in proportion to ϵ, $t \approx t_0(1 + \epsilon)$. The stress ratio under strain, therefore, is $\sigma_{max}/\sigma_{avg} \approx 1 + 2w_0/t_0(1 + \epsilon)$. For most materials ϵ is small compared to unity, so that the stress ratio is $\sigma_{max}/\sigma_{avg} \approx 1 + 2w_0/t_0$. For materials such as rubber and some plastics, however, the strain is large and considerably reduces $\sigma_{max}/\sigma_{avg}$ from the value it otherwise would have. Figure 4 illustrates a rubber band with two degrees of extension, showing the marked decrease in severity of the notch with strain.

It is clear that changes in ϵ with stress cannot affect the failure of materials such as inorganic glasses to the same extent as rubber, for the average strain at failure is of the order of 10^{-3}, or so, for glass. Yet there is a type of recoverable deformation in glasses that might tend

Fig. 4. Strain-induced reduction of the severity of a notch in rubber.

to reduce their notch sensitivity as the applied stress increases. Some simple experiments can illustrate this type of deformation.

Figure 5a shows the permanent deformation produced in a glass fiber when the fiber was formed in a loop to obtain an extreme fiber stress of about 250,000 psi, heated to a temperature of 150°C for 2 hours, and then quenched to room temperature. (The strain point for the glass from which the fiber was drawn was about 515°C, indicating that the possibility of viscous flow at the test temperature was remote.) The maximum deformation of the fiber in Fig. 5a corresponds to about $\frac{1}{2}\%$ inelastic strain. The bent fiber was heated once more for 2 hours at 150°C without any applied stress and, as shown in Fig. 5b, it almost resumed its original shape. This behavior is a good example of the anelastic effects that can be obtained in glasses at moderate temperatures, and it illustrates that very high stresses may bring about local distortions that can diminish the effectiveness of stress-concentrating defects.

In plastics, even more than in glasses, anelastic strain and creep should be effective in reducing the very high stresses in the neighborhood of the tip of a sharp crack. Furthermore, creep should alter the bulk properties of the material so that the stress required to propagate cracks is either increased or decreased.

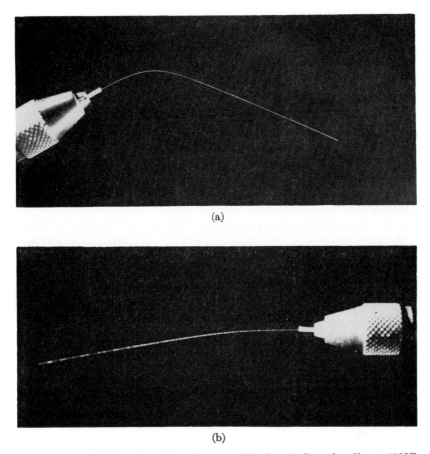

(a)

(b)

Fig. 5. Anelastic deformation (a), and recovery (b), of a soda-lime glass fiber at 150°C.

Requirements of a More Complete Theory of Fracture

In many instances the failure of amorphous solids is strongly influenced by time-dependent phenomena. A question arises as to the means whereby these time-dependent processes can be included within the framework of the statistical theory of fracture, if indeed they can be so included at all. Three classes of time-dependent phenomena are of interest:

1. If the time-dependent process is one of stress corrosion, where pre-existing cracks grow as a function of time, or of stress relaxation, where the tip of the flaw is rounded by local inelastic deformation, then the

fracture properties at any given time can be expressed in terms of a probability distribution of fracture stresses $f(s)$ *that depends upon the time*. In general, then, the probability distribution will be a function $f(s, t)$ that depends upon both stress and time, and the problem that must be solved by an adequate theory is to relate the time-dependence of $f(s, t)$ to the loading history and to the initial distribution of flaws.

2. If the time-dependent process involves creep, relaxation, chemical change, or any other process that alters the bulk properties of the material without changing the geometry of the flaw spectrum, the statistical theory still will be valid with a time-dependent probability distribution of flaw strengths $f(s, t)$, the time-dependence now coming about because of the changing substrate through which the flaws must grow to cause fracture.

3. If, however, there is a time-dependent process that is associated with single time-dependent causes, such as single critical thermal fluctuations, a new mode of description is required. No probability distribution function $f(s, t)$ is adequate. [Coleman (1956), for example, has suggested that fracture may occur as a result of a first-order process with kinetics similar to radioactive decay. Yokobori (1953) has made a similar proposal. They retain some of the characteristics of the flaw theory because larger specimens, with more volume in which the critical process can occur, fail sooner. Yet there is no function $f(s, t)$ that can describe this situation, for changes in the distribution of flaws play no role here. The only requirement is that sufficient time elapse for action of the random process that triggers fracture.]

The first two classes of time-dependent phenomena are such that the occurrence or non-occurrence of fracture depends upon the *state* of the material. If there is a sufficiently deep flaw in relation to the bulk properties of the material, prompt fracture is certain; and, if there is no such flaw, the sample is sure to hold together until a flaw qualifies, whether through flaw growth, stress increase, or time-dependent changes in bulk properties. The third class of phenomena does not relate the occurrence or non-occurrence of fracture to the state of the material, except statistically: whatever the state of the material, there is a probability that it will break during the next increment of time.

We tend to believe that the fracture of amorphous solids can be accounted for by a statistical theory wherein the important element is a time-dependent probability distribution of flaw strengths $f(s, t)$. In other words, we feel that the experimental evidence so far available supports the idea that fracture depends primarily upon the state of the material, including the distribution of flaws within it.

REFERENCES

Brenner, S. S., *J. Appl. Phys.* **27**, 1484 (1956).

Charles, R. J., *J. Appl. Phys.* **29**, 1554 (1958).

Coleman, B. D., *J. Appl. Phys.* **27**, 862 (1956).

Epstein, B., *J. Appl. Phys.* **19**, 140 (1948).

Fisher, J. C., and Hollomon, J. H., *Trans. AIME* **171**, 546 (1947).

Frenkel, J. I., and Kontorova, T. A., *J. Tech. Phys. (U.S.S.R.)* **7**, 108 (1943).

Greene, C. H., *J. Am. Ceram. Soc.* **39**, 66 (1956).

Griffith, A. A., *Phil. Trans. Roy. Soc. London* **A221**, 163 (1921).

Kase, S., *J. Polymer Sci.* **11**, 425 (1953).

Kase, S., *J. Polymer Sci.* **14**, 497 (1954).

Kontorova, T. A., *J. Tech. Phys. (U.S.S.R.)* **10**, 886 (1940).

Norton, F. J., *Gen. Elec. Rev.* **43**, 93 (1940).

Weibull, W., *Ing. Vetenskaps Akad. Handl.* **No. 151** (1939); **No. 153**, (1939).

Yokobori, T., *J. Phys. Soc. Japan* **8**, 104 (1953).

DISCUSSION

H. L. FRISCH

The statistical theories of fracture which have been described have one important common feature, namely, they assume that the flaws of the sample act independently of one another. More generally one would expect that, if one flaw lets go, the next would let go more easily, i.e., the flaw strength distribution would be correlated in time (and possibly in space) and fracture would result from a cooperative phenomenon. The extension of the statistical framework for such theories involving the non-independence of the fundamental events can, of course, be carried through in a straightforward manner, particularly if the fundamental events possess the Markov property. The principal difficulties lie in a closer analysis of the physical situation involved in strength and fracture of materials rather than in the probabilistic treatment. The success of the statistical theories summarized by Epstein may be due in part to the fact that, by choosing an appropriate time scale for one's experimental observations, even a highly correlated process can be approximated by a purely random process.

J. C. FISHER

The experimental evidence is not complete. However, Greene, for example, has found that the assumption of single events is sufficient to account for the dispersion in most experiments.

O. L. ANDERSON

The data that are most lacking in all experiments are those pertaining to dispersion. Nearly all experiments report only a few (perhaps 20) tests under controlled conditions. This is not sufficient to determine the nature of distribution in strength, nor enough to decide how the dispersion varies as the median varies. If a large number of tests were performed (say 500) and the distribution was found to be log-normal rather than normal, then the events could not be independent.

R. E. MOULD

I agree that the general qualitative picture which the authors present is correct, namely, that static fatigue involves the growth of surface flaws, and that an interaction between water and glass plays a vital role in this growth. There are, however, other reasonable mechanisms for the reaction at the root of the crack.

There is, for instance, the lowering of the surface energy of the freshly formed surface by the chemical adsorption of water, as Orowan has proposed [*Nature* **154,** 341 (1944)]. There is also the possibility, as Elliott has suggested, that the diffusion of water in surface layers may limit the rate of the reaction [*J. Appl. Phys.* **29**, 224 (1958)]. It probably will turn out that different mechanisms apply under different experimental conditions.

I would also like to comment on the nature and origin of flaws in glass. At our laboratory [Preston Laboratories, Inc.] we have attempted to determine the distribution of flaws by the direct method of varying the area under high stress with emphasis on very small areas [Mould, *J. Appl. Phys.* **29**, 1263 (1958)]. The smallest area was obtained by testing small fibers in crossbending, in which case the area under high stress was no larger than 10^{-6} sq in. With the stressed area this small, the strength for moderate durations was about 500,000 psi, and, of more interest, the dispersion was no greater than could be accounted for by the apparatus (about 2% of the mean value). Further refinements of the apparatus and methods by O. C. Hansen resulted in still smaller dispersions and higher strengths. This leads us to believe that in this case we are dealing with specimen areas with either no flaws or with very uniform flaws of molecular size (of the order of 7 Å by the Griffith relation).

From a phenomenological point of view, it would appear that there are three classes of flaws and three corresponding strength ranges:

1. The gross flaw, visible and resulting from mechanical damage, which reduces strength to the usual technical levels.

2. The intermediate flaw, invisible and apparently related to forming procedures, which limits the strength of pristine bulk glass and glass fibers to the range 100,000–500,000 psi.

3. The intrinsic structural flaw of molecular size (or perhaps lack of any flaw) associated with the very high strengths in our micro-crossbending tests. In contrast to (1) and (2), this condition produces little if any variability in strength values.

In all three ranges we find experimentally a similar dependence of strength on load duration and test conditions (especially relative humidity) and thus believe that the fracture mechanism is essentially the same in all three cases.

J. C. FISHER

The absence of dispersion is remarkable at the half a million psi level. In addition to your two reasons for the lack of dispersion, it may be possible that chemical attack is making all the flaws equivalent by the time it breaks.

J. W. MICHENER

The concept of slow crack growth may be sufficient to explain the fracture of large samples, but there is doubt that it can apply to fine fibers breaking near 400,000 psi. Instead, it is conceivable that the strength is governed by statistical fluctuation in the strength of surface bonds. This is the so-called "single bond catastrophe" which is based upon the idea that all bonds are so highly stressed that neighboring bonds cannot absorb the energy of a fractured bond. All known effects on fibers can be explained by this mechanism.

It is worth mentioning that O. C. Hansen has obtained 985,000 psi on 0.0017-inch glass fibers (Owens Corning E glass) by reducing the time of loading below 0.01 second and controlling the atmosphere.

R. J. CHARLES (in reply to Dr. Mould)

The conclusion that the water reaction leading to failure was a consequence of sodium ion self-diffusion in the bulk glass near an interface arose from the fact that the same temperature dependence was observed in complementary experiments on strength and corrosion of a soda lime glass. The corrosion mechanisms clearly seemed to depend on the alkali ions and the rates could be shown to be dependent on the volume expansion of the glass structure.

R. J. CHARLES (in reply to Dr. Michener)

It would seem that, if statistical fluctuations in the strength of surface bonds were the prime reason for failure at around 400,000 psi, then it would be difficult to explain the continuous and rapid effect of atmosphere on strength at those levels. At strength values that are more nearly at the theoretical level the single bond idea may have a great deal of merit.

T. H. DAVIES

There are two ways of getting sodium out of glass. One is to withdraw sodium oxide, in which case the activation energy is about 40 kcal/mole if a detailed balance of charges is to be preserved. The other is an ion exchange in which the sodium ion comes out and a hydrogen ion enters. In this process the activation energy is about 15 kcal/mole. Is your process the ion exchange type?

R. J. CHARLES

The reaction we think occurs is of the ion exchange type with about the same activation energy as you have mentioned.

H. A. ELLIOTT

I agree with Charles and Fisher that the mechanism of stress corrosion fracture in materials is due to slow growth of Griffith cracks. I discussed these problems at some length for the case of metals and more briefly for glass [Thesis, University of Bristol, 1947, and *J. Appl. Phys.* **29**, 224 (1958)]. I feel, however, that the authors somewhat simplify the problem.

At least five different possible mechanisms are involved, and it is not yet clear experimentally which is the most important in any individual case. The mechanisms are briefly as follows:

1. Diffusion of the corrosive atmosphere or solution in the opened crack from the exposed free surface.

2. Diffusion of the corrosive atmosphere, or of the reacting component from the solid through any corrosion products left in the crack as a loose amorphous aggregate.

3. Diffusion of the reacting component (probably ionic) within the solid to the root of the crack.

4. An activated process at the root of the crack, probably either the actual chemical reaction or merely the interface potential barrier, here assisted very strongly by the stress energy concentration of the usual Griffith theory.

5. An activated process at the corrosion product-atmosphere interface, again either a chemical reaction or an interface potential barrier.

It must be noted that, owing to the narrow nature of the cracks and more especially to the possible forms of the corrosion product, the "diffusion" referred to in items (1) and (2) may not obey Frick's law but may be more in the nature of a permeation process, as in the case of some highly fissured thick oxide films.

In fitting existing results it appears that mechanism (2), assuming that the crack is almost filled with a fissured corrosion product, is the controlling one for glass.

Fisher has indicated that such mechanisms as the above can account for the differing effects of the strength of the corrosion atmosphere. This is certainly the case, and my previous work gives explanation for the work of Preston and Baker [*J. Appl. Phys.* **17**, 170 (1946)] on glass in an autoclave and for the familiar results of Ioffe on the strengthening of rock salt in warm water.

It should be noted that in any one experiment different mechanisms may control the growth rate, and so the fracture strength, in different time ranges. The controlling process near the actual time of fracture is always the Griffith criterion as modified in (4).

More detailed analyses of the reaction and diffusion mechanisms than the simple one-dimensional analysis of my earlier work are now being studied, and it is hoped that the results will be published in the near future.

R. J. CHARLES

In a recent work [*J. Appl. Phys.* **29**, 1544, 1549 (1958)] it is shown, at least macroscopically, that the water corrosion of a simple glass seems to be limited by an interface reaction, and consequently we would favor a combination of the effects (3) and (4) listed by Elliott as the mechanisms responsible for fatigue. The question is, of course, not settled, for many experiments remain to be done.

Elliott makes the point that different mechanisms might operate according to the time ranges involved. We concur and would like to add that temperature appears to have an analogous effect.

E. PONCELET

The mechanism of fracture which the authors describe is identical with that I gave in my lectures at the Owens Illinois General Research Laboratory in 1947, and which I published in great detail ten years ago [*Verres et réfractaires*

2, 203 (1948); **3,** 149, 289 (1949); **4,** 158 (1950); **5,** 69 (1951); reprinted in 1951 in book form, *La Fracture*].

The chemical equations which the authors use as an example of the mechanism appear verbatim in these publications [*Verres et réfractaires* **2,** 209 (1948); **3,** 150 (1949); *La Fracture*, pp. 7, 8, 10].

I do not agree that (spontaneous) fracture sets in at any definite stress concentration level. A fracture consists of the propagation of a crack under the influence of the tensile stress that exists at the crack tip. Since for very small cracks the crack tip stress increases as the crack grows, the fracture propagation rate rises steeply until a limiting rate of about half the transverse wave velocity is reached. While it may take a long time for a microscopic flow to reach visible dimensions, the fracture appears to be over as soon as the crack length reaches the visible range, giving the impression that the whole process occurs suddenly at an unpredictable instant. Fracture propagation velocities have been measured accurately for the past twenty years, and their theory has been published in several papers and books for the past fifteen, as for instance, in *Fracturing of Metals*, pp. 201–227, published by American Society for Metals, Cleveland, 1948.

Any proposal for further research should be based on the present knowledge of the art.

J. C. FISHER AND R. J. CHARLES

We regret that we did not draw attention in our chapter to Dr. Poncelet's valuable and comprehensive analysis of fracture [*La Fracture, Verres et réfractaires* (1951), pp. 1–57], wherein he treats many aspects of fracture including the time-dependent growth of cracks. However, we feel that our contribution to this subject is an extension, rather than a repetition, of his work. Whereas he focuses attention upon the importance of thermal fluctuations in rupturing bonds and causing a crack to progress, we have focused attention in more detail upon the specific chemical reactions that may be responsible. Where he indicates the over-all reactions that characterize the dissolution of silica by water, we have suggested and shown evidence supporting possible intermediate reactions and sequences of ionic movements: in particular, the momentary motion of a sodium ion from its equilibrium position, allowing a water molecule to react with the revealed unbounded oxygen.

We may disagree to some extent when it comes to the question of the initiation of rapid fracture. It is our belief that thermally induced bond rupture alone will not cause a subcritical crack to grow indefinitely, for the reverse reaction of bond renewal will cause subcritical cracks to heal on average. With chemical corrosion present, on the other hand, the effective surface energy that enters Griffith's formula can become very small or negative for slow crack growth. As a result, small cracks can grow through stress corrosion until they qualify for the more rapid failure envisioned by Griffith. The kinetics of flaw growth during stress corrosion should be describable by equations similar to or identical with those derived by Poncelet for crack growth through the successive rupture of bonds.

by

P. G. Klemens

Commonwealth Scientific and Industrial
Research Organization, Sydney

The Thermal Conductivity of Glass

In non-metallic solids the conduction of heat takes place through the medium of the lattice vibrations. The theoretical treatment of lattice vibrations has been largely confined to perfect, or nearly perfect, crystals, whose normal modes of vibration are traveling elastic waves (lattice waves). When considering the thermal conduction process, it is found that the thermal resistivity arises from imperfectness of the crystal lattice (structural defects and anharmonic components of the lattice forces). These departures from perfection must therefore be taken account of explicitly, but, since the carriers of thermal energy are still pictured as lattice waves, these departures are treated as a weak perturbation only. Thus the present theory of thermal conduction applies only to nearly perfect crystals.

Since amorphous solids deviate very much from being perfect crystals, their thermal resistivity is very high. We shall discuss their resistivity by extrapolating the theory of nearly perfect crystals to the case of strong imperfections. This procedure is not justified in general, but it can be justified at low temperatures, where the important waves are long and the effect of the microscopic disorder is sufficiently small.

We shall therefore first recapitulate the theory of thermal conduction in almost perfect crystals. We shall then consider the observed thermal conductivities of amorphous solids, particularly at low temperatures, to see what conclusions may be drawn concerning their microscopic structure.

Unfortunately, the number of materials studied at low temperatures is not large, and the present discussion will be concerned mainly with vitreous silica.

Thermal Conductivity of Crystals

In a perfect crystal with harmonic lattice forces, the atomic displacements can be resolved into normal coordinates which are waves of the form

$$\mathbf{u(x)} = \frac{1}{\sqrt{G}} \sum_j \sum_{\mathbf{k}} b_j(\mathbf{k})\epsilon_j(\mathbf{k}) \exp\left[i(\mathbf{k \cdot x} + \omega t)\right] \tag{1}$$

where $G = G_1 G_2 G_3$ is the number of unit cells in the crystal, $\mathbf{x}$ is a lattice site, $b_j(\mathbf{k})$ the amplitude of the wave $(\mathbf{k}, j)$, and ϵ is a unit vector specifying the polarization j. There are three polarization branches, and, for a given $\mathbf{k}$, the three directions ϵ_j are mutually perpendicular.

The vibrational energy of the crystal is the sum of the energies of the normal modes, the Hamiltonian being of the form

$$H = \sum_{\mathbf{k},j} H_j(\mathbf{k}) = M\sum_{\mathbf{k},j} \omega_j^2(\mathbf{k})b_j^*(\mathbf{k})b_j(\mathbf{k}) \tag{2}$$

Only a discrete set of values of $\mathbf{k}$ are admissible, namely integral combinations of $2\pi/\mathbf{a}_i G_i$, where $\mathbf{a}_i$ are the three periodicity vectors and $\mathbf{a}_i G_i$ the linear dimensions of the crystal.

The waves in a discrete lattice differ from the elastic waves in a continuum in the following respects.

1. $\mathbf{u(x)}$ is defined only for a discrete set of lattice points, so that a transformation

$$\mathbf{k} \rightarrow \mathbf{k} + \mathbf{b} \tag{3}$$

leaves $\mathbf{u(x)}$ invariant at the lattice points, where $\mathbf{b}$ is an integral combination of the inverse lattice vectors defined by

$$\mathbf{a}_i \cdot \mathbf{b}_j = 2\pi \, \delta_{ij} \tag{4}$$

2. The frequency $\omega(\mathbf{k})$ is not a linear function of k, and $\mathbf{v(k)} = \partial\omega/\partial\mathbf{k}$ is not independent of k, though this dispersion is not pronounced for long waves.

3. The polarization directions bear no simple relation to the direction of $\mathbf{k}$, and the waves of the highest frequency branch, the "longitudinal" branch in the present context, are not necessarily polarized in the direction of propagation.

The energy of each normal mode is not continuously variable, but quantized, the eigenvalues of $H_j(\mathbf{k})$ being

$$E_j(\mathbf{k}) = [N_j(\mathbf{k}) + \tfrac{1}{2}]\hbar\omega_j(\mathbf{k}) \tag{5}$$

so that the energy of the modes may be pictured to reside in an integral number of phonons N, each of energy $\hbar\omega$ and quasi-momentum $\hbar\mathbf{k}$, moving with a velocity $\mathbf{v}(\mathbf{k})$.

Owing to the slight deviations from crystal perfection, there is a slow exchange of energy among the normal modes, and in equilibrium the excitation of each mode is given by

$$N^0 = [\exp(\hbar\omega/KT) - 1]^{-1} \tag{6}$$

where K is the Boltzmann constant. Moreover, if the number of phonons in a mode is disturbed to $N = N^0 + n$, and if the system is then left undisturbed, the deviation from equilibrium will disappear with a rate given by

$$\frac{dN(\mathbf{k})}{dt}\Bigg] = -\frac{n(\mathbf{k})}{\tau(\mathbf{k})} \tag{7}$$

where $\tau(\mathbf{k})$, defined by (7), is a relaxation time, and $l(\mathbf{k}) = v\tau(\mathbf{k})$ can be regarded as the phonon mean free path.

The rate of change of $N(\mathbf{k})$ due to a temperature gradient, which tends to disturb the equilibrium, is given by

$$-\mathbf{v}\cdot\operatorname{grad} N = -(\mathbf{v}\cdot\operatorname{grad} T)\,(dN^0/dT) \tag{8}$$

and, since the total rate of change vanishes in the steady state, there will be a deviation from equilibrium in the presence of a temperature gradient given by

$$n = -(\mathbf{v}\cdot\operatorname{grad} T)\tau\,(dN^0/dT) \tag{9}$$

The energy current density is $(V)^{-1}\Sigma_\mathbf{k}\hbar\omega\mathbf{v}N$, and the specific heat per unit volume is $(V)^{-1}\Sigma_\mathbf{k}\hbar\omega\,(dN^0/dT)$, where V is the volume of the crystal, so that the thermal conductivity becomes

$$\kappa = \frac{1}{3}\sum_{\mathbf{k},j} v^2\tau\hbar\omega\,\frac{dN^0}{dT}$$

$$= \frac{1}{3}\sum_j \int d\omega\, S\cdot(\omega)vl(\omega) \tag{10}$$

where $S(\omega)\,d\omega$ is the contribution to the specific heat per unit volume from waves of polarization j and frequency ω, $d\omega$.

The following processes contribute to $dN/dt]$ of (7), and thus to $1/\tau$.

1. Scattering of lattice waves by static imperfections of the lattice structure (point defects, dislocations, grain boundaries, etc.) and by the external boundaries. This can be regarded as scattering of phonons from a state $\mathbf{k}$ to a state $\mathbf{k}'$ such that $\omega = \omega'$ (elastic scattering).

2. Interactions due to cubic anharmonicities of the lattice forces. The interchange of energy among modes may be pictured as three-phonon interaction processes such that a phonon $\mathbf{k}$ and a phonon $\mathbf{k}'$ combine to form a phonon $\mathbf{k}''$. Such processes can occur only if energy is conserved; i.e., if

$$\omega + \omega' = \omega'' \tag{11}$$

and if either of the following interference conditions is satisfied:

$$\mathbf{k} + \mathbf{k}' = \mathbf{k}'' \tag{12a}$$

or

$$\mathbf{k} + \mathbf{k}' = \mathbf{k}'' + \mathbf{b} \tag{12b}$$

where $\mathbf{b}$ is an integral combination of the inverse lattice vectors (equation 4). Processes like (12b) are called Umklapp processes.

The central problem in the theory of thermal conductivity is to find the effective relaxation time $\tau(\mathbf{k})$ from a solution of the transport equation if the transition probabilities for these various interaction processes are explicitly substituted into equation (7). Let us briefly summarize this problem, which has been reviewed elsewhere; see, for example, Klemens (1956a, 1958). There are two types of processes: processes which conserve the quasi-momentum $\Sigma\hbar\mathbf{k}N(\mathbf{k})$ of the phonon gas, namely three-phonon processes (12a), and processes which do not, namely Umklapp processes (12b) and elastic scattering processes.

Since the effect of the drift term (equation 8) is continuously to increase the momentum of the phonon gas, a steady state can be maintained only by processes which obliterate this excess momentum, and only such processes (Umklapp and elastic scattering processes) contribute to the thermal resistance.

Using second-order perturbation theory, one can calculate the scattering cross section and hence the phonon mean free path $l'(\omega)$ for the various static imperfections; it is also possible to define a mean free path for Umklapp processes. If several such processes (designated by a suffix α) are acting together, the scattering probabilities combine additively, so that

$$\frac{1}{l'} = \sum_{(\alpha)} \left(\frac{1}{l'_{(\alpha)}} \right) \tag{13}$$

If processes (12a) are disregarded, $l = l'$.

Processes (12a) will tend to make the effective value of $v_j l_j(\omega)$ the same for modes of all frequencies and polarization, because, if $\Sigma \mathbf{k} N$ as well as $\Sigma \omega N$ are conserved in all interactions, all distributions of the following form would be stationary:

$$N_\lambda^0 = [\exp[(\hbar\omega - \boldsymbol{\lambda}\cdot k)/KT]-1]^{-1} \simeq N^0 + (\boldsymbol{\lambda}\cdot k/\hbar\omega)T\,(dN^0/dT) \quad (14)$$

where $\boldsymbol{\lambda}$ is a constant, being a measure of the momentum of the phonon gas. One may regard (14) as the distribution function of a phonon gas with a bulk flow; processes (12a) do not affect the bulk velocity.

However, this distribution is of the form (9) if we equate $\boldsymbol{\lambda}$ with $-v^2\tau\hbar \operatorname{grad} T/T$, and, since processes (12a) will tend to make $\boldsymbol{\lambda}$ the same for all modes, they will tend to make $vl(\omega)$ constant. As long as $l'(\omega)$ is the same for all frequencies and polarizations, processes (12a) will have no effect on the steady state distribution and $l = l'$; however, if $l'(\omega)$ varies rapidly with frequency or is very different for different polarizations, such processes must be considered.

The temperature dependence of κ is governed by the frequency dependence, as well as by a possible intrinsic temperature dependence, of $l(\omega)$. At low temperatures, in particular

$$\kappa \propto T^{3-n} \quad \text{if} \quad l(\omega) \propto \omega^{-n} \quad (15)$$

Different types of imperfections have different frequency variations of $l'(\omega)$ and thus give rise to thermal resistivities of different temperature dependence at low temperatures. The frequency variations of $l'(\omega)$ for the principal scattering processes and the temperature variation of the resulting resistivities are summarized in Table 1. Thus one may deduce, under favorable circumstances, the nature of the principal imperfections from observations of low temperature thermal conductivities.

If more than one resistive process is operative, the over-all conductivity is calculated from (13). This is equivalent, very approximately, to an additive compounding of the individual resistivities, though deviations become appreciable if the individual mean free paths have widely different frequency variations. If, in equation (15), $n > 2$, equation (10) would diverge; however, the effect of processes (12a) is to make $l(\omega)$ almost frequency-independent if $\omega < KT/\hbar$.

The intrinsic thermal resistivity is due to Umklapp processes (12b). At high temperatures $(T > \theta)$ the resulting resistivity is proportional to T, as has already been shown classically by Debye (1914). At low temperatures the intrinsic resistivity decreases exponentially, for, in order to satisfy (11) and (12b), at least two participating modes must have values of $\mathbf{k}$ near the zone boundary.

Table 1

FREQUENCY VARIATION OF SCATTERING PROBABILITY AND
TEMPERATURE VARIATION OF THERMAL RESISTANCE
FOR VARIOUS INTERACTION MECHANISMS

Interaction	$1/l(\omega)$	$1/\kappa(T)$
Low temperatures, $T < \theta$		
External boundaries	ω^0	T^{-3}
Grain boundaries	ω^0	T^{-3}
Thin sheets in continuous crystal and stacking faults	ω^2	T^{-1}
Conduction electrons in metals	ω^1	T^{-2}
Dislocations (strain field)	ω^1	T^{-2}
Long cylinders and dislocation core	ω^3	T^0
Point defects	ω^4	T^1
Umklapp processes		$T^{-3} \exp(-\theta/\alpha T)$
High temperatures, $T > \theta$		
Umklapp processes	—	T^1
All static imperfections	—	T^0

This is illustrated in Fig. 1, which shows the thermal conductivity of artificial sapphire, measured by Berman (1951). Above the temperature T_m of the maximum, $\kappa(T)$ decreases in the exponential fashion characteristic of Umklapp resistance; around T_m the conductivity is limited by imperfections; below T_m it is limited by the external boundary and depends upon the specimen size. In the boundary region the average phonon mean free path

$$\bar{l} = \frac{3\kappa}{Sv} \tag{16}$$

is comparable to the smallest external dimension of the specimen, in this case the diameter.

Berman (1952) also measured a polycrystalline specimen. Here an upper limit to $\bar{l}$ is provided by the grain size, for now the grain boundaries scatter the phonons, and T_m is shifted to higher temperatures (see Fig. 1).

While in some crystals $\kappa(T)$ varies in an exponential fashion above T_m, owing to the predominance of the Umklapp resistance, in other crystals this resistance is overshadowed by the resistance due to structural imperfections. Point defects, in particular, cause a resistivity proportional to T. In some materials the mass fluctuation due to the isotopic

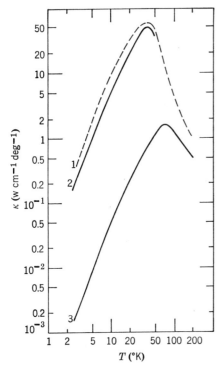

constitution provides an appreciable point defect resistance (Slack, 1957) and overshadows the Umklapp resistance in the exponential region.

Figure 2 shows the thermal conductivity of crystalline quartz, of quartz after various amounts of neutron irradiation, and of vitreous silica (Berman, 1951). Neutron irradiation damage provides additional thermal resistance. This resistance can be divided into two components: one component, increasing with temperature, is due to small defects, probably individual vacancies and interstitials, while the other component, which increases with decreasing temperature, is due to large regions of damage, suggestive of displacement spikes (Berman, Simon, Klemens, and Fry, 1950; Klemens, 1951). The thermal conductivity after heavy irradiation gradually approaches the conductivity of glass; it is possible that

Fig. 1. Thermal conductivity of aluminium oxide according to Berman (1951, 1952). Curve 1, single-crystal sapphire, 3 mm diameter; curve 2, single crystal, 1.5 mm diameter; curve 3, sintered alumina.

neutron damage produces vitreous inclusions wherever a large number of displacements occurred close together, as at the end of the range of a primary displacement.

The thermal conductivity of amorphous silica is considerably lower than that of the corresponding single crystal. Amorphous solids in general have a low thermal conductivity: this is no doubt due to a considerable reduction of the phonon mean free path resulting from the lack of order. Grain boundary scattering also causes a reduction of the thermal conductivity (see Fig. 1), but the change from a single crystal to the vitreous form is accompanied by an even greater change in the thermal conductivity; furthermore, the temperature dependence of the conductivity at low temperatures is different.

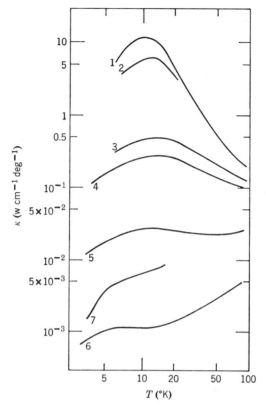

Fig. 2. Thermal conductivity of silica according to Berman (1953) and Cohen (1958). Curve 1, quartz crystal (rod cut perpendicular to axis); 2, after 0.03 unit of neutron irradiation; 3, after 1 unit; 4, after 2.4 units; 5, after 19 units; 1 unit approx. 1.8 × 10^{18} cm^{-2}. Curve 6, fused quartz (Berman, 1951); 7, fused quartz (Cohen, 1958).

Lattice Waves in Amorphous Solids

Although the atoms of an amorphous solid do not form a regular array, each atom still has an equilibrium site, as in a crystal, and vibrates about that site. An amorphous solid, as every other mechanical system in equilibrium, has in principle normal modes of vibration, though in practice it has not been possible to determine them. Qualitatively we can say the following.

1. Below the temperature at which structural changes occur, the specific heat does not differ greatly from that of the corresponding crystalline solid. Thus the frequency spectrum of the normal modes

does not differ substantially from the spectrum of the lattice waves of a crystal, except possibly at the highest frequencies.

2. The normal modes of low frequency must be similar in character to the waves in an elastic continuum, for in the limit of long waves the atomic structure is unimportant; only the macroscopic elastic constants are relevant.

3. There are low frequency transverse waves. In this respect glasses differ from liquids, which can propagate low frequency longitudinal waves but not low frequency transverse waves.

4. Normal modes of high frequency (approaching the Debye frequency) differ profoundly in character from lattice waves.

In the case of a nearly perfect crystal the displacements can be resolved, at any instant, into lattice waves (equation 1); these lattice waves are a superposition of normal modes, and the energy content of each wave varies with time. Since the normal modes do not differ greatly from lattice waves, so that each wave is compounded mainly of one mode, the energy variation is slow and τ of equation (7) is long.

In an amorphous solid the instantaneous displacements can still be resolved into Fourier components of the form (1), except that $b \exp(i\omega t)$ are now replaced by a set of coefficients whose time dependence is different. Each Fourier component is composed of contributions from several normal modes, and a lattice wave loses its shape rapidly; that is, τ is short. If the interchange of energy is too rapid, $\tau \gtrsim 1/\omega$, and it is not possible to speak of lattice waves at all, since each Fourier component of instantaneous displacement has changed shape while traveling through a distance of a wavelength.

Thermal Conductivity of Glass: The Phonon Mean Free Path

We shall avoid the difficult theoretical problem of attempting to resolve lattice waves into the normal modes and studying their dispersion: instead we shall assume the existence of lattice waves and derive the phonon mean free path from the observed conductivities using (16). If the mean free path thus derived satisfies either

$$\bar{l} > \theta a/T \qquad (\text{if } T < \theta)$$

or (17)

$$\bar{l} > a \qquad (\text{if } T > \theta)$$

then the concept of lattice waves was justified; otherwise the concept was inapplicable, and the quantity $\bar{l}$ cannot necessarily be regarded as a phonon mean free path.

Figure 3 shows a schematic plot of $\bar{l}$ against T for a hypothetical substance occurring as a single crystal, as a polycrystalline aggregate, and as a glass. Actually, no single substance has been measured in all these three forms, and Fig. 3 is compounded from the behavior of Al_2O_3 (single crystal and polycrystalline) and of SiO_2 (single crystal and glass).

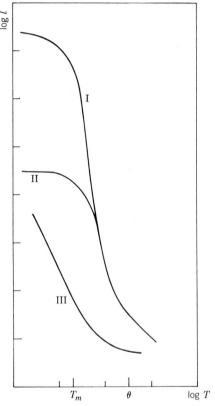

Fig. 3. Average mean free path $\bar{l}$ of equation (16) plotted schematically as function of temperature on logarithmic scale (decades marked). Curve I, single crystal; II, polycrystalline solid; III, glass.

It is interesting to note that $\bar{l}$ of the glass increases rapidly with decreasing temperature at low temperatures, so that (17) is satisfied at low temperatures even if it is not satisfied at intermediate or high temperatures. This confirms the previous expectation that low frequency elastic waves exist in a solid, irrespective of disorder on an atomic scale. Correspondingly, the theory of the nearly perfect crystal can be applied to the problem of the thermal conductivity at low temperatures.

At high temperatures the thermal conductivity of many glasses as a function of temperature is proportional to their specific heat, as pointed out by Kittel (1949). This indicates that $l(\omega)$ is independent of frequency at high frequencies. The magnitude of $l(\omega)$ is quite small, being only of the order of a few interatomic distances.

This property was made plausible by Kittel, who pointed out that the range of order in a vitreous structure is very short and of that magnitude. If glass is regarded as a polycrystalline aggregate, then the size of the crystallites appears to be of the order of the elementary structural units (silicon-oxygen tetrahedra in fused quartz); if it is regarded as a random network, it is reasonable that the mean free path should be of the order of the coherence length, which again is of the same order.

Kittel also noted the increase of $\bar{l}$ with decreasing temperature which he explained in terms of the relative homogeneity of the glass to long waves. The first measurements of the thermal conductivity of a glass over a wide range of low temperatures were published soon afterwards (Berman, 1949), and it appeared that at low temperatures $\bar{l}(T)$ was roughly proportional to T^{-2}, which would indicate from (10) that $l(\omega) \propto \omega^{-2}$ for low frequencies.

In order to make such a frequency variation plausible, Klemens (1951) argued as follows:

A low frequency lattice wave is composed of a superposition of true normal modes. Some of these modes are of low frequency and are themselves similar in character to lattice waves; other modes are of high frequency. A high frequency lattice wave consists mainly of high frequency normal modes, and has, as was empirically observed, a short mean free path l_0. Now it is reasonable to assume that the high frequency modes describe mainly the relative motion of neighboring atoms. Consider the energy content of a low frequency wave: the major portion is associated with over-all motion of an element of the solid containing many atoms, but a fraction of the energy is the energy of relative motion of neighboring atoms. It will be assumed that the latter fraction is the energy content of the high frequency components of the wave, which is dissipated with a mean free path l_0, while the energy of over-all motion is supposed to be retained by the wave.

Consider a wave of type (1) of wave number k. The relative displacement of two neighbors of separation a is

$$\Delta u \sim i(ak)u \qquad (18)$$

The kinetic energy content per unit volume is

$$E_{\text{kin}} = \tfrac{1}{2}\rho(\dot{u})^2 \qquad (19)$$

where ρ is the density. The kinetic energy of relative motion is

$$E_{\text{kin}} = \tfrac{1}{2}\rho \, (\Delta \dot{u})^2 \sim (ak)^2 E_{\text{kin}} \tag{20}$$

The rate of energy dissipation is

$$\frac{dE}{dt} \equiv -v\frac{E}{l} = \frac{d\,\Delta E}{dt} = -v\frac{\Delta E}{l_0} \tag{21}$$

so that

$$l \sim l_0(ak)^2 \tag{22}$$

The above argument is certainly not rigorous, because the separation of the wave into two groups of normal modes is only a surmise.

If (22) is fitted to the thermal conductivity of fused quartz as measured by Berman (1951) (see Fig. 4), it is found that the high temperature results indicate $\bar{l} = l_0 = 12 \times 10^{-8}$ cm, while the results below 8°K indicate that, in (22), $l_0 \simeq 300 \times 10^{-8}$ cm, if we take $a = 5 \times 10^{-8}$ cm. Also, because of the "knee" in the thermal conductivity curve around

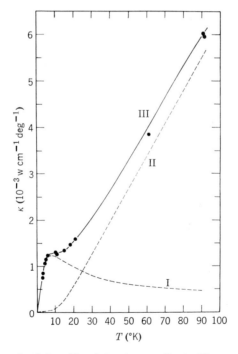

Fig. 4. Thermal conductivity of fused quartz according to Klemens (1951). Curve I, κ_{I}; curve II, κ_{II}; curve III, $\kappa = \kappa_{\text{I}} + \kappa_{\text{II}}$. Circles mark experimental points of Berman (1951).

$10°K$, it is not possible to represent the conductivity by means of equation (10) with a mean free path $l(\omega) \propto \omega^{-n}$ if n is to vary monotonically with frequency.

This difficulty was avoided by assuming a much longer mean free path for structure scattering for longitudinal than for transverse waves (Klemens, 1951); that is, the constant l_0 in (22) for longitudinal waves is much bigger ($\sim 900 \times 10^{-8}$ cm). At high frequencies and temperatures there is strong interaction between the two polarization branches by means of three-phonon processes of type (12a). As explained earlier, this results in the effective mean free path of the longitudinal waves being the same as that of the transverse waves (i.e., the apparent value of l_0 is 12×10^{-8} cm): the resulting conductivity is κ_{II}, given by curve II of Fig. 4.

At lower frequencies the three-phonon processes are not sufficiently numerous to tie the mean free path of the longitudinal waves to that of the transverse waves; this results in an additional conductivity κ_I. At lowest frequencies and temperatures the longitudinal waves are completely uncoupled from the transverse waves, and their effective mean free path is given by (22) with $l_0 \simeq 900 \times 10^{-8}$ cm, so that $\kappa_I \propto T$. At higher temperatures there is partial coupling and κ_I gradually decreases. The "knee" in the curve of the total conductivity $\kappa = \kappa_I + \kappa_{II}$ corresponds to the maximum in κ_I. An expression for κ_I in terms of (22) and the strength of the three-phonon interactions has been given by Klemens (1951). The total conductivity can be made to fit the observed conductivity fairly well (see Fig. 4) by choosing the above values for the constants l_0 for the two polarizations, and by adjusting the strength of the three-phonon interactions. The thermal conductivity of glass provided the first experimental information concerning the strength of interactions of type (12a); the observed strength of interaction exceeds the theoretical value by a factor of order 10 (Klemens, 1956a).

Thermal Conductivity of Vitreous Silica at Very Low Temperatures

It appears possible to draw some conclusions about the nature of the vitreous state from the thermal conductivity at very low temperatures, where the phonon mean free path is substantially greater than the wavelength, so that the weak perturbation theory, as used for crystals, can be applied with confidence.

Berman (1951) had found that, below $8°K$, $\kappa \propto T$, although Bijl (1949) found $\kappa \propto T^{1.3}$ between $1.5°$ and $3°K$ for some silica-based glasses †, and

† Jena Geraete 20, Jena 16^{III}, Thuringian and Monax.

Cohen (1958) found for fused quartz that $\kappa \propto T^{2.2}$ below 5°K. This suggests that there is no unique vitreous state, and that the chemical composition plays only a secondary role, since glasses of the same composition can behave differently. Since Cohen's sample had a higher conductivity (see Fig. 2) as well as a slower temperature variation of $\bar{l}$, it seems that this sample tends to be more coherent and to have at least some crystalline regions of dimensions at least of the wavelength of the important phonons($\sim$100 atom spacings). We have also seen that Berman's linear variation was not implausible in a random network. We shall now attempt to replace these vague considerations by a more specific argument.

To a first approximation, correct in the limit of very long waves, a glass may be regarded as a homogeneous isotropic elastic continuum, whose Hamiltonian is of the form (2):

$$H^0 = M \sum_{\mathbf{k},j} \bar{v}^2 k^2 b_j^*(k) b_j(k) \tag{23}$$

where $\bar{v}$ is the sound velocity. In actual fact, the solid is built up of structural units (e.g., silicon-oxygen tetrahedra) any one of which is oriented at random, though the direction of neighboring units may be correlated.

In an imperfect crystal, phonons are scattered by variations in the mass of unit cells, and by variations in strength or direction of interatomic linkages. It is probable that in a glass the mass variations are less important as a source of phonon scattering than the misorientations of the structural units. These variations of orientation are roughly equivalent to fluctuations of the interatomic forces resolved in fixed directions. Since the strength of the linkages is related to the velocity of sound, these fluctuations can be represented by local fluctuations in the velocity of waves of given directions. Thus the perturbation Hamiltonian is of the form

$$H' = \sum_{\mathbf{k}} \sum_{\mathbf{k}'} \sum_{\mathbf{x}} A(\mathbf{x}) k k' b^*(\mathbf{k}') b(\mathbf{k}) \exp\left[i(\mathbf{k} - \mathbf{k}') \cdot x\right] \exp\left[i(\omega - \omega')t\right] \tag{24}$$

where the summation is over all positions $\mathbf{x}$ of the structural units. The perturbation $A(\mathbf{x})$ is a stochastic variable. If H^0 has been properly chosen so that $\bar{A} = 0$, i.e.,

$$\sum_{\mathbf{x}} A(\mathbf{x}) = 0 \tag{25}$$

then H' has no diagonal terms. The magnitude of $A(\mathbf{x})$ can be related to the variation with direction of v^2 in the crystal. In (22) we have used for $\bar{v}^2$ the value $\overline{v^2}$, i.e., v^2 averaged over all directions. Thus, if $v(\mathbf{x}) = \bar{v} + \delta v(\mathbf{x})$,

$$A(\mathbf{x}) = 2MG^{-1}\bar{v}\,\delta v(\mathbf{x}) \tag{26}$$

or

$$\overline{A^2} = 4M^2G^{-2}\bar{v}^2\,\overline{\delta v^2} \tag{27}$$

where G is the number of structural units in the solid.

The scattering of lattice waves may be calculated by second-order perturbation theory in terms of H' (Klemens, 1955). If

$$H' = \sum_{\mathbf{k}} \sum_{\mathbf{k}'} c(\mathbf{k}, \mathbf{k}')b^*(\mathbf{k}')b(\mathbf{k})$$

then

$$\frac{1}{\tau(\mathbf{k})} \propto \sum_{\mathbf{k}'} c^2(\mathbf{k}, \mathbf{k}')\frac{1}{\omega\omega'} \tag{28}$$

where the summation is over all states $\mathbf{k}'$ such that $\omega' = \omega$. For imperfections of spherical symmetry, in particular, $\sum_{\mathbf{k}'} \propto k^2$, so that the frequency variation of τ is given by

$$1/\tau(\omega) \propto c^2(\mathbf{k}, \mathbf{k}') \tag{29}$$

Let us consider two states $\mathbf{k}$ and $\mathbf{k}' = \mathbf{k} + \mathbf{q}$, such that $\omega = \omega'$. From (24),

$$c^2(\mathbf{k}, \mathbf{k}') = [\sum_{\mathbf{x}} A(\mathbf{x})k^2 \exp(i\mathbf{q}\cdot\mathbf{x})]^2$$

$$= \sum_{\mathbf{x}} \sum_{\mathbf{r}} A(\mathbf{x})A(\mathbf{x} + \mathbf{r})k^4 \exp(i\mathbf{q}\cdot\mathbf{r}) \tag{30}$$

We may write

$$\sum_{\mathbf{x}} A(\mathbf{x})A(\mathbf{x} + \mathbf{r}) = G\overline{A^2}f(\mathbf{r}) \tag{31}$$

where $\overline{A^2}$ is the mean square value (equation 27) of A, and equation (31) defines a correlation function $f(\mathbf{r})$. In particular, $f(\mathbf{r}) = 1$ if $\mathbf{r} = 0$, and in an amorphous solid we would expect absence of long range order, so that $f(\mathbf{r}) \to 0$ as $r \to \infty$. Thus

$$c^2 = k^4\overline{A^2}G \sum_{\mathbf{r}} f(\mathbf{r}) \exp(i\mathbf{q}\cdot\mathbf{r}) \tag{32}$$

In the special case when $f(\mathbf{r})$ has spherical symmetry and is in the limit of long waves, (32) becomes

$$c^2 \propto k^4 \int \sin (qr) f(r) \frac{r}{q} dr \qquad (33)$$

While amorphous solids are macroscopically isotropic, it does not follow that they must be isotropic on a microscopic scale, so that $f(\mathbf{r})$ is not necessarily of spherical symmetry. In glasses which are built up of structural units which are of the same extent in all directions (e.g., silica-based glasses), the correlation function $f(\mathbf{r})$ is probably indeed of spherical symmetry, but in structures which can be regarded as a random arrangement of chains (e.g., rubber, vitreous selenium) a cylindrical symmetry of $f(\mathbf{r})$ seems more appropriate.

If there is no correlation between the directions of neighboring structural units, $f(\mathbf{r}) = \delta(\mathbf{r})$ and in equation (32) the Fourier transform of $f(\mathbf{r})$ is independent of $\mathbf{q}$, so that $c^2 \propto k^4$. From (29), this implies that $\tau(\omega) \propto \omega^{-4}$; in other words, in the absence of correlation each unit scatters independently as a point defect (Rayleigh scattering). Conversely, if $f(\mathbf{r}) = 1$ for all $\mathbf{r}$ (perfect correlation; the substance is a crystal), $c^2(\mathbf{k}, \mathbf{k}') \propto \delta(\mathbf{k} - \mathbf{k}')$, so that there is no scattering.

A case of some interest is a polycrystalline aggregate. This cannot be treated by the present formalism, since the orientation-averaged Hamiltonian (equation 23) would be an inadequate starting point for the application of a perturbation calculation. However, the scattering by small angle grain boundaries may be treated in a different manner (Klemens, 1955) in the case when the grain size is large compared with the phonon wavelength. In this case, scattering is frequency independent. It may be presumed that scattering is also frequency-independent in the case of large angle grain boundaries.

If the size of the crystallites is small, so that their linear dimension is comparable to the wavelength, scattering is no longer independent of frequency. In the extreme case when the wavelength is small compared with the grain size, we can treat each grain as a structural unit and apply the theory leading to (30); however, in (27), G now denotes the number of grains, so that scattering is enhanced by a factor equal to the square of the number of elementary units per grain. If there is no correlation in the direction of neighboring grains, reinforced Rayleigh scattering results; in other cases a correlation function may be defined analogous to equation (21).

Consider now the variation $l(\omega) \propto \omega^{-2}$ found by Berman (1951). Since this variation seems to hold over a fairly wide range of frequencies, it is unlikely to be produced by a polycrystalline structure in the intermediate region where the grain size is comparable to the phonon wavelength, nor would such a large grain size be in accord with the short mean free path at high temperatures.

In order that $\tau(\omega) \propto \omega^{-2}$, we require from (29) that $c^2 \propto \omega^2$, or

$$\sum_{\mathbf{r}} f(\mathbf{r}) \exp{(i\mathbf{q} \cdot \mathbf{r})} \propto q^{-2} \quad \text{for} \quad q \ll \frac{1}{a} \tag{34}$$

where $a \sim 5 \times 10^{-8}$ cm. Assuming spherical symmetry, this implies (from equation 33), that

$$\int_0^\infty \sin{(qr)} f(r) r \, dr \propto 1/q \tag{35}$$

whence

$$f(r) \propto 1/r \tag{36}$$

in the region $r \gg a$, in particular for distances r comparable to the wavelength of the important phonons at liquid helium temperatures ($\sim 5 \times 10^{-6}$ cm).

In order to explain why the mean free path of the longitudinal waves is so much larger than that of the transverse waves, one requires that $\overline{A^2}$ be considerably smaller for longitudinal waves. This would imply that longitudinal waves are less affected by disorientation, i.e., that in the crystal the velocity of longitudinal waves is less anisotropic than the velocity of transverse waves.

One can thus conclude that, in the case of Berman's specimen of fused quartz, the structure is essentially a random network. If it were polycrystalline, the grain size could not exceed $\sim 3 \times 10^{-6}$ cm, but such a large grain size is in conflict with the high temperature data. It is still possible to have a grain size much smaller than the phonon wavelength; however, the direction of individual grains cannot then be uncorrelated: this would have led to $l(\omega) \propto \omega^{-4}$. In all probability we have a gradual loss of coherence—that is, $f(r) \propto r^{-1}$—at large distances; at small distances probably $f(r) = 1$, but from the high temperature data this region of complete coherence cannot exceed $\sim 10^{-7}$ cm, say 2×10^{-7} cm at most. Whether we should speak of a random network in which each silicon-oxygen tetrahedron is slightly misoriented relative to its neighbor, or whether we should regard as the unit structure a small group of such tetrahedra (not exceeding, say, 2×10^{-7} cm in linear dimensions) cannot easily be determined by the present considerations.

When we now consider Cohen's sample of fused quartz, where $\kappa(T) \propto T^{2.2}$, so that $l(\omega)$ varies very slowly with frequency (slower than ω^{-1}), it appears that here $f(r)$ falls off more slowly than $1/r$ at large distances. This would indicate a fairly large grain size, at least comparable to the phonon wavelength at helium temperatures. However, the conductivity of this sample exceeds Berman's merely by a factor ~ 4, and its room temperature value probably does not differ substantially either.

The present data therefore seem to suggest that Cohen's sample was not homogeneously coarse-grained but contained crystalline inclusions of dimensions at least comparable to, if not larger than, the phonon wavelength, and that these inclusions have a relatively large effect on the low temperature thermal conductivity, but relatively less effect at higher temperatures.

Effect of Neutron Irradiation

It is well known that heavy neutron irradiation turns a quartz crystal into an amorphous solid (Wittels and Sherrill, 1954; Primak, 1955); this is also borne out by the gradual change in character of the thermal conductivity curves of Fig. 2. However, the amorphous state attained by prolonged irradiation differs from the state of fused silica, for it has a density about 2% higher than that of ordinary quartz glass, which in turn has a density about 15% less than that of crystalline quartz (Wittels and Sherrill, 1954). Furthermore, if quartz glass is exposed to prolonged neutron irradiation, its density increases by about 2%, apparently attaining the same final state as a heavily irradiated crystal.

It would thus appear that the saturation structure of heavily irradiated quartz is more ordered than that of quartz glass, and on a naive view one would expect it to have a higher conductivity (Klemens, 1956b). This expectation was borne out by Cohen's (1958) measurements: the sample of fused quartz was measured after irradiation, and it was found that neutron bombardment caused a substantial increase in conductivity. However, there was no obvious correlation with density changes, for the density change saturated at neutron exposures of about 6×10^{19} particles/cm^2, while the thermal conductivity change had not yet saturated, though saturation would probably occur at higher dosages.

On the basis of the present perturbation treatment an increase in short range order (i.e., an increase in $f(r)$ for $r \ll 1/q$) should lead to reinforced scattering and cause a decrease in the conductivity, unless balanced by a corresponding increase in $f(r)$ at $r \gtrsim 1/q$. It is probable that neutron irradiation caused a decrease of short range order, leading to a decrease in scattering of long waves, though it is not easy to reconcile this with the density change. Of course, there may be no direct connection between these two properties. Again, it is possible that neutron irradiation caused a growth of the crystalline inclusions which may have been present initially, though no obvious reason for such a growth suggests itself. Thus, although the behavior of glass under neutron irradiation may easily hold a vital clue to our understanding of the thermal conductivity of glass, the present picture is far from clear.

Other Amorphous Solids

The general considerations outlined here should apply to all amorphous solids, although we must expect some variety in detail. Kittel's (1949) suggestion of a constant mean free path $\bar{l}$ at and above the Debye temperature should probably apply to all such solids, while at low temperatures one would in general expect $\bar{l}$ to increase with decreasing temperature.

In the case of rubber, whose thermal conductivity was measured by Schallamach (1941) down to liquid oxygen temperatures, the conductivity was indeed found to be roughly proportional to the specific heat with a mean free path of the order of 10^{-8} cm; however, the measurements did not extend to sufficiently low temperatures to give information about the expected increase of $\bar{l}$ at low temperatures.

Because of their low thermal diffusivity, amorphous solids are distinctly unattractive to workers in the thermal conductivity field, for in most cases their equipment is designed for rod-shaped specimens and uses a steady heat flow technique. For amorphous solids the time of establishment of steady heat flow is often excessive; furthermore, heat losses by radiation are more important and are a source of difficulty. Although these difficulties can be overcome, particularly at low temperatures where $\bar{l}$ (and thus the diffusivity) increases again and radiation is less troublesome, it would probably be advantageous to design thermal conductivity equipment specifically for the study of amorphous solids, using a more advantageous specimen geometry.

It is therefore not surprising that there are relatively few observations of low temperature thermal conductivity of amorphous solids, and fewer still over a wide range of temperatures. In addition to the observations on glass referred to above, there are only measurements by Berman (1951) on Perspex and on nylon (Berman, 1953), and by G. K. White (unpublished) on vitreous selenium. For Perspex and nylon there are as yet no corresponding specific heat measurements.

Several years ago White measured the thermal conductivity of vitreous selenium from 2° to 90°K. Specific heat measurements of crystalline selenium down to 15°K were subsequently published by de Sorbo (1953), and it is possible to extrapolate the specific heat below 15°K by a T^3 law without much error. In this way it is possible to deduce $\bar{l}$, and it is found that, while $\bar{l}$ tends toward a constant value at temperatures above $\sim$40°K, at very low temperatures $\bar{l} \propto T^{-2.6}$.

We may interpret this variation as follows. If $f(\mathbf{r})$ has cylindrical symmetry—i.e., $\mathbf{r} = (z, r)$—and if $f(\mathbf{r}) = \delta(r)$, but independent of z, so that the individual scattering units are long, thin cylinders, then $l(\omega) \propto \omega^{-3}$ (two-dimensional Rayleigh scattering). Since $l(\omega) \propto \omega^{-2.6}$, $f(\mathbf{r})$ does not fall off quite so rapidly with r. Thus the perturbations from the homogeneous isotropic solid appear to be cylinders, with some correlation between neighboring cylinders. In view of the chain-like structure of selenium, this is quite a plausible model: in vitreous selenium the chains are arranged at random, with some tendency for neighboring chains to be parallel.

It remains to be seen whether rubber and amorphous sulfur show a similar variation of $\bar{l}$ at low temperatures.

Conclusion

While the low thermal conductivity of amorphous solids can be understood in general terms as the result of a very short phonon mean free path (though this concept is of doubtful validity at high temperatures), it is only at low temperatures that it is possible to interpret the observed conductivities in terms of the present theory.

The only substance which has been studied reasonably well is fused quartz, and in this case no unique vitreous state was found. Variations in the behavior of the thermal conductivity seem to be associated with variations in the basic structure, while the chemical composition seems to play only a secondary role. The changes in the thermal conductivity on neutron irradiation appear to be particularly interesting and still defy interpretation.

There is a general lack of experimental material. What is required are measurements of the thermal conductivity and of the specific heat (or measurements of the thermal diffusivity directly) over a wide range of low temperatures of a variety of amorphous materials: glasses from different sources (attention being paid to the basic reason for the variation between specimens), as well as rubbers and other polymers, and the amorphous forms of elements. Such an extensive program of measurements would be best carried out by equipment specifically designed for this purpose.

It is probable that such a program of investigations would result in much information about the structure of amorphous solids, and that some of this information could not be obtained by other methods. Furthermore, the low temperature thermal conductivity may prove to be a sensitive, and perhaps not altogether inconvenient, indicator of crystallinity.

REFERENCES

Berman, R., *Phys. Rev.* **76**, 315 (1949).
Berman, R., *Proc. Roy. Soc. (London)* **A208**, 90 (1951).
Berman, R., *Proc. Phys. Soc. (London)* **A65**, 1029 (1952).
Berman, R., *Advances in Physics* **2**, 103 (1953).
Berman, R., Simon, F. E., Klemens, P. G., and Fry, T. M., *Nature* **166**, 864 (1950).
Bijl, D., *Physica* **14**, 684 (1949).
Cohen, Anna F., *J. Appl. Phys.* **29**, 591 (1958).
Debye, P., 1914, in *Vortraege ueber die kinetische Theorie und der Materie und Elektrizitaet*, Teubner, Berlin, pp. 19–60.
de Sorbo, W., *J. Chem. Phys.* **21**, 1144 (1953).
Kittel, C., *Phys. Rev.* **75**, 972 (1949).
Klemens, P. G., *Proc. Roy. Soc. (London)* **A208**, 108 (1954).
Klemens, P. G., *Proc. Phys. Soc. (London)* **A68**, 1113 (1955).
Klemens, P. G., *Encyclopedia of Physics*, Vol. 14 (1956) (a), Springer, Berlin, p. 198.
Klemens, P. G., *Phil. Mag.* **1**, 938 (1956) (b).
Klemens, P. G., *Solid State Physics*, Vol. 7, 1958, Academic Press, New York, p. 1.
Primak, W., *Phys. Rev.* **98**, 1708 (1955).
Schallamach, R., *Proc. Phys. Soc. (London)* **53**, 214 (1941).
Slack, G. A., *Phys. Rev.* **105**, 829 (1957).
White, G. K., unpublished data. See also White, Woods, and Elford, *Phys. Rev.* **112**, 111 (1958).
Wittels, M., and Sherrill, F. A., *Phys. Rev.* **93**, 1117 (1954).

DISCUSSION

ROMAN SMOLUCHOWSKI

In so far as the results of Cohen at Oak Ridge are concerned, there is the possibility that the effects she sees in vitreous silica are due to irradiation-induced strains. This has happened in KCl.

P. G. KLEMENS

In crystals like KCl, strains may make a difference, while in solids with low conductivity they would not.

R. W. DOUGLAS

When vitreous silica is irradiated, the damage may be caused by a thermal spike. It is observed that neutron irradiation increases the density.

Years ago Izard and I found that, the higher the "fictive" temperature of vitreous silica, the greater is the density. If we imagine that the irradiated centers of damage cool very quickly, these centers will have a higher fictive temperature and therefore a higher density. Your observations on neutron irradiation are in qualitative, at least, accord with our observations.

R. MAURER

I would like to add that, if Douglas' curves are extrapolated to the density of heavily irradiated vitreous silica, a fictive temperature of about 7000° is obtained which is thought to be that of a thermal spike. Furthermore, if the relaxation times are extrapolated to that temperature, the relaxation time obtained is roughly of the same order as the quenching time of a thermal spike.

H. L. FRISCH

Your scattering theory in the region of high concentration of scattering centers may apply very well because of the fact that waves, in first approximation, see their space-averaged potential (optical model) with superimposed fluctuations. For low enough densities I suppose only correlations between pairs of scattering centers are important. Would there be any convergence difficulties in your theory?

P. G. KLEMENS

The perturbation theory is essentially a Born approximation. That is, an incident wave is scattered by a perturbed region, but to first order it is not affected. This gives one the various interaction probabilities which are fed into the Boltzmann equation.

This works very well for one isolated imperfection. It also seems to work very well for a large number of imperfections, provided they are very weak scatterers, such as for the isotopic mass variation.

In the case which I have treated here, it perhaps works very well, because, as you said, we have taken, as a starting point, a uniform medium whose sound velocity is the average velocity of sound and just considered local fluctuations.

I haven't investigated the convergence in all respects. As a rough criterion, I will just say that, unless the scattering mean free path turns ought to be long compared to the wavelength, there might be convergence difficulties.

J. A. KRUMHANSL

Is there not a conceptional difference between the formation of a theory for crystalline and non-crystalline solids. For example, how can one treat the Umklapp process in the absence of lattice? Or, how does one formulate the problem of the inelastic intrinsic resistance?

P. G. KLEMENS

In a practical sense, the intrinsic resistance is not important because of the resistance due to the imperfections. In the fundamental sense, it would be necessary to go back to the original Debye formulation. In so far as high temperatures are concerned, the whole concept of phonons is doubtful.

G. J. DIENES

There are indications that when vitreous silica and quartz are heavily irradiated with neutrons they approach an intermediate state (sometimes called the metamict state). In this state the densities, as well as the thermal conductivity, of the two phases approach each other. If the radiation dosage is not too great, the two phases will return to the original state upon reheating. But, if the dosage is sufficiently large, the two phases come to a new stable phase which is more dense than vitreous silica.

The color centers that are created come from both thermal spikes and displaced atoms, but I believe the displaced atom mechanism dominates.

N. KREIDL

I agree that both thermal spikes and point defects are present in highly irradiated silica.

When neutron-irradiated quartz is annealed, it relaxes in a complicated way, suggesting that at low dose part of the material remembers the original state while, with increasing dose, an increasing portion (and finally the entire sample) does not and becomes identical with vitreous silica [Primak, *Phys. Rev.* **110**, 1240 (1958)]. Consequently, the "metamict state" appears not to be homogeneous in a wide dose range.

A. J. COHEN

I would like to mention that silica upon fast neutron irradiation develops a band at 2420 Å with intensity proportional to dosage [Cohen, *Phys. Rev.* **105**, 1151 (1957)]. An interesting feature of this band is that it is most likely due to Si(II), which would indicate that SiO can exist in the solid state under special conditions.

Index